GEOMETRY

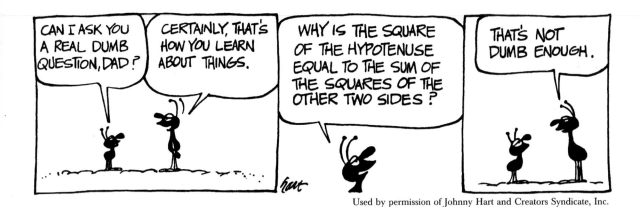

GEOMETRY
Seeing, Doing, Understanding
Third Edition

Harold R. Jacobs

MY FATHER'S WORLD®

Printed in China

January 2014

Published by My Father's World®
PO Box 2140
Rolla, MO 65402
(573) 202-2000   info@mfwbooks.com

www.mfwbooks.com

Contents

1

An Introduction to Geometry   7

2

The Nature of Deductive Reasoning   41

6

Parallel Lines   211

7

Quadrilaterals   257

8

Transformations   297

Midterm Review   330

15

Geometric Solids   617

16

Non-Euclidean Geometries   689

Final Review   718

Forewords

This is one of the great geometry books of all time. It is the book that I would like to have had for the geometry classes that I taught at Menlo School and College. It is the finest example of instructional artistry that I have encountered.

When I taught statistics courses, I used the counting and probability chapters from *Mathematics: A Human Endeavor* by Jacobs. His approach engaged my students and enabled them to discover and master this subject. In the present book, Jacobs does the same thing for geometry.

Harold Jacobs–author and master teacher–loves geometry, and this book shows it. Its thousands of photographs, diagrams, and figures draw the reader into the material. Jacobs has a genius for finding illustrations that reveal a subject and make it come alive. A look at his sources shows the broad search that he made to assemble this visual feast.

Teachers know that in most classes the goal for students is to complete the homework exercises with as little pain as possible. When students get their assignment, they first go to the exercises. If the teacher worked an example in class, the student follows that. If not, then the student scans the text in search of an example that is similar to the exercise. So many textbooks are little more than a bunch of examples, followed by exercises that can be solved by using the methods of the examples. And the student learns by creative copying.

As you page through this book, you will be struck by how few words Jacobs uses in introducing each lesson. Jacobs knows that students will probably not read much introductory material and want to get to the exercises as quickly as possible–solutions are still the goal. But, for Jacobs, the exercises are the beating heart of the book. You will first notice that they are beautifully illustrated with real-world material. As you read, you will discover that they are engaging, carefully sequenced, and structured so that students discover ideas for themselves. Students come away from his exercise sets empowered, because the ideas have become "their" ideas. Students using this book, working alone or in groups, will learn geometry by doing it. The result is that they will enjoy learning a body of integrated concepts that has become their intellectual possession.

Donald J. Albers

Donald J. Albers
The Mathematical Association of America

Twenty-six hundred years ago Thales of Miletus launched the idea that Nature itself is subject to the laws of logic. Geometry, which had previously existed as a practical science, was found during the next few centuries to be tightly bound by logic. Some complex geometric facts were shown to be consequences of far simpler facts, and soon similar analyses of more general ideas about the world became standard for the Greek philosophers. The principle of stitching a few fundamental ideas together by logical analysis is at the heart of all modern science.

About 300 B.C.E., Euclid compiled his famous *Elements,* containing much of the geometry known at the time. Although the *Elements* does not fully meet today's standards of rigor, it quite rightly became and remained the principal textbook for teaching geometry for more than 2,000 years. In the past 100 years, however, the idea of *proof* has slowly receded (from American textbooks, at least), and now there is often little distinction between statements that have been proved formally and those that appear true on the basis of a drawing or a few measurements. This is an immense loss for American education, especially for science education. Some have tried to introduce formal proofs in algebra in place of those in geometry, but the results in algebra do not have the appeal of theorems such as that of Pythagoras. Geometry offers surprising theorems that can be proved by ingenious reasoning.

This book restores the idea of *proof* to its rightful place in geometry. Whoever studies this text will know what a proof is, what has been proved, and what has not.

Andrew M. Gleason

Andrew M. Gleason
Harvard University

Photograph by Roy Bishop

A Letter to the Student

The most useful question in the history of science is, Why?
Because mathematics is the language of science, the same question
is important in mathematics as well.

The oldest standing examples of applied geometry are the
pyramids of Egypt, built about 2600 B.C. The bases of these
structures are almost perfect squares, and their faces are precisely
constructed triangles. There is evidence that the Egyptians even
knew how to compute the *volume* of a pyramid but no evidence that
they ever tried to understand or explain their methods by asking,
"Why?" Their mathematics was based on intuition and experience;
even for other ancient civilizations from Babylon to Rome, intuition
and experience were as far as geometry went. The subject consisted
of disconnected rules, and the fact that these rules "worked" in
measuring land and constructing buildings seemed to be enough.

Your understanding of geometry has been like that of these
people of long ago. You have a good intuitive knowledge of the
subject simply by growing up in the world. As a small child, you
may have played with blocks in the shape of *cubes*. On the playground, you have played with balls in the shape of *spheres*. In school,
you use paper ruled with *parallel* and *perpendicular lines*. You drink
from cans in the shape of *cylinders* and eat ice cream from containers
in the shape of *cones*. Geometry is everywhere, and so it is natural
for you to take it for granted without ever asking, "Why?"

About 600 B.C., the Greeks made a discovery that led to a new way of looking at mathematics. Thales, one of the seven wise men of antiquity, saw how geometric ideas that had been discovered intuitively could be related to one another logically. If some were true, then others must follow without question. He raised the question Why? about a mathematical idea and then successfully answered it. For example, the four edges of the Great Pyramid that meet at its top are equal in length. Thales explained why it follows from this fact that the angles that these edges form with the sides of the base also must be equal.

After Thales came other Greek mathematicians, including Pythagoras, Hippocrates, and, eventually, Euclid. Euclid, about whom you will learn more in this book, presented geometry as a logical system of connected ideas so well that his book titled the *Elements* became the most widely used textbook ever written. Euclid's approach to geometry, centered on the question *why,* was so successful that it even inspired writers in other fields to organize their ideas in the same way. One of the most influential books of modern science, the *Principia* by Sir Isaac Newton, was modeled after Euclid's *Elements.*

The word *geometry* derives from the Greek words for "earth" and "measure" and in some languages is still used today to mean "earth measurement" or "surveying." Remarkably, although Euclid's *Elements* is the most famous geometry book of all time, the Greek word for geometry never appears in it. The *Elements* was not a book about measuring the earth; rather, by bringing geometry together as a coherent whole, it made geometry understandable *and* provided a model for other sciences.

As you pursue your study of geometry, you will encounter not only many familiar ideas but also many ideas new to you that are both beautiful and surprising. As the title of this book suggests, it is about seeing, doing, and understanding. As you read the lessons, you will *see* the main ideas and some of their applications. With the exercises comes your chance to *do, understand,* and, consequently, know *why.* I hope that in using this book you will discover for yourself the wonder and excitement of geometry so that you will find your study of it to be an enjoyable and rewarding endeavor.

Acknowledgments

Since beginning work on the first edition of *Geometry* some 30 years ago, I have benefited from the comments and suggestions of many people. Many teachers have been generous in sharing their ideas, both at conferences and through correspondence, and students have contributed as well.

I am especially grateful to Peter Renz, for his unflagging effort and support during the development of all three editions of this book; to Donald J. Albers, Andrew M. Gleason, Keith Henderson, and Thomas Rike, for their detailed comments on the preliminary manuscript of the third edition; and to Patricia Zimmerman, for her expertise and patience in editing this edition and the first. I am also indebted to many colleagues throughout the United States for their various contributions and helpful advice: to Thomas Banchoff, James A. Barys, Charles Bigelow, Richard D. Bourgin, William R. Chambers, Charles Herbert Clemens, Kevin DeVizia, Russel L. Drylie, Kate Epstein, Dani Falcioni, Frederick P. Greenleaf, Shirley S. Holm, Kris Holmes, Jane Jelinek, Ellen Kaplan, Laurence Kaplan, Robert Kaplan, Lehman Kapp, John Larsen, Joseph Malkevitch, Otis W. Milton III, Harry D. Peterson, Gwen Roberts, Doris Schattschneider, Dennis Simons, Wolfe Snow, John W. Sperry, and Clem Wings, in regard to this edition, and to Dennis Anderson, Steven Bergen, Richard Brady, Don Chakerian, Barbara Fracassa, Gary Froelich, Hector Hirigoyen, Geoffrey Hirsch, Mel Noble, Linda Rasmussen, Sy Schuster, Bill Shutters, Ross Taylor, and Sharon Tello, in regard to earlier editions.

Putting a book such as this one together is a formidable task. Without the patience and support of the dedicated staff at W. H. Freeman and Company, it would not have been possible. For their valued efforts, many times above and beyond the call of duty, I would like to thank Mary Johenk, Craig Bleyer, Jane O'Neill, Paul Rohloff, Diana Blume, and Vikii Wong. I remain grateful to Robert Ishi and Heather Wiley for their efforts on earlier editions and their influence on the present one.

I would also like to acknowledge my indebtedness to other authors whose work has been especially helpful to me in this revision: Benno Artmann, H. S. M. Coxeter, John L. Heilbron, David W. Henderson, Dan Pedoe, and David Wells. Finally, I want to express my gratitude to Martin Gardner, for his seemingly endless ideas and inspiring enthusiasm, and to Howard Eves, Morris Kline, George Polya, and W. W. Sawyer, for showing us by example what good mathematics teaching is all about.

Old Euclid drew a circle
On a sand-beach long ago.
He bounded and enclosed it
With angles thus and so.
His set of solemn graybeards
Nodded and argued much
Of arc and of circumference,
Diameters and such.
A silent child stood by them
From morning until noon
Because they drew such charming
Round pictures of the moon.

VACHEL LINDSAY

INTRODUCTION

Euclid, the Surfer, and the Spotter

In about 300 B.C., a man named Euclid wrote what has become one of the most successful books of all time. Euclid taught at the university at Alexandria, the main seaport of Egypt, and his book, the *Elements,* contained much of the mathematics then known. Its fame was almost immediate. The *Elements* has been translated into more languages and published in more editions than any other book except the Bible.

The poem "Euclid" is reprinted with the permission of Macmillian Publishing Co., from *Collected Poems* by Vachel Lindsay. Copyright 1914 by Macmillan Publishing Co., renewed in 1942 by Elizabeth C. Lindsay.

Although very little of the mathematics in the *Elements* was original, what made the book unique was its logical organization of the subject, beginning with a few simple principles and deriving everything else from them.

The *Elements* begins with an explanation of how to draw an *equilateral triangle,* that is, a triangle with three sides of equal length. Euclid's method requires the use of two tools: a straightedge for drawing straight lines and a compass for drawing circles. These tools have been used to make geometric drawings called *constructions* ever since Euclid's time.

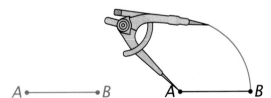
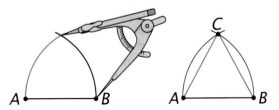

To construct an equilateral triangle, we begin by using the straightedge to draw a segment for one side. The segment is named AB in the figure at the left above. We set the metal point of the compass at A and adjust the compass so that the pencil point falls on B. The compass is now set to draw a circle with radius AB about point A. We draw an arc of this circle above the segment AB as shown in the second figure. Next we move the metal point of the compass to point B and, keeping the compass set at the same radius, cross the arc that we just drew with a second arc, as shown in the third figure. Finally, we draw two line segments from the point of intersection (labeled C in the last figure) to points A and B to form the triangle.

Exercises

1. Use a ruler to draw a line segment 12 centimeters long and then use a straightedge and compass to construct an equilateral triangle having this segment as one of its sides.

Next, we will consider two geometric problems about equilateral triangles. To make them easier to understand, they will be presented in the form of a story.

The Puzzles of the Surfer and the Spotter

One night a ship is wrecked in a storm at sea and only two members of the crew survive. They manage to swim to a deserted tropical island where they fall asleep exhausted. After exploring the island the next morning, one of the men decides that he would like to spend some time there surfing from the beaches. The other man, however, wants to escape and decides to use his time looking for a ship that might rescue him.

The island is overgrown with vegetation and happens to be in the shape of an equilateral triangle, each side being 12 kilometers (about 7.5 miles) long.

Wanting to be in the best possible position to spot any ship that might sail by, the man who hopes to escape (we will call him the "spotter") goes to one of the corners of the island. Because he doesn't know which corner is best, he decides to rotate from one to another, spending a day on each. He wants to build a shelter somewhere on the island and a path from it to each corner so that the sum of the lengths of the three paths is a minimum. (Digging up the vegetation to clear the paths is not an easy job.) Where should the spotter build his house?

The figure below is a scale drawing of the island in which 1 centimeter (cm) represents 1 kilometer (km). Suppose that the spotter builds his house at point D. The three paths that he has to clear have the following lengths: DA = 4.4 km, DB = 9.1 km, and DC = 7.9 km. Check these measurements with your ruler, remembering that 1 cm represents 1 km. The sum of these lengths is 21.4 km.

If the spotter builds his house at point E, the path lengths are: EA = 10.4 km, EB = 5.1 km, and EC = 6.9 km, and their sum is 22.4 km. So point D is a better place for him to build than point E. But where is the best place?

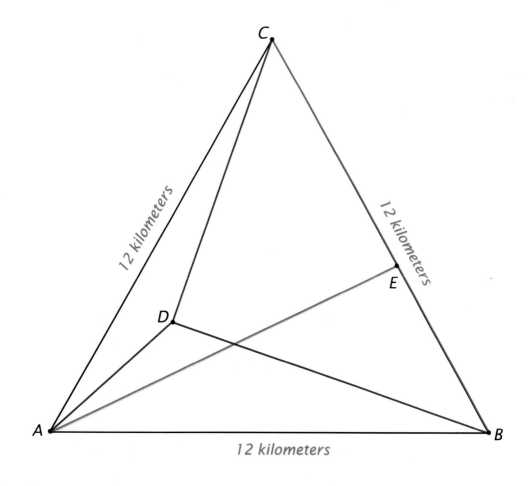

12 kilometers

2. Use the equilateral triangle that you drew in the first exercise to represent the island. Choose several different points on it; for each point, measure the distance between it and each of the corners to the nearest 0.1 cm, and find their sum, as illustrated for points D and E on page 3.

3. On the basis of your work in exercise 2, where do you think is the best place for the spotter to build his house? And how many kilometers of path does he have to clear? (Remember that 1 cm on your map represents 1 km.)

4. Where do you think is the *worst* place on the island for the spotter to locate? How many kilometers of path would he have to clear from it?

Now consider the problem of where the surfer should build *his* house. He likes the beaches along all three sides of the island and decides to spend an equal amount of time on each beach. To make the paths from his house to each beach as short as possible, he constructs them so that they are *perpendicular* to the lines of the beaches.

Perpendicular lines form right angles, 90 degrees (90°) on a protractor or the angle formed by the edges of a file card. An easy way to draw a line that is perpendicular to another line is to use a file card as shown in the figures below. Small squares are usually used to indicate that lines are perpendicular.

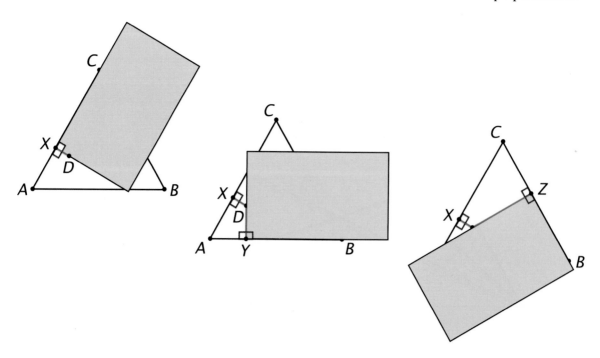

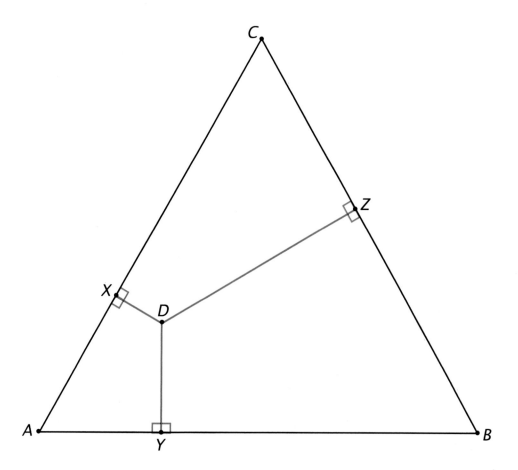

In the figure above, if the surfer built his house at point D, the three paths to the beaches would be as shown. Path DX is perpendicular to beach AC, path DY is perpendicular to beach AB, and path DZ is perpendicular to beach BC. The lengths of the three paths are: DX = 1.4 km, DY = 2.9 km, and DZ = 6.0 km; so their sum is 10.3 km.

The surfer, like the spotter, wants to locate his house so that the sum of the lengths of the paths is a minimum. Where is the best place on the island for him?

5. Use a straightedge and compass to construct another equilateral triangle whose sides are 12 centimeters long. Choose several different points on it; for each point, measure the perpendicular distance from it to each of the sides to the nearest 0.1 cm, and find their sum as illustrated for point D above.

6. On the basis of your work in exercise 5, where do you think is the best place for the surfer to build his house? And how many kilometers of path does he have to clear?

7. Where do you think is the worst place for the surfer to locate? How many kilometers of path would he have to clear from it?

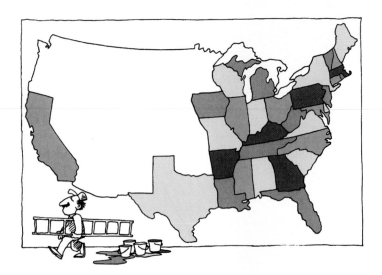

Inductive Reasoning

In thinking about the puzzles of the surfer and the spotter, you first collected some evidence–you made drawings and measured them. Then you looked for conclusions based on what you had observed.

This method of reasoning is used in both science and mathematics. You will be using it throughout this book. The scientist who makes observations, discovers regularities, and formulates general laws of nature calls this process the *scientific method*. Mathematicians refer to it as *inductive reasoning*. It is the method used for drawing conclusions from a limited set of observations.

We use inductive reasoning regularly in everyday life. Its conclusions are generally reliable and useful, but they are sometimes wrong. For this reason, scientists call such conclusions *conjectures.*

In 1852, a young English mathematician named Francis Guthrie noticed that he could color every map that he could draw or had seen with only four colors in such a way that no two regions having a common border were the same color. The map of the United States of 1852 shown above is an example. Many people tried to draw maps that would require more than four colors, but no one succeeded, which seemed to confirm that "four colors suffice" but did not prove it.

In 1976, more than a century after Guthrie made his conjecture, Wolfgang Haken and Kenneth Appel proved that Guthrie was right. To celebrate Haken and Appel's proof, the University of Illinois used the postage-meter message that you see here. The method that they used, *deductive reasoning*, uses logic to draw conclusions from statements already accepted as true.

FOUR COLORS SUFFICE

In addition to using inductive reasoning throughout your study of geometry to discover *what* is true, you will also learn how to reason deductively to be able to understand *why.*

Chapter 1

An Introduction to Geometry

In this chapter, you will see how practical problems ranging from designing a city and measuring the earth to using shadows to tell time led to the development of geometry. The ideas that come from these problems are important because they lead to the solutions of other problems. As you proceed, you will become acquainted with geometric terms and ideas that will be useful as you continue your study of geometry.

City wall

Aqueduct

Light-
house

Great
harbor

Pharos
town

City wall

LESSON 1

Lines in Designing a City

Alexandria, the city in which Euclid wrote his famous book on geometry, is named for Alexander the Great. Alexander had conquered much of the ancient world by the time of his death in 323 B.C. He is thought to have planned the streets of Alexandria, which today has become the second largest city in Egypt.

The map above shows the arrangement of the streets in ancient Alexandria. It also suggests some of the basic terms used in geometry. The streets lie along straight *lines;* they intersect in *points* and lie in a common *plane.*

•A

B•   •C

Some points

Euclid described a *point* as "that which has no part." This description conveys the idea that, when we draw a dot on paper to represent a point, the point, unlike the dot, has a location only, without physical extent. The points in a figure to which we want to refer are labeled with capital letters.

Euclid described a *line* as having "breadthless length" and said that "the extremities of a line are points." These statements reveal that he was thinking of what we would now call a *line segment.*

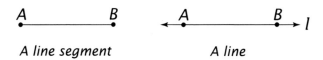

A line segment   A line

A *line segment* is part of a line bounded by two endpoints; it has a length that can be measured. Line segment AB in the figure at the left above has a length of 1 inch. A *line,* however, cannot be measured. The arrows on the figure of the line at the right above indicate that a line extends without end in both directions. These figures also suggest that lines, and hence line segments, are always *straight,* like a stretched string or the edge of a ruler.

Lines are usually named either by two points that they contain, such as line AB above, or by a single small letter. The line in the figure could be simply named line *l.*

The map of Alexandria is printed on a flat surface, which illustrates part of a *plane.* Planes are usually represented by figures such as the two at the right and are usually named, like points, with capital letters. These figures are useful in suggesting that planes are always *flat* but are unfortunately misleading in suggesting that planes have edges. In geometry, we think of a plane as having *no boundaries.* Although the parts of the planes shown here are bounded by edges, the complete planes extend beyond them, just as the line AB extends beyond the endpoints of the segment determined by A and B.

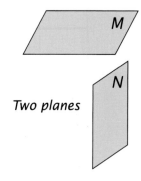

Two planes

Some additional terms relating *points, lines,* and *planes* are illustrated and defined below.

Definitions

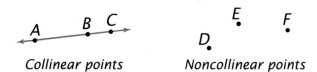

Collinear points   Noncollinear points

Points are *collinear* if there is a line that contains all of them. Points are *noncollinear* if no single line contains them all.

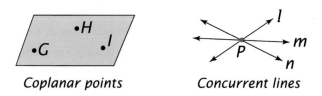

Coplanar points   Concurrent lines

Points are *coplanar* if there is a plane that contains all of them. Lines are *concurrent* if they contain the same point.

In the figure at the right above, lines *l, m,* and *n* all contain point P, their common *intersection.*

Exercises

Set I

This map shows the plan of the main streets of the ancient Chinese city Ch'ang-an.

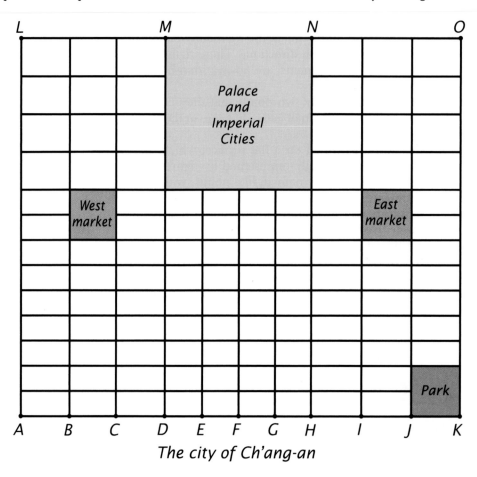

The city of Ch'ang-an

The intersections of the street at the bottom of the map with the streets above it are labeled A through K.

1. What word is used to describe points such as these, given that one line contains them all?

Use your ruler to find the lengths of the following line segments in centimeters.

2. AK.
5. AB.
3. AF.
6. AL.
4. AD.

If the map is accurately drawn and the street from A to K is 6 miles long,

7. how many miles is it from A to F?
8. how many miles does 1 cm of the map represent?
9. how many miles is it from A to L?
10. Is the city square? Why or why not?
11. What regions of the city do appear to be square?

The city, whose name means "long security," was protected by a surrounding wall.

12. Use the lengths of the streets bordering the city to figure out how many miles long the wall was that surrounded it.

If the city were perfectly flat, then all of the points in it would lie in one plane.

13. What word is used to describe points such as these?

14. Are the streets in the map represented by *lines* or *line segments?*

15. What is the difference between a line and a line segment?

Notice that AB, CD, and HK are three different segments, yet they all lie in *one* line.

16. On how many different lines do all the segments in this map lie?

Set II

The points and lines in the figure below are related in some unusual ways.

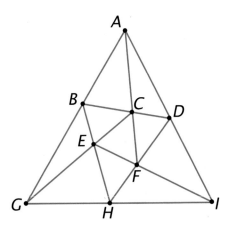

Each point in which line segments intersect has been labeled with a letter.

17. How many such points does the figure contain?

18. What does the word *collinear* mean?

The figure has been drawn so that each set of points that *appears* to be collinear actually *is.*

For example, points E, F, and I are collinear and lie on the line EI.

19. How many sets of three collinear points does the figure contain? List them, beginning with E-F-I.

20. What does the word *concurrent* mean?

How many different *lines* in the figure are concurrent at

21. point A?

22. point B?

23. point C?

24. each of the other points?

And now some very tricky questions about the line segments that can be named by using the letters in the figure.

25. How many different line segments in the figure meet at point A? Name them.

How many different line segments meet at

26. point B? Name them.

27. point C? Name them.

Set III

On a sheet of graph paper, draw a figure similar to, but much larger than, the one below.

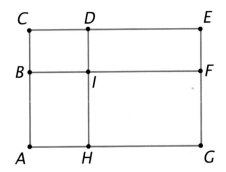

1. Use a colored pen or pencil to draw the following three lines:

   AI, CF, and DG.

   Draw enough of each line so that it crosses the entire figure.

2. What seems to be true about the three lines AI, CF, and DG?

Now use a pen or pencil of a different color to draw these three lines:

AF, CI, and EH.

Extend each line to the edges of the figure.

3. Describe what you see.

Now use a pen or pencil of a third color to draw these three lines:

BG, CH, and EI.

Extend each line to the edges of the figure.

4. What do you notice?

5. Draw the figure again, but change it so that it is taller or shorter, BF is higher or lower, and DH is farther to the left or right. An example of such a figure is shown here, but choose your own.

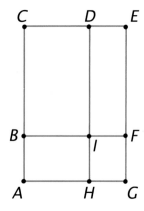

6. Now try drawing all the lines again and see what happens. What do you think?

7. Try changing the figure in other ways to see what happens to the lines drawn in the three colors. Some examples of altered figures are shown here. (Be sure to make your drawings much larger!)

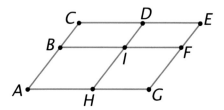

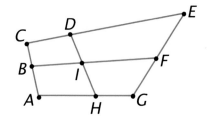

8. What do you think?

LESSON 2

Angles in Measuring the Earth

The ancient Greeks knew that the world was round. Eratosthenes, the head of the library in Alexandria where Euclid lived, figured out a clever way to estimate the distance around the world. His method depended on measuring an *angle*.

Euclid described an *angle* as "the inclination to one another of two lines in a plane which meet one another." If we draw a figure showing two lines, *l* and *m*, meeting at a point P, several angles are formed.

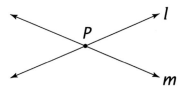

The figure can also be described as consisting of four *rays* starting from point P. As the figure suggests, a *ray* is part of a line that extends endlessly in one direction. To refer to a ray, we always name its endpoint first, followed by the name of any other point on it. The name of the ray in the first figure at the right is PA.

An *angle* is a pair of rays that have the same endpoint. The rays are called the *sides* of the angle and their common endpoint is called the *vertex* of the angle. Angles can be named in several ways. Using the symbol ∠ to mean "angle," we can name the angle in the second figure at the right ∠P or ∠1 or ∠APB or ∠BPA. Notice that, if the angle is named with three letters, the vertex is named in the middle.

A ray

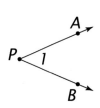

Two rays that form an angle

Before learning how Eratosthenes measured the earth, we will review the way in which angles are measured. To measure an angle, we need a *protractor*.

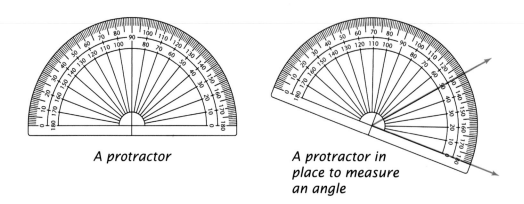

A protractor

A protractor in place to measure an angle

The protractor measures angles in *degrees* and has two scales, each numbered from 0 to 180. The center of the protractor is placed on the vertex of the angle so that the 0 on one of the scales falls on one side of the angle. The number that falls on the other side of the *same* scale gives the measurement of the angle in degrees. Look carefully at the scales on the protractor in the figure above to see why the angle has a measure of 50° and *not* 130°.

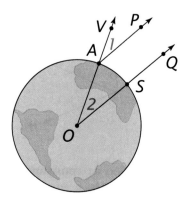

The diagram above illustrates the method that Eratosthenes used to measure the earth. He knew that Alexandria was about 500 miles north of the city of Syene (now called Aswan). The points A and S represent Alexandria and Syene, respectively, and the rays AP and SQ represent the direction of the sun as seen from each city. At noon on a certain day of the year, the sun was directly overhead in Syene, as shown by SQ. In Alexandria at the same time, the direction of the sun was along AP, in contrast with the overhead direction AV.

Eratosthenes measured the angle between these two directions, ∠1, and found that it was about 7.5°. Euclid had shown why it was reasonable to conclude that ∠1 was equal to ∠2, the angle with its vertex at the center of the earth. By dividing 7.5° into 360° (the measure of the degrees of a full circle), we get 48; so the full circle is 48 times the angle from Alexandria to Syene:

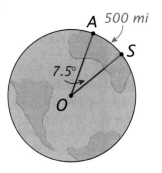

$$48 \times 7.5° = 360°.$$

Eratosthenes concluded that the earth's circumference (the entire distance around the circle) was 48 times the distance from Alexandria to Syene:

$$48 \times 500 \text{ miles} = 24{,}000 \text{ miles}.$$

The modern value of the circumference of the earth is about 25,000 miles; so Eratosthenes' estimate was remarkably accurate.

Exercises

Set I

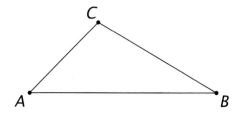

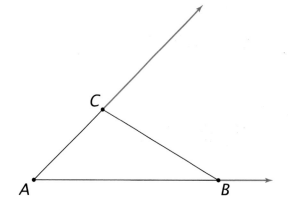

Triangle Measurements. Each side and angle of the triangle above has a different measure. If you simply look at the figure without doing any measuring,

1. which side is the longest?

2. which angle is the largest?

3. which side is the shortest?

4. which angle is the smallest?

5. Use your ruler to measure the sides of the triangle, each to the nearest 0.1 cm.

Most protractors are too large to be able to measure the angles of a figure such as this triangle easily. For example, to measure ∠A, it is easiest to extend its sides as shown in color in the figure at the right above.

6. Name the two rays that are the sides of ∠A.

7. Use your protractor to measure ∠A.

8. Carefully trace triangle ABC on your paper and then extend the sides of ∠B.

9. Name the two rays that are the sides of ∠B.

10. Measure ∠B.

Go back to the figure you drew for exercise 8 and extend the sides of ∠C.

11. Name the two rays that are the sides of ∠C.

12. Measure ∠C.

Constellation Angles.
Eudoxus, a Greek mathematician, was the first to write about constellations, groupings of stars in the sky, in the fourth century B.C.

Two of the ten stars in the constellation Orion are among the brightest in the sky: Betelgeuse and Rigel. They appear as points B and R in the figure below.

Use a protractor to measure each of the four angles to check your guesses.

16. ∠1.   **18.** ∠2.

17. ∠B.   **19.** ∠R.

One of the most well-known constellations is Ursa Major, or the Big Dipper.

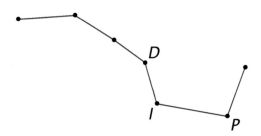

20. Carefully trace the figure above and then extend the sides of the angles as necessary to measure each of the following angles.

21. ∠D.

22. ∠I.

23. ∠P.

Set II

The Sliding Ladder. This figure represents a ladder 6 feet long leaning against a wall.

13. What word describes the apparent relation of the points labeled X, Y, and Z in Orion's belt?

Look carefully at the four angles, ∠1, ∠B, ∠2, and ∠R. Without measuring, guess which of these four angles is

14. smallest.

15. largest.

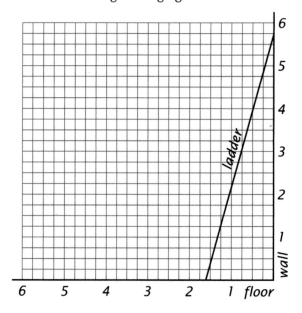

24. On a sheet of graph paper that is 4 units per inch, draw two lines to represent the wall and floor as shown in the figure. Mark a scale on the wall, letting 1 inch (4 units) represent 1 foot.

   The safest position in which to place the ladder is with its top $5^3/_4$ feet above the floor. Place the end of your ruler at the $5^3/_4$-foot point on the wall and turn the ruler until its 6-inch mark just touches the floor. Trace this safe position for the ladder on your paper.

25. Approximately how far is the foot of the ladder from the wall?

Use your protractor to measure the angle that the ladder makes

26. with the floor.

27. with the wall.

Now suppose that the ladder slips down the wall. Place the end of your ruler at the 5-foot point on the wall and turn it until its 6-inch mark touches the floor. Trace this position on your paper.

28. About how far is the foot of the ladder from the wall now?

Measure the angle that the ladder now makes

29. with the floor.

30. with the wall.

Place the end of your ruler at the 3-foot point on the wall, again being sure to turn it so that its 6-inch mark touches the floor.

31. About how far is the foot of the ladder from the wall now?

Measure the angle that the ladder now makes

32. with the floor.

33. with the wall.

Notice that, as the ladder's angle with the floor becomes smaller, its angle with the wall becomes larger.

34. How big do you suppose each angle would be when the angles are equal?

Set III

Measuring Mars. The above map of the planet Mars was drawn in 1903 by the astronomer Percival Lowell. It shows canals and cities that he thought had been built by intelligent beings on the planet.

   Suppose that the Martians discovered that, when the sun is directly overhead at Botrodus (point B below), it is 24° from the vertical at Aquae Calidae (point A).[*]

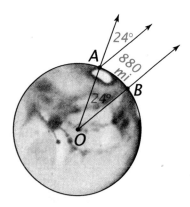

If the distance between the two cities is 880 miles, what is the distance around Mars? (Show your reasoning.)

---

[*]For convenience, we will assume that the Martians use the same units of measure that we do.

Polygons and Polyhedra: Pyramid Architecture

More than 2,000 years before Euclid was born, the ancient Egyptians used their knowledge of geometry to build the Great Pyramid at Giza, the only one of the "seven wonders of the world" still in existence. This pyramid is comparable in height to a building 40 stories high and covers an area of more than 13 acres. It was put together from more than 2 million stone blocks, weighing between 2 and 150 tons each!

Its base is almost a perfect square, and its four faces are in the shape of triangles. Squares and triangles are special types of *polygons,* and the pyramid itself is an example of a *polyhedron.* The words polygon and polyhedron are Greek in origin and, although the plural of polygon is polygons, the plural of polyhedron is *polyhedra.*

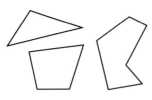

Polygons

Polyhedra

Polygons and polyhedra are related to line segments in a simple way. As you know, a line segment is part of a line bounded by two endpoints; it is a one-dimensional figure. A *polygon* is bounded by line segments and lies in a plane; it is a two-dimensional figure. A *polyhedron* is bounded by polygons and exists in space; it is a three-dimensional figure.

Figure	*Dimensions*	*Example*
line segment	1	
polygon	2	
polyhedron	3	

The most basic way to name polygons is according to their number of sides. Some of them are illustrated here.

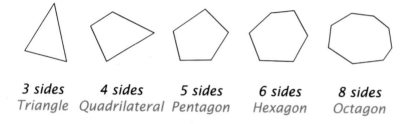

3 sides	4 sides	5 sides	6 sides	8 sides
Triangle	Quadrilateral	Pentagon	Hexagon	Octagon

The ways for naming polyhedra are more complicated. Some words, such as *cube* and *pyramid,* are already familiar to you. Others, such as *tetrahedron* and *parallelepiped,* are probably not.

Whenever polygons or polyhedra are in practical problems, their measurements are often important. Consider the Great Pyramid, for example. A person seeing it for the first time might wonder how much ground it covers. In other words, what is the *area* of the polygon that is its base? Another question might concern how long it would take to walk around the pyramid. The answer depends on the *perimeter* of its base. A third question might concern how much stone was required to build the pyramid. This answer is related to the *volume* of the polyhedron that is its shape.

In this lesson, we will review two of these terms. The easiest one is perimeter. The *perimeter* of a polygon is the sum of the lengths of its sides.

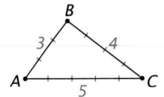

The perimeter of
triangle ABC is
$3 + 4 + 5 = 12$ units.

1 unit

1 square unit

The second term is *area*. According to one dictionary, area is "the surface included within a set of lines; specifically, the number of unit squares equal in measure to the surface."* This definition is obvious for a simple figure such as this rectangle.

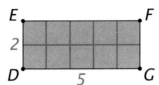

The area of
rectangle DEFG is
$2 \times 5 = 10$ square units.

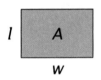

The figure even suggests the simple formula for the area of any rectangle. A rectangle with length l and width w has area A given by

$$A = lw.$$

The base of the Great Pyramid is square, with sides 756 feet long.

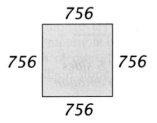

Its perimeter, then, is

756 feet + 756 feet + 756 feet + 756 feet =
4×756 feet =
3,024 feet.

A square is also a rectangle; so its area is

756 feet $\times$ 756 feet =
571,536 square feet.

Merriam-Webster's Collegiate Dictionary.

Exercises

Set I

The Perimeter and Area of a Square. The base of the Great Pyramid is in the shape of a square. A square is a rectangle all of whose sides are of equal length. Because a square is a *rectangle,* each of its angles is a *right angle;* that is, each angle has a measure of 90°.

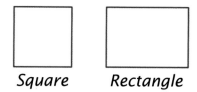

Square   Rectangle

1. Use your ruler and protractor to accurately draw a square whose sides are 3 inches long. Then divide it into smaller squares whose sides are 1 inch long.

2. What is the area of the square?

3. What is its perimeter?

Without drawing it, imagine a square whose sides are 6 inches long.

4. What is its area?

5. What is its perimeter?

Without drawing it, imagine a square whose sides are 1 foot long.

6. What is its area in square feet?

7. What is its perimeter in feet?

Now think of the same square as having sides 12 inches long.

8. What is its area in square inches?

9. What is its perimeter in inches?

If a square has sides that are x units long, what, in terms of x, is its

10. area?

11. perimeter?

Pentominoes. A game called Pentominoes uses the 12 pieces shown here. Their names are suggested by their shapes.

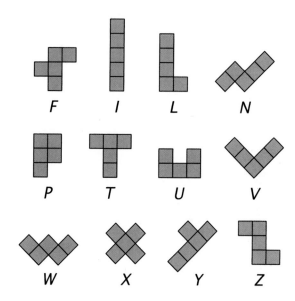

F   I   L   N

P   T   U   V

W   X   Y   Z

12. Each piece is in the shape of a *polygon.* What is a polygon?

13. Which piece is in the shape of a *quadrilateral?* Why?

14. All 12 pieces have the same area. What is it?

15. All 12 pieces have the same perimeter *except for one.* Which one is it?

Texas Ranches. Two ranches are for sale in Texas. Each is in the shape of a rectangle and their dimensions are as follows:

Ranch A: 4 miles wide, 14 miles long.
Ranch B: 6 miles wide, 10 miles long.

16. Suppose that neither ranch has a fence. Which one would need more fencing to surround it?

17. Both ranches are the same price and you want to buy the bigger one. Which one should you buy?

18. Which is more important in this situation: *perimeter* or *area?*

Set II

A Model of the Great Pyramid. While on a trip to study the Great Pyramid in 1799, Napoleon made this sketch together with some notes.

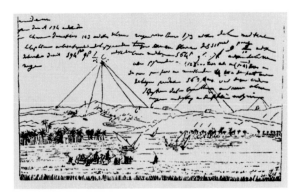

Use your ruler and protractor to draw a square 10 cm on each side for the base of the pyramid on a heavy sheet of paper.

The other four faces of the pyramid are in the shape of triangles. Use the measurements shown in the figure below to draw four triangles on a sheet of heavy paper.

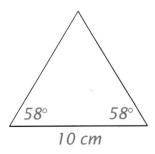

10 cm

19. Use your protractor to measure the angle at the top of one of these triangles.

20. Do any sides of the triangle appear to be equal? Use your ruler to check your answer.

21. Cut out the square and four triangles and tape them together to make a scale model of the Great Pyramid.

22. Make a drawing of the pyramid.

The pyramid has five faces altogether: its square base and its four triangular faces.

23. What kind of figures are squares and triangles?

24. What kind of figure is the pyramid itself?

The line segments in which the faces of the pyramid meet are called its *edges.*

25. How many edges does the pyramid have?

26. How many corners does it have?

27. How many edges meet at the top of the pyramid?

28. How many edges meet at each corner of the base?

Each face of the pyramid lies in a *plane.*

29. In how many different planes do the faces of the pyramid lie?

30. If two *lines* intersect, they intersect in a *point.* If two *planes* intersect, in what do they intersect?

31. Use your ruler to estimate, as best as you can, the height of your model in centimeters.

In your model, 10 cm represent 756 feet, the length of one edge of the base of the pyramid.

32. How many feet does 1 cm represent?

33. Use this result and your estimate of the height of your model in centimeters to estimate the height of the Great Pyramid in feet.

34. What view of the Great Pyramid does this drawing appear to show?

Set III

A Square Puzzle. The book *Mathematical Snapshots* by the Polish mathematician Hugo Steinhaus begins with an illustration of four polygons arranged to form a square.*

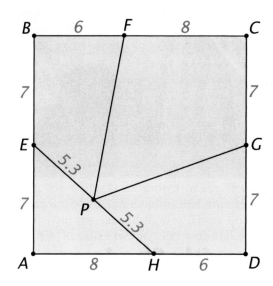

Use your ruler and protractor to make an enlargement of this figure on a sheet of heavy paper by doing each of the following:

(1) Draw a square 14 cm on each side and label its corners A, B, C, and D as shown in the figure.

(2) Mark the points E, F, G, and H at the indicated distances from the corners.

(3) Draw EH.

(4) Mark point P on EH.

(5) Draw PF and PG.

Test the accuracy of your drawing and your ability to measure angles by doing each of the following.

1. ∠EPF, ∠FPG, and ∠GPH should appear to be equal. What is the measure of each of these angles? Write the measure inside each angle.

2. ∠BFP should appear to be 30° larger than ∠AEH. What is the measure of each of these angles?

3. ∠BEH should appear to be 90° larger than ∠EHA. What is the measure of each of these angles?

4. Two other line segments in the figure should appear to have the same length as that of EH. Which are they?

5. Carefully cut the four polygons out. Try to rearrange them to form an equilateral triangle (a triangle all of whose sides are equal). Trace the arrangement on your paper.

6. About how many centimeters long is each side of the equilateral triangle?

7. How large is each of its three angles?

8. How does the area of the triangle compare with that of the original square? Why?

9. What is the area of the triangle?

10. How does the perimeter of the triangle compare with that of the original square?

---

*The figure is the solution to a puzzle created in 1902 by Henry Dudeney, England's greatest inventor of mathematical puzzles. The lengths in it have been rounded for convenience.

Constructions: Telling Time with Shadows

The largest sundial in the world, built in 1724 in Jaipur, India, is shown in the photograph above. Its gnomon (the object that casts the shadow) is a ramp that rises 90 feet above the ground. The shadow cast by the ramp moves at a rate of about two inches per minute, making it possible to accurately tell the local time within seconds!

Sundials were the main instrument for keeping time from the days of ancient Egypt until the sixteenth century. At noon, the sun is at its highest in the sky, the shadow cast by the gnomon is at its shortest, and, in the northern hemisphere, the shadow points northward.

The Egyptians were aware of these facts and put them to use in constructing their pyramids so that their sides faced directly north, south, east, and west. The method that they are thought to have used for finding map directions is related to a geometric construction.

Since the time of Euclid, two tools have been used in making geometric drawings: the *straightedge* and *compass*. The straightedge is used for drawing *lines* (actually *line segments*), and the compass is used for drawing *circles* or parts of circles called *arcs*. A *circle* is the set of all points in a plane that are a fixed distance from a given point in the plane. The fixed distance is called the *radius* of the circle and the given point is called its *center*.

Drawings made with just a straightedge and compass are called *constructions* to distinguish them from those made with other tools such as a ruler and protractor.

In this lesson, we will learn simple constructions for bisecting line segments and angles. To *bisect* something means to divide it into two equal parts.

Construction 1
To bisect a line segment.

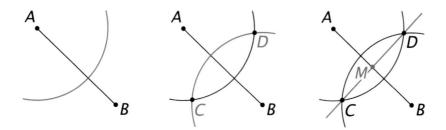

Let AB be the given line segment. With A as center, draw an arc intersecting the segment as shown in the first figure. With B as center, draw an arc of the same radius that intersects the first arc in two points (C and D in the second figure). Draw line CD. Line CD bisects segment AB. In other words, AM and MB have the same length.

There is a simple way to prove that this method does what we have claimed. You will learn how it works later in your study of geometry.

Angles can also be bisected with a straightedge and compass.

Construction 2
To bisect an angle.

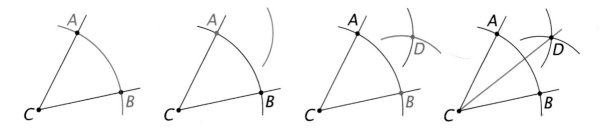

Let ∠C be the given angle. With point C as center, draw an arc that intersects the sides of the angle (at points A and B in the figure). With A as center, draw an arc inside the angle as shown in the second figure. With B as center, draw an arc of the same radius that intersects the arc drawn from point A (at point D in the third figure). Draw line CD. It bisects ∠C. In other words, ∠ACD and ∠DCB are equal in measure.

This equality also can be easily proved, as you will learn later.

Exercises

Set I

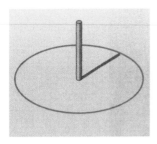

Finding North by Shadows. The ancient Egyptians are thought to have used the shadow of a vertical post to find north. The figure below is an overhead view of some level ground into which a post has been stuck at point P. Once in the morning the tip of the post's shadow touches the circle at A, and once in the afternoon it touches the circle at B. These two positions of the shadow, PA and PB, form ∠P.

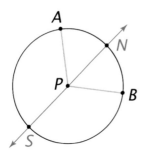

1. Draw a circle larger than this one, label its center P, mark two points on the circle A and B, and draw PA and PB. Bisect ∠P.

   The ray that bisects ∠P points north. Label the point in which it intersects the circle N. Also draw the ray from P that points south.

2. Check the accuracy of your drawing by using your protractor to measure ∠APB and ∠APN. What measurements do you get?

3. Apply the directions given for exercise 1 to the following figure.

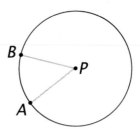

4. Check the accuracy of your drawing by using your protractor to measure ∠APB and ∠APN.

   In each of your drawings, points P, A, and B do not lie on the same line.

5. What word describes such points?

   On the other hand, points P, A, and B do lie in the same *plane.*

6. What word describes these points?

   Suppose line NS in the figure below points north and south.

7. Draw a figure like this one on your paper and then use your straightedge and compass to construct the line that bisects segment NS. In what directions do you think this line points? Label them on the line.

8. Use your protractor to measure the angles formed by NS and EW. Do you get the results that you would expect?

9. What is the sum of all four angles? What do you expect it to be?

Bisectors in a Triangle.

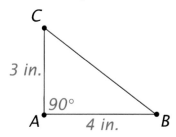

10. Use your ruler and protractor to draw a triangle with the measurements shown in the figure above. Then use your straightedge and compass to bisect each side of the triangle.

11. What relation do the three bisecting lines that you drew seem to have to each other?

12. Where do the lines seem to meet?

Label the point in which they meet P and draw PA.

13. How do the distances from point P to the corners of the triangle, A, B, and C, seem to compare?

14. Make another copy of the same triangle. This time, use your straightedge and compass to bisect its angles.

15. What seems to be true about the three lines that you drew?

Label the point in which they meet S.

16. Are the distances from point S to the corners of the triangle equal?

Set II

About Sundials. A sundial was once featured on boxes of Kellogg's Raisin Bran. When the gnomon (shadow pointer) was cut out and put in place, its shadow moved around the dial during the day. The way in which the hour lines are spaced suggests that the shadow does not always move at the same speed.

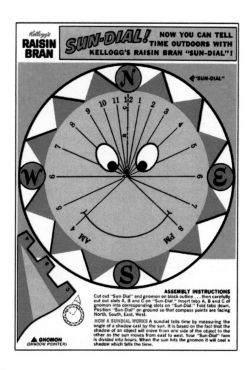

In what map direction does the shadow

17. point at 6 o'clock in the morning?

18. point at noon?

19. never point?

20. At what time of the day do you think the shadow moves the most slowly?

21. When does it appear to move fastest?

The hour lines of the Kellogg sundial have been redrawn and lettered in the figure below.

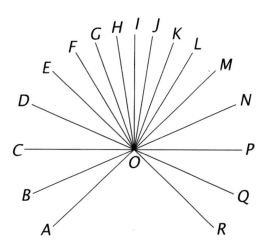

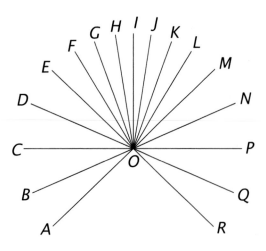

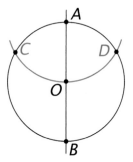

Draw a line through O as shown in the figure at the bottom of the preceding column and label the points in which it intersects the circle A and B.

With your compass, draw an arc centered at A and passing through O as shown in the figure below. Label the points in which the arc intersects the circle C and D.

22. Which angle in the figure seems to be equal to ∠HOI?

23. If your answer to exercise 22 is true, what does OI do to ∠HOJ?

24. Does OQ seem to bisect ∠POR? Why or why not?

25. Name two angles in the figure that OC seems to bisect.

26. Which angle seems to be equal to ∠COF?

27. Name three angles in the figure that seem to be equal to ∠COD.

28. Which angle seems to be equal to ∠AOR?

A sundial in which the hour lines are evenly spaced is simpler to make but harder to use. A straightedge and compass can be used to construct such a sundial without the use of a protractor.

29. Use your compass to draw a circle with a radius of 3 inches. Label its center O.

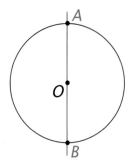

Draw another arc centered at B and passing through O as shown in the left-hand figure below. Label the points in which the arc intersects the circle E and F.

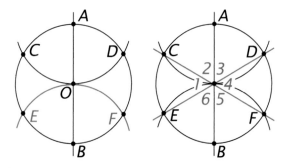

If you have drawn your figure accurately, points C, O, and F should appear to be collinear, as should points E, O, and D.

30. What does collinear mean?

Draw the lines CF and ED and number the angles at the center as shown in the right-hand figure above. Each of the six numbered angles in your drawing should appear to be equal. Measure them with your protractor.

31. What does the measure of each angle appear to be?

Use your straightedge and compass to bisect ∠1, ∠2, ∠3, and ∠4. The lines in your drawing should now look like this.

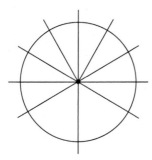

32. What is the measure of each of the eight smaller angles in the figure?

Use your straightedge and compass to bisect each of these angles. The lines in your drawing should now look like this.

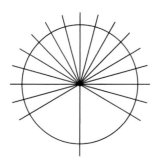

Compare your drawing with the Kellogg's sundial and number the hour spokes appropriately.

If your sundial had a gnomon perpendicular to its base and if the sundial were tilted in the right direction, the shadow would move at a steady speed across the hour lines.

Through how many degrees would the shadow turn

33. between 6 A.M. and 6 P.M.?

34. between noon and 6 P.M.?

35. during one hour?

36. How long would it take the shadow to turn 1 degree?

Set III

Angle Bisectors in a Rectangle. Something rather surprising usually happens when the angles of a rectangle are bisected. The following exercises will help you discover what it is.

1. On a sheet of graph paper ruled 4 units per inch, draw a rectangle having sides with lengths 1.5 and 2 inches.

2. Draw the four lines that bisect the angles of the rectangle. What polygon do they seem to form?

3. Draw another rectangle having sides of lengths 2 inches and 3 inches. Draw the lines that bisect its angles. What do you notice?

4. Follow the directions given in exercise 3 but with a rectangle of sides 2 inches and 4 inches. What do you notice?

5. Follow the directions given in exercise 3 but with a rectangle of sides 1 inch and 4 inches. What do you notice?

6. Is the size of the polygon formed related in any way to the shape of the rectangle? Explain.

7. Do you think there is any rectangle for which the polygon would shrink to a point? Explain.

An overhead view of plots of land
in the shape of quadrilaterals not
far from Alexandria.

We Can't Go On Like This

This title may seem to be a very strange one for a geometry lesson, but it points out a troubling problem with what we have been doing so far.

We have become acquainted with many important ideas in geometry, mostly in an informal way. We have learned how to make simple constructions with a straightedge and compass, yet we don't really know how they work. We have guessed some conclusions on the basis of the appearance of things, not always being certain that they were true. Our approach to geometry to this point has been comparable to that of the ancient Egyptians, long before the time of Euclid.

What has survived of Egyptian mathematics as it existed 4,000 years ago reveals an accumulation of rules and results seemingly based on trial and error. The Egyptians were evidently satisfied with ideas that appeared to be useful, without concerning themselves about why they might or might not always be true.

Here is an example of the difficulties to which this approach to geometry leads. To find the areas of fields in the shape of quadrilaterals, the Egyptians used the formula

$$A = \frac{1}{4}(a + c)(b + d)$$

in which *a, b, c,* and *d* are the lengths of the consecutive sides. They had gotten this formula from the ancient Babylonians. The trouble with it is that sometimes it gives the correct answer and sometimes it does not.

Thus when tax assessors used it to figure out the areas of four-sided fields, some landowners were charged correctly and some were not. In fact, those who were not were cheated every time! The tax assessors may have known that these charges were incorrect, but apparently no one could figure out what was wrong with the formula to cause it to give such undependable results.

We will explore this problem and some other similarly troubling ones in this lesson.

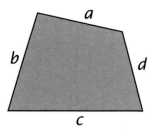

Exercises

Set I

The Egyptian Tax Assessor. We are back in 2500 B.C. and three Egyptians, Ramses, Cheops, and Ptahotep, have recently purchased plots of land in the shapes shown here.

The tax assessor uses his formula for the area of a quadrilateral,

$$A = \frac{1}{4}(a + c)(b + d)$$

in which *a, b, c,* and *d* are the lengths of the consecutive sides.

What area does he calculate for the plot belonging to

1. Ramses?

2. Cheops?

3. Ptahotep?

The bigger the plot, the higher the tax.

4. According to these results, who has to pay the highest tax?

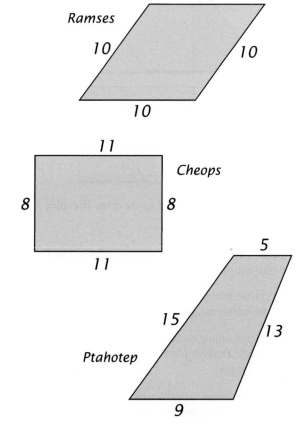

The area of Cheops's plot, being rectangular in shape, is easiest to check.

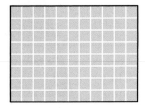

5. Does it contain as many square units as the tax assessor says?

Before we try to count the number of squares in each of the other plots, making some changes in the figures will make the job easier.

For Ramses' plot, we can imagine cutting off the triangular part on the left and moving it to the right.

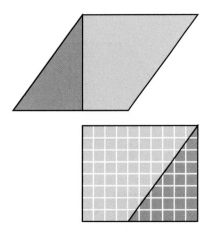

6. How many square units does the plot contain?

For Ptahotep's plot, we can add some lines as shown at the top of the next column.

7. How many square units does the left-hand rectangle contain?

8. How many square units do you think Ptahotep's part of this rectangle contains?

9. How many square units does the right-hand rectangle contain?

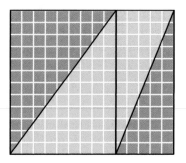

10. How many square units do you think Ptahotep's part of this rectangle contains?

11. Use these results to determine how many square units Ptahotep's property contains.

12. Which one of the three is cheated the most by the tax assessor's formula? Why?

How to calculate area correctly is an important topic in geometry. Having worked through these exercises, you will probably agree that it would be convenient to have easier methods whose logic we really understand.

Set II

Trisection Problems. The methods for bisecting line segments and angles by using just a straightedge and compass were known to the ancient Greeks long before Euclid was born. Having solved these two problems, the Greeks naturally wondered if just these two tools could be used to *trisect* a line segment or angle, that is, divide them into *three* equal parts.

The trisection problem for line segments was solved almost immediately. Here is one way to do it.

13. For convenience in checking the result at the end, draw a line segment AB 3 inches long.

A   *B*
3 inches

First, use your straightedge and compass to construct the line, *l*, that bisects AB. Label the midpoint C.

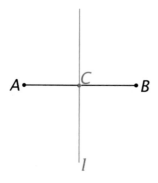

With C as center, draw a circle through A and B. Label the points in which line *l* intersects the circle D and E. Draw AD and BE.

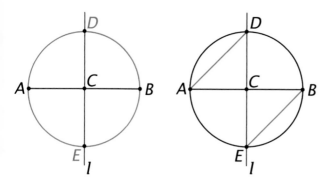

Construct the line that bisects AD and label it *m*. (You should notice that line *m* goes through C, the center of the circle.)

Where line *m* intersects AD and BE, label the points F and G as shown here. Draw DG and FE.

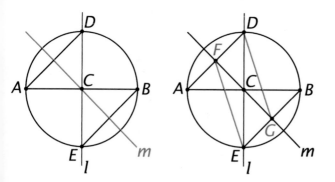

These two line segments trisect the original line segment AB, which you can check with your ruler.

An early method proposed for trisecting angles is illustrated below.

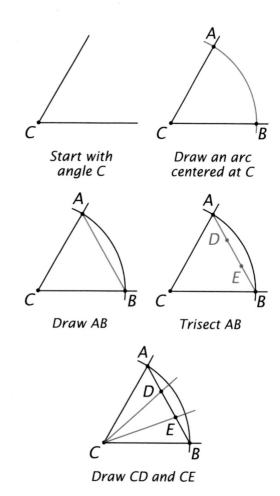

Start with angle C

Draw an arc centered at C

Draw AB

Trisect AB

Draw CD and CE

Rather than carrying out this construction with straightedge and compass, we will draw an accurate figure to test the results.

14. Use your ruler and compass to draw an equilateral triangle, each of whose sides is 3 inches long. Label its vertices A, B, and C to correspond to the third figure above. Use your ruler to find the points D and E on side AB that trisect it. Draw CD and CE.

15. Center your protractor on C and carefully measure ∠ACD, ∠DCE, and ∠ECB. What does the measure of each angle seem to be?

Because we can neither draw nor measure things perfectly, it is not easy to tell whether the original angle has been trisected. In fact, it *has not.* As surprising as it may seem, since the time of Euclid, no one has ever found a way that can be used to trisect any angle by using just a straightedge and compass!

We have made two drawings, both of which might *seem* to be correct, yet one is not. The title of this lesson, "We Can't Go On Like This," describes our dilemma. It is not possible to be sure of what we are doing in geometry without developing a deeper understanding of the subject.

Set III

Cutting Up a Circle. Here is a simple problem about points and circles that has become famous because it is so baffling.

If four points are chosen on a circle and connected with line segments in every possible way, the result might look something like this. Notice that the circle is separated into eight regions.

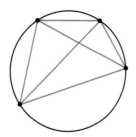

1. Draw a circle, choose five points on it, and connect them with line segments in every possible way.

2. Into how many regions is the circle separated?

How many regions would be formed if you started with

3. just two points?

4. three points?

5. Put all of these results together by making a table like this:

Number of points connected: 2 3 4 5
Number of regions formed: ? ? 8 ?

6. What happens to the number of regions each time one more point is added to the circle?

How many regions would you expect to be formed if you started with

7. six points?

8. seven points?

9. Make drawings of circles having six and seven points. Start with large circles.

10. Are the results what you expected?

This engraving from 1630 is titled *Dido Purchases Land for the Foundation of Carthage*. It depicts the hide of an ox being cut to solve a problem in geometry considered in this review.

CHAPTER 1 Summary and Review

Introduction *(pp. 1–2)*

Since about 300 B.C., Euclid's book titled the *Elements* has been the model for presenting geometry in a logical way. We will become acquainted with Euclid's approach to mathematics in our study of geometry.

Lesson 1 *(pp. 8–9)*

Some basic terms used in geometry are *point, line,* and *plane.* A *line segment* is part of a line bounded by two endpoints.

Some terms relating points, lines, and planes are *collinear* (points that are on the same line), *noncollinear* (points that are not on the same line), *coplanar* (points that are in the same plane), and *concurrent* (lines that contain the same point).

Lesson 2 *(pp. 13–15)*

A *ray* is part of a line that extends endlessly in one direction. An *angle* is a pair of rays (called its *sides*) that have the same endpoint (called its *vertex*).

A *protractor* measures angles in *degrees.*

Lesson 3 *(pp. 18–20)*

A *polygon* is bounded by line segments and lies in a plane. A *polyhedron* (plural *polyhedra*) is bounded by polygons and exists in space.

Names for some common polygons include: *triangle* (three sides), *quadrilateral* (four sides), *pentagon* (five sides), *hexagon* (six sides), and *octagon* (eight sides).

Two numbers associated with a polygon are its *perimeter* (the sum of the lengths of its sides) and its *area* (the number of unit squares equal in measure to its surface).

A rectangle with length *l* and width *w* has area *A* given by

$$A = lw.$$

Lesson 4 (pp. 24–25)

Geometric drawings called *constructions* are made with just two tools: the *straightedge* (for drawing lines) and the *compass* (for drawing circles).

Two simple constructions are to *bisect a line segment* and to *bisect an angle*. To bisect something means to divide it into two equal parts.

Lesson 5 (pp. 30–31)

The study of geometry in an informal way, as we have done in this chapter, can lead to many interesting and practical results. This informal approach is ultimately unsatisfactory, however, because conclusions based on appearances or guessing may not always be correct.

Exercises

Set I

The die shown in the photograph above was made in Italy in about 700 B.C. and is in the shape of a cube.

The corners of a cube are *points*. What kind of geometric figure

1. are its edges?

2. are its faces?

3. is the cube itself?

The figure below is a transparent view of a cube.

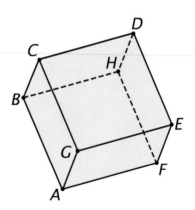

How many edges

4. meet at each corner of a cube?

5. does a cube have altogether?

How many faces

6. meet at each corner of a cube?

7. does a cube have altogether?

The corners A, G, and C of the cube are noncollinear.

8. What is another word that describes them?

The following pattern can be used to form a cube.

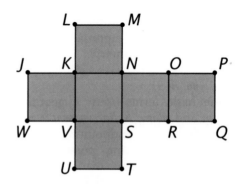

9. In how many lines do the edges of the pattern lie?

Some harder questions

Suppose the pattern is cut out and folded together to form a cube.

With which edge would each of the following edges come together?

10. JW.

11. MN.

12. LM.

With which corner(s) would each of the following corners come together?

13. R.

14. W.

Here is another transparent view of a cube.

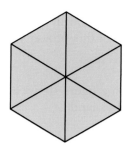

15. Looking at this figure as flat rather than three-dimensional, what polygons do you see in it?

16. Make a copy of the figure, but make the figure look three-dimensional by drawing it with the hidden edges as dashed line segments.

17. What is the greatest number of faces of a die that can be seen at any one time?

Set II

Some drawings in geometry are made with a ruler and protractor, and others are made with just a straightedge and compass.

18. What are drawings made with just a straightedge and compass called?

19. Use your ruler and protractor to draw a triangle with the measurements shown below in the *center* of a sheet of paper.

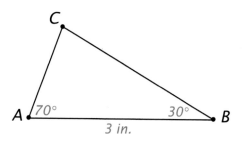

Extend the lines of the sides CA and CB, marking two points D and E on them as shown below.

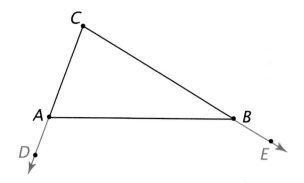

Measure each of the following angles:

20. ∠DAB.

21. ∠ABE.

22. ∠DCE.

Now use your straightedge and compass to bisect ∠DAB and ∠ABE. Draw the two bisectors long enough so that they meet in a point; label it F.

Check the accuracy of your drawing by measuring these angles:

23. ∠DAF and ∠FAB.

24. ∠ABF and ∠FBE.

Draw CF.

25. Measure ∠DCF and ∠FCE.

26. What does the line CF seem to do to ∠DCE?

27. Draw a quadrilateral of about this shape on your paper.

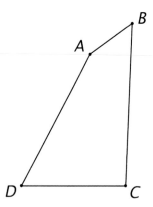

Use your straightedge and compass to bisect the four sides of the quadrilateral. Use the letter M to label the midpoint of side AB, the letter N for the midpoint of BC, the letter O for the midpoint of CD, and the letter P for the midpoint of DA.

Connect M, N, O, and P with line segments to form quadrilateral MNOP.

28. What do you notice about the sides of this quadrilateral?

29. What is its perimeter in centimeters?

Draw AC and BD. These line segments are called the *diagonals* of quadrilateral ABCD.

30. Measure AC and BD in centimeters and add their lengths.

If you have drawn and measured everything accurately, your answers to exercises 29 and 30 should be the same, even though your original copy of quadrilateral ABCD may not look exactly like the one above!

Set III

According to the Roman poet Virgil, a princess named Dido wanted to buy some land in Africa in about 900 B.C. She was told that she could buy as much land as she could enclose with the skin of an ox.

Dido is said to have had the hide cut into thin strips which were then tied together to form as long a cord as possible.

Suppose that her plot of land had to be in the shape of a rectangle, that it could face a river so that the cord would have to stretch only along three sides, and that the cord was 900 yards long.

If the land were in the shape of a square, it would look like this.

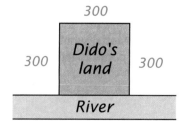

1. Including the fourth side, what is the perimeter of this property?

2. What is its area?

The following figure shows another possible shape for Dido's land.

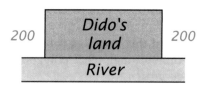

3. In this case, how far would the cord reach across the top side?

4. What is the perimeter of this property?

5. What is its area?

6. What length and width should the rectangle have for Dido to get *as much* land as possible? Make some more drawings to try to find out.

Simplifying Expressions

The operations of addition and multiplication have these basic properties:

	Addition	*Multiplication*
Commutative	$a + b = b + a$	$ab = ba$
Associative	$(a + b) + c = a + (b + c)$	$(ab)c = a(bc)$
Identity	$a + 0 = a$	$1 \cdot a = a$
Inverse	$a + (-a) = 0$	$a \cdot \dfrac{1}{a} = 1$

The *commutative property* tells you that the result of operating on two numbers is independent of their order.

The *associative property* tells you that the result of operating on three numbers is independent of the way in which they are grouped.

The *additive identity* is 0 and the *multiplicative identity* is 1.

The *additive inverse* of a number, a, is its *opposite*, $-a$, and the *multicative inverse* of a number, a, is its *reciprocal*, $\dfrac{1}{a}$.

Multiplication can often be understood as *repeated addition*; for example, $3a$ means $a + a + a$. The 3 in the expression $3a$ is called the *coefficient*.

Raising to a power can often be understood as *repeated multiplication*; for example, a^3 means $a \cdot a \cdot a$. The 3 in the expression a^3 is called an *exponent*.

Subtraction and Division

The operations of subtraction and division are not listed above because they are defined in terms of addition and multiplication, respectively.

Subtracting a number is defined as *adding its opposite*.

  Example: $a - b = a + (-b)$

Dividing by a number is defined as *multiplying by its reciprocal*.

  Example: $\dfrac{a}{b} = a \cdot \dfrac{1}{b}$

This figure illustrating the associative property of multiplication is from a Korean mathematics book.

Exercises

Name the property or definition illustrated by each of the following equations.

1. $(x + 1) + 2 = x + (1 + 2)$
2. $3 \cdot 4 = 4 \cdot 3$
3. $x - (-5) = x + 5$
4. $100 + 0 = 100$
5. $\dfrac{x}{6} = x \cdot \dfrac{1}{6}$
6. $7 \cdot \dfrac{1}{7} = 1$

Write each of the following expressions as a single integer.

7. 12^3
8. 12×10^3
9. $5 - (-15)$
10. $5(-15)$
11. $17^2 - 8^2$
12. $(17 - 8)^2$

Simplify the following expressions.

13. $\pi(7)^2$
14. $2\pi(7)$
15. $x + x + x + x + x$

16. $x \cdot x \cdot x \cdot x \cdot x$
17. $2x + 3x$
18. $x^2 \cdot x^3$
19. $x + x + y + y + y$
20. $x \cdot x \cdot y \cdot y \cdot y$
21. $x \cdot x + y \cdot y \cdot y$
22. $x \cdot x \cdot x + y \cdot y$
23. $(x + y) + y$
24. $(xy)y$
25. $(x^2 + x^2 + x^2 + x^2) + (x^2 + x^2 + x^2)$
26. $4x^2 + 3x^2$
27. $(x^2 + x^2 + x^2 + x^2 + x^2 + x^2) - x^2$
28. $6x^2 - x^2$
29. $(x^2 + x^2 + x^2 + x^2) + (x + x + x)$
30. $x^3 + x^3 + x^3 + x^2 + x^2 + x$
31. $(x^2 \cdot x^2 \cdot x^2 \cdot x^2)(x^2 \cdot x^2 \cdot x^2)$
32. $(x^8)(x^6)$
33. $(2x^3)(3x^2)$
34. $(x^3 + x^3)(x^2 + x^2 + x^2)$
35. $(2x + 2x + 2x)(3x + 3x)$
36. $(2x \cdot 2x \cdot 2x)(3x \cdot 3x)$
37. $(x + x + x + y + y) + (x + y + y)$
38. $(3x + 2y) + (x + 2y)$
39. $(x + x + x + y + y) - (x + y + y)$
40. $(3x + 2y) - (x + 2y)$
41. $(x + y) + -(x + y)$
42. $(x + y)\dfrac{1}{x + y}$
43. $(4x + 7y) + (x + 3y)$
44. $(4x + 7y) - (x + 3y)$
45. $(4x - 7y) + (x - 3y)$
46. $(4x - 7y) - (x - 3y)$
47. $(4x)(7y) + (x)(3y)$
48. $(4x)(7y) - (x)(3y)$
49. $(2 + x^3) + (5 + x^5)$
50. $(2x^3)(5x^5)$

Chapter 2

The Nature of Deductive Reasoning

The last chapter closed with a lesson titled "We Can't Go On Like This." It revealed that we need a stronger foundation for our study of geometry than the informal approach that we have used so far.

Euclid led the way by organizing geometry into a deductive system with definitions, assumptions called *postulates*, and logical methods for proving our conclusions, called the *theorems* of geometry. In this chapter, you will become acquainted with this system and the nature of deductive reasoning.

Conditional Statements

A goal in studying geometry is to develop the ability to think critically. Deductive reasoning is fundamental to critical thinking, and so we now turn our attention to this subject.

Deductive reasoning is used by both real and fictional detectives. In Agatha Christie's *Murder on the Orient Express,* the detective Hercule Poirot says:

> We have to rely solely on deduction. That to me, makes the matter very much more interesting. . . . It is all a matter of intellect.

Toward the end of the mystery, Poirot reasons:

> If Ratchett had been heavily drugged, he could not have cried out.
> If he had been capable of crying out, he would have been capable of making some kind of struggle to defend himself.

Statements such as the last two are called *conditional statements*. A conditional statement consists of two clauses, one of which begins with the word "if" or "when" or some equivalent word. Such statements are used by detectives and others to establish conclusions, and they are important in mathematics in writing deductive proofs.

A conditional statement can be represented symbolically by

$$a \rightarrow b.$$

This is read "If *a*, then *b*." The letter *a* represents the "if" clause, or *hypothesis*, and the letter *b* represents the "then" clause, or *conclusion*. (The word "then," being understood, is often omitted.) For example, in the statement

If the crime was committed at a quarter past one, the murderer cannot have left the train,

a represents the words "the crime was committed at a quarter past one" and *b* represents the words "the murderer cannot have left the train."

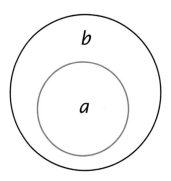

To see how conditional statements relate to each other, you can represent them by using circle diagrams. These diagrams are called *Euler diagrams* after an eighteenth-century Swiss mathematician, Leonhard Euler (pronounced "Oiler"), who first used them.

To make an Euler diagram, we draw two circles, one inside the other. The interior of the smaller circle represents *a*, the hypothesis; the interior of the larger circle represents *b*, the conclusion. Note that, if a point is inside circle *a*, it is also inside circle *b*. Or, briefly, "if *a*, then *b*," which is what the diagram is intended to represent. The diagram at the right, for example, represents the statement

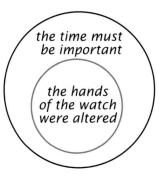

If the hands of the watch were altered, then the time must be important.

We will explore conditional statements in this lesson and put them to work drawing conclusions in Lessons 3 and 4.

Exercises

Set I

1. What is a statement that can be represented symbolically by "If *a*, then *b*" called?

2. In the statement "If *a*, then *b*," what do the letters "*a*" and "*b*" represent?

3. Draw and describe the Euler diagram for "If *a*, then *b*."

Sometimes the conclusion of a conditional statement is stated before the hypothesis. Compare the following statements:

You live in the United States
if you live in the Ozarks.

If you live in the Ozarks,
then you live in the United States.

4. Both statements have the same hypothesis. What is it?

5. Both statements have the same conclusion. What is it?

6. Are they both true?

Compare these two statements:

If it is snowing, then it is cold outside.

If it is cold outside, then it is snowing.

7. Do both statements have the same hypothesis?

8. Are they both true? Why or why not?

9. Do they mean the same thing?

10. Rewrite the first statement so that the conclusion is stated before the hypothesis.

11. Is the statement that you wrote true?

It is possible to compare the following three statements, even though you probably don't know what they mean.

(1) Two quoits cancel each other if they ring the same bob.
(2) If two quoits cancel each other, they ring the same bob.
(3) If two quoits ring the same bob, they cancel each other.

12. Which two statements have the same hypothesis and the same conclusion?

13. Do those two statements mean the same thing?

Rewrite each of the following sentences in "if-then" form. You may change some of the words, but be careful not to change the meanings of the sentences; for example, if you write a true statement in "if-then" form so that it turns out to be false, something is wrong.

Example: Genuine phone numbers do not begin with 555.

Possible answers:
If a phone number is genuine, it does not begin with 555.
If a phone number begins with 555, it is not genuine.

14. Koala bears eat only eucalyptus leaves.

15. When the cat is in the birdcage, it isn't there to sing.

16. Smokey Bear wouldn't have to do commercials for a living if money grew on trees.

17. All architects use geometry.

18. I ask questions whenever I don't understand.

19. Use the stairs instead of the elevator in case of fire.

20. No vampire casts a shadow.

Set II

21. Write the conditional statement represented by the Euler diagram below in the form "if *a*, then *b*."

22. Rewrite the conditional statement that you just wrote in the form "*b* if *a*."

An Euler diagram, such as the one shown below, separates the paper into three regions; they are numbered 1, 2, and 3 in the figure.

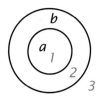

23. Which region is inside circle *a*?

24. Which *regions* are inside circle *b*?

25. Which *regions* are outside circle *a*?

26. Which region is outside circle *b*?

27. Draw an Euler diagram to represent the statement

If *x*, then *y*

and a second Euler diagram to represent the statement

If *y*, then *x*.

28. Which of your diagrams, the first or the second, also illustrates the statement

If not *x*, then not *y*?

29. Which diagram also illustrates the statement

If not *y*, then not *x*?

30. How many "if-then" statements does a given Euler diagram represent?

31. Draw an Euler diagram to represent the following statement:

All players for the Yankees make a lot of money.

32. Which of the following statements are illustrated by your diagram?

a) If you play for the Yankees, then you make a lot of money.
b) If you make a lot of money, then you play for the Yankees.
c) If you don't play for the Yankees, then you don't make a lot of money.
d) If you don't make a lot of money, then you don't play for the Yankees.

33. Which of the statements listed in exercise 32 are true, given that all players for the Yankees make a lot of money?

34. Draw an Euler diagram to represent the following statement:

If you have lived a long time, then you are an octagenarian.

35. Which of the following statements are illustrated by your diagram?

a) If you are an octagenarian, then you have lived a long time.
b) If you have not lived a long time, then you are not an octagenarian.
c) If you are not an octagenarian, then you have not lived a long time.
d) You are an octagenarian if you have lived a long time.

36. Which of the statements listed in exercise 35 do you think are true?

Set III

In language experiments with chimpanzees, the biologist David Premack used plastic shapes to represent words. A chimp named Sarah learned to interpret sentences, including conditional statements, built from these shapes.[*]

One of these statements looked like this.

The green triangle with the three holes represented "if then" and the statement said:

If Sarah takes the apple, then Mary will give chocolate to Sarah.

1. What shape do you think represented the word Sarah?

2. Where does the hypothesis appear in the arrangement of the shapes?

A second statement shown to the monkey, in which the word "banana" appeared, looked like this.

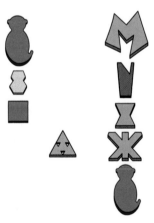

3. What shape do you think represented the word "banana"?

4. What do you suppose the statement said?

_____

[*] *The Animal Mind*, by James L. Gould and Carol Grant Gould (Scientific American Library, 1994).

Horse by Any Other Name Is Still a Horse?

■ **Zoning:** Rancher faces jail time for having too many equines if the definition is not changed.

By ALAN ABRAHAMSON
TIMES STAFF WRITER

A horse is a horse, of course. Of course?

Not quite, says Yucca Valley breeder James K. Walker Jr. He owns three horses, which he says the breeding industry defines precisely as male animals at least five years old and 58 inches high at the base of the neck. The rest of the 29-animal herd at Clover J Arabians, he insists, consists of equines called mares, colts, fillies, geldings and foals.

It's All in the Name

Horses, horses: From the left, a mare, a gelding, and a colt.

What is a horse? That may depend on the source. Here is a look at several definitions:

ACCORDING TO A HORSEMAN:

"...In a horseman's terminology a **colt** is a male horse under five years of age and a **filly** is the female counterpart. Youngsters of both sexes are **foals** until they reach the age for weaning. Then they are called **weanlings**, and later **yearlings**. After that, they are colts and fillies and after five they are **horses** and **mares**."
    —Complete Book of Horses and Horsemanship, C.W. Anderson

ACCORDING TO THE DICTIONARY:

LESSON 2

Definitions

Several years ago a rancher in Yucca Valley, California, got into trouble for having too many horses. He said that he had only 3, but the local officials said that he had 29. The disagreement centered on the definition of a horse.

According to the breeding industry, a horse is "a male animal at least five years old and 58 inches high at the base of the neck." "Horsefeathers," said the officials, "If it looks like a horse, trots like a horse and smells like a horse, it *is* a horse."

Disagreements about the meanings of words frequently come up in courts of law. To prevent arguments in debates, key terms are often defined first. Variations in a word's meaning seldom cause much of a problem in everyday communication, but they are serious when we are trying to reason precisely. For this reason, definitions play an important role in mathematics.

When we define a word in geometry, the word and its definition are understood to have exactly the same meaning. For example, when we define a "triangle" as "a polygon that has three sides," we can say not only that

If a figure is a triangle, then it is a polygon that has three sides but also that

> If a figure is a polygon that has three sides, then it is a triangle.

Notice that the hypothesis and conclusion of the first statement are interchanged in the second. The second statement is called the *converse* of the first.

The *converse* of a conditional statement is found by interchanging its hypothesis and conclusion. In symbols, the converse of $a \rightarrow b$ is $b \rightarrow a$.

You have seen in the preceding lesson that the converse of a true statement may be false. Because a statement and its converse do not have the same meaning, accepting a statement as true does not require us to accept its converse as true.

For a definition, however, the converse is *always* true. Because "*a*," the word being defined, and "*b*," its definition, have the same meaning, "*a*" and "*b*" are interchangeable. Consequently, for definitions, either form, $a \rightarrow b$ or $b \rightarrow a$, implies the other. This is *not true* for ordinary conditional statements.

The two Euler diagrams shown here represent $a \rightarrow b$ and $b \rightarrow a$. Notice that the second diagram also illustrates "*a*, if *b*" because in it a point is inside circle *a* if it is inside circle *b*. The first diagram also illustrates "*a* only if *b*" because in it a point is inside circle *a* only if it is inside circle *b*. These observations show that, if both a statement and its converse are true, we can write

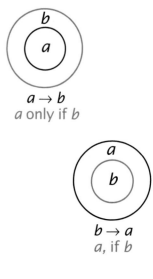

$a \rightarrow b$
a only if *b*

$b \rightarrow a$
a, if *b*

> "*a* if *b*" and "*a* only if *b*,"

or, more briefly,

> "*a* if and only if *b*."

The phrase "if and only if" is represented by the abbreviation "iff" and by the symbol $\leftrightarrow$; $a \leftrightarrow b$ means both $a \rightarrow b$ and $b \rightarrow a$.

Because the converse of every definition is true, we usually write definitions in the form "*a* iff *b*." For example, the definition of a triangle given in this lesson can be written as

> A figure is a triangle if and only if it is a polygon that has three sides.

Exercises

Set I

Consider the statement

> All geese have two legs.

1. Write this statement in "if-then" form.

2. Illustrate it with an Euler diagram.

3. Write the converse of the statement.

4. If we assume that the original statement is true, does it follow that the converse is true?

Consider the true statement

> If you are an astronaut, you are not more than six feet tall.

5. What is the conclusion of this statement?

6. Write the converse of the statement.

7. Is the converse true?

8. Does it have the same meaning as the original statement?

Consider the statement

> You cannot comprehend geometry if you do not know how to reason deductively.

9. What is the hypothesis of this statement?

10. Write the converse of the statement.

11. What is the conclusion of the converse?

Consider the true definition

> You have *arachibutyrophobia* iff you have the fear of peanut butter sticking to the roof of your mouth.

12. What does the abbreviation "iff" stand for?

13. From this definition, what can you conclude about the word "arachibutyrophobia" and the words "the fear of peanut butter sticking to the roof of your mouth"?

If the definition were represented in symbols as $a \leftrightarrow b$ and "*a*" represents "arachibutyrophobia," what does

14. " $\leftrightarrow$ " represent?

15. "*b*" represent?

In words, "$a \rightarrow b$" for this definition is "If you have arachibutyrophobia, then you are afraid of peanut butter sticking to the roof of your mouth."

16. Write in words, "$b \rightarrow a$" for this definition.

17. Is the sentence that you wrote necessarily true? Explain.

For a definition to be understood, it is necessary to know the meanings of the words used in it. The following definition of *vulgar fraction* is correct but not necessarily helpful.

> A *vulgar fraction* is a common fraction that is either proper or improper.

18. Which words in this definition might not be understood?

19. Write the definition in "if-then" form.

20. Write its converse.

21. Is the converse necessarily true? Why or why not?

In writing a definition, we try to say no more than is necessary. Consider the following possible definition of *New Year's Day*.

> *New Year's Day* is a holiday that is the first day of the year.

Suppose this definition were shortened to

> *New Year's Day* is a holiday.

22. Why wouldn't this shortened version be a good definition of *New Year's Day*?

Suppose instead that the definition were shortened to

> *New Year's Day* is the first day of the year.

23. Would this version be a good definition of *New Year's Day*? Explain.

Set II

Compare the following two sentences:

(1) If it is your birthday,
   then you get some presents.
(2) Only if it is your birthday,
   do you get some presents.

24. Is the first sentence true for you?

25. Is the second sentence true for you?

26. Do both sentences say the same thing?

27. Which sentence does this Euler diagram illustrate?

it is your birthday

you get some presents

Compare the following two sentences, both of which are true:

(1) If it is dry ice, then it is frozen carbon dioxide.

(2) Only if it is dry ice is it frozen carbon dioxide.

28. What relation does the second sentence have to the first?

29. Draw an Euler diagram to illustrate the second sentence.

30. Combine the two sentences into a single sentence by using the words "if and only if."

Suppose that on an English test you wrote the sentence

It is a whodunit iff it is a detective story

and that the teacher crossed out the second "f" with a red pencil.

31. What kind of mistake did the teacher think you made?

32. To which one of these sentences would the "corrected" statement be equivalent?

(1) If it is a whodunit, then it is a detective story.

(2) If it is a detective story, then it is a whodunit.

33. Would it be safe to conclude that your English teacher's knowledge of mathematics is "iffy"?

Consider this statement:

A car is a convertible iff it has a removable top.

34. Write the two conditional statements that are equivalent to this statement.

35. What relation does the second of your statements have to the first?

Here is an interesting definition:

A *wolf pack* is two wolves or is a wolf pack together with a wolf.

36. According to this definition, how many wolves are in a pack?

37. Why is it appropriate that this definition is used as an example in a book titled *Keys to Infinity?**

Set III

Here is a puzzle in logical reasoning called the Wason test, named after the British psychologist Peter Wason who created it.[†]

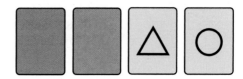

Four cards lie on a table; each card is either red or blue on one side and has a triangle or circle on the other side.

The following conditional statement supposedly describes the way that the cards are made:

If a card is blue on one side, it has a circle on the other side.

The puzzle is to figure out which cards have to be turned over to find out if this statement is true. It turns out that the "obvious" answer, chosen by most people, is wrong.

Which cards would you choose? Explain your reasoning.

---

*Keys to Infinity, by Clifford A. Pickover (Wiley, 1995).
†*The Math Gene,* by Keith Devlin (Basic Books, 2000).

Raising spoon to mouth (**A**) pulls string (**B**), thereby jerking ladle (**C**), which throws cracker (**D**) past parrot (**E**). Parrot jumps after cracker, and perch (**F**) tilts, upsetting seeds (**G**) into pail (**H**). Extra weight in pail pulls cord (**I**), which opens and lights automatic cigar lighter (**J**), setting off skyrocket (**K**), which causes sickle (**L**) to cut string (**M**) and allows pendulum with attached napkin (**N**) to swing back and forth, thereby wiping off your chin.

Rube Goldberg is a trademark and copyright of Rube Goldberg, Inc.

LESSON 3

Direct Proof

The artist Rube Goldberg was so well known for his cleverly ridiculous inventions that his name has come to be associated with any complicated and impractical way of performing a simple task. His "self-operating napkin," pictured above, has been featured in *Scientific American* and even on a U.S. postage stamp.

The cartoon illustrates a chain of events that begins as follows:

> If you raise the spoon of soup to your mouth, the string is pulled.
> If the string is pulled, the ladle is jerked.
> If the ladle is jerked, it throws a cracker past the parrot.

Notice how the hypothesis of each successive statement matches the conclusion of the preceding one. The chain continues, finally ending with

> If the napkin swings back and forth, the napkin wipes your chin.

What makes this series of events so preposterous is that it seems unlikely that the conditional statements describing them are all true. If they are, however, then it follows from taking them all together that

> If you raise the spoon of soup to your mouth, then the napkin wipes your chin.

The shortest and simplest case of this sort begins with just two conditional statements from which a third conditional statement follows. Such an argument is called a *syllogism*.

A *syllogism* is an argument of the form

$$a \rightarrow b$$
$$b \rightarrow c$$

Therefore, $a \rightarrow c$.

If we illustrate the statements $a \rightarrow b$ and $b \rightarrow c$ with Euler diagrams and combine them into one, it is easy to see why the third statement, $a \rightarrow c$, follows.

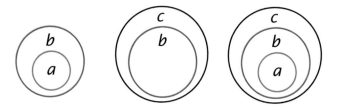

Extending this pattern to the situation illustrated in the Rube Goldberg cartoon, we get

$$a \rightarrow b,\ b \rightarrow c,\ c \rightarrow d,\ d \rightarrow e,\ e \rightarrow f, f \rightarrow g,\ g \rightarrow h,$$
$$h \rightarrow i,\ i \rightarrow j, j \rightarrow k,\ k \rightarrow l,\ l \rightarrow m,\ m \rightarrow n$$

from which it follows that

$$a \rightarrow n.$$

This argument is an example of a *direct proof*. The statements $a \rightarrow b$, $b \rightarrow c$, ... , $m \rightarrow n$ are called the *premises* of the argument, and the statement $a \rightarrow n$ is called the *conclusion* of the argument. The conclusion might be considered a *theorem*.

A *theorem* is a statement that is proved by reasoning deductively from already accepted statements.

If all of the premises of an argument are true and the logic of the argument is correct, then the conclusion *must be true*. As the old saying goes, however, "a chain is no stronger than its weakest link." If one of the premises is false or the logic is faulty, then the conclusion may be false as well. For this reason, we have to pay close attention to the premises and the logic used in any proof. More on this subject will be included in a future lesson.

Exercises

Set I

In the *Encyclopedia Britannica,* a syllogism is described as a "valid deductive argument that has two premises and a conclusion having between them three terms."

Suppose that the three terms of a syllogism are:

    a, "you keep quiet"
    b, "others will never hear you make a mistake"
    c, "others will think you are wise."

1. Write the two premises of the syllogism as conditional statements.

2. Write its conclusion as a conditional statement.

3. Write the pattern of the syllogism in terms of the symbols *a, b,* and *c.*

Syllogisms were discussed by the Greek philosopher Aristotle in the fourth century B.C. Write the syllogisms illustrated by the following Euler diagrams.

4.   **5.**

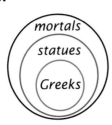

6. If the premises of a syllogism are true, does it follow that its conclusion must be true?

7. If the premises of a syllogism are false, does it follow that its conclusion must be false?

Aristotle made the following statement about how you can argue correctly, yet arrive at a false conclusion: "Admit one ridiculous premise and the rest follows."

Consider the following argument:

    If you live at the South Pole, you live in the Antarctic.
    If you live in the Antarctic, you live where it is cold.
    If you live where it is cold, you see a lot of penguins.
    Therefore, if you live at the South Pole, you see a lot of penguins.

What part of the second premise matches

8. the conclusion of the first premise?

9. the hypothesis of the third premise?

10. Starting with $a \rightarrow b$ to represent the first premise, represent the entire argument in symbols.

11. Which premise is ridiculous (false)?

12. What does the fact that one premise is false indicate about the conclusion of the argument?

Consider the following premises:

    If Captain Spaulding is in the jungle, there are too many cheetahs.
    If there are too many cheetahs, Captain Spaulding can't play cards.

13. What conclusion follows from them?

14. If the two premises are true, does it follow that the conclusion must be true?

Consider these premises:

    If NASA launched some cows into space, they would be put into low earth orbit.
    If some cows were put into low earth orbit, they would be the herd shot around the world.

15. What conclusion follows from the two premises?

16. What is a statement called that is proved from already accepted premises?

Consider the following statements:

> If you take a plane, you will go to the airport.
>
> If you go to Dallas, you will take a plane.
>
> If you see all the cabs lined up, you will see the yellow rows of taxis.
>
> If you go to the airport, you will see all the cabs lined up.

17. Copy the statements, rearranging them in logical order.

18. What "theorem" do they prove?

Consider the following statements:

> A duck would ask for some Chapstick if he went to a drugstore.
>
> If a duck had sore lips, he would go to a drugstore.
>
> A duck would ask to have it put on his bill if he asked for some Chapstick.

19. Copy the statements, writing them in "if-then" form and rearranging them in logical order.

Each of the following exercises consists of a "theorem" and a proof in which two statements have been omitted. After studying the relations of the statements given, write the missing statements.

20. *Theorem.*
If two hungry vultures took an airplane, they would be told that there is a limit of two carrion per passenger.
Proof.
If two hungry vultures took an airplane, they would want to take along some food.
(What is the second statement?)
If they tried to carry on six dead raccoons, the flight attendant would object.
(What is the last statement?)

21. *Theorem.*
If a group of chess players checked into a hotel, the manager would say "I can't stand chess nuts boasting in an open foyer."
Proof.
(What is the first statement?)
If they stood in the lobby bragging about their tournament victories, the manager would ask them to leave.
(What is the third statement?)
If they asked why, the manager would say "I can't stand chess nuts boasting in an open foyer."

The arguments in exercises 15 through 21 are based on pun stories in *A Prairie Home Companion Pretty Good Joke Book* (Highbridge Company, 2000).

Set II

The reasoning in each of the following puzzles illustrates the pattern of a direct proof.

Dice Proof. Dice players know that the numbers on the opposite faces of an ordinary die such as the one shown here always total the same.

22. What is the sum of the numbers of all six faces of a die?

23. Because the numbers on each pair of opposite faces totals the same, what number do they total?

24. What number is on the face opposite the 5?

25. What number must be on the bottom of the die in the picture?

Matchbox Proof. The figure above shows three matchboxes. One contains two red marbles, one contains two white marbles, and one contains a red marble and a white marble. The labels telling the contents of the boxes have been switched, however, so that *the label on each box is wrong.*

You may choose just one box and open it far enough to see just one marble.

Suppose that you open the box labeled "1 red, 1 white" and that you see a red marble.

26. If you see a red marble, then what color is the other marble in the box? Why?

27. What would be in the box labeled "2 white"?

28. What would be in the box labeled "2 red"?

Tick-tack-toe Proofs. The sequence of moves in tick-tack-toe can resemble the pattern of a direct proof.*

Suppose the first two moves in a game are as shown here (your opponent marks Xs and you mark Os).

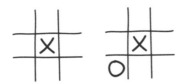

29. Copy the second figure on your paper and mark it as needed to copy and complete the following sequence of conditional statements.

30. If your opponent marks an X in the upper left, then . . .
If . . . , then . . .
If . . . , then . . .

At this point, it is evident that the game will end in a draw.

Now consider a second game in which the first three moves are shown here (again your opponent marks Xs and you mark Os).

31. Make several copies of the third figure on your paper and continue the game in various ways.

32. Can you draw any conclusions about whether this game will end in a win or draw? Explain.

Set III

A "word ladder" is a sequence of words in which one letter is changed at a time. For example, the following word ladder

> COLD
> CORD
> CARD
> WARD
> WARM

transforms COLD into WARM.

The mathematician and writer Rudy Rucker compares word ladders to direct proofs in the sense that successive words are linked to one another just as the conditional statements in a direct proof are linked to one another.

Can you figure out a word ladder that transforms

1. LESS into MORE?
2. HEAD into TAIL?

---

*Based on ideas in the chapter on tick-tack-toe in *The Scientific American Book of Mathematical Puzzles and Diversions*, by Martin Gardner (Simon and Schuster, 1959).

ANNO'S HAT TRICKS

Akihiro Nozaki and Mitsumasa Anno

Indirect Proof

In the book *Anno's Hat Tricks,* the mathematician Akihiro Nozaki wrote:

> "If" is a very small word, but it is one of the most powerful ones in our language. It is the key to imaginative thinking, a key that opens the door to new ideas. Yet "if" can also be used very strictly, to test the truth of an idea or a supposition in a logical way. . . . The pattern of reasoning that goes "if . . ., then . . ." is very useful. It is no exaggeration to say that modern mathematics has been developed by using the word "if."*

Anno's Hat Tricks begins with a hatter who has lots of hats in a box. In the first trick, he takes one red hat and one white hat and puts one on you and one on a friend named Tom while your eyes are closed.

Anno's Hat Tricks, by Akihiro Nozaki and Mitsumasa Anno (Philomel Books, 1985).

When you open your eyes, you see a red hat on Tom. What color is your hat?

Putting the word "if" to work, you reason that

If Tom's hat is red, then mine must be white.

In the second hat trick, the hatter starts with *three* hats—two red and one white. He puts one on you and one on Tom while your eyes are closed. When you open your eyes, you again see a red hat on Tom and, when Tom looks at your hat, he is sure that his hat is red. What color is your hat?

This time we might start by assuming that your hat is red. If your hat is red, then Tom wouldn't know whether his hat is white or red because there are two red hats. This contradicts the fact that Tom is sure that his hat is red. Therefore, the assumption that your hat is red is wrong and your hat must be white.

We have arrived at this conclusion by reasoning *indirectly*.

In an *indirect proof*, an assumption is made at the beginning that leads to a contradiction. The contradiction indicates that the assumption is false and the desired conclusion is true.

The hatter's third hat trick provides another example of indirect reasoning. Again, the hatter starts with three hats, two red and one white. Again, he puts one on you and one on Tom while your eyes are closed. When you open your eyes, you again see a red hat on Tom but this time, when Tom looks at your hat, he doesn't know what color his hat is. What color is your hat?

It must be red. Do you see why?

This time we will put our argument into the format of an indirect proof.

Proof

Suppose that your hat is not red.	← We assume the *opposite of the desired conclusion.*
If your hat is not red, then it is white.	
If your hat is white, then Tom would know that his hat is red.	
This contradicts the fact that he doesn't know what color his hat is.	← The contradiction.
Therefore, what we supposed is false, and your hat must be red.	← We end with the *desired conclusion.*

Both the direct and the indirect methods of proof require making a chain of conditional statements. In the direct method, the chain begins with the *hypothesis* of the theorem and ends with its *conclusion*. In the indirect method, the chain begins with the *opposite of the conclusion* of the theorem. From here, the chain leads to a contradiction, revealing that the opposite of the conclusion is *false,* and so the conclusion itself is *true.*

Patterns of two short proofs of the theorem "If *a*, then *d*."

Direct proof	*Indirect proof*
If *a*, then *b*.	Suppose *not d* is true.
If *b*, then *c*.	If *not d*, then *e*.
If *c*, then *d*.	If *e*, then *f*,
Therefore, if *a*, then *d*.	and so on, until we come to a *contradiction.*
	Therefore, *not d* is false; so *d* is true.

Exercises

Set I

The movie producer Sam Goldwyn once said: "I'll tell you what I think in two words: im–possible!"

This statement describes what is eventually reached in a certain kind of proof.

1. What is it (in one word)?

2. According to the way that Goldwyn would say it, name this kind of proof in "two words."

To prove a theorem indirectly, we begin by assuming the opposite of the conclusion. List the assumption with which an indirect proof of each of the following statements would begin.

Example. If a tailor wants to make a coat last, he makes the pants first.

Answer. Suppose that he does not make the pants first.

3. If a chicken could talk, it would speak foul language.

4. If a teacher is cross-eyed, he has no control over his pupils.

5. If a proof is indirect, then it leads to a contradiction.

Canton, Mississippi, once resolved to:
  A. build a new jail.
  B. build it out of the materials of the old jail.
  C. use the old jail until the new jail is finished.

Tell whether the resolutions in each of the following pairs conflict with each other.

6. A and B.

7. B and C.

8. A and C.

The mathematician and author Keith Devlin recently wrote:

As so often happens in mathematics, the best bet is to look for a proof by contradiction. . . . Once you have obtained your contradiction, you will have achieved your goal, since contradictory conclusions can be obtained only from false assumptions.[*]

9. What kind of proof is the author describing?

10. How is the assumption that is proved false related to the theorem being proved?

---

[*]*Mathematics, The New Golden Age,* by Keith Devlin (Columbia University Press, 1999, p. 270).

In a book written in the thirteenth century on the shape of the earth, the author reasoned:

> If the earth were flat, the stars would rise at the same time for everyone, which they do not.[*]

11. What is the author trying to prove?
12. With what assumption does the author begin?
13. What is the contradiction?
14. What does the contradiction prove about the author's beginning assumption?

Set II

After studying the relations of the statements given in each of the following indirect proofs, write the missing statements.

Trading Desks Proof. A classroom has five rows of five desks per row. The teacher asks the pupils to change their seats by moving either one seat forward or back or one seat to the left or right.[†]

15. *Theorem.* The pupils can't obey the teacher.
    Proof.
    (What is the beginning assumption?)

    If they can obey the teacher, the 13 pupils at the black desks will move to the brown desks.
    (Look at the figure to tell what this contradicts.)

    Therefore, our assumption is false and
    (what conclusion follows?)

[*] *The Sphere,* by Johannes de Sacrobosco.
[†] A problem from *Mathematical Gems,* by Ross Honsberger (M.A.A., 1973).

Ammonia Molecule Proof. The ammonia molecule consists of three hydrogen atoms bonded to a nitrogen atom as shown in this figure.

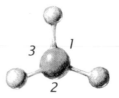

The fact that chemists have found that each bond angle is 107° can be used to prove the following theorem.

16. *Theorem.* The atoms of an ammonia molecule are not coplanar.
    Proof.
    (What is the beginning assumption?)

    If the atoms are coplanar, then the sum of the three bond angles is 360°.
    If the sum of the three bond angles is 360°, then each angle is 120°. (What does this contradict?)

    Therefore, our assumption is false and
    (what conclusion follows?)

Poker Proof. John Scarne, for many years the world's foremost authority on gambling, once said of the game of poker: "Poker is a game of strategy, deception, mathematics and psychology."[‡] Here is an obvious case in which indirect reasoning is used in the game.

In a poker game with no "wild cards," you have been dealt the "four of a kind" hand shown in the figure above.

[‡] *Scarne's New Complete Guide to Gambling,* by John Scarne (Simon & Schuster, 1974).

17. *Theorem.* In this deal of the cards, no one holds a royal flush.
Proof.
  (What is the beginning assumption?)

  If someone holds a royal flush, then one of the "10" cards would be in his or her hand. (What does this contradict?)
  Therefore, our assumption is false and
  (what conclusion follows?)

Balanced Weights Proofs. Here are two puzzles about weights and a scale with two pans. In each case, the puzzle is to separate the weights into two sets so that one set will exactly balance the other.

Puzzle 1

Puzzle 2

18. Can you solve either puzzle?

Consider this argument about these puzzles.

  If a puzzle of this type has a solution, then the weights of the two sets will be equal.
  If the weights of the two sets are equal, then each set will weigh half the total weight.

19. What conclusion follows from these two premises?

Consider this argument in the form of an indirect proof about these puzzles.

20. *Theorem.* If the sum of all of the weights is odd, there is no solution.
Proof.
  (What is the beginning assumption?)

  If there is a solution, let the weights in one set add up to *S*.

If the weights in each set add up to *S*, then the weights in both sets add up to *S* + *S* = 2*S*, an even number. (What does this contradict?)

  Therefore, our assumption is false and
  (what conclusion follows?)

Athletes Puzzle. This puzzle is from the book *Are You as Smart as You Think?* and can be solved by reasoning indirectly.[*]

At a sports banquet there are 100 famous athletes. Each one is either a football or a basketball player. At least one is a football player. Given any two of the athletes, at least one is a basketball player.

21. How many of the athletes are football players, and how many are basketball players? Explain your reasoning.

Set III

The following puzzle, adapted from one by David L. Silverman, is to decide which of the following statements must be true and which false to avoid any contradictions.[†]

A. Exactly one statement on this list is false.
B. Exactly two statements on this list are false.
C. Exactly three statements on this list are false.
D. Exactly four statements on this list are false.

1. Can two of the statements be true? Why or why not?

2. Can all of the statements be false? Why or why not?

3. Can three of the statements be true?

4. Can all of the statements be true?

5. How many statements are true? Explain.

[*]*Are You as Smart as You Think?*, by Terry Stickels (Thomas Dunne Books, 2000).
[†]*Journal of Recreational Mathematics* (January 1969).

e·col'o·gy n.

the cycle of life.

cycle n.
to move in
a circle.

cir'cle n.
to end up where
you began.

ecol'o·gy n.

Used by permission of Johnny Hart and Creators Syndicate, Inc.

LESSON 5

A Deductive System

B. C.'s predicament in trying to learn the meaning of "ecology" from Wiley's dictionary pokes fun at a problem that every dictionary maker has. A dictionary attempts to provide the meaning of every word in simpler words or words that the user already understands. These words, in turn, are defined by even simpler words, but the process cannot go backward without an end. Every dictionary solves this problem by going around in circles.

Definitions are extremely important in mathematics because, without them, a word can have different meanings for different people. To avoid the problem of the dictionary maker—that is, coming back to the point from which we begin—we must have a starting point: some words that we leave undefined. Among these words, the *undefined terms,* are "point," "line," and "plane."

You have already seen in the first lesson of Chapter 1 how these terms can then be used to define other terms. Here are two examples, restated in "if and only if" terms:

Definition. Points are *collinear* iff there is a line that contains all of them.
Definition. Lines are *concurrent* iff they contain the same point.

For the same reason that it is impossible to define everything without going around in circles, it is impossible to *prove* everything. To avoid eventually coming back to the point from which we begin, we must leave a few statements unproved. These statements, called *postulates,* can then be used as a basis for building proofs of other statements.

A *postulate* is a statement that is assumed to be true without proof.

We begin with some useful postulates concerning our undefined terms.

Postulate 1
Two points determine a line.

This postulate is suggested by the observation that, if we draw a line, just two points are sufficient to locate its position. The word "determine" in the postulate indicates that, if there are two points, then there is *exactly one* line that contains them.

The postulate gives some meaning to the word "line" because, for it to be true, it would seem that a line not only must be *straight,* but also must *extend without end* in both directions.

Postulate 2
Three noncollinear points determine a plane.

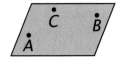

This postulate is suggested by the observation that, although a line cannot be drawn so that it contains three noncollinear points, it is always possible to imagine a *plane* that contains them. The postulate gives some meaning to the word plane because, for it to be true, it would seem that a plane must be *flat,* and have *no boundaries.*

From the *undefined terms,* then, we can construct definitions of other words. From the *definitions* and *postulates,* we can construct proofs, either directly or indirectly, of the statements that we call *theorems.* The structure that is built by means of logic in this way is called a *deductive system.*

Exercises

Set I

The *American Heritage Dictionary of the English Language* gives 34 definitions for the word "point." The definition given for a point in geometry is "a dimensionless geometric object having no property but location."

1. According to this definition, would it be correct to say that the period at the end of a sentence is a point?

2. What about an atom?

The definition says that the only property of a point is "location." "Location" is defined as a "site or situation." "Site" is defined as "the place or setting of an event." "Place" is defined as "a definite location."

3. What happens when, as in a dictionary, you try to define everything?

Another Mammoth Box-office Attraction with...

WARNER BROS

RIN-TIN-TIN

'Dog Wonder of the Screen

The following dialogue is from a scene in a classroom in the Laurel and Hardy film *Pardon Us.*

> *Teacher:* What is a comet?
> *A student:* A star with a tail on it.
> *Teacher:* Can anyone give us an example?
> *Laurel:* Rin-Tin-Tin?

4. Which words in the other student's answer did Laurel misunderstand?

5. Why did he say "Rin-Tin-Tin"?

If a weight is hung on the end of a piece of string, the string hangs along a *vertical* line, a line that goes through the center of the earth.

6. From whatever point you suspend the weight with the string, the string will have exactly one position. What postulate is illustrated here?

7. Why does the string in this position make a better model of a line than when the string is lying on the floor?

The philosopher Bertrand Russell wrote:

> I had been told that Euclid proved things, and was much disappointed that he started with postulates. At first I refused to accept them unless my brother could offer me some reason for doing so, but he said:
> "If you don't accept them we cannot go on."

8. What are the statements that are proved called?

9. What is a postulate?

10. Is it possible to prove everything without going around in circles?

Questions 11 through 15 have been removed by the author.

Points are *coplanar* iff there is a plane that contains all of them.

16. What does "iff" mean?

17. Write the two "if-then" statements that follow from this definition.

18. What word names the relation that your two statements have to each other?

Intersecting Cubes. This figure shows two intersecting cubes.

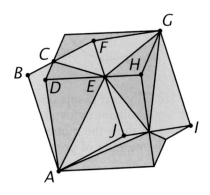

Tell whether each of the following statements is true or false.

19. Points B, C, and F are collinear.
20. Points B and C determine a line.
21. Points F, E, and J are coplanar.
22. Points F, E, and J determine a plane.
23. Points A, E, and G are collinear.
24. Points A, B, C, and J are coplanar.
25. Lines DH, FJ, and EG are concurrent.

Set II

Japanese Weights. According to the *Macmillan Dictionary of Measurement*, a *picul* is a Japanese unit of weight equal to 16 *kwan*. A *kwan* is a unit of weight equal to 100 *taels*. A *tael* is a unit of weight equal to 10 *momme*.

26. How would you define *picul* in terms of *tael?*
27. How would you define *picul* in terms of *momme?*
28. How would you define *momme* in terms of *tael?*
29. From these definitions, can you estimate your weight in piculs? Explain.

The dictionary also says that the term *picul* derives from an expression for "the load that can be carried by one man."

30. Can you conclude anything from this derivation about how the weight of an elephant compares with a weight of 1 picul?
31. Why not simply define a *picul* as "the load that can be carried by one man"?

Credit Card Rules. The following statements appear on the customer agreement for obtaining a credit card.

(1) A transaction finance charge is a charge made if a new advance is added to your account.
(2) If you go over your credit limit, you will be charged a fee.
(3) A supercheck is a check designed for use with your credit card account.
(4) If you are charged a fee, the fee will be added to your balance.
(5) If your card is lost or stolen, you agree to report it immediately.

32. Which of these statements are definitions?
33. What words do they define?
34. Which statements are postulates?
35. Which two statements can be combined to form a syllogism?
36. What theorem is proved by the syllogism?

Crooked Lines. Obtuse Ollie refuses to use a ruler. He drew the following figure to illustrate, as he described it, "two lines that intersect in two points."

Acute Alice says that his description contradicts one of our postulates.

37. What does the postulate say?
38. Is Acute Alice correct in saying that there is a contradiction?

39. Why would it be incorrect to criticize Ollie's drawing by saying that our definition of a line says that a line is straight?

Obtuse Ollie's drawing and the criticism of it suggest a theorem.

40. What is a *theorem?*

The theorem is:

> Two lines cannot intersect in more than one point.

Study the outline of the following indirect proof of this theorem and write the missing statements.

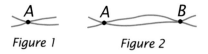

Figure 1   Figure 2

41. *Proof*
(What is the beginning assumption?)

If they intersect in more than one point, then two points do not determine a line. (What does this contradict?)

Therefore, our assumption is false and
(what conclusion follows?)

Set III

You know that two points determine a line. How many lines could 20 points determine?

The figure at the right shows 20 points arranged in a circle and all of the lines determined by them. Although it would be a challenge to try to count them from the figure, you may be able to guess the correct number by "sneaking up" on the problem.

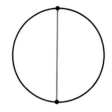

If there were only two points on the circle, there would obviously be just one line.

Draw figures to show the number of lines determined if the number of points on the circle is

1. three.

2. four.

3. five.

4. six.

5. Do you see any kind of pattern in your results that would enable you to guess the number of lines for 20 points? If so, show your method.

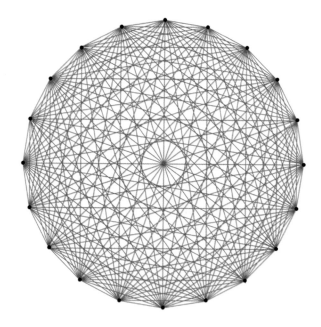

Used by permission of Johnny Hart and Creators Syndicate, Inc.

Some Famous Theorems of Geometry

In his book *Euclid–The Creation of Mathematics,* Benno Artmann wrote:

> The Greek word *theorema* is related to *theater* and means
> *something seen,* or, in mathematics, *an insight,* understanding, or
> knowledge. A mathematical theorem should answer a question
> or solve a problem that posed itself during the discussion of a
> mathematical subject.[*]

The most famous theorem in all of geometry is the one named for
Pythagoras, a Greek mathematician who lived more than 200 years before
Euclid. The fame of the Pythagorean Theorem is due to its impor-
tance in nearly every branch of mathematics. You may have become
acquainted with it in your study of algebra as the equation $c^2 = a^2 + b^2$.
In the B. C. strip above, it is stated in words:

The Pythagorean Theorem

The square of the hypotenuse of a right triangle is equal to the sum
of the squares of the other two sides.

The Greeks did not use algebraic symbols, so the equation
$c^2 = a^2 + b^2$ would not have meant anything to them. They thought of
the Pythagorean Theorem in terms of the areas of geometric squares.

---

[*]Springer, 1999.

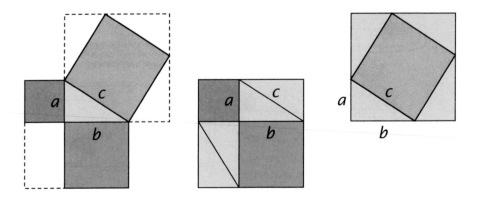

In the figures above, the right triangle is shaded yellow. The hypotenuse, the side of the triangle opposite the right angle, is labeled c, and the other two sides are labeled a and b. The area of the square on the hypotenuse, shaded red, is c^2, and the areas of the squares on the other two sides, shaded blue and green, are a^2 and b^2. The theorem claims that, in the first figure, the red area is equal to the sum of the blue and green areas; the other two figures suggest why this claim is true.

Another theorem about triangles with which you may be acquainted concerns their angles:

The Triangle Angle Sum Theorem
The sum of the angles of a triangle is 180°.

This theorem claims that $\angle 1 + \angle 2 + \angle 3 = 180°$ in the first figure below; the second figure suggests why this claim is true.

Two more famous theorems with which most students become acquainted before studying geometry concern measuring the circle.

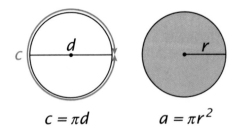

$$c = \pi d \qquad a = \pi r^2$$

Two Circle Theorems
If the diameter of a circle is d, its circumference is πd.
If the radius of a circle is r, its area is πr^2.

Because the diameter of a circle is twice its radius, the formula for the circumference of a circle is often stated as $c = 2\pi r$.

You may remember that π, the number called "pi," is approximately 3.14. No one will ever know its *exact* value in decimal form, because its decimal form has no known patterns and never ends! Because of the complexity of π, it is impossible to suggest with pictures why the theorems about the circumference and area of a circle are true.

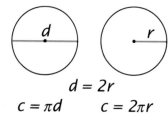

$d = 2r$

$c = \pi d \qquad c = 2\pi r$

In an earlier lesson, we learned that a theorem is a statement that is proved by reasoning deductively from already accepted statements. Although we are not yet able to prove the theorems considered in this lesson, we will begin now to apply them to solving problems. Eventually, we will return to these theorems as we arrive at the points at which we *will be* able to prove them and, hence, include them in our deductive system.

Exercises

Set I

In a survey of the "10 mathematical formulas that changed the face of the world," "$e = mc^2$" ranked first, followed by "$a^2 + b^2 = c^2$."* It is interesting to note that c^2 appears in both of these formulas.

1. What does the c in the formula $a^2 + b^2 = c^2$ stand for?

2. Do you know what the c in the formula $e = mc^2$ stands for?

3. What does the c in the formula $c = \pi d$ stand for?

4. What does the a in the formula $a^2 + b^2 = c^2$ stand for?

5. What does the a in the formula $a = \pi r^2$ stand for?

This stamp, issued by Greece in 1955, illustrates a special case of one of the theorems in this lesson.

Wonders of Numbers, by Clifford A. Pickover (Oxford University Press, 2001).

6. Which theorem is it?

7. How do the checkerboard patterns on the three sides of the triangle illustrate the theorem?

A contest was held in 1025 A.D. between two of the most learned men in Europe, Raoul and Raimbeau.†

After throwing dust into each other's eyes(!), Raimbeau challenged Raoul to prove a theorem. The best that Raoul could do was to draw a triangle on paper, cut off its corners, and put them together as shown here.

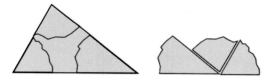

8. What theorem was Raoul trying to prove?

9. Does his method prove it?

10. If he had drawn and cut out a lot of triangles of different shapes and gotten similar results, would he have proved the theorem?

†*Geometry Civilized,* by J. L. Heilbron (Clarendon Press, 1998).

Target Circles. This "target" figure consists of five circles with radii of 1, 2, 3, 4, and 5 units.

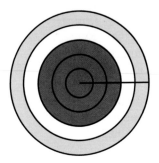

11. What are the diameters of the five circles?

12. What are the exact circumferences of the five circles?

13. What is the exact area of the purple region?

14. What is the exact area of the yellow region?

15. Why do you suppose that this figure sometimes appears in books on optical illusions?

In each of the following figures, squares have been drawn on the sides of a right triangle. Given the two areas shown in each figure, find the third area. Show your methods.

16.

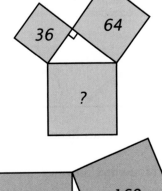

17.

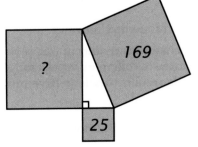

When a bird is gliding, its wings produce a lifting force that makes a 90° angle with the direction of the air flow at the leading edge of the wing.

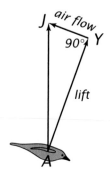

18. Find ∠A if ∠J = 60°.

19. Find ∠A if ∠J = 45°.

20. Find ∠A in terms of n if ∠J = n°.

This figure shows an overhead view of someone at C listening to stereo speakers at A and B. For the sound to be balanced, ∠A = ∠B.

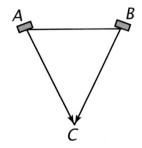

21. Find ∠A if ∠C = 40°.

22. Find ∠A if ∠C = 50°.

23. Find ∠A in terms of n if ∠C = n°.

Notice that the Pythagorean Theorem consists of more than simply "$a^2 + b^2 = c^2$." Expressed as a conditional statement about the figure shown below, it says:

> If this figure is a right triangle with hypotenuse c, then $a^2 + b^2 = c^2$.

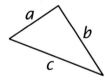

24. Given that this statement is true, does it necessarily follow that

> If $a^2 + b^2 = c^2$, then this figure is a right triangle?

25. Why or why not?

Set II

Eye Pupil. The pupil of the eye controls the amount of light entering the eye. The widest that it gets, in dim light, is about 8 mm in diameter. In very bright light, it gets as narrow as 2 mm.*

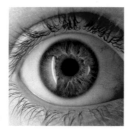

What is the approximate area of the pupil when its diameter is

26. 8 mm?

27. 2 mm?

28. Approximately how many times as much light does the pupil let in when it is biggest as when it is smallest?

Triangle Angle Sum Theorem. Use the theorem about the sum of the angles of a triangle to answer the following questions.

29. If one angle of a triangle has a measure of 90°, what is the sum of the other two angles?

30. If all three angles of a triangle are equal, how large is each angle?

31. Can a triangle have two 90° angles? Why or why not?

32. Can one angle of a triangle have a measure of 179°? Why or why not?

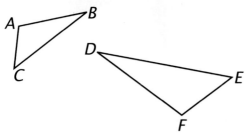

33. If two angles of one triangle are equal to two angles of another triangle, does it follow that the third pair of angles have to be equal? Why or why not?

Human Information Processing: An Introduction to Psychology, by Peter H. Lindsay and Donald A. Norman (Harcourt Brace Jovanovich, 1977).

The Stretched Cord. Baudhayana, a mathematician of ancient India, wrote in a book titled *Manual of the Cord:*

If a cord [AB in the figure] is stretched across the diagonal of a square, the cord is the side of a square double the area of the original square.

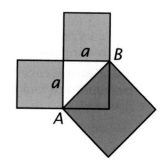

34. If the side of the original square is *a,* what is its area?

35. What is the combined area of the two light-green squares?

36. What is the area of the dark-green square?

37. How do you know?

Pencil Experiment. Imagine a large triangle on which a pencil is placed pointing to the right as shown in the first figure below. If the pencil is pivoted about ∠A, then about ∠B, and then about ∠C, it ends up as shown in the last figure.

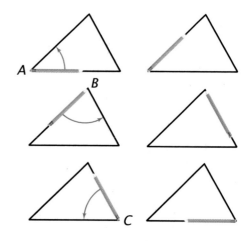

38. In what direction is the pencil pointing at the end?

39. What does this direction suggest about the number of degrees through which it

has turned in pivoting about the three angles?

40. What theorem does this experiment seem to demonstrate?

Aryabhata on the Circle. In the sixth century, the Indian astronomer Aryabhata wrote:

The area of a circle is half of the circumference multiplied by half of the diameter.

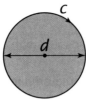

41. Is this statement correct? Show why or why not.

Aryabhata also said:

Add 4 to 100, multiply the result by 8 and then add 62,000; the result is approximately the circumference of a circle of diameter 20,000.

42. If this result were exact rather than approximate, to what number would π be equal?

When asked to write down a number used to measure circles, a backward geometry student named Dilcue wrote:

ꟼI.Ɛ

43. Do you think he should get any credit for this answer? Explain.

Set III

The following figures show three pieces hinged into a chain. If the two triangles are rotated downward, they form the second figure. If they are rotated upward, they form the fourth figure.[*]

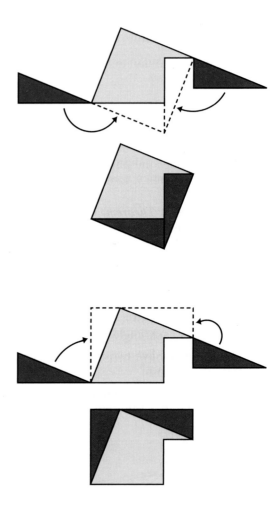

What do the two arrangements of the three pieces illustrate? Explain.

---

[*]From *Dissections, Plane and Fancy,* by Greg N. Frederickson (Cambridge University Press, 1997).

Summary and Review

You should be familiar with the following concepts introduced in Chapter 2.

Basic Ideas

Postulates

1. Two points determine a line.   61
2. Three noncollinear points determine a plane.   61

Theorems

The Pythagorean Theorem. The square of the hypotenuse of a right triangle is equal to the sum of the squares of the other two sides.   65

The Triangle Angle Sum Theorem. The sum of the angles of a triangle is 180°.   66

If the diameter of a circle is d, its circumference is πd.   66

If the radius of a circle is r, its area is πr^2.   66

Exercises

Set I

Write in "if-then" form:

1. All limericks have five lines.

2. I will make a fortune when I perfect my perpetual motion machine.

3. No toadstools are edible.

In his book *Take Time for Paradise,* A. Bartlett Giamatti wrote:

> If we have known freedom, then we love it.
> If we love freedom,
>   then we fear its loss.[*]

These are the two premises of a syllogism.

4. What is the pattern of a syllogism?

5. What, in words, is the conclusion of this syllogism?

6. What might allow the conclusion of a syllogism to be false?

The following statement is a definition of *daredevil:*

> You are a daredevil iff
> you are recklessly bold.

7. Write the two conditional statements that are equivalent to this statement.

8. How is one of your statements related to the other?

The figure below shows three birds perched on a power line.

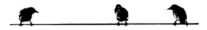

9. If we think of the birds as points on the line, what word describes their relation?

10. How many points does it take to determine a line?

11. On what type of statement in our deductive system is your answer to the preceding question based?

---

[*]Summit Books, 1989.

The figure below represents the advertising slogan of the Morton Salt Company.

12. What is this type of figure called?

13. Write the slogan in "if *a*, then *b*" form.

14. Rewrite it in the form "*b* if *a*."

15. Write the converse of the slogan in "if-then" form.

16. If the slogan is true, does it follow that its converse also is true?

The figure below appeared in a problem on an SAT exam.

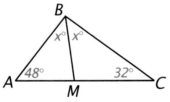

Find each of the following:

17. ∠ABC.

18. *x*.

19. ∠BMC.

A tripod is a device used to provide steady support to a camera.

20. State the postulate that is the basis for the fact that a tripod has three legs.

21. What might happen if a tripod had four legs instead of three?

Geometry in Spanish. The following sentence appears in a geometry book written in Spanish:

> En todo triángulo rectángulo el cuadrado de la longitud de la hipotenusa es igual a la suma de los cuadrados de las longitudes de los catetos.

22. Translate the sentence into English.

23. What does the word *cuadrado* mean?

24. What does the word *igual* mean?

The second word in the sentence is *todo.* Looking in a Spanish dictionary, we find *todo* defined as *entero, entero* defined as *completo,* and *completo* defined as *entero.*

25. What do these findings illustrate about the way in which words have to be defined in dictionaries?

26. What are some of the undefined terms of geometry?

27. Why are these words left undefined?

Courtroom Questions. The following conversation took place in a recent criminal trial in California.[*]

Attorney: Can you calculate the area of a circle with a 5 mm diameter?
Witness: I mean I could . . . I don't know right now what it is.
Attorney: Well, what is the formula for the area of a circle?
Witness: Pi R Squared.
Attorney: What is pi?
Witness: Boy, you are really testing me. 2.12 . . . 2.17 . . .
Judge: How about 3.1214?

. . .

Attorney: And what is the radius?
Witness: It would be half the diameter: 2.5.
Attorney: 2.5 squared, right?
Witness: Right.

. . .

_____
*Reported in *The Joy of π,* by David Blatner (Walker, 1997).

Attorney: Tell me what pi times 2.5
  squared is.
Witness: 19.

28. What mistakes did the witness make?

29. Was the judge correct? Why or why
  not?

30. Did the attorney make any mistakes?

Set II

Euclid gathered together the
geometric knowledge of his time,
and arranged it
not just in a hodge-podge manner,
but,
he started with what he thought were
self-evident truths
and then proceeded to
PROVE all the rest by
LOGIC.
A splendid idea, as you will admit
And his system has served
as a model
ever since.

Lillian Lieber
The Education of T. C. Mits

31. What are Euclid's "self-evident truths"
  called?

32. What are the rest of the truths proved
  by logic called?

33. What are the names of the two types of
  proofs used to prove these truths?

In the figure below, squares have been drawn
on the sides of a right triangle.

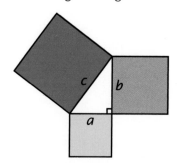

Given that $a = 12$ and $b = 16$, find the area
of

34. the yellow square.

35. the orange square.

36. the red square.

Heron of Alexandria wrote:

How many times in an attack on a
stronghold have we arrived at the foot
of the ramparts and found that we
had made our ladders too short![*]

Suppose that a ladder just reaches the top of a
wall 16 feet high and that the closest the base
of the ladder can be placed to the foot of the
wall is 12 feet.

37. How long must the ladder be to reach
  the top of the wall?

From this diagram from the Rhind papyrus,
we know that the ancient Egyptians calculated the area of a circle as

$$\left(\frac{16}{9}r\right)^2.$$

38. If this method were correct, then to what
  fraction would π be equal?

39. How do the areas of circles given by this
  method compare with their actual areas?

---

[*]*Geometry Civilized,* by J. L. Heilbron (Clarendon
Press, 1998).

Panda Proof. Here is another story from *A Prairie Home Companion Pretty Good Joke Book.* After studying the relations of the statements given in the proof, write the missing statements.

40. *Theorem.* If a panda went to a restaurant, then he eats shoots and leaves.
    Proof.
    If a panda went to a restaurant, he would have a sandwich.
    (What is the second statement?)
    If he took out a gun, he would shoot the waiter.
    (What is the fourth statement?)
    If he leaves without paying, then the panda eats shoots and leaves.

41. What kind of proof is this?

Clue Proof. Mr. Boddy has been the victim of foul play. It happened after 4 P.M. After studying the relations of the statements given in the following proof, write the missing statements.

42. *Theorem.* Colonel Mustard did it.
    Proof.
    (What is the beginning assumption?)
    If Colonel Mustard didn't do it, then Miss Scarlet did it.
    (What statement belongs here?)
    If it was done in the dining room, then it happened before noon.
    (What does this contradict?)
    Therefore, our assumption is false and (what conclusion follows?)

43. What kind of proof is this?

Circle in the Square. This figure shows a circle drawn inside a square.

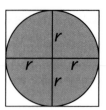

44. What is the exact circumference of the circle in terms of r?

45. What is the perimeter of the square?

46. What fraction of the perimeter of the square is the circumference of the circle?

47. What is the exact area of the circle in terms of r?

48. What is the area of the square?

49. What fraction of the area of the square is the area of the circle?

In one of his books, Lewis Carroll described a planet so small that someone can walk around it in 20 minutes!

50. If someone can walk three miles in an hour, what is the approximate diameter of that planet? Explain your reasoning. (1 mile = 5,280 feet.)

Solving Linear Equations

The Distributive Rule

The distributive rule relates the operations of multiplication and addition. For any numbers a, b, and c,

$$a(b + c) = ab + ac.$$

From the definition of subtraction in terms of addition, it follows that

$$a(b - c) = ab - ac.$$

Here are some examples of how the distributive rule is used to eliminate parentheses.

Example 1: $5(x + 7)$
Solution: $5x + 35$

Example 2: $x^2(x - y)$
Solution: $x^3 - x^2y$

Solving Linear Equations

Some useful steps in solving linear equations are:

Step 1.   Use the distributive rule to eliminate parentheses.
Step 2.   Simplify both sides of the equation as much as you can.
Step 3.   Add and subtract as necessary to get all of the terms containing the variable on one side of the equation and all of the other terms on the other side.
Step 4.   Multiply or divide to get the variable alone on one side.

Example 1:
$$2(x + 8) = x + 20$$
Solution:

$2x + 16 = x + 20$	(using the distributive rule)
$x + 16 = 20$	(subtracting x from each side)
$x = 4$	(subtracting 16 from each side)

Example 2:
$$4(2x - 7) + 10 = 3x$$
Solution:

$8x - 28 + 10 = 3x$	(using the distributive rule)
$8x - 18 = 3x$	(simplifying the left side)
$5x - 18 = 0$	(subtracting $3x$ from each side)
$5x = 18$	(adding 18 to each side)
$x = \dfrac{18}{5} = 3.6$	(dividing each side by 5)

The whetstone
of witte,

whiche is the seconde parte of
Arithmetike: containyng thextrac-
tion of Rootes: The Cossike practise,
with the rule of Equation: and
the woorkes of Surde
Nombers.

Though many stones doo beare greate price,
The whetstone is for exersice
As needefull, and in woorke as straunge:
Dulle thinges and harde it will so chaunge,
And make them sharpe, to right good vse:
All artesmen knowe, thei can not chuse,
But vse his helpe, yet as men see,
Noe sharpenesse semeth in it to bee.
The grounde of artes did brede this stone:
His vse is greate, and moare then one.
Here if you lift your wittes to whette,
Muche sharpenesse therby shall you gette.
Dulle wittes hereby doe greately mende,
Sharpe wittes are fined to their fulle ende.
Now proue, and praise, as you doe finde,
And to your self be not vnkinde.

These Bookes are to bee solde, at
the Weste doore of Poules,
by Jhon Kyngstone.

The Arte

as their workes doe extende) to distincte it onely into
twoo partes. Whereof the firste is, when one number is
equalle vnto one other. And the seconde is, when one nomber is compared as equalle vnto .2. other nombers.

Alwaies willyng you to remēber, that you reduce
your nombers, to their leaste denominations, and
smalleste formes, before you procede any farther.

And again, if your equation be soche, that the greateste denomination Cossike, be ioined to any parte of a
compounde nomber, you shall tourne it so, that the
nomber of the greateste signe alone, maie stande as
equalle to the reste.

And this is all that neadeth to be taughte, concer-
nyng this woorke.

Howbeit, for easie alteratiō of equations. I will pro-
pounde a fewe exāples, bicause the extraction of their
rootes, maie the more aptly bee wroughte. And to a-
uoide the tediouse repetition of these woordes: is e-
qualle to: I will sette as I doe often in woorke vse, a
paire of paralleles, or Gemowe lines of one lengthe,
thus:————, bicause noe .2. thynges, can be moare
equalle. And now marke these nombers.

1. $14.\not z. ———— .15.\not q. ———— 71.\not q.$
2. $20.\not z. ————.18.\not q. ————.102.\not q.$
3. $26.\not z. ———— 10\not z ———— 9.\not z ———— 10\not z ———— 213.\not q.$
4. $19.\not z ———— 192.\not q ———— 10\not z ———— 108\not q ———— 19\not z$
5. $18.\not z ———— 24.\not q. ———— 8.\not z. ———— 2.\not z.$
6. $34\not z ———— 12\not z ———— 40\not z ———— 480\not q ———— 9.\not z.$
1. In the firste there appeareth. 2. nombers, that is
    $14.\not z.$

The first algebra book in English, titled The Whetstone of Witte, *was written by Robert Recorde and published in 1557. It was in this book that the equal sign was used for the first time in history.*

Exercises

Simplify the following expressions.

1. $8x + 2x$
2. $(8x)(2x)$
3. $5x + x + 5$
4. $5x - x - 5$
5. $7x^2 - x^2$
6. $x^2 - 7x^2$
7. $6x + 3y + 3x + y$
8. $6x + 3y - 3x - y$

Use the distributive rule to eliminate the parentheses.

9. $5(x + 3)$
10. $11(4 - x)$
11. $6(3x + 1)$
12. $8(5 - 7x)$
13. $9x(x - 2)$
14. $2x(10 + 3x)$
15. $xy(x + y)$
16. $2(x^2 - 2x + 4)$

Solve the following equations.

17. $5x - 3 = 47$
18. $9 + 2x = 25$
19. $4x + 7x = 33$
20. $10x = x + 54$
21. $6x - 1 = 5x + 12$
22. $2x + 9 = 7x - 36$
23. $8 - x = x + 22$
24. $3x - 5 = 10x + 30$
25. $4(x - 11) = 3x + 16$
26. $x(x + 7) = x^2$
27. $5(x + 2) = 2(x - 13)$
28. $6(4x - 1) = 7(15 + 3x)$
29. $8 + 2(x + 3) = 10$
30. $x + 7(x - 5) = 2(5 - x)$
31. $4(x + 9) + x(x - 1) = x(6 + x)$
32. $2x(x + 3) + x(x + 4) = 5x(x + 2) - 2x^2$

Chapter 3

Lines and Angles

Where is the five-pointed star?

In this chapter, we begin with the algebraic tools used in geometry and then apply them to the measurement of line segments and angles. In doing so, we look at the ways in which rulers and protractors work. These ideas are then applied to exploring relations between angles with respect to both their measures and the positions of their sides. The chapter closes with a look at two important relations between lines.

© 2003 Harold R. Jacobs

"That, in itself, is a breakthrough."

LESSON 1

Number Operations and Equality

In your study of algebra, you learned some properties that are true for all numbers. Here are some examples.

1. $a = a$. Any number is equal to itself (called the "reflexive" property of equality).

2. $a + b = b + a$. The order in which two numbers are added doesn't matter (addition is "commutative").

3. $a(b + c) = ab + ac$. (The "distributive" property.)

4. $(a + b)^2 = a^2 + 2ab + b^2$. ("Squaring a binomial.")

5. $a^2 - b^2 = (a + b)(a - b)$. ("Factoring the difference of two squares.")

The first three properties are examples of statements that are accepted in algebra as true without proof. They are some of the *postulates*, also called "axioms," of algebra. The word "axiom" means "a self-evident or accepted rule," and so the words *postulate* and *axiom* convey the same idea.

The last two properties in the list are statements that are often *proved* in algebra, and so they are examples of algebraic *theorems*.

We will use some of the postulates (axioms) of algebra when reasoning about figures in geometry. These algebraic postulates about numbers will be just as important as our geometric postulates about points, lines, and planes.

Each algebraic postulate below states that two algebraic expressions are *equal* to each other. If the symbols *a* and *b* represent real numbers, what do we mean by the statement *a* = *b*? Simply that *a* and *b* *represent the same number*. The statements below are direct consequences of this idea. For simplicity, they are stated symbolically, the letters representing real numbers. The postulates have been given names with which you can identify them when you use them.

The Reflexive Property
a = *a*. (Any number is equal to itself.)

The Substitution Property
If *a* = *b*, then *a* can be substituted for *b* in any expression.

The Addition Property
If *a* = *b*, then *a* + *c* = *b* + *c*.

The Subtraction Property
If *a* = *b*, then *a* − *c* = *b* − *c*.

The Multiplication Property
If *a* = *b*, then *ac* = *bc*.

The Division Property
If *a* = *b* and *c* ≠ 0, then $\dfrac{a}{c} = \dfrac{b}{c}$.

Here is an example of how some of these postulates are used in reasoning about a geometric figure.

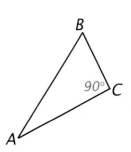

In triangle ABC, ∠C = 90° and ∠B is twice as large as ∠A. How large is ∠A?

∠A + ∠B + ∠C = 180°.
    (The sum of the angles of a triangle is 180°.)

If ∠C = 90°, ∠A + ∠B + 90° = 180°.
    (Substitution.)

If ∠A + ∠B + 90° = 180°, then ∠A + ∠B = 90°.
    (Subtraction. 90° was subtracted from each side.)

If ∠A + ∠B = 90° and ∠B = 2∠A, then ∠A + 2∠A = 90°.
    (Substitution.)

If 3∠A = 90°, then ∠A = 30°.
    (Division. Each side was divided by 3.)

Exercises

Set I

Name the property of equality illustrated by each of the following statements.

1. If $a^2 + b^2 = c^2$, then $b^2 = c^2 - a^2$.
2. If $b^2 = c^2 - a^2$ and $c^2 - a^2 = (c + a)(c - a)$, then $b^2 = (c + a)(c - a)$.
3. If $\dfrac{c}{d} = \pi$, then $c = \pi d$.
4. If $\angle A + \angle B + \angle C = 180°$ and $\angle C = \angle A + \angle B$, then $\angle C + \angle C = 180°$.
5. If $2\angle C = 180°$, then $\angle C = 90°$.

In this figure, the perimeter of the green region is equal to the perimeter of the red region.

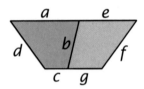

6. Write an equation to show this equality.
7. Why is $a + c + d = e + f + g$?

This figure shows two lines intersecting to form several angles, three of which are numbered.

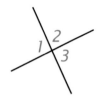

8. If $\angle 1 + \angle 2 = \angle 2 + \angle 3$, then $\angle 1 = \angle 3$. Why?
9. If $\angle 1 = \angle 2$ and $\angle 2 = \angle 3$, then $\angle 1 = \angle 3$. Why?
10. If $\angle 1 = x°$ and $\angle 3 = x°$, then $\angle 1 + \angle 3 = (2x)°$. Why?

This figure shows how we bisected an angle by using a straightedge and compass. Let's check the algebra to see that $\angle 1$ is the size that we would expect.

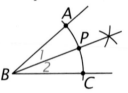

11. If $\angle ABC = \angle 1 + \angle 2$ and $\angle 1 = \angle 2$, then $\angle ABC = \angle 1 + \angle 1 = 2\angle 1$. Why?
12. If $\angle ABC = 2\angle 1$, then $\angle 1 = \dfrac{1}{2}\angle ABC$. Why?

The division property does not allow division by 0, because, if it did, some strange things could happen. To see why, try to tell what number should replace ? to make each of the following statements true.

13. $\dfrac{6}{3} = ?$ because $3 \times ? = 6$.
14. $\dfrac{6}{0} = ?$ because $0 \times ? = 6$.
15. $\dfrac{0}{6} = ?$ because $6 \times ? = 0$.
16. $\dfrac{0}{0} = ?$ because $0 \times ? = 0$.
17. What is strange about the equations in exercise 16?

Euclid listed five "common notions" at the beginning of the *Elements*. One of them is:
> If equals are added to equals, the wholes are equal.

In the symbols of algebra, this notion says:
> If $a = b$ and $c = d$, then $a + c = b + d$.

It is easy to prove this statement by using our statement of the addition property:
> If $a = b$, then $a + c = b + c$.

18. If $a + c = b + c$ and $c = d$, then $a + c = b + d$. Why?

19. Use the same reasoning to show that

If $a = b$ and $c = d \neq 0$,

then $\dfrac{a}{c} = \dfrac{b}{d}$.

Correcting Mistakes. An algebraic mistake can give a wrong solution. Here is an example:

Solve for x: $2x + 7 = 19$

Solution: $2x + 7 = 19$
$2x = 26$ (Addition)
$x = 13$ (Division)

20. What mistake was made here?

Logical thinking helps find and fix such errors.
Check:
Suppose $x = 13$.

21. If $2x + 7 = 19$ and $x = 13$, then
$2(13) + 7 = 19$. Why?

If $2(13) + 7 = 19$, then $26 + 7 = 19$.
If $26 + 7 = 19$, then $33 = 19$.
This contradicts the fact that $33 \neq 19$.
Therefore, our assumption that $x = 13$
is wrong.

22. What kind of proof is this?

Set II

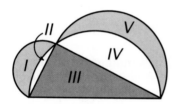

Triangle and Crescents. In this figure, the Roman numerals represent the areas of the five colored regions and

$$I + II + IV + V = II + III + IV.$$

23. What can you conclude about how the total area shaded light blue compares with the area shaded dark blue?

24. Why?

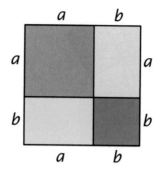

Binomial Square. The figure above shows a large square divided into two smaller squares and two rectangles. The letters a and b represent the lengths indicated.

25. What are the areas of the two smaller squares?

26. What is the total area of the two rectangles?

27. How long is each side of the entire figure?

Write an expression for the area of the entire figure

28. in terms of the length of its side.

29. as the sum of the areas of the four parts.

30. Write an equation to indicate that these two expressions are equal.

Chinese Proof. The figure below is from a Chinese textbook of 1607.

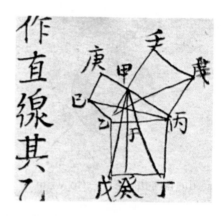

31. What theorem does it seem to illustrate?

Lesson 1: Number Operations and Equality   **81**

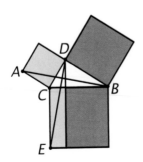

Part of the proof of this theorem shows that

Area of triangle ABC = area of triangle CDE.
Area of yellow square = 2 × area of triangle ABC.
Area of yellow rectangle = 2 × area of triangle CDE.

Another part of the proof shows that

Area of red square = area of red rectangle.

Which property of equality tells why each of the following conclusions is true?

32. Area of yellow square = 2 × area of triangle CDE.

33. Area of yellow square = area of yellow rectangle.

34. Area of yellow square + area of red square = area of yellow rectangle + area of red rectangle.

35. State the theorem that this proof demonstrates as a complete sentence.

Circle Formula. There is a formula other than $a = \pi r^2$ for the area of a circle that can be found by algebra.

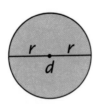

36. Use the fact that $r = \dfrac{d}{2}$ to write a formula for a in terms of d rather than in terms of r. Show your method.

Quadratic Formula. A famous theorem of algebra is the quadratic formula:

If $ax^2 + bx + c = 0$, then $x = \dfrac{-b \pm \sqrt{b^2 - 4ac}}{2a}$.

37. What is the hypothesis of this theorem?

Name the postulate that is the reason for each of the following first three steps in its proof:

38. If $ax^2 + bx + c = 0$, then $x^2 + \dfrac{b}{a}x + \dfrac{c}{a} = 0$.

39. If $x^2 + \dfrac{b}{a}x + \dfrac{c}{a} = 0$, then $x^2 + \dfrac{b}{a}x = -\dfrac{c}{a}$.

40. If $x^2 + \dfrac{b}{a}x = -\dfrac{c}{a}$, then

$$x^2 + \dfrac{b}{a}x + \left(\dfrac{b}{2a}\right)^2 = -\dfrac{c}{a} + \left(\dfrac{b}{2a}\right)^2.$$

41. What kind of proof begins like this?

When the quadratic formula is used to solve an equation such as

$$2x^2 + 5x + 3 = 0$$

in which $a = 2$, $b = 5$, and $c = 3$, the solution begins with

$$x = \dfrac{-5 \pm \sqrt{5^2 - 4(2)(3)}}{2(2)}.$$

42. What postulate is being used here?

43. Simplify the expression and find x.

Dilcue's Pie. Dilcue's mother baked him a pie for his birthday and everyone in the neighborhood agreed that it was the largest pie that they had ever seen. Dilcue was so impressed that he decided to figure out its circumference in feet. He used the *wrong* expression, πr^2, to do it but still got the right answer!

44. How could this have happened if using the wrong expression was his only mistake?

45. What was the circumference of the pie? Show your reasoning.

46. What was its area?

Set III

Lewis Carroll once posed the following problem in a letter to a young friend who was studying algebra.*

Understanding you to be a distinguished algebraist (i.e. distinguished from other algebraists by different face, different height, etc.) I beg to submit to you a difficulty which distresses me much.

If x and y are each equal to "1," it is plain that $2(x^2 - y^2) = 0$ and also that $5(x - y) = 0$. Hence $2(x^2 - y^2) = 5(x - y)$.

Now divide each side of this equation by $(x - y)$.

Then $2(x + y) = 5$.

But $(x + y) = (1 + 1)$, i.e. $= 2$.

So that $2 \times 2 = 5$.

Ever since this painful fact has been forced upon me, I have not slept more than 8 hours a night, and have not been able to eat more than 3 meals a day.

I trust you will pity me and will kindly explain the difficulty.

Can *you?*

---

*_The Universe in a Handerchief,_ by Martin Gardner (Copernicus, 1996).

LESSON 2

The Ruler and Distance

As surprising as it may seem, there are no measurements in Euclid's *Elements.* Tools such as the ruler and protractor are never mentioned.

Although Euclid did not attach numbers to line segments, angles or areas, he did *compare* them with statements such as

All right angles are *equal* to one another

and

In any triangle the *greater* side subtends the *greater* angle.

Numbers are now taken for granted in geometry. In fact, applications such as computer graphics could not exist without them. In this lesson, we will consider how numbers are used in measuring distances.

Our first postulate says that

Two points determine a line.

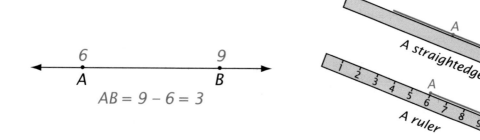

$$AB = 9 - 6 = 3$$

If we merely want to *draw* the line determined by two points, we can use a simple *straightedge* to do so. If we want to measure the *distance* between the points, we need a *ruler*. If point A falls on the 6 and point B falls on the 9, as happened in measuring Snoopy's mouth, then AB, the distance from A to B, is 9 − 6 = 3. Because the numbers on the ruler being used are 1 inch apart, Snoopy's mouth measures 3 inches across.

It is convenient to think of a ruler as an infinite number line. The points on the line are numbered so that to every point there corresponds exactly one real number called its *coordinate* and, conversely, to every real number there corresponds exactly one point. Furthermore, to every pair of points on the line there corresponds a real number called the *distance* between them. As illustrated in the example of measuring Snoopy's mouth, this distance is the *positive difference* between their coordinates. We will summarize this description of a ruler as the Ruler Postulate.

Postulate 3. The Ruler Postulate
The points on a line can be numbered so that positive number differences measure distances.

The figure at the right shows three points, A, B, and C, on a line and the numbers that are their coordinates, *a*, *b*, and *c*. We will use the symbol "A-B-C" (or "C-B-A") to indicate that point B is between points A and C. Because point B is between the other two points, its coordinate, *b*, must be between their coordinates. In other words, *b* is greater than one of them and less than the other; either $a < b < c$ or $a > b > c$, which suggests a way to *define* what it means for one point to be *between* two others.

Definition (Betweenness of Points)
A *point is between two other points on the same line* iff its coordinate is between their coordinates. (More briefly, A-B-C iff $a < b < c$ or $a > b > c$.)

Here is another example. In the figure at the right, the coordinates of U, S, and A are 9, 4, and 1. Computing distances, we get US = 9 − 4 = 5, SA = 4 − 1 = 3, and UA = 9 − 1 = 8:

$$US + SA = UA \text{ because } 5 + 3 = 8.$$

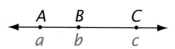

These results are just what we would expect from the figure and can be easily proved as our first theorem.

As you know, a theorem is a statement that is proved by reasoning deductively from already accepted statements, including both definitions and postulates. Our proof is a direct one. To make it easier to read, the statements in it are listed at the left and the reasons for them at the right.

Theorem 1. The Betweenness of Points Theorem
If A-B-C, then $AB + BC = AC$.

Proof for case in which $a < b < c$

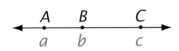

Statements	*Reasons*
1. A-B-C.	The hypothesis.
2. $a < b < c$.	Definition of betweenness of points and this case.
3. $AB = b - a$ and $BC = c - b$.	Ruler Postulate.
4. $AB + BC = (b - a) + (c - b)$ $= c - a$.	Addition (and simplification).
5. $AC = c - a$.	Ruler Postulate.
6. $AB + BC = AC$.	Substitution (steps 4 and 5).

Exercises

Set I

Three important ideas have been introduced in this lesson that you should get to know. Write each of them as a complete sentence.

1. The Ruler Postulate.

2. The definition of betweenness of points.

3. The Betweenness of Points Theorem.

Three points on a line have the following coordinates: point A, 123; point T, 1; and point W, 12. Which idea in exercises 1 through 3 is the reason for each statement below?

4. T-W-A because $1 < 12 < 123$.

5. TW + WA = TA because T-W-A.

Triple Jump. The figure above shows a triple jump with the jumper taking off from A and landing at B, C, and D. A typical jumper runs about 40 meters to get to the takeoff point.

Use the numbers on the figure to find:

6. The total distance of the jump, AD.

7. The coordinate of C.

8. The distance CD.

Because A-B-C, AB + BC = AC, or 7 + 5 = 12, according to the Betweenness of Points Theorem.

Use the Betweenness of Points Theorem to complete the following statements.

9. Because B-C-D, BC + ? = ?, or 5 + ? = ?.

10. Because A-B-D, AB + ? = ?, or 7 + ? = ?.

11. Because A-C-D, AC + ? = ?, or ? + ? + ?.

Eclipse Problems. Eclipses occur when the earth, sun, and moon are in line with each other.

12. What are points that lie on the same line called?

The figures below (not to scale) represent the possible positions of the sun, S, earth, E, and moon, M, during an eclipse.

S	E	M	S	M	E
•	•	•	•	•	•

| Figure A | Figure B |

13. Which figure illustrates an eclipse of the sun?

If the distance from the earth to the moon is 240,000 miles and the distance from the earth to the sun is 93,000,000 miles, find the distance between the moon and the sun when

14. S-E-M.

15. S-M-E.

Seven League Boots. According to legend, "seven league boots" allow whoever wears them to travel 7 leagues at each step. (A league is about 3 miles!)

Home 4 *A* 7 *B* 7 *C* 7 *D* 7 *E* 7 *F*
  0 4

Suppose someone puts them on 4 leagues away from home and walks as shown in the figure above.

16. What are the coordinates of points B, C, D, E, and F?

How many leagues away from home is the person after taking

17. two steps?

18. five steps?

19. If *n* represents the number of steps taken, what does $4 + 7n$ represent?

Skyscraper. A side view of the lower floors of a skyscraper is shown in the figure at the right.
 Use the Ruler Postulate to find the distance in floors between

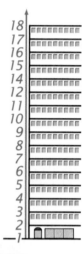

20. the 2nd and 9th floors.

21. the 5th and 15th floors.

22. Are both of these answers correct? Why or why not?

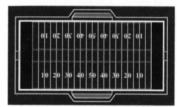

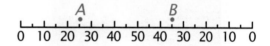

Football Field. The yard lines on a football field are spaced at 5-yard intervals and numbered as shown in the figures above and below.

23. At what yard lines are points A and B?

24. If these numbers were coordinates as in the Ruler Postulate, then the distance from A to B would be 10 yards. Why?

25. Why can't we think of the numbers of yard lines as coordinates?

Suppose the lines on a football field were numbered like this instead.

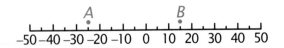

26. What are the coordinates of points A and B now?

27. What distance does the Ruler Postulate give for AB now?

28. Is this distance correct?

SAT Problem. The figure below appeared in a problem on an SAT exam.

On this number line, the numbers 3, −1, 5, 0, and 1 are indicated by the arrows.

29. Copy the figure and write the numbers in the appropriate places.

30. Which arrow indicates 0?

31. What is the distance from the first arrow to the last arrow?

Set II

Pole Vaulter. This time sequence photograph shows a pole vaulter in action.

Although it seems that the points at which the vaulter's hands hold the pole are *between* the endpoints of the pole, this does not agree with the definition of betweenness of points.

32. Without looking it up, try to write the definition of betweenness of points as a complete sentence.

33. What is it about the pole that does not fit this definition?

34. Without looking it up, try to write the Betweenness of Points Theorem as a complete sentence.

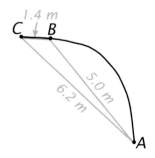

The figure above shows the distances between one hand and the ends of the pole at one moment of the vault.

35. How does AB + BC compare with AC in this figure?

36. Do you think AB + BC could ever be less than AC?

Ladder Problem 1.
The extension ladder in the figure at the right can be adjusted to different lengths. The upper distance (AB in the diagram) looks as if it might be equal to the lower distance (CD).

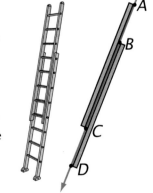

37. Do you think these two distances would still look equal to each other if the ladder were extended by sliding the sections as indicated?

Suppose that the two parts of the ladder, AC and BD, are the same length (that is, AC = BD).

Complete the following two statements.

38. Because A-B-C, AC = ?.

39. Because B-C-D, BD = ?.

40. Why is AB + BC = BC + CD?

41. Why is AB = CD?

Ladder Problem 2. The first rung of the ladder shown in the figure below is 11 inches from the bottom of the ladder and the last rung is 11 inches from the top of the ladder. The other rungs are spaced 12 inches apart.

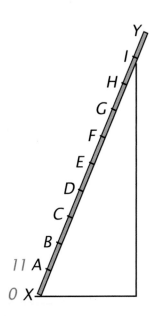

42. If the coordinate of X, the bottom of the ladder, is 0 and the coordinate of the first rung is 11, find the coordinates of the other rungs and of the top of the ladder, Y.

Check your work by comparing

43. the coordinates of the first and last rungs with the distance between them.

44. the coordinate of Y, the top of the ladder, with XY, the total length of the ladder.

Stars Proof. The figure at the right shows three stars as seen from the earth. The distances between the stars, in light-years, are:
XY = 7.2, YZ = 9.8, and XZ = 16.6.

● *Star X*

● *Star Y*

● *Star Z*

45. *Copy and complete* the following indirect proof that, contrary to their appearance, star Y is not between star X and star Z.

Proof

(What is the beginning assumption?)

(What statement follows from the Betweenness of Points Theorem?)

If XY + YZ = XZ, then 7.2 + 9.8 = 16.6.

(What is the contradiction?)

Therefore, our assumption is false and (what conclusion follows?)

Signal Problem. Suppose you are approaching an intersection at a speed of 30 miles per hour (44 feet per second) and the signal turns yellow. The intersection is 60 feet wide and the signal stays yellow for 3 seconds.

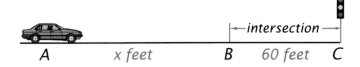

46. If you don't change your speed, how far can you be from the intersection to get through it before the light turns red? Show how the Betweenness of Points Theorem can be used to find the answer.

Our first theorem, the Betweenness of Points Theorem, was proved in this lesson only for the case in which $a < b < c$. The proof for the case in which $a > b > c$ is almost exactly the same.

47. Using the proof on page 86 as a guide, write the proof for this case. (Include the figure with your proof.)

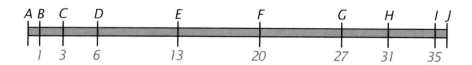

Yardstick Distances. A yardstick 36 inches long is represented in the figure above. Even though it has only eight marks on it, it can be used to measure every whole-number distance from 1 to 36 inches!*

48. Show how by making a list of the numbers from 1 through 36 and naming at least one pair of points that can be used to measure each distance.

For example, the beginning of your list would look like this:

```
1   AB (or IJ)
2   BC
3   AC (or CD) and so forth
```

Set III

You have inherited a rowboat with no oars. According to Shaw and Tenney, a company in Maine that manufactures oars, the handles of a pair of oars should overlap by 4 inches.†

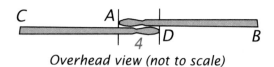

Overhead view (not to scale)

1. If the distance between the oarlocks, BC, is 42 inches and the overlap, AD, is 4 inches, how long should AB and CD be? Show your reasoning.

For efficient rowing, Shaw and Tenney recommend that the inboard part of each oar (AB in each figure) should be 7/25ths of the overall length of the oar. The paddle, EF, is 26 inches long.

2. According to this information, how long should the oars for your boat be? Show your method.

Oars come in lengths from 6 feet to 10 feet in 6-inch increments.

3. What length of oars would you order for your boat?

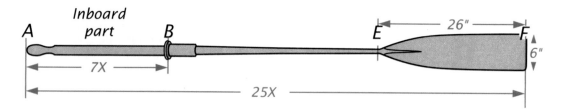

The Incredible Dr. Matrix, by Martin Gardner (Scribners, 1976).
† *Sizes,* by John Lord (Harper Collins, 1995).

Used by permission of Johnny Hart and Creators Syndicate, Inc.

The Protractor and Angle Measure

Although a vast number of different units have been invented through-out history to measure distance, the unit chosen by the ancient Babylonians for measuring angles more than 4,000 years ago is still in use today. No other unit of measurement even comes close to having lasted as long as the *degree*.

The scale on a circular protractor is divided into 360 equal parts, each part measuring 1 degree. If we imagine a ray with its endpoint at the center of the protractor turning exactly once around the scale, we might think of all of the positions through which it moves as a *rotation of rays*.

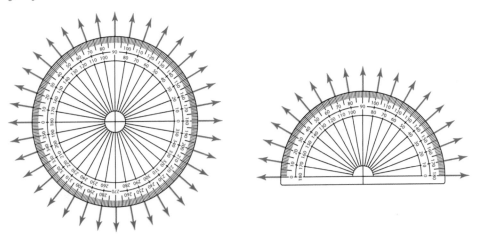

The largest angle usually considered in geometry, however, has a measure of only 180°; so the protractor in most common use is the semicircular protractor. We will refer to all of the rays that correspond to it as a *half-rotation* of rays.

When an angle is measured with a protractor, *the center of the protractor **must** be placed on the vertex of the angle.* It isn't necessary, however, for the 0 mark on the protractor to be placed on one side of the angle.

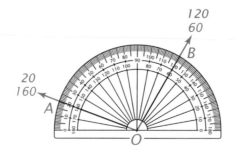

$$\angle AOB = 160 - 60 = 100°$$
or
$$\angle AOB = 120 - 20 = 100°$$

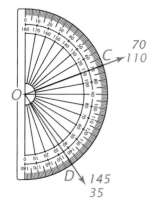

$$\angle COD = 110 - 35 = 75°$$
or
$$\angle COD = 145 - 70 = 75°$$

In the figure above, $\angle AOB = 160 - 60 = 100°$ (or $120 - 20 = 100°$, depending on which scale you choose) and, in the figure at the left, $\angle COD = 110 - 35 = 75°$ (or $145 - 70 = 75°$).

Although every protractor is numbered with two scales, only one of them is needed. In fact, in describing how a protractor works, we will find that it is convenient to think of it as having only one scale. With this in mind, we can say that the rays in a half-rotation can be numbered so that to every ray there corresponds exactly one real number called its *coordinate*, and to every real number from 0 to 180 inclusive there corresponds exactly one ray. Moreover, to every pair of rays there corresponds a real number called the *measure of the angle* that the rays determine. The measure of this angle is the positive difference between the coordinates of the rays. This description of a protractor is very much like our description of a ruler. We will summarize it as the Protractor Postulate.

Postulate 4. The Protractor Postulate

The rays in a half-rotation can be numbered from 0 to 180 so that positive number differences measure angles.

Angles are classified according to their measures as follows.

Definitions

An angle is

  acute iff it is less than 90°.
  right iff it is 90°.
  obtuse iff it is more than 90° but less than 180°.
  straight iff it is 180°.

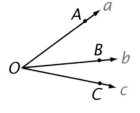

In the figure at the left, rays OA, OB, and OC have a common endpoint, O, and coordinates *a*, *b*, and *c*. It seems reasonable to say that ray OB is *between* rays OA and OC and to use the abbreviation "OA-OB-OC" (or "OC-OB-OA"). As we did in defining *betweenness of points*, we can use coordinates to define *betweenness of rays*.

Definition (Betweenness of Rays)
A *ray is between two others in the same half-rotation* iff its
coordinate is between their coordinates. (More briefly, OA-OB-OC
iff $a < b < c$ or $a > b > c$.)

In the figure at the right, the coordinates of rays IF, IT, and IS are
135, 90, and 20. Calculating angles, we get $\angle FIT = 135 - 90 = 45°$,
$\angle TIS = 90 - 20 = 70°$, and $\angle FIS = 135 - 20 = 115°$:

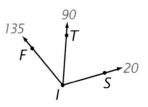

$$\angle FIT + \angle TIS = \angle FIS \text{ because } 45° + 70° = 115°.$$

Such results are true whenever one ray is between two others, and we
prove it as our second theorem.

Theorem 2. The Betweenness of Rays Theorem
If OA-OB-OC, then $\angle AOB + \angle BOC = \angle AOC$.

Proof for case in which $a > b > c$

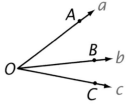

Statements	*Reasons*
1. OA-OB-OC.	The hypothesis.
2. $a > b > c$.	Definition of betweenness of rays and this case.
3. $\angle AOB = a - b$ and $\angle BOC = b - c$.	Protractor Postulate.
4. $\angle AOB + \angle BOC = (a - b) + (b - c) = a - c$.	Addition (and simplification).
5. $\angle AOC = a - c$.	Protractor Postulate.
6. $\angle AOB + \angle BOC = \angle AOC$.	Substitution (steps 4 and 5).

Exercises

Set I

Three more important ideas have been introduced in this lesson that you should get to
know. Write each of them as a complete
sentence.

1. The Protractor Postulate.

2. The definition of betweenness of rays.

3. The Betweenness of Rays Theorem.

Three rays in a half-rotation have the following coordinates: ray HE, 81; ray HI, 18; and
ray HO, 180.

4. Which ray is between the other two? Use
   your protractor to draw a figure.

5. Name and find the measures of the three
   angles formed by the rays.

Which statement in exercises 1 through 3 is
the reason for your answer to

6. exercise 4?

7. exercise 5?

The following definition is from an old book titled *First Book of Geometry.**

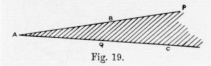
8. What do we call "half-lines"?

9. What do we call the "arms" of an angle?

10. Which of the following also are correct names for the angle shown in the figure?

∠A, ∠ABC, ∠CAB, ∠PAC, ∠AQP.

Danger Area. One of the many ways in which angles are used in navigation is in the directions of signal lights warning mariners of hazardous areas. The figure at the right shows a "red sector," the interior of an angle marking a dangerous area.[†]

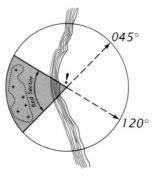

11. What are the numbers 45 and 120 called with respect to the sides of the angle opposite the danger angle?

12. What is the measure of this angle?

13. What kind of angle is it?

_____

*Written by Grace Chisholm Young and W. H. Young and published in London in 1905.
[†]From *Dutton's Navigation and Piloting*, by Elbert E. Maloney (Naval Institute Press, 1985).

Although angles in geometry have measures of no more than 180°, the number of degrees through which something can turn is unlimited. Two examples from sports are listed below.

14. A spectacular move in basketball is the "360." What do you think that means?

15. A dive in springboard diving is the "one-and-a-half" somersault. What do you think that means?

The apparent size of an angle depends on your point of view.

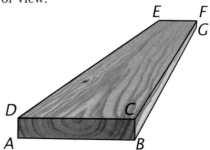

16. How many angles do you see in this picture?

17. Assuming that it is an ordinary board, how many of them are right angles?

If you measured the angles as they appear in this picture, which angles do you think would be

18. acute?

19. obtuse?

Birds and planes sometimes form angles in the sky. The photograph below shows geese flying in "V formation."

20. Is it possible to tell from the photograph what type of angle the birds are flying in? Explain.

Bubble Angles. If four bubbles in a foam come together as shown in the figure at the left below, they quickly rearrange themselves to form the figure shown at the right.

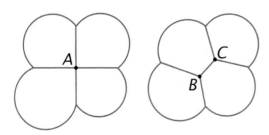

What type of angles seem to surround

21. point A?

22. points B and C?

23. If the four angles surrounding point A are equal, how large is each angle?

24. If the three angles surrounding point B and point C are equal, how large is each angle?

Cactus Spokes. The "spokes" coming from the center of this cactus seem to be evenly spaced around it.

25. If this is the case, find the measure of one of the angles formed by two adjacent spokes.

Some of the spokes of the cactus are represented in this figure by rays; the numbers are their coordinates.

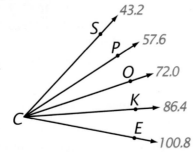

26. Would it be correct to say that ray CP is between ray CS and ray CK?

27. Use the definition of betweenness of rays to explain why or why not.

Use the coordinates of the rays to find the measures of the following angles.

28. ∠SCP.

29. ∠PCK.

30. ∠SCK.

31. Write an equation relating the measures of these three angles.

32. What theorem does this equation illustrate?

33. State the theorem as a complete sentence.

Set II

Runway Numbers. Airport runways have numbers on them indicating in what direction a plane is heading when it takes off. A runway numbered 0 points due north and a runway numbered 9 points due east.

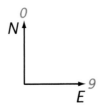

What do you think is the number of a runway pointing

34. due south?

35. due west?

36. In what way are the numbers of airport runways related to the numbers on a circular protractor?

Airplanes sometimes take off from either end of a runway, depending on conditions.

37. If one end of a runway is numbered 5, what do you think the opposite end is numbered?

Two runways at an airport may have the same number, such as the ones in this photograph.

38. What does this numbering indicate about the directions of the two runways?

39. What angle do these runways make with "due north"? Make a drawing to illustrate your answer.

40. What do the letters represent in the photograph?

Pool Ball Angles. In this overhead view of a pool table, the cue ball (white) is shown banking off the lower cushion to nudge the 1-ball into the corner pocket.*

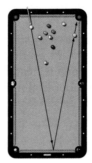

When a pool ball banks off a cushion, the angles that its path forms with the cushion are equal. For example, in the figure below, a ball from point A hitting the cushion at P makes $\angle 1 = \angle 2$. A ball from C hitting the cushion at P makes $\angle CPX = \angle DPY$.

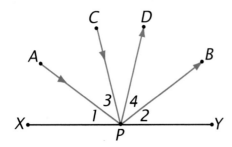

*From *Billiards,* by John Grissim (St. Martin's Press, 1979).

It is easy to prove from these facts that $\angle 3$ and $\angle 4$ in this figure also must be equal. Tell why each of the following statements in the proof is true.

41. $\angle CPX = \angle 1 + \angle 3$ because PX-PA-PC and $\angle DPY = \angle 2 + \angle 4$ because PD-PB-PY.

42. $\angle 1 + \angle 3 = \angle 2 + \angle 4$ because $\angle CPX = \angle DPY$.

43. $\angle 3 = \angle 4$ because $\angle 1 = \angle 2$.

NBC Peacock. When color television first began, NBC chose a peacock with 11 feathers as a symbol for its programs broadcast in color.

How many degrees do you think the angle of each feather would be if the peacock had

44. 9 feathers?

45. 10 feathers?

46. 12 feathers?

47. How many degrees does the angle of each feather in the actual symbol seem to be?

Minutes and Seconds. Units of angle measure smaller than the degree are the *minute* and *second.* One degree is equal to 60 minutes and 1 minute is equal to 60 seconds.

48. What unit besides the degree also is equal to 60 minutes, with a minute being equal to 60 seconds?

49. How many seconds are there in 1 degree?

The earth makes one rotation on its axis in 24 hours.

50. How many degrees are in one rotation?

51. Through how many degrees does the earth turn in 1 hour?

52. Through how many (angular) minutes does the earth turn in 1 minute of time?

53. Through how many (angular) seconds does the earth turn in 1 second of time?

Our second theorem, the Betweenness of Rays Theorem, was proved in this lesson only for the case in which $a > b > c$. The proof for the case in which $a < b < c$ is almost exactly the same.

54. Using the proof on page 93 as a guide, write the proof for this case. (Include the figure with your proof.)

Set III

In 1995, a geometrical puzzle in the *Washington Post* attracted more attention than its author could have imagined. As J. L. Heilbron relates in his book *Geometry Civilized,*

> The United Press Syndicate, which had carried the quiz in which the puzzle first appeared, insisted it could be solved, but by a method too long to print. The man who set the puzzle . . . said that he had forgotten how to do it and could not repeat his lost performance. He had recourse to three dozen geometers, none of whom, he said, could find a solution.*

The problem was to find the measure of ∠EFB in the figure at the right without measuring or using any advanced mathematics.

1. Use a ruler and protractor to make an accurate drawing of the figure. Make it as large as you can.

Several angles in the figure can be figured out by using the theorem about the sum of the angles of a triangle.

2. Which angles are they and what are their measures?

Obviously, the measure of ∠EFB cannot be figured out as easily or the puzzle would not have given so much trouble. If your drawing is reasonably accurate, however, you may be able to make a good guess.

3. What do you think the measure of ∠EFB might be?

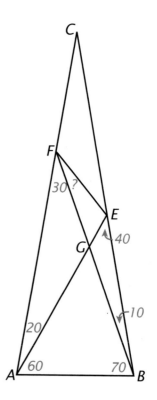

---

*Clarendon Press, 1998.

Lesson 3: The Protractor and Angle Measure   **97**

Bisection

A fellow in Central City, Kentucky, was upset because his wife had filed for divorce and demanded an equal property settlement. Using drills and saws, he started to "bisect" their house into two equal parts, which he called "His" and "Hers." His wife got a restraining order to stop him from finishing the job.*

In Lesson 4 of Chapter 1, you learned how to bisect line segments and angles with a straightedge and compass. Such figures can also be bisected by *folding*. If a line segment is drawn on tracing paper and one endpoint is folded onto the other, the crease divides the line segment into two equal parts. The fold line *bisects* the line segment and intersects it at its *midpoint*.

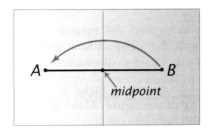

midpoint

Definition

A point is the *midpoint of a line segment* iff it divides the line segment into two equal segments.

———————————

*Associated Press, January 21, 1983, as reported by Martin Gardner in *Penrose Tiles to Trapdoor Ciphers* (W. H. Freeman and Company, 1989).

If an angle is drawn on tracing paper, it can be bisected by folding one side onto the other. The crease line goes through its vertex and forms two equal angles with the sides of the angle.

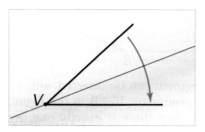

Definition
A line *bisects an angle* iff it divides the angle into two equal angles.

When we use the word "equal" in these folding examples, we are not thinking of numbers; we are using the word in the sense that Euclid used it. At the beginning of the *Elements,* Euclid assumed that "things which coincide with one another are equal to one another." The word *congruent* is defined in the dictionary as "coinciding exactly when superimposed." So we can say that, when something is bisected, it is divided into two congruent parts. Clearly, line segments are congruent if they have equal lengths, and angles are congruent if they have equal measures.

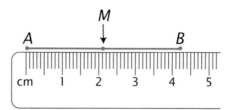

Another way to bisect a line segment is to use a ruler. If line segment AB in the figure above is exactly 4.2 centimeters long, then there is exactly one point on it, M, that divides it into two equal segments:

$$\frac{4.2 \text{ cm}}{2} = 2.1 \text{ cm},$$

and so the point is 2.1 cm from each end. In our description of how a ruler works, we assumed that to each number there corresponds exactly one point; so the idea that a line segment has exactly one midpoint follows directly from the Ruler Postulate. A statement that follows directly from another statement is called a *corollary* to it.

A *corollary* is a theorem that can be easily proved as a consequence of a postulate or another theorem.

We will call our conclusion about a midpoint a

Corollary to the Ruler Postulate
A line segment has exactly one midpoint.

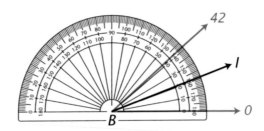

Just as a line segment can be bisected with a ruler, an angle can be bisected with a protractor. If ∠B in the figure above has a measure of exactly 42°, then there is exactly one ray inside it, BI, that divides it into two equal angles:

$$\frac{42°}{2} = 21°,$$

and so the ray is 21° from each side.

Our description of how a protractor works includes the assumption that to each number from 0 to 180 there corresponds exactly one ray, so the idea that an angle has exactly one ray that bisects it follows directly from the Protractor Postulate.

Corollary to the Protractor Postulate
An angle has exactly one ray that bisects it.

Exercises

Set I

Many important words in geometry begin with the letter C. Explain in a few words what each of the following words means.

1. Collinear.
2. Concurrent.
3. Congruent.
4. Construction.
5. Converse.
6. Corollary.

The definition of *midpoint,* like all definitions, can be written as two different if-then statements.

7. The hypothesis of one of them is "If a point is the midpoint of a line segment." What is its conclusion?
8. Write the other if-then statement as a complete sentence.

9. What relation do the two if-then statements have to each other?

State each of the following as a sentence.

10. The corollary to the Ruler Postulate.
11. The corollary to the Protractor Postulate.

Arrow Illusion. In this "arrow" figure, two points, M and N, have been marked on AB.

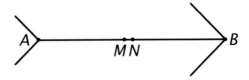

12. Which one looks like the midpoint of AB?
13. Could they *both* be midpoints of AB? Why or why not?
14. Which two line segments along line AB are equal? (Check your answer with your ruler.)

Origami Duck. Origami, the Japanese art of paper folding, was used to create this duck.*

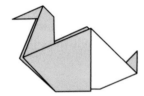

Starting with a square sheet of paper, corner B is folded onto D. Then sides BC and DC are folded onto the fold AC.

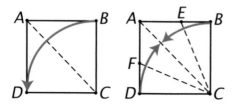

15. Does point E appear to be the midpoint of AB?

16. Is point E between points A and B?

Because ∠BAC fits onto ∠DAC, ∠BAC and ∠DAC are congruent.

17. Which angle is bisected if ∠BAC = ∠DAC?

18. Name three more angles that are bisected in the folding process.

Angle BCD is a right angle because the process starts with a square. Find the number of degrees in each of the following angles.

19. ∠ACD.

20. ∠FCD.

21. ∠FCE.

22. ∠DCE.

23. ∠DFC.

Bisection Constructions. Because this lesson is about bisection, this is a good place to review the two bisection constructions.

_____
Folding the Universe, by Peter Engel (Vintage Books, 1989).

24. *The origami bisections by construction.*
    Use your protractor to make a large drawing of ∠BCD (the lower right corner of the square of origami paper). Then use your *straightedge and compass* to bisect ∠BCD.
    Also bisect both of the angles formed. Finally, measure the angles with your protractor to check your accuracy.

25. *A short ruler construction.*
    Use your ruler to draw a line segment AB 8 centimeters long. Then use your straightedge and compass to bisect AB.
    Also bisect both of the segments formed. Finally, measure the segments with your ruler to check your accuracy.

Clock Puzzle. An old puzzle asks, if a clock takes 3 seconds to chime 3 o'clock, how long does it take to chime 6 o'clock?
    The figures below reveal the answer. (The points indicate the chimes and the coordinates represent the time in seconds.)

3 o'clock

A	B	C
0	?	3

26. Because B is the midpoint of AC, AB = BC. Why?

27. What is the length of AB?

28. What is the coordinate of B?

6 o'clock

A	B	C	D	E	F
0		3	?	?	?

29. What are the coordinates of D, E, and F?

30. What is the answer to the puzzle?

Set II

Yen Measurement. The Japanese one-yen coin is unusual in that it is just the right size for measuring distances in centimeters. A row of five of these coins is 10 cm long.

0   10

31. What is the diameter of a one-yen coin?

Suppose a one-yen coin rolls exactly one revolution along a line without slipping, as shown in the figure below.

0   ?   ?

What would be the coordinate of the point at which the coin touches the line

32. at the end?

33. midway between?

Acetylene Proofs. Molecules of acetylene, a gas used in welding, contain four atoms, as shown in the figure below.*

In the figure at the top of the next column, the points represent the atoms and the line segments represent the bonds between them.

_____

The Architecture of Molecules, by Linus Pauling and Roger Hayward (W. H. Freeman and Company, 1964).

A   B   C   D

In the acetylene molecule, AB = CD, A-B-C, and B-C-D. Use these facts to supply the reasons for the following direct proof that AC = BD.

34. *Proof.*
   AB = CD. (By hypothesis.)
   AB + BC = BC + CD. (Why?)
   A-B-C and B-C-D. (By hypothesis.)
   AB + BC = AC and BC + CD = BD. (Why?)
   Therefore, AC = BD. (Why?)

Use the additional fact that AC > 2AB to supply the missing statements and reasons in this indirect proof that B is *not* the midpoint of AC.

35. *Proof.*
   (What is the beginning assumption?)
   If B is the midpoint of AC, then AB = BC. (Why?)
   Because AB + BC = AC, 2AB = AC. (Why?)
   (What does this statement contradict?)
   Therefore, our assumption is false and (what conclusion follows?)

Miter Joint Proof. In carpentry, a miter joint is formed when two pieces of wood cut at an angle are joined together.

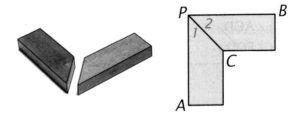

If the pieces are cut correctly, when they are glued together so that PA-PC-PB, PC bisects ∠APB.
   Copy and complete the following proof that
$$\angle 1 = \frac{\angle APB}{2}.$$

36. *Proof*

Statements	*Reasons*
1. PA-PC-PB.	By hypothesis.
2. ∠1 + ∠2 = ?.	Betweenness of Rays Theorem.
3. PB bisects ∠APB.	By hypothesis.
4. ∠1 = ?.	If a line bisects an angle, it divides the angle into two equal angles.
5. ∠1 + ∠1 = ∠APB; so 2∠1 = ∠APB.	Why?
6. $∠1 = \dfrac{∠APB}{2}$.	Why?

Angle Definition. It may surprise you that not everyone agrees on the best way to define some of the terms of geometry. An example is "angle."

Compare these figures of an obtuse angle and a straight angle.

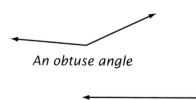

An obtuse angle

A straight angle

37. Would you think that both of these figures were angles if they were not so labeled? Explain.

We defined an angle as "a pair of rays that have the same endpoint" and called the common endpoint the vertex of the angle.

38. What is strange about the vertex of a straight angle?

In the figure below, some of the rays between the sides of the obtuse angle are shown.

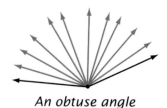

An obtuse angle

39. Where are the rays between the sides of the straight angle?

40. Although the corollary to the Protractor Postulate says that an angle has exactly one ray that bisects it, someone might say that the corollary is not true for a straight angle. Why?

Passion Flower. A passion flower has three stigmas, five stamens, and ten petals.*

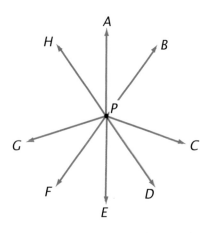

In the figure below, drawn from the photograph, the stigmas are represented by the red rays and the stamens by the green rays. Imagine a circular protractor placed with its center at P so that the coordinate of ray PA is 0 and the numbers on the scale increase in a clockwise direction.

41. Copy the figure and mark it appropriately to answer the following questions.

Numbers: Facts, Figures and Fiction, by Richard Phillips (Cambridge University Press, 1994).

42. If points A, P, and E are collinear, what is the coordinate of ray PE?

43. If the stamens are equally spaced around P, how large is ∠EPC?

44. If ray PD bisects ∠EPC and ray PF bisects ∠GPE, how large are ∠FPE and ∠EPD?

45. Put all of these assumptions together to find the coordinates of the other rays.

46. Would it be correct to say that ray PA is between rays PG and PC? Why or why not?

47. Would it be correct to say that ray PE bisects ∠GPC? Why or why not?

Set III

Rusty Compass Constructions. In about 980 A.D., the Persian mathematician Abul Wefa explored making constructions with a straightedge and a compass whose radius cannot be changed. Such a compass is called a "rusty compass."

1. Use your ruler to draw a line segment AB 5 inches long. Set the radius of your compass to 1 inch. Can you figure out a way to bisect the line segment with your straightedge and compass without changing the radius of the compass?

2. Use your protractor to draw a 50° angle and bisect it with your rusty compass.

3. Draw a 150° angle and try to bisect it with your rusty compass.

If a rusty compass had a radius of 1 inch, the easiest line segment to bisect would be one 2 inches long.

4. Can you guess the size of the angle that would be easiest to bisect with such a compass?

Complementary and Supplementary Angles

If you ride a bicycle in a circle, the bicycle automatically leans toward the center of the circle. The angle at which the bicycle leans depends on its speed and the size of the circle. It is measured from the vertical because that is the "normal" direction of the bicycle.

In the photograph, this angle is labeled A and has a measure of $32°$. If the angle of the bicycle with the horizontal were measured instead, $\angle B$ in the diagram at the right, what would its measure be? Because $\angle A + \angle B = 90°$, $\angle B = 90° - \angle A = 90° - 32° = 58°$.

Two angles whose sum is $90°$ are *complementary*. Such angles are frequent in geometry; so *complementary* is an important word to know.

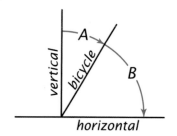

Definition
Two angles are *complementary* iff their sum is $90°$.

Each angle is called the *complement* of the other. Because the sum of two complementary angles is $90°$, the complement of an angle is formed by subtracting the angle from $90°$.

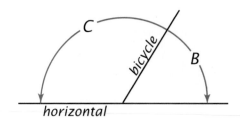

The figure above shows that there are two ways to choose the angle between the bicycle and the horizontal. If ∠B = 58°, what would be the measure of ∠C? Because ∠B + ∠C = 180°, ∠C = 180° − ∠B = 180° − 58° = 122°.

Two angles whose sum is 180° are called *supplementary,* another important word to know.

Definition

Two angles are ***supplementary*** iff their sum is 180°.

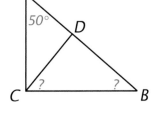

Each angle is called the ***supplement*** of the other, and the supplement of an angle is found by subtracting the angle from 180°.

Although complementary angles often share a common side, as do supplementary angles, our definitions say nothing about their positions. For example, in the figure at the left, ∠A and ∠B are complementary; ∠DCB and ∠B also are complementary. Given that ∠A = 50°, how large is ∠B? How large is ∠DCB?

That ∠DCB = ∠A in this figure is no accident. It is easy to prove that two angles that are complements of the same angle must be equal. The proof, which we write in two-column form, is presented below. The hypothesis of a theorem is often referred to as "given" and the conclusion as "prove," as is done here.

Theorem 3

Complements of the same angle are equal.

> *Given:* ∠1 and ∠2 are complements of ∠3.
> *Prove:* ∠1 = ∠2.

Proof

Statements	Reasons
1. ∠1 and ∠2 are complements of ∠3.	Given.
2. ∠1 + ∠3 = 90°; ∠2 + ∠3 = 90°.	If two angles are complementary, their sum is 90°.
3. ∠1 + ∠3 = ∠2 + ∠3.	Substitution.
4. ∠1 = ∠2.	Subtraction.

A similar theorem with an almost identical proof is true for supplementary angles.

Theorem 4

Supplements of the same angle are equal.

Exercises

Set I

The definitions in the dictionary for "complement" and "supplement" are quite similar. *Complement* is defined as "something that completes or makes up a whole" and *supplement* is defined as "something added to complete a thing, or strengthen the whole."

To what number does the word "whole" refer with respect to

1. complementary angles?

2. supplementary angles?

The word *complement* is easily confused with the word *compliment*.

3. Which one would you rather get from a friend?

Safe Angle. The lights at the end of a runway tell a pilot if the plane is approaching it at the safe angle of 3°. Above this angle, the lights look white; below it, they look red.

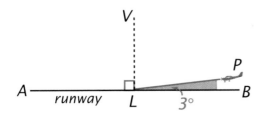

4. If the plane is approaching the runway at the safe angle, what angle (∠VLP) does its path make with the vertical?

5. What relation does ∠VLP have to ∠BLP?

6. What angle should the path of the plane, LP, make with LA?

7. What relation does ∠PLA have to ∠BLP?

Sign Measure. An old unit of angle measure, the "sign," comes from astrology: 12 signs were equal to 360°.

8. To how many degrees was one sign equal?

How many degrees were in

9. the supplement of a sign?

10. the complement of a sign?

11. Where do you suppose the name "sign" came from?

Suppose that a right angle is bisected and each of the two angles that result is *trisected*.

12. Sketch a figure to illustrate this.

13. How large is each of the smallest angles formed?

14. What do the measures of *all* of the angles in the figure have in common?

Skier Forces. The figure below shows the forces acting on a skier skiing downhill.*

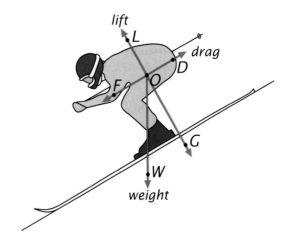

If a protractor is placed on the figure so that OD has the coordinate 0, the coordinates of some of the other rays are:

OG, 90; OW, 117; OF, 180.

15. Draw and label the rays on your paper and mark their coordinates.

———————

The Physics of Skiing, by David Lind and Scott P. Sanders (AIP Press, 1996).

16. Write the equation that follows from the fact that OD-OW-OF.

17. Find the measures of ∠DOW, ∠WOF, and ∠DOF.

18. What relation does ∠DOW have to ∠WOF?

19. Find the measure of ∠WOG.

20. What relation does ∠WOG have to ∠WOF?

Name two angles in the figure that are

21. acute.   22. obtuse.

Triangle in the Woods. While on a walk in the woods, Obtuse Ollie made a very large triangle by stretching a long rope around three trees. He told Acute Alice that its three angles were supplementary.

23. Without even looking at it, Alice said that that was nonsense. Why?

Ollie then claimed that *two* of its angles were supplementary.

24. Is this possible? Why or why not?

Alice looked at the triangle and said that she thought two of its angles were complementary.

25. Is this possible? Explain.

Hammer Throw. The direction, OH, of launching the hammer in the hammer throw is shown in this figure. If the hammer is thrown in the ideal direction, then OH bisects ∠YOX.

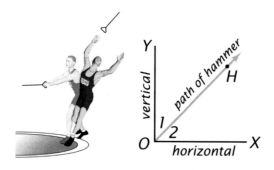

26. Because OY-OH-OX, why does it follow that ∠1 + ∠2 = ∠YOX?

27. Given that ∠YOX is a right angle, why is ∠YOX = 90°?

28. Why does it follow that ∠1 + ∠2 = 90°?

29. If OH bisects ∠YOX, why is ∠1 = ∠2?

30. Why does it follow that ∠2 + ∠2 = 90°, or 2∠2 = 90°?

31. Why does it follow that ∠2 = 45°?

Set II

Clock Hands. A small child just learning to tell time was told that she could stay up until "the big hand is on the 6 and the little hand is on the 8."

32. What time was she supposed to go to bed? Draw a picture of a clock to illustrate it.

33. According to the description of the clock, what angle would the hands make?

34. If what the child was told was true, how is it that she might have been able to stay up all night?

35. What angle would the hands actually make at the bedtime intended?

Complement and Supplement. Suppose that ∠C is the complement of ∠A and that ∠S is the supplement of ∠A.

36. Copy and complete the following table.

∠A	∠C	∠S
10°	?	?
20°	?	?
30°	?	?

37. How does ∠S seem to compare with ∠C?

38. If ∠A = $x°$, what are the measures of ∠C and ∠S in terms of *x?*

39. Use the two expressions and some algebra to show that the conclusion suggested by the table is always true.

Earth Angles. The Arctic Circle connects the points on the earth that are 66.54° north of the equator. The tropic of Capricorn connects the points on the earth that are 23.46° south of the equator.

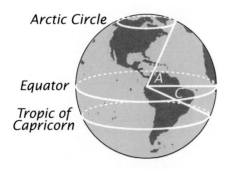

Arctic Circle

Equator

Tropic of Capricorn

40. What relation do these angles have to each other?

On the first day of winter in North America, the sun is directly overhead at noon on the tropic of Capricorn.

41. Where do you suppose the sun appears to be at the same time on the Arctic Circle?

The North and South Poles are the points that are 90° north and 90° south of the equator.

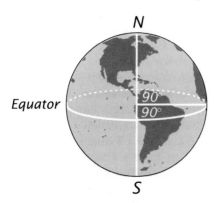

N

Equator 90° 90°

S

42. What relation other than being equal do these angles have to each other?

On the first day of winter in North America, the sun never sets at the South Pole.

43. What do you suppose is true of the first day of winter at the North Pole?

In the figure below, ∠1 and ∠2 are both complements of ∠AOC.

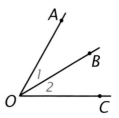

44. What else seems to be true? Explain why.

45. Is it possible to figure out the size of each angle in the figure without measuring them? Explain.

The proof of Theorem 4 is almost identical with that of Theorem 3.

46. Write it, using the proof of Theorem 3 as a guide.

Set III

This pattern is made from 15 squares.*

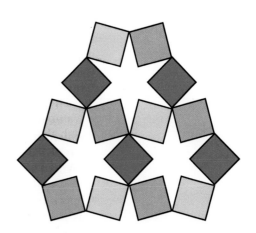

From the appearance of the figure, how large do you think the angles at the points of the stars are? Show your reasoning.

———————

Numbers: Facts, Figures and Fiction, by Richard Phillips (Cambridge University Press, 1994).

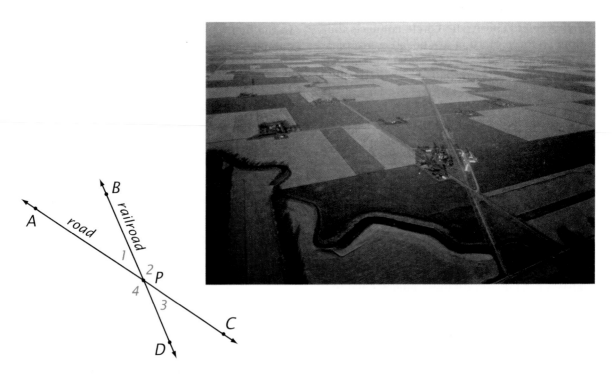

Linear Pairs and Vertical Angles

Much of the American landscape is divided by section lines that run north–south and east–west. An exception to this pattern are the railroads. In the photograph above of Castleton, North Dakota, a railroad intersects a road at a fairly sharp angle.

The lines of the road and railroad actually form four angles, which are numbered in the diagram above. Notice also that the point in which the lines intersect, P, divides each line into two rays. Because the rays point in opposite directions, they are called *opposite rays*: rays PA and PC are opposite rays, as are rays PB and PD.

Angles such as $\angle 1$ and $\angle 2$ that have a common side and have opposite rays as their other sides are called a *linear pair*. Angles such as $\angle 1$ and $\angle 3$ in which the sides of one angle are opposite rays to the sides of the other are called *vertical angles*.* Because we will be using these terms throughout our study of geometry, their definitions are repeated here.

---

*"Opposite angles" seems like a more appropriate name because "vertical" suggests a connection to vertical lines, and vertical angles have nothing to do with vertical lines. The dictionary definition for "vertical angle" is, in fact, "one of two *opposite* angles formed by two intersecting lines."

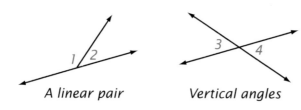

| A linear pair | Vertical angles |

Definitions

Two angles are a ***linear pair*** iff they have a common side and their other sides are opposite rays.

Two angles are *vertical angles* iff the sides of one angle are opposite rays to the sides of the other.

In Lesson 5 of this chapter, we considered relations between pairs of angles that concerned only their measures. The definitions of complementary angles and supplementary angles say nothing about their sides.

Although the definitions of linear pair and vertical angles say nothing about their measures, the figures at the top of this page suggest some possible conclusions about them. The angles in a linear pair, such as $\angle 1$ and $\angle 2$, seem to be supplementary. Vertical angles, such as $\angle 3$ and $\angle 4$, seem to be equal. Because both of these observations are useful and can be proved on the basis of what we already know, we add them to our list of theorems.

Theorem 5

The angles in a linear pair are supplementary.

    Given: $\angle 1$ and $\angle 2$ are a linear pair.
    Prove: $\angle 1$ and $\angle 2$ are supplementary.

Proof

Statements	Reasons
1. $\angle 1$ and $\angle 2$ are a linear pair.	Given.
2. Rays OA and OC are opposite rays.	If two angles are a linear pair, they have a common side and their other sides are opposite rays.
3. Let the coordinates of OA, OB, and OC be 0, n, and 180.	Protractor Postulate.
4. $\angle 1 = n - 0 = n°$, $\angle 2 = (180 - n)°$.	Protractor Postulate.
5. $\angle 1 + \angle 2 = n° + (180 - n)° = 180°$.	Addition.
6. $\angle 1$ and $\angle 2$ are supplementary.	Two angles are supplementary if their sum is 180°.

Theorem 6

Vertical angles are equal.

Given: ∠1 and ∠3 are vertical angles.
Prove: ∠1 = ∠3.

Proof

Statements	Reasons
1. ∠1 and ∠3 are vertical angles.	Given.
2. The sides of ∠1 are opposite rays to the sides of ∠3.	If two angles are vertical angles, the sides of one are opposite rays to the sides of the other.
3. ∠1 and ∠2 are a linear pair; ∠2 and ∠3 are a linear pair.	Two angles are a linear pair if they have a common side and their other sides are opposite rays.
4. ∠1 and ∠2 are supplementary; ∠2 and ∠3 are supplementary.	The angles in a linear pair are supplementary.
5. ∠1 = ∠3.	Supplements of the same angle are equal.

Exercises

Set I

When this chair is closed up, the angles of the braces between its legs change in size. No matter whether the chair is open or closed, however, the way in which these angles are related to one another never changes.

1. Why are some of them always equal?

2. Why are some of them always supplementary?

Figures such as the one below are used in tests of perception. For example, it might be seen as a four-sided figure and two triangles.

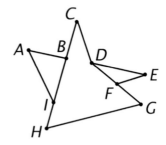

3. What other way do you think it might be seen?

4. Name the sets of points in the figure that seem to be collinear.

5. Name the pairs of angles that seem to be linear pairs.

6. Does the figure contain any vertical angles?

An intersection of two roads can be dangerous if they do not form 90° angles. In this figure, road X intersects road Y at P.

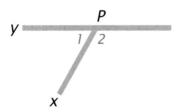

7. Name two relations of ∠1 and ∠2.
8. If ∠1 = 55°, how large is ∠2?
9. How large is ∠1 if ∠2 = x°?
10. If you went from one road onto the other, through which angle would it be more dangerous to turn?

Sun Directions. Four special directions of the sun in the course of a year are shown along the lines AD and BC in the figure below.* The lines of the map directions bisect the angles formed by these lines.

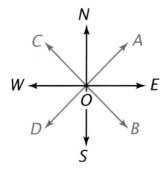

If a circular protractor is centered on point O so that ON has the coordinate 0, the coordinate of OA is 50.

11. Copy the figure and write the coordinates of all of the rays on it.

Rays OA and OB show the directions of the sun at sunrise in midsummer and midwinter.

12. How large is ∠AOB?

Stonehenge Complete, by Christopher Chippindale (Cornell University Press, 1983).

Rays OC and OD show the directions of the sun at sunset in midsummer and midwinter.

13. How large is ∠COD?
14. Why must ∠AOB = ∠COD?
15. How large are ∠AOC and ∠BOD?

In the following figure, ∠1 = ∠2 = ∠3.

16. Can you conclude from this that ∠1 and ∠2 must be vertical angles?

The theorem about vertical angles can be written in the form of a conditional statement:

> If two angles are vertical angles, then they are equal.

17. Write the converse of this statement.
18. Is it true?
19. If two angles are not equal, can they be vertical angles?
20. If two angles are not vertical angles, can they be equal?

Ship Position. Navigators ordinarily use three lines to determine a ship's position. If the lines are accurate, they intersect in a single point locating the ship as shown in the figure below.

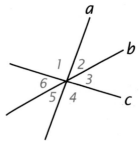

21. What word describes lines that contain the same point?

22. Draw and label a large figure similar to the one below. Use your protractor to measure the six numbered angles in your figure.

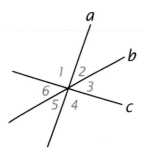

23. How many of the six angles do you need to measure to be able to figure out the rest?

Without knowing the measures of any of the angles, it is still possible to know what number three consecutive angles add up to.

24. To what number is ∠1 + ∠2 + ∠3 equal?

25. Is it possible to tell to what number ∠1 + ∠3 + ∠5 is equal? Explain.

Because of small errors, when a navigator draws the three lines, they may form a triangle such as the one shown in the figure below.

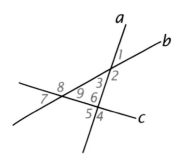

Regardless of the shape of the triangle, it is possible to draw some conclusions about the numbered angles.

26. To what number is ∠3 + ∠6 + ∠9 equal?

27. How do you know?

28. To what number is ∠1 + ∠4 + ∠7 equal?

29. Explain your reasoning.

30. Why are ∠2 + ∠3 = 180°, ∠5 + ∠6 = 180°, and ∠8 + ∠9 = 180°?

31. Why is ∠2 + ∠3 + ∠5 + ∠6 + ∠8 + ∠9 = 540°?

32. To what number is ∠2 + ∠5 + ∠8 equal?

33. Explain your reasoning.

Set II

Steep Slope. Trees sometimes grow on very steep slopes. In the figure below, a vertical line along which the tree grows is shown intersecting a line representing the slope.

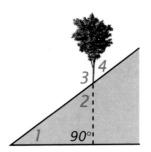

34. Copy and complete this table for various measures of the angles in the figure.

∠1	∠2	∠3	∠4
25°	?	?	?
33°	?	?	?
48°	?	?	?

35. How does ∠4 compare with ∠2?

36. Why?

37. How does ∠3 seem to compare with ∠1?

38. If ∠1 = x°, what are the measures of ∠2, ∠3, and ∠4 in terms of x?

39. Use the expressions for ∠1 and ∠3 and some algebra to show that the conclusion suggested by the table is always true.

Hedge Shears. A pair of hedge shears is shown in this figure.

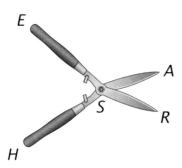

40. As the shears are opened and closed, most of the angles vary in size, but two angles never change and are always equal. Which two angles are they?

41. As the shears are used, which of the rays with endpoint at S are always between two other rays?

42. What pair of angles can change in size but are always equal to each other?

43. Show in a short proof why the angles you named in exercise 42 are always equal.

Bent Light Ray. According to Einstein's theory of relativity, a ray of light passing by the sun is bent by an angle of 1.75 *seconds.*

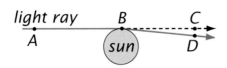

The figure above is a highly exaggerated illustration of how the light is bent.

44. How many minutes are in 1 degree and how many seconds are in 1 minute?

45. Given that $\angle CBD = 1.75$ seconds, how large is $\angle ABD$?

Pinhole Camera. The angle of view of a pinhole camera is shown as $\angle 1$ in this figure.

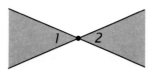

Given: $\angle 1$ and $\angle 2$ are vertical angles and $\angle 1$ and $\angle 2$ are complementary.

46. How large do you think the angle of view of this camera is?

47. *Copy and complete* the following proof by using the facts given about the lens.

Proof

Statements	Reasons
1. $\angle 1$ and $\angle 2$ are vertical angles.	Given.
2. $\angle 1 = \angle 2$.	Why?
3. $\angle 1$ and $\angle 2$ are complementary.	Why?
4. $\angle 1 + \angle 2 = ?$.	Why?
5. $\angle 1 + \angle 1 = ?$ and so $2\angle 1 = ?$.	Why?
6. $\angle 1 = ?$.	Why?

SAT Problem. The following figure appeared in a problem on an SAT exam.

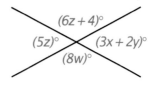

It shows two intersecting lines and the measures of the angles that they form in terms of w, x, y, and z.

48. What is the value of w? Show your reasoning.

Set III

The proof of the vertical angle theorem as it appears in a Chinese geometry book is shown here.

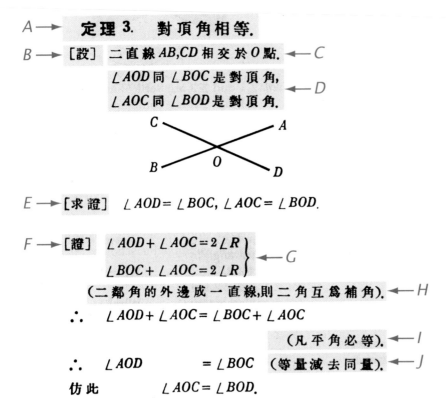

The symbols in the box labeled A say: "Theorem 3. Vertical angles are equal." The symbol in the box labeled B says: "Given."

1. What do you think the symbols in box C say?

2. Box D?

3. Box E?

4. Box F?

5. What do you think the symbols $2\angle$R mean in box G, given that there is no angle R in the figure?

6. The symbols in box H are the reason for the equations in box G. State the theorem in this lesson that you think they represent.

7. What do you think the symbols in box I say?

8. Box J?

Perpendicular and Parallel Lines

Four Corners is an unusual place. It is the only place in the United States where you can be in four states at once! It is the point in which the border lines of Utah, Colorado, Arizona, and New Mexico intersect. The border lines are *perpendicular* because they form right angles.

Definition

Two lines are *perpendicular* iff they form a right angle.

In the figure at the right, lines AB and CD form the right angle AOC, marked by the small square shown in the figure. As we will see, this fact implies that all four angles at O are right angles. The symbol for "perpendicular" is ⊥ and, to indicate that lines AB and CD are perpendicular, we write AB ⊥ CD.

It is easy to prove that, if two lines form a right angle, the other angles must be right angles as well. The proof follows from what we know about linear pairs and vertical angles.

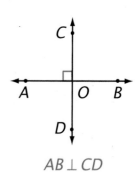

AB ⊥ CD

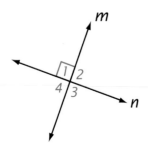

Theorem 7

Perpendicular lines form four right angles.

> *Given:* $m \perp n$.
> *Prove:* m and n form four right angles.

Proof

Because $m \perp n$, we know that they form a right angle, which we name $\angle 1$. Because $\angle 1$ is a right angle, $\angle 1 = 90°$. Because $\angle 1$ forms a linear pair with $\angle 2$, they are supplementary. Because $\angle 1 + \angle 2 = 180°$ and $\angle 1 = 90°$, $\angle 2$ also is 90°.

Because $\angle 1$ and $\angle 3$ are vertical angles, as are $\angle 2$ and $\angle 4$, and vertical angles are equal, $\angle 3 = \angle 1 = 90°$ and $\angle 4 = \angle 2 = 90°$. So all four angles are right angles.

Because every right angle has a measure of 90°, we know that all right angles are equal. We will occasionally use this fact in proofs, so we state it as a

Corollary to the definition of a right angle

All right angles are equal.

The first figure at the left below shows a linear pair, $\angle 1$ and $\angle 2$, in which $\angle 1 = \angle 2$. It is easy to prove from what we know about linear pairs that OB, the line of the common side of the two angles, must be perpendicular to AC, the line of their other two sides.

Theorem 8

If the angles in a linear pair are equal, then their sides are perpendicular.

> *Given:* $\angle 1$ and $\angle 2$ are a linear pair and $\angle 1 = \angle 2$.
> *Prove:* OB $\perp$ AC.

Proof

Because $\angle 1$ and $\angle 2$ are a linear pair, they are supplementary; so $\angle 1 + \angle 2 = 180°$. Because $\angle 1 = \angle 2$, $\angle 1 + \angle 1 = 180°$; so $2\angle 1 = 180°$ by substitution. Dividing by 2 gives $\angle 1 = 90°$; so $\angle 1$ is a right angle. By definition, two lines that form a right angle are perpendicular; so OB $\perp$ AC.

Another word that names a relation between two lines is *parallel.*

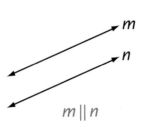

Definition

Two lines are *parallel* iff they lie in the same plane and do not intersect.

The symbol for "parallel" is $\parallel$. To indicate that lines m and n are parallel, we write $m \parallel n$. Our definitions for the words *perpendicular* and *parallel* are about lines. Because line segments and rays are parts of lines, we also refer to them as being perpendicular or parallel if they lie in lines that are perpendicular or parallel.

Exercises

Set I

When light travels from air into water, it is partly reflected and partly refracted (bent).* In this figure, AB intersects CE at W.

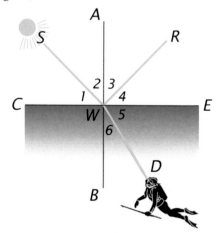

State the reason for each of the following.

1. If ∠5 + ∠6 = 90°, then ∠5 and ∠6 are complementary.
2. If ∠SWR is a right angle, then SW ⊥ WR.
3. If ∠SWR and ∠AWE are right angles, then ∠SWR = ∠AWE.
4. If ∠2 and ∠3 are supplements of ∠RWB, then ∠2 = ∠3.
5. If ∠2 = ∠3, then WA bisects ∠SWR.
6. If ∠AWC = ∠AWE, then AB ⊥ CE.

The parallel bars used in gymnastics are a good illustration of parallel lines.

7. Write the definition of parallel lines as a complete sentence.
8. What are two reasons why parallel bars may not actually be parallel?

---

*Introductory Physics, by Mashuri L. Warren (W. H. Freeman and Company, 1979).

A dartboard is divided into sectors by ten lines through its center.

9. What relation do the ten lines have to one another?
10. Why must the angles of the opposite sectors be equal?
11. Why must some of the pairs of angles in the figure be supplementary?
12. How many pairs of perpendicular lines do there appear to be on the board?

Cube Illusion. The "Necker cube" illusion is named after the Swiss scientist who first studied it in 1832.[†] It shows the edges of an ordinary cube.

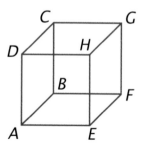

13. Name the edges of the cube that appear to be parallel to AB.
14. Name the edges that appear to be perpendicular to HE.
15. Name an edge that appears to be neither parallel nor perpendicular to CG.
16. Which edge of the cube is "in back": CB or HE?

[†]*Visual Intelligence: How We Create What We See,* by Donald D. Hoffman (Norton, 1998).

Mud Cracks. This photograph shows cracks in mud that has dried up in the sun.*

Many of the cracks seem to meet at right angles. The line segments in the figure below represent two cracks, AB and CD, meeting at point B.

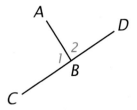

What relation do $\angle 1$ and $\angle 2$ have with respect to

17. their sides?

18. their measures?

When mud cracks, these angles tend to be equal. If they are equal,

19. what is the measure of each angle?

20. what kind of angle is $\angle 1$?

21. What does this prove about the cracks AB and CD?

22. State the theorem of this lesson to which all of these ideas are related as a complete sentence.

Mathematical Snapshots, by H. Steinhaus (Oxford University Press, 1969).

Set II

A Deceptive Figure. Appearances can sometimes be deceiving. In this figure, $\angle 1$ is a right angle but $\angle 2$, $\angle 3$, and $\angle 4$ are not.

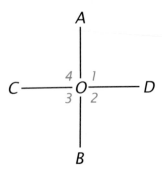

23. Is it correct to conclude that any lines in the figure are perpendicular? Explain.

The figure seems to contradict several of our theorems. How does it seem to contradict the theorem

24. about vertical angles?

25. about a linear pair?

26. about perpendicular lines?

27. Is it possible that $\angle 2$ and $\angle 4$ could be vertical angles? Explain.

Bisecting a Linear Pair. This figure shows a linear pair in which $\angle AOB = 50°$.

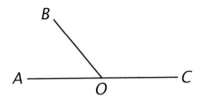

28. How large is $\angle BOC$?

29. Use your ruler and protractor to make an accurate enlargement of the figure. Then use your straightedge and compass to bisect $\angle AOB$ and $\angle BOC$. Label a point X on the bisector of $\angle AOB$ and a point Y on the bisector of $\angle BOC$.

30. How large should ∠BOX and ∠BOY be? Check the accuracy of your construction by using your protractor to measure these angles.

31. How large is ∠XOY?

This figure shows a linear pair in which OX bisects ∠AOB and OY bisects ∠BOC.

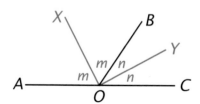

32. Why are ∠AOB and ∠BOC supplementary?

33. To what number is $2m + 2n$ equal?

34. To what number is $m + n$ equal?

35. What kind of angle is ∠XOY?

36. Why?

37. How are OX and OY related?

38. Why?

In the figure below, $a \perp b$, ∠2 = $n°$, ∠3 = $2n°$, and ∠4 = $3n°$.

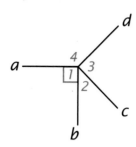

39. Write an equation for the sum of the four numbered angles and solve it for n.

40. Find the measures of the four angles.

41. What relation does ∠1 have to ∠3?

42. What relation does ∠2 have to ∠4?

Gravity pulls the water in a waterfall vertically downward to the horizontal surface of the lake below. In the diagram, WA represents the line of the waterfall and points A, B, and C represent points in the plane of the lake's surface.

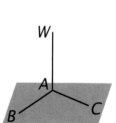

43. *Copy and complete* this proof.

Given: WA ⊥ AB and WA ⊥ AC.
Prove: ∠WAB = ∠WAC.

Proof

Statements	Reasons
1. WA ⊥ AB and WA ⊥ AC.	Why?
2. ∠WAB and ∠WAC are right angles.	Why?
3. ∠WAB = ∠WAC.	Why?

44. *Copy and complete* the following proof.

Given: ∠1 and ∠2 are complementary and PB-PC-PD.
Prove: AB ⊥ PD.

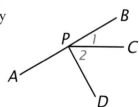

Proof

Statements	Reasons
1. ∠1 and ∠2 are complementary.	Why?
2. ∠1 + ∠2 = ?.	Why?
3. PB-PC-PD.	Why?
4. ∠BPD = ∠1 + ∠2.	Why?
5. ∠BPD = 90°.	Why?
6. ∠BPD is a right angle.	Why?
7. ?.	Why?

Set III

Just a few letters of the alphabet contain both parallel and perpendicular lines. One of them is F, the first initial of Franklin Delano Roosevelt. It and Roosevelt's second initial were made into puzzles in 1933, the year Roosevelt first became president.*

Copy the five pieces shown below onto a file card or stiff sheet of paper, cut them out, and see if you can arrange them to form the letter F.

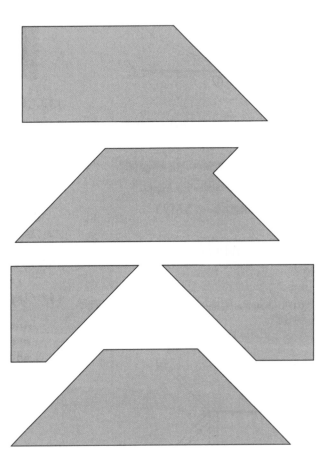

Either draw a diagram of the arrangement or tape the pieces to your paper.

---

*New Book of Puzzles, by Jerry Slocum and Jack Botermans (W. H. Freeman and Company, 1992).

Basic Ideas

Postulates

3. *The Ruler Postulate.* The points on a line can be numbered so that positive number differences measure distances. 85

4. *The Protractor Postulate.* The rays in a half-rotation can be numbered from 0 to 180 so that positive number differences measure angles. 92

Theorems

1. *The Betweenness of Points Theorem.* If A-B-C, then AB + BC = AC. 86

2. *The Betweenness of Rays Theorem.* If OA-OB-OC, then ∠AOB + ∠BOC = ∠AOC. 93

Corollary to the Ruler Postulate. A line segment has exactly one midpoint. 99

Corollary to the Protractor Postulate. An angle has exactly one ray that bisects it. 100

3. Complements of the same angle are equal. 106

4. Supplements of the same angle are equal. 106

5. The angles in a linear pair are supplementary. 111

6. Vertical angles are equal. 112

7. Perpendicular lines form four right angles. 118

Corollary to the definition of a right angle. All right angles are equal. 118

8. If the angles in a linear pair are equal, then their sides are perpendicular. 118

Exercises

Set I

The Very Large Array is a radio telescope in New Mexico consisting of 27 dishes. The dishes can be moved along three straight tracks, each about 12 miles long.

Suppose the centers of the dishes along one track are in a line and have the coordinates shown in the figure below.

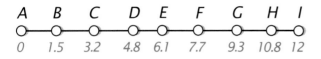

1. Is F between E and H? Use the definition of betweenness of points to explain why or why not.

2. Which point is closer to C: point B or point D? Explain.

3. Is E midway between A and I? Show why or why not.

Sliding Bevel. The handle and blade of a sliding bevel, a tool used in carpentry, can be adjusted to different angles.

Regardless of the angle, ∠BEV and ∠VEL always form a linear pair.

4. What other relation do they always have?

5. If ∠BEV = $x°$, what is the measure of ∠VEL in terms of x?

6. If ∠BEV is larger than ∠VEL, what type of angle is ∠BEV? ∠VEL?

7. If ∠BEV = ∠VEL, how large is each angle?

8. If ∠BEV = ∠VEL, what can you conclude about the handle?

9. State the theorem that is the basis for your answer.

Old Quadrant. The figure below, from a book published in 1542, shows an astronomical quadrant used to measure the direction of the sun.

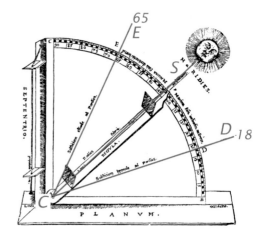

The rays CE and CD have coordinates 65 and 18.

10. Find the measure of ∠ECD.

11. Write the fact that ray CS is between rays CE and CD in symbols.

The ray CS pointing toward the sun looks as if it might bisect ∠ECD.

12. What would be the measure of ∠ECS if it did?

13. What would be the coordinate of CS?

14. Check your work by using the coordinate of CS to find the measure of ∠SCD.

Ollie's Logic. Obtuse Ollie thought it over and decided: "Either two lines intersect or they do not." He then reasoned:
"If they intersect, they are perpendicular. If they don't intersect, they must be parallel."

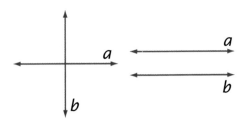

After thinking about Ollie's reasoning, Acute Alice decided that most of it was nonsense.

15. Does anything that Ollie said make sense? If so, what?

16. Explain what is wrong with his reasoning.

SAT Problem. The figure below appeared in a problem on an SAT exam.

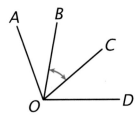

∠AOC = 70°, ∠BOD = 80°, and ∠AOD = 110°.

17. Copy the figure and mark the coordinates 0 and 70 on rays OA and OC.

18. What is the coordinate of ray OD?

19. What is the coordinate of ray OB?

20. What is the measure of ∠BOC?

Shoe Laces. A common way of lacing shoes is shown in the figure below.

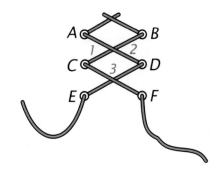

21. What are two ways in which ∠1 and ∠2 are related?

22. If ∠1 and ∠2 were complementary, how many degrees would each one measure?

23. If ∠1 and ∠2 were supplementary, what would be true about AD and BC?

24. If ∠1 and ∠3 were both supplementary to ∠2, what could you conclude about ∠1 and ∠3?

25. Why?

Axioms and Corollaries. Oliver Wendell Holmes, a Supreme Court justice for many years, once said:

The law embodies the story of a nation's development through many centuries, and it cannot be dealt with as if it contained only the axioms and corollaries of a book of mathematics.

26. What is an axiom?

27. What is a corollary?

One of the axioms of algebra used in geometry is the reflexive property of equality.

28. State it as a sentence.

Complete the following statements of the corollaries of this chapter.

29. A line segment has . . .

30. An angle has exactly one ray . . .

31. All right angles . . .

Set II

Clock Problems.

Clock Problems. The following two questions are from an old geometry book.*

How many degrees are there in the angle formed by the hands of a clock

(1) at 5 o'clock?

(2) at 10 o'clock?

32. What is the answer to each question?

If you reasoned that 10 is twice 5, you might think that the second answer should be twice the first.

33. How *can* the second answer be correctly obtained from twice the first? Draw a figure showing both times on the same clock to illustrate your answer.

Stilt Distances. Suppose a person 6 feet tall puts on stilts 6 feet long so that his or her feet are on cleats *x* feet above the ground.

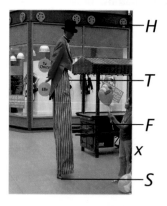

34. How "tall," in terms of *x*, is the person when wearing the stilts?

Wentworth's Plane Geometry, by George Wentworth and David Eugene Smith (Ginn, 1910).

35. How far, in terms of *x*, is it from the top of the stilts to the top of the person's head?

36. *Copy and complete* the following proof for the stilts figure.

> *Given:* S-F-T, F-T-H, and ST = FH.
> *Prove:* SF = TH.

Proof

Statements	Reasons
1. S-F-T and F-T-H.	Why?
2. SF + FT = ? and FT + TH = ?.	Why?
3. ST = FH.	Why?
4. SF + FT = FT + TH.	Why?
5. ?.	Why?

Chair Design. In the design of a comfortable chair, the seat is normally slanted between 5 and 8 degrees from the horizontal and the back is tilted between 20 and 25 degrees from the vertical.

In the diagram below, OA and OB represent the seat and back of the chair; VT ⊥ HZ.

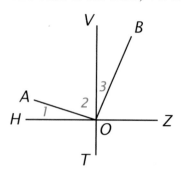

Given that $\angle 1 = x°$ and $\angle 3 = y°$, find

37. $\angle 2$ in terms of *x*.

38. $\angle AOB$ in terms of x and y.

39. *Copy and complete* the following indirect proof that, for a comfortable chair, $\angle AOB$ cannot be a right angle.

Proof.
(What is the beginning assumption?)

$\angle AOB = 90°$. (Why?)

$90 - x + y = 90$. (Why?)

$-x + y = 0$. (Why?)

$y = x$. (Why?)

This contradicts the fact that, if x is between 5 and 8 degrees and y is between 20 and 25 degrees, $y \neq x$.

Therefore, our assumption is false and (what conclusion follows?)

40. According to the chair-design rules on page 126, can the back of a comfortable chair be perpendicular to the seat?

Another SAT Problem. This description appeared in a problem on an SAT exam:

A, B, C, and D are points on a line, with D the midpoint of segment BC. The lengths of segments AB, AC, and BC are 10, 2, and 12, respectively.

41. Draw a figure to illustrate what is being described.

42. What is the length of segment AD?

Graphite and Diamond. Although both graphite and diamond consist of carbon atoms, the different geometrical arrangements of the atoms in them give the minerals very different properties.

Carbon atoms in graphite, a very soft mineral, are arranged in flat sheets as shown in the figure below. The points represent the atoms and the line segments represent the bonds between them. All of the angles are equal.

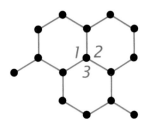

43. What kind of polygons do the bonds between the atoms form?

44. To how many degrees do you think the angles of one of the polygons add up?

45. *Copy and complete* the following proof.

Given: $\angle 1 + \angle 2 + \angle 3 = 360°$ and all of the angles in the figure are equal.

Proof

Statements	Reasons
1. $\angle 1 + \angle 2 + \angle 3 = 360°$ and all of the angles in the figure are equal.	Why?
2. $\angle 1 + \angle 1 + \angle 1 = 360°$, so $3\angle 1 = 360°$.	Why?
3. $6\angle 1 = ?$.	Why?

Carbon atoms in diamond, the hardest mineral at the earth's surface, are arranged in space as shown in this figure. (The green segments have been added to make the figure look more three-dimensional.)

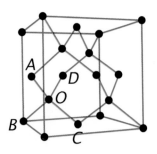

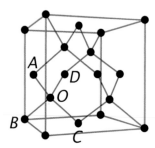

The atom at O is bonded to four atoms at A, B, C, and D.

46. How many angles do the bonds from O make with one another?

47. Name them.

Chemists have found that each of these angles has a measure of 109.5°.

48. *Copy and complete* the following indirect proof.

Given: Each angle whose vertex is O has a measure of 109.5°.
Prove: ∠AOB and ∠BOC cannot be a linear pair.

Proof
(What is the beginning assumption?)

∠AOB and ∠BOC are supplementary. (Why?)

∠AOB + ∠BOC = 180°. (Why?)

This contradicts that fact that ∠AOB + ∠BOC = 109.5° + 109.5° = 219°.

Therefore, our assumption is false and (what conclusion follows?)

49. Because ∠AOB and ∠BOC cannot be a linear pair, would it be correct to conclude that points A, B, and C are not coplanar? Explain.

March Times. In military marching, "quick time" corresponds to taking 120 steps, each 30 inches long, per minute.

1st step	2nd step	3rd step	4th step

0   30   60   90   120

If a marcher starts at 0 and marches along a line, what is the coordinate of the end of the

50. fifth step?

51. 100th step?

52. nth step?

What is the marcher's "speed" in

53. steps per minute?

54. inches per minute?

55. miles per hour? (1 mile = 5280 feet.)

"Double time" is 180 steps, each 36 inches long, per minute.

56. What is the speed of a marcher doing "double time" in inches per minute?

57. Is the speed of a marcher doing "double time" double the speed of a marcher doing "quick time"? Explain.

Operations with Polynomials

Addition and Subtraction

To add or subtract polynomials, add or subtract like terms (those having the same degree and variable).

Example 1:	$(5x^2 + 3x - 10) + (x^2 + 8)$
Solution:	$(5x^2 + x^2) + (3x) + (-10 + 8) =$
	$6x^2 + 3x - 2$

Example 2:	$(2x + 5y + 4) + (7x - 9y - 1)$
Solution:	$(2x + 7x) + (5y - 9y) + (4 - 1) =$
	$9x - 4y + 3$

Example 3:	$(8x + 7) - (3x - 2)$
Solution:	$(8x - 3x) + (7 - -2) =$
	$5x + 9$

Example 4:	$(7x^2 - 5x + 1) - (4x^2 - x + 3)$
Solution:	$(7x^2 - 4x^2) + (-5x + x) + (1 - 3) =$
	$3x^2 - 4x - 2$

Multiplication

To multiply two polynomials, multiply each term of one polynomial by each term of the other and then add the resulting terms. (This method uses the distributive rule, as the first example below illustrates.)

Example 1:	$(7x + 4)(3x + 5)$
Solution:	$(7x + 4)(3x + 5) =$
	$(7x + 4)(3x) + (7x + 4)(5) =$
	$(7x)(3x) + (4)(3x) + (7x)(5) + (4)(5) =$
	$21x^2 + 12x + 35x + 20 =$
	$21x^2 + 47x + 20$

Example 1 again:
A briefer solution:

$$(7x + 4)(3x + 5) =$$

$$21x^2 + 35x + 12x + 20 =$$
$$21x^2 + 47x + 20$$

59

8 times 10 are 80.

I think he's pretty weighty.

A page from a nineteenth-century book titled Marmaduke Multiply. *The book was used in many elementary schools to help children learn the multiplication table by using pictures and rhymes.*

Example 2: $(x - 3)(x^2 - 6x + 2)$
Solution:

$$(x - 3)(x^2 - 6x + 2) =$$

$$x^3 - 6x^2 + 2x - 3x^2 + 18x - 6 =$$
$$x^3 - 9x^2 + 20x - 6$$

Example 3: $(5x - 9)^2$
Solution: $(5x - 9)(5x - 9) =$
$25x^2 - 45x - 45x + 81 =$
$25x^2 - 90x + 81$

Example 4: $(x + 1)(x + 2)(x - 4)$
Solution: $(x + 1)(x + 2)(x - 4) =$
$(x^2 + 3x + 2)(x - 4) =$
$x^3 - 4x^2 + 3x^2 - 12x + 2x - 8 =$
$x^3 - x^2 - 10x - 8$

Exercises

Add.

1. $(5x + 9) + (x - 8)$

2. $(x - 3y) + (x - y)$

3. $(3x^2 - 2) + (x^2 + 10)$

4. $(x^2 + 6x - 1) + (2x^2 - 4)$

5. $(2x + 4) + (3x - 2) + (7x - 5)$

6. $(x^3 - x^2) + (5x^2 - 3x) + (2x - 8)$

7. $(6x + 2y + 3) + (7x - 2y - 9) + (x - 5y + 6)$

Subtract.

8. $(11x + 3) - (4x - 1)$

9. $(7x - 7y) - (x - 7y)$

10. $(x^2 - 8x) - (2x^2 + 3x)$

11. $(5x^2 + 9x + 6) - (3x^2 - x + 7)$

12. $(3x^3 + 2y^3 - z^3) - (x^3 + y^3 - z^3)$

Multiply.

13. $(x + 12)(x + 2)$

14. $(3x + 4)(2x - 5)$

15. $(4x + 1)(4x - 1)$

16. $(x - 3)(x^2 - 7x - 2)$

17. $(2y - 1)(2y^2 - 3y + 5)$

18. $(x + y)(x^2 - xy + y^2)$

19. $(5x + 3)(x^2 - 4)$

20. $(x + 2)(x - 3)(x + 6)$

Do the indicated operations.

21. $5(2x - 7) - 2(5x + 7)$

22. $(10x - 1)^2$

23. $(x + 4)^3$

24. $x^2 - (x + 5)(x - 1)$

Chapter 4

Congruence

Design drawing for intarsia wood panels with fish—Maurits Escher

Two figures are said to be congruent if they have the same size and shape. Congruent triangles, in particular, appear in many important applications of geometry; therefore much of this chapter deals with the conditions needed to prove them so. Along the way, we will review coordinates in two dimensions, look at several important types of triangles, and learn how congruence is the basis for geometric constructions.

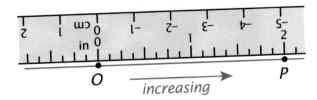

LESSON 1

Coordinates and Distance

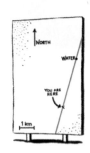

Maps usually include roads and landmarks. The one in this cartoon gives this poor fellow no help because it shows neither. If the man were on a road and the map looked like the one at the left, he could know that he was headed in the right direction and he could figure out how far he had to go.

Locating points on a line is easy. First, we choose a starting point O, the *origin*. Next, we decide which is to be the increasing direction. We can use a ruler as shown above to find that the coordinate of point P is 2 and that for point O is 0. The distance from O to P is the difference between their coordinates, $2 - 0$, in inches. By the Ruler Postulate, we get the correct distance however the ruler is placed and whatever units are used. Recall that the numbers assigned to points in this way are called *coordinates*. Choosing an origin and ruler gives us a *one-dimensional coordinate system*. In the figure at the left, point B has coordinate -2. What are the coordinates of points A and C?

To locate points in a plane, we use a *two-dimensional coordinate system*. We begin by taking two perpendicular lines as *axes*. Their intersection gives our origin, O. The line with the same direction as that of the bottom of this page is the horizontal axis, or the *x-axis*, as the label "*x*" shows. The other axis is called the vertical axis, or *y-axis*, labeled "*y*." Using our ruler, we establish coordinates on each axis as shown in the figure at the right. The axes separate the plane into four regions called *quadrants*. The quadrants are identified by numbers, shown as Roman numerals in the figure.

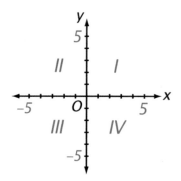

Two *coordinates* in our system locate a point in the plane. They are found by drawing perpendicular lines from the point to the axes as shown in the figures below.

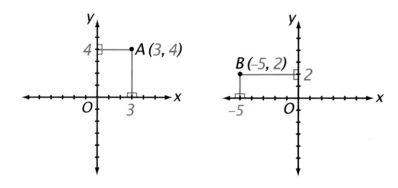

The coordinates of a point are written in parentheses and separated by a comma, the *x*-coordinate always being listed first: (x, y).

Coordinates can be used to find the distances between points in the plane. In the figure at the right, the grid lines drawn at unit intervals make it easy to see that the lengths of the legs of right triangle ABC are

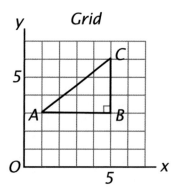

Grid

$$AB = 4 \text{ units and } BC = 3 \text{ units.}$$

The length of AC is not obvious, but we can find it by using the Pythagorean Theorem:

$$AB^2 + BC^2 = AC^2$$

and so $AC = \sqrt{AB^2 + BC^2} = \sqrt{4^2 + 3^2} = \sqrt{16 + 9} = \sqrt{25} = 5$, in the same units as were used on the axes.

We can find the distances between the points even without the grid, as long as we know their coordinates:

$$AB = 5 - 1 = 4, \ BC = 6 - 3 = 3, \text{ and}$$

$$AC = \sqrt{AB^2 + BC^2} = \sqrt{(5 - 1)^2 + (6 - 3)^2} = \sqrt{4^2 + 3^2}, \text{ etc.}$$

Coordinates

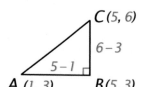

Using the same units for all distances, we can find the distances in terms of *general* coordinates as the figure at the left shows:

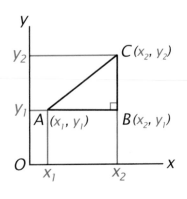

$$AB = x_2 - x_1, \ BC = y_2 - y_1, \text{ and}$$

$$AC = \sqrt{AB^2 + BC^2} = \sqrt{(x_2 - x_1)^2 + (y_2 - y_1)^2}.$$

The Pythagorean Theorem gives us this useful *distance formula* for any two points in the coordinate plane.

The Distance Formula

The distance between the points $P_1 \ (x_1, y_1)$ and $P_2 \ (x_2, y_2)$ is

$$\sqrt{(x_2 - x_1)^2 + (y_2 - y_1)^2}.$$

Exercises

Set I

Pin-Board Geometry. A blind mathematician, Nicholas Saunderson, invented the "pin board," a device in which pins mark the positions of the intersections on a coordinate grid. To form geometric figures, rubber bands are stretched around the pins.

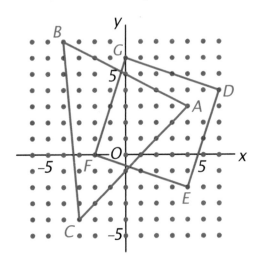

1. What are the lines labeled *x* and *y* called?

2. What is the point labeled O called?

Which of the lettered points

3. have an *x*-coordinate of 4?

4. has a *y*-coordinate of 4?

5. is in the second quadrant?

6. is on the *y*-axis?

The coordinates of point B are $(-4, 7)$.

7. What are the coordinates of the other two corners of the triangle?

8. What are the coordinates of the four corners of the square?

9. If the *x*-coordinate of a point is 0, where must it be?

10. If the *y*-coordinate of a point is 0, where must it be?

Grids. One dictionary definition of "grid" is "a pattern of horizontal and vertical lines forming squares of uniform size on a map, chart, or aerial photograph, used as a reference for locating points."*

11. To which axis of a graph are the horizontal lines parallel?

12. How many numbers are needed to locate a point on a grid?

––––––––––––

* The American Heritage Dictionary of the English Language.

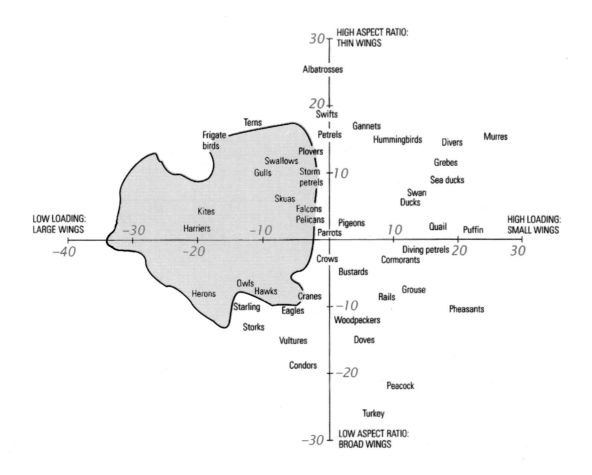

The figure below shows the design of a grid map that soldiers learn to read.

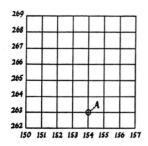

13. Why do you suppose they are told to memorize the phrase "Read right up"?

14. What are the coordinates of point A?

Another definition of "grid" is "a football field."

15. What does a football field have in common with a grid map?

Birds and Bats. The graph above compares different groups of birds according to their ability to fly. The region in yellow shows the area occupied by bats.* Numbers have been added to the axes for reference.

16. In which quadrant are the birds whose wings are small and broad?

17. In which quadrants are the bats?

Which group of birds seems to be closest to the point

18. $(0, 0)$?   20. $(-10, -15)$?

19. $(10, 15)$?   21. $(0, 25)$?

22. What are the approximate coordinates of the two points in which the "bats region" intersects the x-axis?

Exploring Biomechanics, by R. McNeill Alexander (Scientific American Library, 1992).

An Early Graph. The figure below, from Newton's *Opticks* (1704), shows part of the first graph to appear in a book in which the axes are perpendicular and all four quadrants are shown.

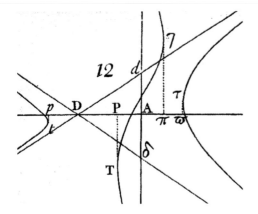

23. Which point is the origin?

What seems to be true about the coordinates of

24. points D and P?

25. point T?

Set II

Tidal Current. The figure below is part of a tidal-current chart for Upper Chesapeake Bay.* The arrows show the direction of the current.

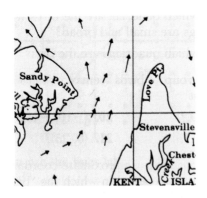

Dutton's Navigation and Piloting, by Elbert S. Maloney (Naval Institute Press, 1985).

Three current arrows are shown in the graph below.

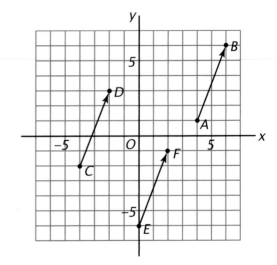

26. What seems to be true about them?

27. Find the coordinates of the endpoints of arrow AB and use them with the distance formula to calculate its length.

28. Do the same for arrow CD.

29. Do the same for arrow EF.

30. Do your results agree with the appearance of the arrows on the graph?

Japanese Floor Plan. In a traditional Japanese home, a grid of points determines the floor plan.[†] The figure at the top of the next page shows both the post pattern and the corresponding floor plan on different parts of the same grid.

Suppose that the origin of the grid is at the lower-left corner and the grid lines are 1 unit apart. What are the coordinates of

31. point A_1 and the corresponding point A_2?

32. point B_1 and the corresponding point B_2?

[†]*Architecture: Form, Space, and Order,* by Francis D. K. Ching (Wiley, 1996).

Traditional Japanese Residence

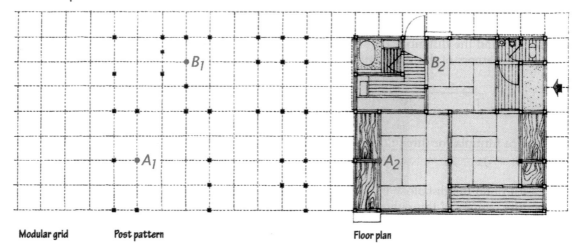

Modular grid   Post pattern   Floor plan

33. How are the coordinates of each point on the floor plan related to the coordinates of the corresponding points in the post pattern?

34. Where would the floor plan appear on the grid if the *x*-coordinates of its points matched those of the post pattern but the *y*-coordinates were 10 units larger?

Computer Screen. The coordinates of a computer screen are usually given in "pixels." Suppose that the coordinates of two corners of a window on the screen are as shown in the figure below.*

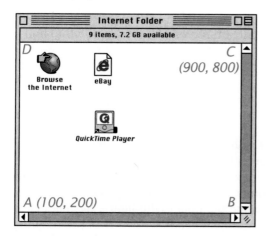

What are the coordinates of

35. the lower-right corner of the window, B?

36. the upper-left corner, D?

If the pixels are 0.25 mm square, what is the distance

37. from A to C?

38. from B to D?

Suppose that you use the computer mouse to click on one of the three icons.

39. If the computer reads the coordinates (410, 670), which icon did you click?

Distance Formulas. There are distance formulas for all numbers of dimensions![†]

40. Write the formula for the distance between two points, $P_1(x_1, y_1)$ and $P_2(x_2, y_2)$ in two dimensions.

41. Use it to find the distance between the opposite corners of this square. Leave your answer in radical form.

(4, 4)

(1, 1)

The Geometry Toolbox for Graphics and Modeling, by Gerald E. Farin and Dianne Hansford (A. K. Peters, 1998).

[†]*Beyond the Third Dimension: Geometry, Computer Graphics, and Higher Dimensions,* by Thomas F. Banchoff (Scientific American Library, 1990).

42. Would it be correct to say that the distance formula for one dimension is $\sqrt{(x_2 - x_1)^2}$?

43. Use it to find the distance between the opposite corners of this line segment.

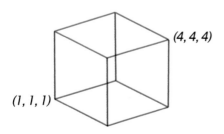

The distance formula for three dimensions is $\sqrt{(x_2 - x_1)^2 + (y_2 - y_1)^2 + (z_2 - z_1)^2}$.

44. Use it to find the distance between the opposite corners of this cube.

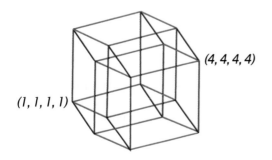

(4, 4, 4)

(1, 1, 1)

45. What do you think the distance formula for four dimensions might be?

46. Use it to find the distance in four dimensions between the opposite corners of this hypercube.

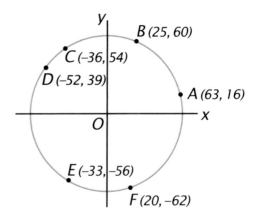

(4, 4, 4, 4)

(1, 1, 1, 1)

Triangle Coordinates. Use the coordinates of the vertices of the two triangles in the figure at the top of the next column to find the lengths of the sides of

47. triangle ABC.

48. triangle CDO.

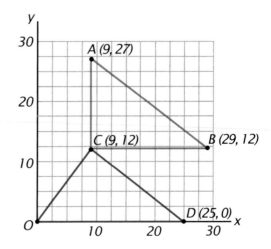

49. If an accurate tracing of triangle ABC were made, do you think you could get it to fit exactly on triangle CDO? Explain why or why not.

Set III

A Circle Challenge. The circle in the figure below has its center at the origin.

B (25, 60)
C (–36, 54)
D (–52, 39)
A (63, 16)
O
E (–33, –56)
F (20, –62)

The figure has been accurately drawn but, even though all six points appear to lie on the circle, two of them do not. (Remember that a point in geometry has a position only and, unlike the dots in the figure, has neither width nor breadth.)

One of the points is actually *inside* the circle and one of them is *outside* it. Which points are they and how can you tell?

Polygons and Congruence

There is not much variety in the housing development in Palm Beach, Florida, pictured above. The lots, houses, and swimming pools look very much alike. Most of the shapes in the photograph are *polygons*.

In an earlier lesson, a polygon was described as a "figure bounded by line segments that lies in a plane." The figure at the right, outlining a section of the roofs of the houses in the photograph, suggests a more precise way to define this word.

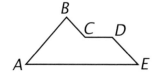

Definition

A *polygon* is a connected set of at least three line segments in the same plane such that each segment intersects exactly two others, one at each endpoint.

The line segments are the *sides* of the polygon and their endpoints are its *vertices*.* Because each side of a polygon intersects exactly two others, a polygon always has the same number of sides as it has vertices. If *n* is this number, the polygon is an "*n*-gon." The roof figure, for example, is a 5-gon.

---

*The word "vertices" is the plural of "vertex," the same word used to name the common endpoint of the sides of an angle.

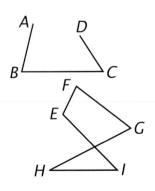

Not polygons

Our definition of "polygon" excludes figures such as those shown at the left. Both figures consist of at least three line segments in the same plane, but in neither figure does each line segment intersect exactly two others, one at each endpoint.

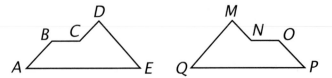

Because the houses in the photograph seem like mirror images of one another, it appears that two roof sections such as those shown above are *congruent;* that is, that they have *the same size and shape.* Therefore, if we traced one polygon, we could place the tracing so that it fits exactly on the other one. For these polygons, we would have to turn the tracing over to get them to coincide. In doing so, we are establishing a *correspondence* between the vertices of the polygons called a *congruence.* When the tracing of polygon ABCDE is made to coincide with polygon MNOPQ, vertex A falls on P, vertex B falls on O, and so forth. To indicate the correspondence of the vertices, we can write A ↔ P, B ↔ O, and so on, or, more briefly, ABCDE ↔ PONMQ.

Because each pair of sides and angles that correspond in a congruence must coincide, each pair of corresponding parts must be equal. Congruence is easiest to define for triangles.

Definition

Two triangles are *congruent* iff there is a correspondence between their vertices such that all of their corresponding sides and angles are equal.

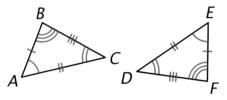

The tick marks and arcs in these triangles indicate the parts of them that are equal. For example, AB = EF and ∠C = ∠D. Triangles ABC and DEF are congruent, but simply saying it does not tell us the correspondence between their vertices that would make them coincide. Writing "△ABC ≅ △EFD" does. The symbol "≅" means "is congruent to," and "△ABC ≅ △EFD" indicates that the congruence correspondence is

ABC ↔ EFD.

From this abbreviated statement, we can tell without even looking at the triangles that

∠A = ∠E, ∠B = ∠F, ∠C = ∠D,
AB = EF, BC = FD, and AC = ED.

It is easy to prove from the definition of congruent triangles that, if two triangles are congruent to a third triangle, then they must also be congruent to each other. The proof is included as an exercise in this lesson.

Corollary to the definition of congruent triangles

Two triangles congruent to a third triangle are congruent to each other.

Exercises

Set I

Connect the Dots. A popular children's puzzle consists of a set of numbered dots that are to be connected in sequence to make a picture. In the example below, the result is a polygon.

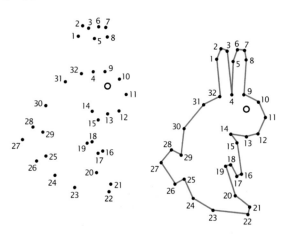

1. What are the line segments called with respect to the polygon?

2. What are the points called?

3. How many sides does this polygon have?

4. What is it called with respect to its number of sides?

5. If the last point had not been connected to the first point, would the figure still have been a polygon? Explain why or why not.

A tracing of the polygon at the right would fit exactly on the polygon at the left.

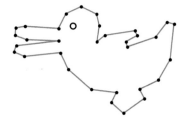

6. What does this indicate about the two polygons?

7. What can you conclude about their corresponding sides and angles?

Paper-Clip Patent. This drawing of a paper clip is from the patent issued to its inventor.* It is a single piece of wire bent into five parts.

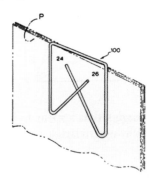

---

*United States Patent 4,949,435 issued to Gary K. Michelson on August 21, 1990. Included in *Invention by Design,* by Henry Petroski (Harvard University Press, 1996).

The figure below shows the five parts as line segments. The inventor described the clip by saying that BC ⊥ CD and DE ⊥ CD.

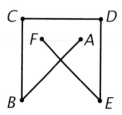

8. What does this tell you about ∠C and ∠D?

He also stated the size of ∠B and ∠E in degrees.

9. How large do you think each one is?

10. Why must some of the angles formed where BA and FE intersect be equal?

11. Explain why the paper-clip diagram is not a polygon.

Origami Duck. The origami duck considered in an earlier lesson is based on folding a square sheet of paper as shown in the figure below.

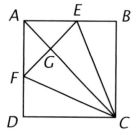

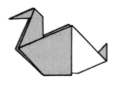

Name the triangles that appear to be congruent to the following triangles.

12. △AFG.

13. △ACD.

14. △CDF.

15. △ACE.

16. Name a triangle that is not congruent to any other triangle in the figure.

Name the quadrilaterals that appear to be congruent to quadrilateral

17. CDFG.

18. BCFE.

19. ADCE.

Art Gallery. The floor plan of an art gallery with four "wings" is shown at the right.

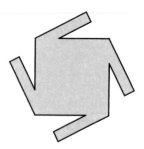

20. How many walls does each wall of the gallery meet?

21. How many walls does the art gallery have altogether?

22. What is a polygon having this number of sides called?

23. How many corners does the floor of the gallery have?

24. How many guards do you suppose would be necessary if the owners want to keep all the walls of the gallery in view at the same time?

Puzzle Figure. This figure once appeared as part of a puzzle in a magic magazine.*

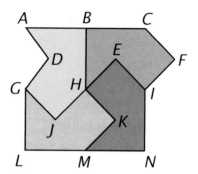

25. What kind of polygon do the outer edges of the figure appear to form?

---

*The Pallbearers Review, July 1969. Reported in Wheels, Life, and Other Mathematical Amusements, by Martin Gardner (W. H. Freeman and Company, 1983).

The figure contains four congruent polygons, each shaded a different color.

26. What kind of polygons are they?

If a tracing of the yellow polygon were placed on the green one, which of its vertices would fit on

27. E?

28. B?

29. C?

Copy and complete the following congruence correspondence between the vertices of the yellow and green polygons.

30. ABHJGD ↔ ?

If a tracing of the green polygon were placed on the red one, which of its vertices would fit on

31. M?

32. I?

33. E?

Copy and complete the following congruence correspondences between the vertices of

34. the green and red polygons:
HBCFIE ↔ ?

35. the green and blue polygons:
HBCFIE ↔ ?

36. the red and blue polygons:
MNIEHK ↔ ?

Set II

Tessellation Pattern. The figure below is a *tessellation,* a pattern of shapes that fit perfectly to cover a surface.

37. What do the two types of polygons in the figure have in common?

All of the line segments in the figure are equal.

38. If the sides of one polygon are equal to the sides of another, does it follow that the polygons must be congruent?

The polygons shaded yellow are *convex* and the polygons shaded blue are *concave.*

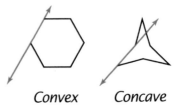

Convex   Concave

39. If a line that contains a side of a polygon lies partly inside the polygon, which kind of polygon is it?

Suppose nails are stuck into the vertices of a polygon and a rubber band is stretched around the nails so that all of the nails are inside it.

40. If the rubber band takes the shape of the polygon, which kind of polygon is it?

Draw and identify examples of

41. two pentagons, one convex and the other concave.

42. two quadrilaterals, one convex and the other concave.

43. Can a triangle be concave?

Polygons on a Grid. On graph paper, draw a pair of axes extending 10 units in each direction from the origin.

44. Plot these points and connect them to form a triangle: (2, 1), (5, 5), (9, 0).

45. Would you get a different triangle if you connected the points in a different order?

44. *(continued)* On the figure that you drew for exercise 44, plot these points and connect them to form a quadrilateral: (−7, 4), (−4, 6), (−4, 8), (0, 3).

46. Do you think someone else could get a different quadrilateral by connecting the same points? Explain.

44. *(continued)* On the figure that you drew for exercise 44, plot the following points and connect them to form a quadrilateral that is *not congruent* to your previous one: $(-6, -4)$, $(-3, -2)$, $(-3, 0)$, $(1, -5)$.

47. How many different quadrilaterals do you think can be drawn that have the same vertices as the one you just drew?

Dividing a Rectangle. An unusual way to divide a 3-by-7 rectangle into six congruent pieces is shown in the following figure.*

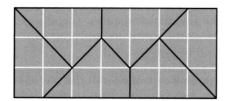

48. What is the area of the rectangle, given its dimensions of 3 and 7?

49. Because each of the six pieces is congruent, how large would you expect the area of each one to be?

50. What are you assuming to be true about the areas of polygons that are congruent?

51. Does your answer to exercise 49 agree with what you see inside each piece? Explain.

52. How large do the angles of each piece appear to be?

53. Do any of the sides in one of the pieces appear to be equal to each other?

54. If a tracing were made of one of the pieces, could it be made to coincide with each of the others without turning it over?

---

*Discovered by Michael Reid and reported in *Tracking the Automatic Ant,* by David Gale (Springer, 1998).

Proof Without a Figure. Although most theorems are much easier to understand and prove with a good diagram, the corollary to the definition of congruent triangles doesn't need one.

55. Give the reasons for the statements in the following proof. (Don't bother to copy the statements.)

Two triangles congruent to a third triangle are congruent to each other.

Given: $\triangle ABC \cong \triangle XYZ$ and $\triangle DEF \cong \triangle XYZ$.
Prove: $\triangle ABC \cong \triangle DEF$.

Proof

Statements	Reasons
1. $\triangle ABC \cong \triangle XYZ$ and $\triangle DEF \cong \triangle XYZ$.	Why?
2. $\angle A = \angle X$, $\angle B = \angle Y$, $\angle C = \angle Z$, $AB = XY$, $BC = YZ$, $AC = XZ$, $\angle D = \angle X$, $\angle E = \angle Y$, $\angle F = \angle Z$, $DE = XY$, $EF = YZ$, $DF = XZ$.	Why?
3. $\angle A = \angle D$, $\angle B = \angle E$, $\angle C = \angle F$, $AB = DE$, $BC = EF$, $AC = DF$.	Why?
4. $\triangle ABC \cong \triangle DEF$.	Why?

Set III

The polygons on the next page were created by the Polish mathematician Waclaw Sierpinski, pictured on this postage stamp issued in honor of his work in 1982.†

---

†*Penrose Tiles to Trapdoor Ciphers,* by Martin Gardner (W. H. Freeman and Company, 1989).

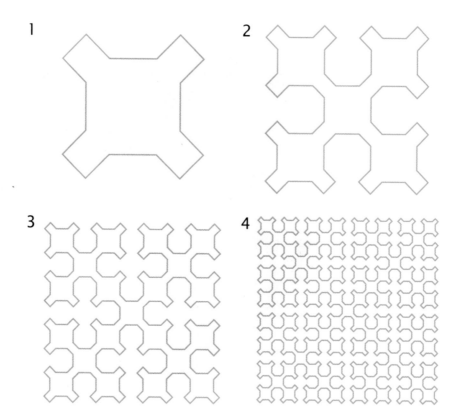

1. How many sides does the first polygon have?

2. The second polygon?

3. Can you figure out how many sides the third and fourth polygons have?

4. If the series of polygons were to continue in this way, how many sides do you think the tenth one would have? (A calculator would help!)

5. How many sides do you think the nth one would have? Show your reasoning.

ASA and SAS Congruence

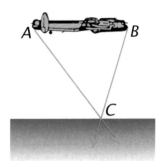

In World War II, the British air force used "skip bombs" to destroy dams that supplied much of the power that ran the Nazi war machine. A feature film titled *The Dam Busters* tells the amazing story of this adventure.

For the bombs to work, they had to be dropped from a plane flying 60 feet above the water. At the time, no instrument on a plane could measure this distance accurately. The problem was solved with two flashlights, one mounted in the airplane's nose and the other in the tail. The flashlights were pointed in fixed directions and, when the two beams of light met on the water's surface, the pilot knew that the plane was at the correct height to release the bomb.

The method worked because the two light beams and the body of the plane formed a triangle. The two angles formed by the beams with the body of the plane and the length of the plane determined the vertices of the triangle and hence its size and shape. Even though a triangle has six parts, three sides and three angles, the airplane triangle shows that just three of them, two angles and their "included" side, are sufficient to determine its size and shape.

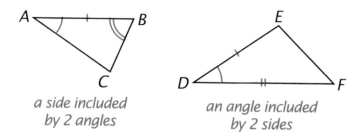

a side included
by 2 angles

an angle included
by 2 sides

The words "included" and "opposite" describe the relative positions of the sides and angles of a triangle. In △ABC, for example, side AB is said to be *included* by ∠A and ∠B and to be *opposite* ∠C. In △DEF, ∠D is said to be *included* by sides DE and DF and to be *opposite* side EF.

The tick marks and arcs in these figures are used to call attention to certain parts of the triangles as well as to identify equal sides and angles. The marks here indicate that AB = DE and ∠A = ∠D.

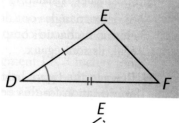

These two triangles are clearly not congruent because they do not have the same size and shape. However, the three parts marked in each triangle determine the size and shape of *that triangle*. If tracing paper were placed over △ABC and AB were traced along with the angles A and B, the tracing paper could be removed and the rest of the triangle could be drawn simply by extending the sides of the angles as shown at the right.

If tracing paper were placed over △DEF and ∠D were traced along with the sides DE and DF, the tracing paper could be removed and the rest of the triangle could be drawn simply by connecting points E and F.

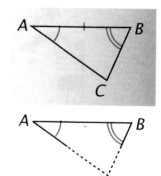

The first of these observations suggests that, if we know that two angles and the included side of one triangle are equal to two angles and the included side of another triangle, that is sufficient to establish that they are congruent. The second observation suggests the same conclusion for two sides and the included angle. We will abbreviate these conclusions as "ASA" and "SAS" and, because they will form the foundation for our reasoning about congruent triangles, we state them as our next postulates.

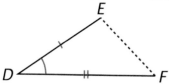

Postulate 5. The ASA Postulate

If two angles and the included side of one triangle are equal to two angles and the included side of another triangle, the triangles are congruent.

Postulate 6. The SAS Postulate

If two sides and the included angle of one triangle are equal to two sides and the included angle of another triangle, the triangles are congruent.

It is important to learn these postulates well enough to be able to say them as complete sentences. The appropriate sentence and figure should come to mind when you see ASA or SAS.

Exercises

Set I

Bermuda Triangle. The triangle on the map below has been featured in both books and movies. Stretching from Bermuda to Florida to Puerto Rico, it is known as "the Bermuda Triangle."

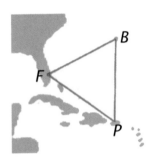

1. Which sides of the triangle include ∠B?
2. Which side is opposite ∠P?
3. Which angle is opposite FP?
4. Which angles include side FB?

French Postulate. In France, one of the congruence postulates is stated in these words:

> Si deux triangles ont deux *côtés* égaux chacun à chacun comprenant un *angle* égal, ils sont égaux.

5. Refer to the figure below and write our abbreviation for this postulate.

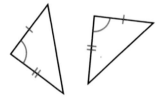

6. State the postulate in English as a complete sentence.
7. What do you think the abbreviation for this postulate is in French?

8. What do you think the abbreviation for the other congruence postulate is in French?
9. State it in English as a complete sentence.

Congruence Correspondences. In a section on triangles in his book *Architecture,** Francis Ching wrote:

> The triangle signifies stability. When resting on one of its sides, the triangle is an extremely stable figure. When tipped to stand on one of its vertices, however, it can either be balanced in a precarious state of equilibrium or be unstable and tend to fall over onto one of its sides.

In the figures below, △TRI ≅ △ANG and △ANG ≅ △LES. Use these congruence correspondences to copy and complete the following equations.

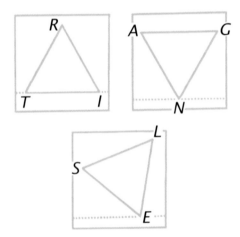

10. TR = ?
11. ∠I = ?
12. IT = ?
13. LS = ?
14. ∠E = ?
15. Why is △TRI ≅ △LES?

_____

Architecture: Form, Space, and Order, by Francis D. K. Ching (Wiley, 1996).

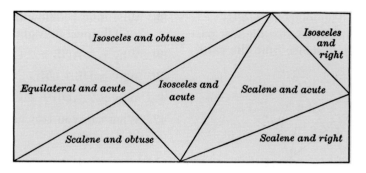

Isosceles and obtuse		Isosceles and right
Equilateral and acute	Isosceles and acute	Scalene and acute
Scalene and obtuse		Scalene and right

Triangle Names. The figure above, from a geometry book published in 1901, illustrates the words that are used to name triangles according to their sides and angles.*

Compare the relative sizes of the sides and angles of the triangles and the words inside them. Use your observations to tell what you think each of the following words means with reference to triangles.

16. Equilateral. **19.** Obtuse.

17. Acute. **20.** Scalene.

18. Isosceles. **21.** Right.

Intersecting a Triangle. In the figure below, line *l* contains vertices A and B of the triangle and line *n* contains vertex C.

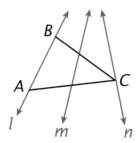

In geometry, two sets of points *intersect* iff they have at least one point in common.

How many sides of △ABC are intersected by

22. line *l?*

23. line *m?*

24. line *n?*

___
First Steps in Geometry, by G. A. Wentworth and G. A. Hill (Ginn, 1901).

Is it possible for a line to intersect

25. exactly one side of a triangle?

26. no sides of a triangle?

Set II

Eye Focus Triangle. When your eyes focus on an object in front of you, your pupils and the object are at the vertices of a triangle.

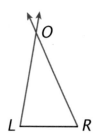

In the figure above, your eyes are at L and R and the object is at O; for most people, the distance between L and R is about 3 inches.

27. Draw a line segment LR 3 inches long near the bottom of a sheet of paper. Use your protractor to draw ∠L = 80° and ∠R = 65°.

28. Approximately how far is the object from your eyes?

29. Measure ∠O with your protractor.

30. Does the measure of ∠O seem to be consistent with the measures of ∠L and ∠R? Explain why or why not.

As the object moves away from you, what happens to

31. the sizes of ∠L and ∠R?

32. the size of ∠O?

Astronomy Problem. The following words from an astronomy book describe the first part of a calculation of the distance from the earth to the moon.*

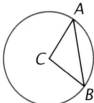

In the triangle ABC, the angle ACB at the center of the earth is known from the difference in latitudes of A and B and in this case is equal to about 94°. AC and BC, the sides of the triangle, are radii of the earth and are known from measurements of the size and shape of the earth. Since two sides and the included angle are known, the third side AB can be computed.

The radius of the earth is approximately 4,000 miles.

33. Use your ruler and protractor to make an accurate drawing of △ABC, making AC = BC = 4 cm and ∠C = 94°.

34. What is the length of AB in centimeters?

35. What is the approximate distance in miles between points A and B on the earth? Explain.

36. Measure ∠A and ∠B with your protractor.

37. What seems to be true about them?

Molecule Path. The figure at the right shows the path of a gas molecule that bounces off a wall; ∠1 = ∠2 and AC ⊥ DB.

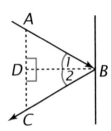

38. Why does it follow that ∠ADB and ∠CDB must be right angles?

39. Why is ∠ADB = ∠CDB?

40. Why is DB = DB?

41. Why is △ADB ≅ △CDB?

42. What can you conclude about AB and BC?

Pond Problem.
The figure at the right shows a way to find the distance across a pond. Posts are put in the ground at the five lettered points so that X-O-A, Y-O-B, XO = OA, and YO = OB.

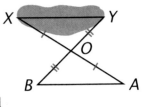

43. What do the symbols X-O-A and Y-O-B mean?

44. What relation does ray OA have to ray OX and ray OB have to ray OY?

45. Why is ∠XOY = ∠AOB?

46. Why is △XOY ≅ △AOB?

47. How do answers to these questions help in finding the distance across the pond?

Set III

Match Puzzles.† Starting each time with the arrangement of matches shown below, can you show how to leave two triangles by removing

1. four matches?

2. three matches?

3. two matches?

Make drawings to illustrate your answers. There must be no "loose ends."

Pictorial Astronomy, by Dinsmore Alter, Clarence H. Cleminshaw, and John G. Phillips (Crowell, 1974).

†From *Mathematical Circus,* by Martin Gardner (Knopf, 1979).

Permission granted by Virgil Partch

"Very, very exclusive."

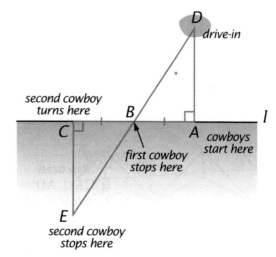

LESSON 4

Congruence Proofs

There does not seem to be any easy way for the two cowboys in the cartoon above to get over to that drive-in. Yet there *is* an easy way for them to find out how far away it is. In fact, if they know the approximate length of their horses' strides, they can measure the distance (AD in the figure) without any special instruments or even getting off their horses! The method, that of a Roman surveyor of long ago, is based on congruent triangles.*

The cowboys start from a position, A, directly across from the drive-in, D. They ride a short distance along a line *l* that is perpendicular to AD, counting strides as they go. One cowboy stops at point B and the other continues an equal distance along *l* to point C.

The second cowboy then turns left and rides until he reaches the point, E, where the first cowboy is in line with him and with the drive-in. The distance from C to E must be equal to the distance from A to D. Do you see why?

*Science Awakening, by B. L. van der Waerden (Oxford University Press, 1961).

It is because the two triangles in the figure (shown at the left below) are congruent and, because CE and AD are corresponding sides of these triangles, CE and AD must be equal. This conclusion comes from our definition of congruent triangles: Two triangles are congruent iff there is a correspondence between their vertices such that all of their corresponding sides and angles are equal. Because we will use this definition frequently when reasoning about congruent triangles, we state part of it more briefly here.

Definition (Brief Restatement)
Corresponding parts of congruent triangles are equal.

The figure at the left shows the triangles with the parts that we know marked. From the method described, the angles at B are vertical angles; so they must be equal. The triangles are congruent by ASA. All of this information is organized below in the form of a two-column proof.

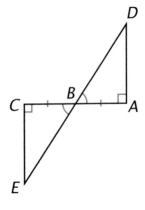

> *Given:* CA ⊥ AD, CB = BA, ∠C is a right angle and
> ∠CBE and ∠DBA are vertical angles.
> *Prove:* CE = AD.

Proof

Statements	Reasons
1. CA ⊥ AD.	Given.
2. ∠A is a right angle.	Perpendicular lines form right angles.
3. ∠C is a right angle.	Given.
4. ∠A = ∠C.	All right angles are equal.
5. ∠CBE and ∠DBA are vertical angles.	Given.
6. ∠CBE = ∠DBA.	Vertical angles are equal.
7. CB = BA.	Given.
8. △CBE ≅ △ABD.	ASA.
9. CE = AD.	Corresponding parts of congruent triangles are equal.

Notice how this proof is organized. To claim that the two triangles are congruent by ASA, we need to show that two pairs of angles and the pair of sides included by them are equal. In other words, we need to write *three equations:* two about the angles (steps 4 and 6) and one about the sides (step 7). Notice how step 4 follows from steps 2 and 3; step 2 in turn follows from step 1. Step 6 follows from step 5, step 8 from the three equation steps, and step 9 from step 8.

The proof didn't have to begin with the statement chosen as step 1. It could just as well have begun with statements 3, 5, or 7 instead. There can be several "correct" orders for the steps of a proof.

Exercises

Set I

Roof Plan. The design usually used for a roof is shown in the figure at the right.*

The following diagram shows a side view of the rafters and ceiling joists. We can prove different things about the figure depending on what we assume about it, that is, what we take as "given."

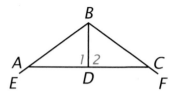

1. Copy the figure and mark the following "given" information on it:

    Given: D is the midpoint of AC, BD ⊥ AC.

2. Why is AD = DC?
3. Why are ∠1 and ∠2 right angles?
4. Why is ∠1 = ∠2?
5. Why is BD = BD?
6. Why is △ABD ≅ △CBD?
7. Why is ∠BAD = ∠BCD?

8. Make another copy of the figure and mark the following "given" information on it instead:

    Given: ∠1 = ∠2, ∠ABD = ∠CBD.

9. Why is BD = BD?
10. Why is △ABD ≅ △CBD?
11. Why is BA = BC?

How to Design and Build Your Own House, by Lupe Di Donno and Phyllis Sperling (Knopf, 1981).

12. Make another copy of the figure and mark the following "given" information on it:

    Given: BA = BC, BD bisects ∠ABC.

13. Why is ∠ABD = ∠CBD?
14. Why is BD = BD?
15. Why is △ABD ≅ △CBD?
16. Why is ∠1 = ∠2?
17. If ∠1 and ∠2 are a linear pair, why is BD ⊥ AC?

Repeating Patterns. The figure below contains several repeating patterns.

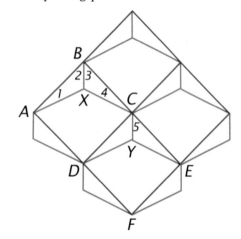

What kind of polygons do

18. the blue lines seem to form?
19. the red line segments form?

In the figure, AB = BC, ∠1 = ∠4, and ∠2 = ∠3.

20. Which triangles must be congruent?
21. Why?

Also, BC = CE, BX = CY, and ∠3 = ∠5.

22. Which triangles must be congruent?
23. Why?
24. Why is △ABX ≅ △ECY?
25. Why is AX = YE?

Set II

Strange Results. If the congruence postulates are not used correctly, some strange conclusions can result. Here are two examples.

Example 1

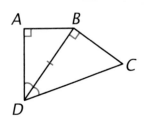

Given: DB bisects ∠ADC; ∠A and
       ∠DBC are right angles.
Prove: △ADB ≅ △BDC.

Proof

Statements	Reasons
1. DB bisects ∠ADC.	Given.
2. ∠ADB = ∠BDC.	If an angle is bisected, it is divided into two equal angles.
3. BD = BD.	Reflexive.
4. ∠A and ∠DBC are right angles.	Given.
5. ∠A = ∠DBC.	All right angles are equal.
6. △ADB ≅ △BDC.	ASA.

The figure for this proof is drawn accurately, and all of the given information is true.

26. Does △BDC look as if it could be congruent to △ADB? Why or why not?

27. What is wrong with the proof?

Example 2

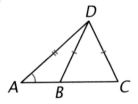

Given: DB = DC.
Prove: AB = AC.

Proof

Statements	Reasons
1. DB = DC.	Given.
2. AD = AD.	Reflexive.
3. ∠DAB = ∠DAC.	Reflexive.
4. △DAB ≅ △DAC.	SAS.
5. AB = AC.	Corresponding parts of congruent triangles are equal.

Again the figure is drawn accurately.

28. What is really true about AB and AC?

29. What is wrong with the proof?

Congruence Proofs. Write complete proofs for each of the following exercises. In each case, copy the figure and mark the given information on it. Also copy the "given" and "prove" before writing your statements and reasons. (Each proof can be written in five steps.)

30.

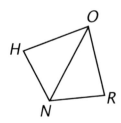

Given: HN = NR; NO bisects ∠HNR.
Prove: △HNO ≅ △RNO.

31.

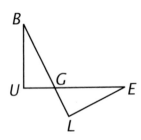

Given: ∠BGU and ∠EGL are vertical
       angles; BG = GE and UG = GL.
Prove: BU = LE.

32.

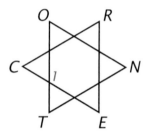

Given: ∠C = ∠O; ∠R and ∠N are
     supplements of ∠1; CR = ON.
Prove: △CRE ≅ △ONT.

33.

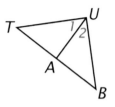

Given: ∠T and ∠2 are complements of
     ∠1; TA = AU and TU = UB.
Prove: AU = AB.

Grid Exercise. On graph paper, draw a pair of
axes extending 10 units in each direction from
the origin.

34. Plot the following points and connect
them to form △ABC: A(3, 1), B(3, 8),
C(7, 1).

35. Find the lengths of its sides.

34. *(continued)* On the figure that you drew
for exercise 34, plot the following points
and connect them to form △DEF:
D(3, −1), E(3, −8), F(7, −1).

36. In which quadrant is △DEF?

37. What would happen if you folded the
graph paper along the *x*-axis?

38. How are the coordinates of the vertices
of △DEF related to those of △ABC?

39. Find the lengths of its sides.

40. From the observation that ∠A and ∠D
are right angles, why does it follow that
△ABC ≅ △DEF?

34. *(continued)* Draw the triangle on which
△ABC would fit if you folded the graph
paper along the *y*-axis. Label its vertices
G, H, and I so that △ABC ≅ △GHI.

41. In which quadrant is △GHI?

42. What are the coordinates of its vertices?

43. How are the coordinates of its vertices
related to those of △ABC?

34. *(continued)* Plot the following points and
connect them to form △JKL: J(1, 3),
K(8, 3), L(1, 7).

44. Is △JKL ≅ △ABC?

45. How are the coordinates of the vertices
of △JKL related to those of △ABC?

46. Is it possible to fold the graph paper so
that the vertices of △ABC and △JKL
would fit together? If so, where would
you fold the paper? Check your answer
by trying it.

River Problem. Acute Alice and Obtuse Ollie
are standing on the bank of Muddy Boggy
Creek. Ollie asks Alice how wide she thinks
the river is. Alice adjusts the rim of her hat as
she looks across the river, then walks along the
river bank and gives Ollie an answer.*
   The "three-dimensional" figure below
illustrates the situation.

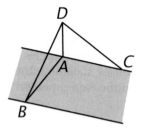

47. Copy it and mark the parts that Alice
used to figure out her answer.

48. Tell how she did it.

---

*Adapted from a problem in *You Are a Mathematician*,
by David Wells (Wiley, 1995).

Set III

*The Problem of the Handcuffed Prisoners**
Nine dangerous prisoners have to be carefully
watched. Each day they are taken out for
exercise, handcuffed in threes as illustrated in
this sketch made by one of their guards. How
can they be handcuffed so that, on four consecutive days, no pair of prisoners are together
in the same group more than once?

Although this puzzle is much more
difficult to solve than it first appears, a solution can be found quite easily by using some
simple geometry.

Draw a circle and write the numbers 1
through 9 (except 3) placed as shown in the
lower figure at the right. Those on the circle
are equally spaced. Draw another circle of the
same size and on it draw the diameter and
two congruent triangles as shown in red.
Write the number 3 in the center of this circle
and cut it out.

Place it on the first circle so that it looks
like the diagram. Copy the set of three numbers on the diameter, and the two sets of three
numbers at the vertices of the two triangles.
You should get a list like this: 123, 456, 789,
corresponding to the way in which the
prisoners are arranged in the sketch.

Now rotate the circle so that the diameter
falls between 4 and 9 and write down the new
sets of numbers (on the diameter and at the
vertices of the triangles). Do this again with
the diameter placed between 7 and 5, and
again with the diameter between 8 and 6.

If you haven't copied any numbers incor-
rectly, you have the solution to the puzzle.
Strange as it may seem, puzzles of this sort
have practical uses, including the statistical
design of scientific experiments!

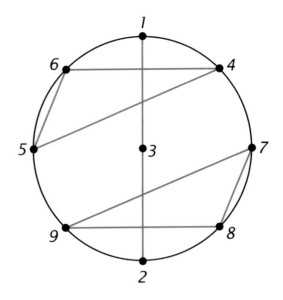

---

*Adapted from a problem by Henry Ernest Dudeney,
Amusements in Mathematics (1917); paperback published
by Dover, 1958.

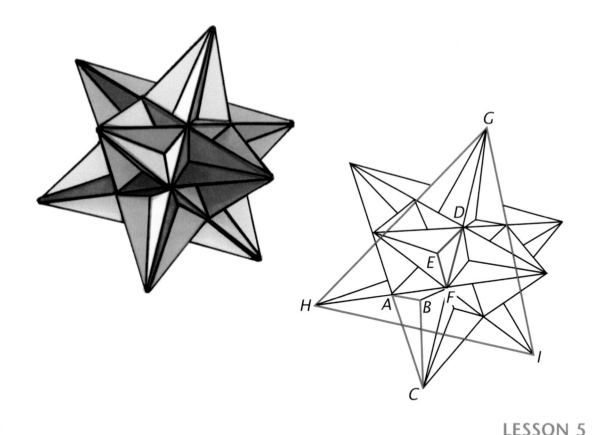

Isosceles and Equilateral Triangles

Euclid began the *Elements* with the construction of an equilateral tri-angle (Book I, Proposition 1). He ended it comparing five geometric solids called the "regular polyhedra" (Book XIII, Proposition 18). A beautiful polyhedron discovered more than 2,000 years later is shown in the figure above. It was discovered by Louis Poinsot, a French mathematician, in 1809 and is called a "great icosahedron."

The edges of the great icosahedron form a large number of tri-angles of various shapes. Most of them, such as △ABC in the figure beside the photograph, are *scalene* because they have no equal sides. Some of the triangles, such as △DEF, are *isosceles* because they have two equal sides, and some, such as △GHI, are *equilateral* because they have three equal sides.

Definitions
A triangle is
    scalene iff it has no equal sides.
    isosceles iff it has at least two equal sides.
    equilateral iff all of its sides are equal.

These definitions depend on the relative lengths of the *sides* of a triangle. Triangles are also classified according to the measures of their *angles*.

Definitions

A triangle is
 obtuse iff it has an obtuse angle.
 right iff it has a right angle.
 acute iff all of its angles are acute.
 equiangular iff all of its angles are equal.

The sides and angles of triangles are related in special ways. For example, if a triangle has a pair of equal sides, it will also have a pair of equal angles, and conversely. Furthermore, a triangle is equiangular iff it is equilateral.

 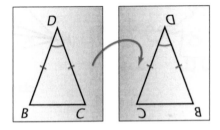 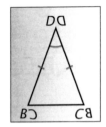

These ideas are easy to prove by using our congruence postulates. Consider △BCD with BD = CD, for example. If you traced it and flipped the tracing over, it would look the same. In fact, if you placed the flipped triangle on the original triangle, the two triangles would coincide. CD would fit on BD because they are equal, ∠D would fit on ∠D, and BD would fit on CD. We have the congruence correspondence, △BCD ≅ △CBD by SAS. It follows that ∠C = ∠B because corresponding parts of congruent triangles are equal. So, if two sides of a triangle are equal, two of its angles also must be equal.

Here is our argument arranged as a proof in two-column form.

Theorem 9

If two sides of a triangle are equal, the angles opposite them are equal.

  Given: In △BCD, BD = CD.
  Prove: ∠C = ∠B.

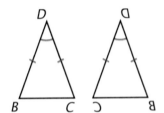

Proof

Statements	Reasons
1. In △BCD, BD = CD.	Given.
2. ∠D = ∠D.	Reflexive.
3. CD = BD.	Given.
4. △BCD ≅ △CBD.	SAS.
5. ∠C = ∠B.	Corresponding parts of congruent triangles are equal.

The converse of this theorem is also true.

Theorem 10
If two angles of a triangle are equal, the sides opposite them are equal.

From these two theorems, it follows that all equilateral triangles must be equiangular and vice versa.

Corollaries to Theorems 9 and 10
An equilateral triangle is equiangular.
An equiangular triangle is equilateral.

These facts are all easy to prove; their proofs are considered in the exercises.

Exercises

Set I

In the figure below, AB = AD and ∠C = ∠BDC.

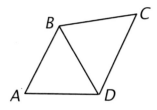

1. Copy the figure and mark the equal parts on it.

2. Which angle of △ABD is opposite AB?

3. Which angles of △ABD must be equal?

4. Which side of △BCD is opposite ∠C?

5. Which sides of △BCD must be equal?

6. Does it follow that △ABD and △BCD are congruent?

The figure at the right appeared in an edition of Euclid's *Elements* published in 1665. In △ABC, AB = AC; AD = AE.

7. What kind of triangle is △ABC?

8. Why is ∠ABC = ∠ACB?

9. What angle do △ACD and △ABE have in common?

10. Why is △ACD ≅ △ABE?

11. Why is ∠D = ∠E?

"Isosceles." "Isosceles" is a strange word. Not only is it strange, it is very old. It comes from the Greek word *isoskeles* and is used only in geometry.

12. What does it mean to say that a triangle is isosceles?

13. Is an equilateral triangle isosceles? Explain why or why not.

According to the dictionary, "isosceles" means "having equal legs."

14. Where are the equal angles in an isosceles triangle with respect to its legs?

If it is possible, draw an example of an isosceles triangle that is also

15. a right triangle.

16. a scalene triangle.

17. an obtuse triangle.

Alcoa Building. The architects who designed the Alcoa building in San Francisco used a grid of isosceles triangles.*

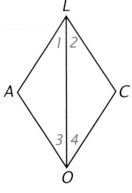

18. Copy this figure based on that grid and mark the following information on it: AL = LC = CO = OA; ∠A = ∠C.

19. What kind of triangles are △LAO and △LCO?

20. Why is ∠1 = ∠3 and ∠2 = ∠4?

21. Why is ∠1 + ∠2 = ∠3 + ∠4?

From the figure, we see that LA-LO-LC and OA-OL-OC.

22. Why is ∠ALC = ∠1 + ∠2 and ∠AOC = ∠3 + ∠4?

23. Why is ∠ALC = ∠AOC?

24. Why is △LAO ≅ △LCO?

25. Why is ∠1 = ∠2 and ∠3 = ∠4?

26. What relation does LO have to ∠ALC and ∠AOC?

Shuffleboard Court. The figure at the right shows one of the scoring zones of a shuffleboard court. SH = HU = UF = FL = LE = EB.

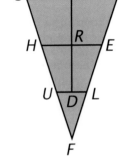

*Geometry in Architecture, by William Blackwell (Wiley, 1984).

27. What relation does OD appear to have to SB, HE, and UL?

28. What relation do SB, HE, and UL appear to have to one another?

29. What kind of triangles are △SBF, △HEF, and △ULF?

Given that ∠F = 36°, find the measures of

30. ∠S and ∠B.

31. ∠LUF and ∠ULF.

32. ∠SUL and ∠BLU.

Set II

Theorem 10 can be proved in a way almost identical with the proof of Theorem 9.

33. Write a complete proof of Theorem 10 by first copying it, the figure, and the "given" and "prove." Use the proof of Theorem 9 as a guide in writing your proof.

Theorem 10. If two angles of a triangle are equal, the sides opposite them are equal.

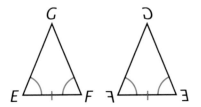

Given: In △EFG, ∠E = ∠F.
Prove: GE = GF.

Theorem 9 can be used to prove its corollary.

34. Write a complete proof of the corollary by first copying it, the figure, and the "given" and "prove." Copy the statements and give the reasons.

Corollary. An equilateral triangle is equiangular.

Given: △ABC is equilateral.
Prove: △ ABC is equiangular.

160   Chapter 4: Congruence

Proof

Statements	*Reasons*
1. △ABC is equilateral.	Why?
2. BC = AC and AC = AB.	Why?
3. ∠A = ∠B and ∠B = ∠C.	Why?
4. ∠A = ∠C.	Why?
5. △ABC is equiangular.	Why?

The proof of the corollary to Theorem 10 is almost the same.

35. Copy the following and use the proof in exercise 34 as a guide in writing your proof.

Corollary. An equiangular triangle is equilateral.

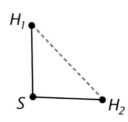

Given: △ABC is equiangular.
Prove: △ABC is equilateral.

Hydrogen Sulfide. One of the reasons that rotten eggs stink is hydrogen sulfide. The hydrogen sulfide molecule consists of a sulfur atom bonded to two hydrogen atoms.*

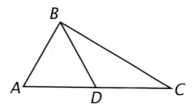

In △SH$_1$H$_2$, S represents the center of the sulfur atom; H$_1$ and H$_2$ represents, the centers of the hydrogen atoms; SH$_1$ = SH$_2$.

36. What kind of triangle is △SH$_1$H$_2$ with respect to its sides?

The measure of ∠H$_1$ is 43.9°. Find the measure of

37. ∠H$_2$.

---

*The Architecture of Molecules, by Linus Pauling and Roger Hayward (W. H. Freeman and Company, 1964).

38. ∠S.

39. What kind of triangle is △SH$_1$H$_2$ with respect to its angles?

40. If you knew that SH$_1$ = SH$_2$ = 1.34 angstroms, could you use the Pythagorean Theorem to find the length of H$_1$H$_2$? Explain.

In the figure below, △ABD is equiangular and D is the midpoint of AC.

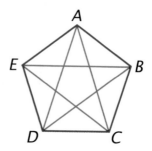

41. Copy the figure and mark this information on it.

△BDC is evidently obtuse.

42. What further conclusions can you draw about △BDC? Explain your reasoning.

Star Puzzles. In the accurately drawn figure below, 10 line segments connect the 5 lettered points.

43. What kind of polygon is the blue polygon?

44. Why isn't the red star a polygon?

All of the sides and angles of the blue polygon are equal.

45. Do you think that the 5 line segments that form the red star also must be equal? Explain why or why not.

In this accurately drawn figure, the 5 line segments that form the red star are equal.

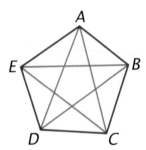

46. Do you think that the 5 sides of the blue polygon also must be equal? Explain why or why not.

47. If you also knew that the angles at the corners of the red star were equal, could you then conclude that the sides of the blue polygon also are equal? Explain why or why not.

SAT Problem. The figure below appeared in a problem on an SAT exam.

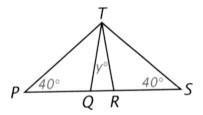

In it, PS is a line segment and PQ = QT = TR = RS.

48. What is the value of *y?* Show your reasoning.

Drawing Exercise.

49. Draw a line segment 3 inches long. Use your straightedge and compass to construct an equilateral triangle with the line segment as one of its sides. Label the corners of the triangle A, B, and C. Use your ruler to mark point X on AB so that AX = 1 inch. Mark point Y on BC so that BY = 1 inch. Mark point Z on AC so that CZ = 1 inch. Connect points X, Y, and Z to form △XYZ.

50. What seems to be true about △AXZ, △BYX, and △CZY?

51. Explain why it must be true.

52. What seems to be true about △XYZ?

53. Explain why it must be true.

Set III

In this remarkable drawing by Maurits Escher, the artist has filled part of a plane with lizards.*

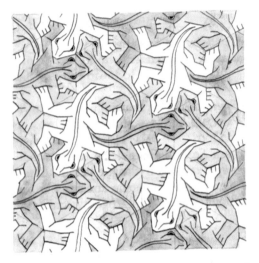

1. In how many different directions are the lizards crawling?

2. Through how many degrees would one of the lizards have to turn to be crawling in the same direction as one of the lizards next to it?

3. The lizard at the bottom of this page looks like the ones in the drawing and yet, other than being blue, it couldn't fit in with all the rest. Why not?

The Magic of M. C. Escher (Abrams, 2000).

SSS Congruence

In 1875, the Reverend Samuel Manning described the experience of riding in a train across a bridge like the one in the picture above:

> The road is carried across valleys hundreds of feet in depth on rude trestle bridges, which creak and groan beneath the weight of the train. Anything apparently more insecure than these structures can hardly be found elsewhere, and I always drew a long breath of relief as I found myself safely on the other side.*

Although the bridge in the photograph doesn't look capable of supporting a heavy train, part of its strength comes from the framework beneath it. The framework is composed of "trusses," based on the triangle, the simplest rigid shape that a structure can have.

If models of a triangle and a quadrilateral are made by threading drinking straws together, the triangle will hold its shape but the quadrilateral will collapse. The shape of the triangle, then, is completely determined by the lengths of its sides.

Thus, if the sides of one triangle are equal to the sides of another, the triangles must be congruent. We now have enough facts about triangles to be able to prove it.

American Pictures (1875).

Theorem 11. The SSS Theorem

If the three sides of one triangle are equal to the three sides of another triangle, the triangles are congruent.

Our proof, after that of Euclid, is based on copying one of the triangles and then showing that the other triangle is congruent to this copy. The figures illustrate the construction and proof.

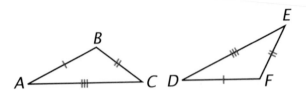

Given: AB = DF, BC = FE, and AC = DE.
Prove: △ABC ≅ △DFE.

Proof
The first part: Drawing a new triangle congruent to △DEF.
First, draw ray AX from point A so that ∠CAX = ∠D (Protractor Postulate). Next, choose point P on ray AX so that AP = DF (Ruler Postulate). Draw CP (two points determine a line). △APC ≅ △DFE (SAS).

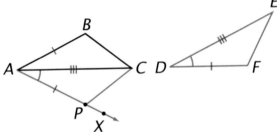

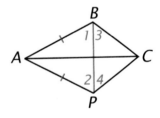

The second part: Showing that the new triangle is congruent to △ABC.
Draw BP. AP = DF (corresponding parts of congruent triangles are equal) and AB = DF (given), so AP = AB (substitution). From this information we know that △ABP is isosceles; so ∠1 = ∠2 (if two sides of a triangle are equal, the angles opposite them are equal).

Also, PC = FE (corresponding parts of congruent triangles are equal) and BC = FE (given); so PC = BC (substitution). So △CBP also is isosceles and ∠3 = ∠4.

Because ∠1 = ∠2 and ∠3 = ∠4, ∠1 + ∠3 = ∠2 + ∠4 (addition). But ∠1 + ∠3 = ∠ABC and ∠2 + ∠4 = ∠APC (Betweenness of Rays Theorem, which holds because BP divides both ∠ABC and ∠APC); so ∠ABC = ∠APC (substitution). From this information we know that △ABC ≅ △APC (SAS). Finally, △ABC ≅ △DFE because two triangles congruent to a third triangle are congruent to each other.

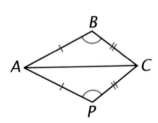

The proof is long but the theorem is easy to use. You should learn the SSS Theorem well enough to be able to recall it as a sentence whenever you see it referred to as SSS.

Exercises

Set I

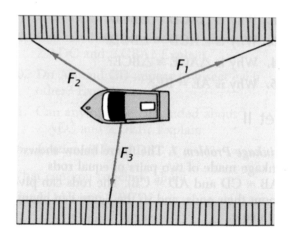

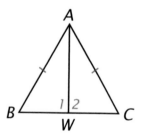

If the weight hangs over the midpoint of BC,

3. why is △ABW ≅ △ACW?

4. why is ∠1 = ∠2?

5. In what other way are ∠1 and ∠2 related?

6. Why is AW ⊥ BC?

The weight causes AW to always be vertical.

7. What can therefore be concluded about BC?

Suppose instead that the weight line bisects ∠BAC.

8. If this is the case, is it still true that △ABW ≅ △ACW? Explain why or why not.

Force Triangles. The figure above shows a boat held in place by three ropes. If the arrows represent the forces acting on the ropes, triangles can be drawn having the arrows as their sides.*

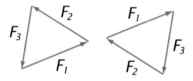

1. How do you know that these triangles are congruent?

2. Why are the angles of one triangle equal to the angles of the other?

Plumb Level. This device, called a plumb level, consists of a wooden frame in the shape of an isosceles triangle. A string with a weight on it is suspended from its vertex.

Equal Parts. The two triangles below have been accurately drawn and their equal parts have been marked.

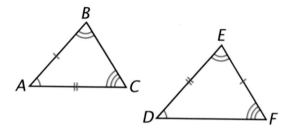

9. Are the triangles congruent? Explain why or why not.

10. How many pairs of equal parts do they have?

---

*Project Physics (Holt, Rinehart and Winston, 1981).

Are two triangles necessarily congruent if they have

11. three pairs of equal parts?

12. four pairs of equal parts?

13. five pairs of equal parts?

14. six pairs of equal parts? Explain.

Angle Bisection. In Chapter 1, you learned *how* to bisect line segments and angles. We can use congruent triangles to understand *why* these constructions work.

15. Use your protractor to draw an angle of 50°. Use your straightedge and compass to bisect the angle. Label your drawing as shown in the figure below. Draw AD and BD.

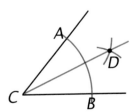

16. Which line segments in your drawing are equal by construction?

17. Why is CD = CD?

18. Why is △ACD ≅ △BCD?

19. Why is ∠ACD = ∠BCD?

Segment Bisection. The method for bisecting a line segment can be understood in a similar, but slightly longer, way.

20. Use your ruler to draw a line segment 6 cm long. Use your straightedge and compass to bisect it. Label your drawing as shown in the figure below.

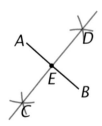

Draw AD, BD, AC, and BC.

21. Which line segments in your drawing are equal because of the way that you constructed them?

22. Why is △ACD ≅ △BCD?

23. Why is ∠ACD = ∠BCD?

24. Why is △ACE ≅ △BCE?

25. Why is AE = BE?

Set II

Linkage Problem 1. The figure below shows a linkage made of two pairs of equal rods (AB = CD and AD = CB). The rods can pivot about their ends, and so the figure can change its shape.

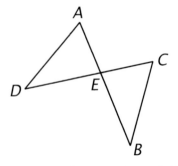

26. Draw the figure by using line segments to represent the rods as shown below. Use tick marks to show AD = CB and draw AC.

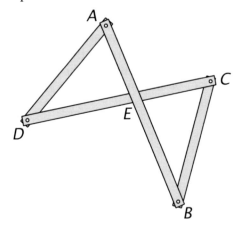

27. What seems to be true about △ADC and △CBA?

Suppose the linkage were adjusted to a slightly different shape.

28. Do you think your observation about △ADC and △CBA would still be true? Explain why or why not.

29. Can anything be concluded about ∠ADC and ∠CBA? Explain.

30. Do AB and CD appear to bisect each other? Explain.

31. Can anything be concluded about ∠AEC and ∠DEB? Explain.

26. *(continued)* Draw DB.

What can you conclude about

32. △DAB and △BCD?

33. ∠DAB and ∠BCD?

34. As the linkage is slightly changed, what is always true about △AED and △CEB? Explain.

35. Can anything be concluded about △AEC and △DEB? Explain.

Linkage Problem 2. The following figure shows another linkage.* In it, OA = OB and AD = DB = BC = CA.

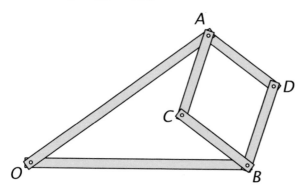

36. Draw the figure, by using line segments to represent the rods, and mark the equal parts on it.

37. What seems to be true about points O, C, and D?

---

*Geometry and the Imagination, by David Hilbert and Stefan Cohn-Vossen (AMS-Chelsea, 1999).

36. *(continued)* Draw OC.

38. No matter what shape the linkage is adjusted to, △AOC is always congruent to △BOC. Why?

39. Why are ∠AOC and ∠BOC always equal?

40. What relation does line OC have to ∠AOB?

36. *(continued)* Draw OD.

41. What relation does line OD have to ∠AOB? Explain.

42. Why must lines OC and OD be the same line?

43. What does this prove about points O, C, and D?

Grid Exercise. On graph paper, draw a pair of axes extending 10 units in each direction from the origin.

44. Plot the following points and connect them to form △ABC: A(−2, 4), B(7, 7), C(5, −2).

45. What kind of triangle do you think △ABC is?

46. Find the lengths of its sides.

47. Do these lengths agree with your answer to exercise 45? If not, what kind of triangle is △ABC?

44. *(continued)* Plot the following points and connect them to form △DEF: D(−9, 0), E(0, −2), F(−6, −9).

48. Find the lengths of its sides.

49. What can you conclude about △ABC and △DEF? Why?

Which angle(s) in your drawing are equal to

50. ∠A?

51. ∠E?

Set III

Bracing the Square. This puzzle once appeared in the "Mathematical Games" column of *Scientific American* magazine.*

Suppose a square is made of four rods, hinged at their ends. How many more rods of the same length and also hinged at their ends are needed to make the square rigid?

The figure below shows a solution with 23 rods that was discovered by a number of readers of the magazine. As long as the rods lie flat in a plane, no arrangement with fewer than 23 rods will work.

1. Trace the figure on your paper and use the facts that the sum of the angles of a triangle is 180° and that each angle of a square is 90° to write down as many of the angle measures in the figure as you can.

The fact that points X, Y, and Z are collinear makes the structure rigid.

2. Draw segments XY and YZ and explain, by using the angles at Y, why X, Y, and Z must be collinear.

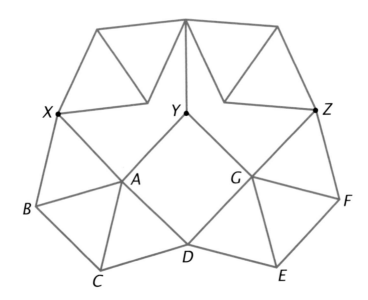

Martin Gardner's Sixth Book of Mathematical Games from Scientific American, by Martin Gardner (W. H. Freeman and Company, 1971).

LESSON 7

Constructions

Vitruvius, a Roman architect of the time of Julius Caesar, wrote in his book *On Architecture:*

> Let the architect be educated, skillful with the pencil, instructed in geometry. . . . Geometry is of much assistance in architecture, and in particular it teaches us the use of the rule and compass.

Euclid established the tools used in making geometric constructions: the pencil for marking *points,* the "rule" (straightedge) for drawing *lines,* and the compass for drawing *circles.* You have learned to use these tools in two constructions:

Construction 1. To bisect a line segment.
Construction 2. To bisect an angle.

You learned in Lesson 6 that both constructions are based on the SSS theorem. In this lesson, we will see how the straightedge and compass can be used to copy simple figures.

The word "compass" (originally "compasses") comes from the Latin word *compassare,* meaning "to measure off by steps." For example, if we have a line segment of length "1 unit," we can use the compass to measure off steps on a line, each 1 unit long.

$$A \underset{1}{\rule{1.5em}{0.4pt}} B \qquad \overset{\displaystyle l}{\underset{\displaystyle 0 \quad 1 \quad 2 \quad 3 \quad 4 \quad 5}{\rule{10em}{0.4pt}}}$$

This example illustrates the basic construction of copying a line segment.

Construction 3
To copy a line segment.

Let AB be the given line segment. Set the *radius* of the compass to the length of AB by putting the metal point on A and the pencil point on B. Draw a line (*l*) and mark a point C on it. With C as center, draw an arc of radius AB that intersects the line (D in the figure at the right above): CD = AB.

Even though we may not know the measure of an angle, we can use a straightedge and compass to copy it.

Construction 4
To copy an angle.

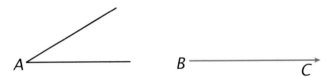

Let ∠A be the angle to be copied. Draw a ray BC as one side of the angle to be drawn. With point A as center, draw an arc that intersects the sides of A (points D and E in the figure at the left below). With point B as center, draw an arc with the same radius as shown in the figure at the right below. This arc intersects BC at point F. We drew it above BC, and that is where the copied angle will be.

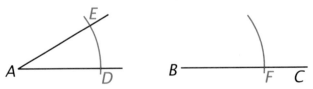

Go back to ∠A and set the radius of the compass to the distance between points D and E. With F as center, draw an arc having this radius so that it intersects the arc through F giving point G.

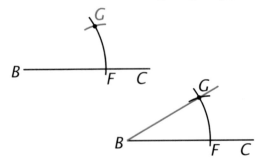

Draw BG to finish the construction: ∠A = ∠B.

Drawing DE and FG shows why this works. △ADE ≅ △BFG by SSS, and so ∠A = ∠B because corresponding parts of congruent triangles are equal.

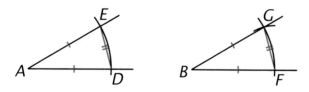

Because of SSS congruence, it is just as easy to copy an entire triangle.

Construction 5
To copy a triangle.

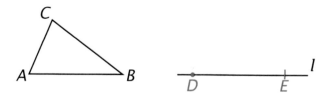

Let △ABC be the triangle to be copied. Draw a line (*l*) and copy AB on it (DE in the figure at the right above).

Return to the triangle and set the radius of the compass to the length of AC. With D as center, draw an arc having this radius, as shown in the figure at the left below.

Reset the radius of the compass to the length of BC. With E as center, draw an arc having this radius so that it intersects the first arc at point F, as shown in the middle figure below.

Draw DF and EF to finish the construction, as shown in the figure at the right below.

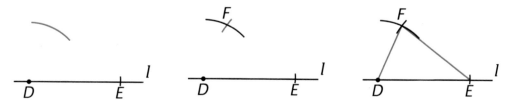

To see why △ABC ≅ △DEF, mark the equal lengths on the sides of the two triangles. They are congruent by SSS.

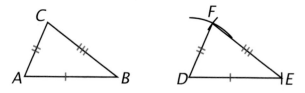

Exercises

Set I

This old engraving shows a geometer standing beside a globe of the earth.

1. What tool is he holding?
2. What could it be used to compare on the globe?
3. Can a circle be drawn on a globe?
4. Can a line be drawn on a globe?

In making constructions, it is customary to draw arcs of circles rather than the entire circles. The following figures show why! Tell what is being constructed in each figure.

5.

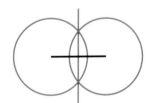

6.

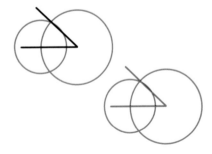

7.

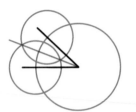

8.

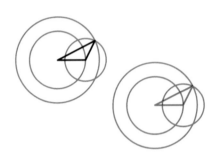

Light Reflection. Euclid's book on light, *Optics,* gives the following rule for light reflected from a mirror: *The angle of incidence is equal to the angle of reflection.* Both angles are measured from a perpendicular line *l,* as shown in the figure below.

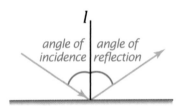

AB represents the mirror and CP the incident ray of light in the figure below. We will use Euclid's rule to find the reflected ray.

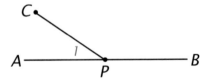

9. Draw a figure similar to the one above. Use your straightedge and compass to bisect ∠APB. Label the bisector line *l.* Write the number 2 inside the angle that line *l* makes with PC.

10. What relation does line *l* have to line AB?

11. What relation does ∠2 have to ∠1?

9. *(continued)* On your drawing, use your straightedge and compass to draw the direction of the light ray after it leaves point P. Name another point on this line D.

12. What construction did you use to find ray PD?

Bridge Girder. This design, a Warren girder, is frequently used in bridge construction.* It is based on equilateral triangles.

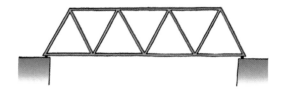

13. Use your straightedge and compass to construct such a row of triangles.

14. Why are they all congruent?

15. Why are all of the angles in the triangles equal? (There are two reasons.)

16. How does the line containing the tops of the triangles appear to be related to the line containing their bases?

Equidistant Points. A cartoon in the *New Yorker* once showed a family on vacation in a car passing a road sign saying "This spot is exactly equidistant between Disneyland and Disney World."

17. Choose two points on your paper several inches apart and label them X and Y. Draw line segment XY and use your straightedge and compass to construct its midpoint. Label the midpoint A. Point A is *equidistant* from X and Y.

18. What do you think "equidistant" means?

19. How many midpoints does a line segment have?

17. *(continued)* On your drawing, use your compass to find several more points, each of which is equidistant from X and Y.

20. How many points do you think can be found that are equidistant from the endpoints of a line segment?

21. Where do all of these points appear to lie?

Car Jack. The car jack in the picture below is a linkage of four bars of equal length. As a screw through A and B is turned, the distance between A and B changes.[†]

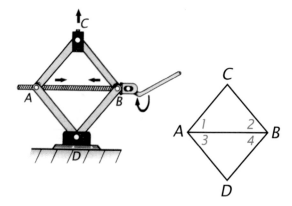

22. Draw a line segment AB and construct two triangles ACB and ADB so that AC = CB = AD = DB as shown in the figure at the right above. Identify the equal lengths with tick marks.

23. What kind of triangles are △ACB and △ADB?

24. Why is ∠1 = ∠2 and ∠3 = ∠4?

25. Why is ∠1 + ∠3 = ∠2 + ∠4?

26. Why is ∠CAD = ∠CBD?

27. Why must △ACB and △ADB be congruent?

28. Why is ∠1 = ∠3 and ∠2 = ∠4?

29. How is AB related to ∠CAD and ∠CBD?

---

*Structures, or Why Things Don't Fall Down, by J. E. Gordon (Plenum, 1978).

†*Mathematics Meets Technology,* by Brian Bolt (Cambridge University Press, 1991).

Set II

A Construction with an Unexpected Result.

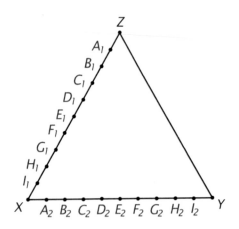

30. Use your ruler to draw a horizontal line segment 5 inches long in the center of a sheet of paper. Label it XY. Construct equilateral triangle XYZ having XY as its base. Use your ruler to mark points on XY 0.5 inch apart; do the same on XZ. Label the points as shown in the figure above.

Now use your straightedge to draw line segments between the points labeled with the same letter (that is, A_1A_2, B_1B_2, etc.)

Something should now appear to be in the figure that isn't really there.

31. What is it?

The finished figure contains many pairs of congruent triangles.

32. To which triangle is $\triangle XA_1A_2$ congruent?

33. How do you know that these triangles are congruent?

Stair Design. In his book *On Architecture,* Vitruvius suggested using steps that are 3 units high, are 4 units wide, and cover a slant distance of 5 units.

34. Use your straightedge to draw a line at the top of a sheet of paper and your

compass to mark off 5 equal units as shown in the figure below.

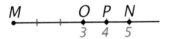

Label your figure as shown and copy the lengths 3, 4, and 5 as needed to do the following construction.

Starting with a side 4 units long, construct near the upper left of your paper a triangle whose other sides are 3 and 5 units long ($\triangle ABC$ as shown in the figure below).

Extend line AC and construct $\triangle CDE$ and $\triangle EFG$ congruent to $\triangle ABC$ as shown in the figure.

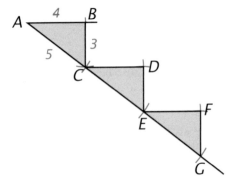

35. What kind of triangles do the triangles appear to be?

36. How do you know that they are congruent?

Suppose a staircase of 16 steps having this design goes up 10 feet between floors.

37. Find the height and width of each step in inches.

38. What horizontal distance will the stairs cover?

Guitar Frets. In 1743, a Swedish craftsman without mathematical training developed an accurate construction for locating the frets on a guitar.*

———————————

Another Fine Math You've Got Me Into . . . , by Ian Stewart (W. H. Freeman and Company, 1992).

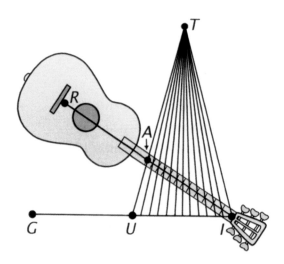

The straightedge and compass have long been used to create all kinds of elaborate designs. The drawing below is based on seven circles.

Although the construction requires just a straightedge and compass, we will start with a ruler to speed up the work. Refer to the figure above and the following directions to do the construction.

39. First, use your ruler to draw a line segment GI 12 cm long and label its midpoint U. Divide UI into 12 equal segments, each 0.5 cm long.

    Put the ruler aside and use your straightedge and compass to do the following.

    Using UI as one side, construct △TUI so that TU = TI = GI. Draw line segments between T and the equally spaced points along UI. Use your scale on UI to set your compass at 3.5 cm. Find A on UT so that UA = 3.5 cm. Draw line segment IA and extend it to R so that AR = IA. If IR is the length of the guitar string, the points of intersection between I and A mark the positions of the 11 frets between I and A.

40. What do you notice about the spacing of the frets along the fingerboard?

The circles suggest how the drawing can be constructed with a straightedge and compass.

1. Use these tools to try to make as accurate an enlargement of the drawing as you can.

How many of each of the following polygons appear to be in the drawing?

2. Squares.

3. Equilateral triangles.

4. Isosceles triangles that are not equilateral.

CHAPTER 4 Summary and Review

Basic Ideas

Postulates

5. *The ASA Postulate.* If two angles and the included side of one triangle are equal to two angles and the included side of another triangle, the triangles are congruent.   147

6. *The SAS Postulate.* If two sides and the included angle of one triangle are equal to two sides and the included angle of another triangle, the triangles are congruent.   147

Theorems

Corollary to the definition of congruent triangles. Two triangles congruent to a third triangle are congruent to each other.   141

9. If two sides of a triangle are equal, the angles opposite them are equal.   158

Corollary. An equilateral triangle is equiangular.   159

10. If two angles of a triangle are equal, the sides opposite them are equal.   159

Corollary. An equiangular triangle is equilateral.   159

11. *The SSS Theorem.* If the three sides of one triangle are equal to the three sides of another triangle, the triangles are congruent.   164

Constructions

1. To bisect a line segment.   23
2. To bisect an angle.   23
3. To copy a line segment.   170
4. To copy an angle.   170
5. To copy a triangle.   171

Exercises

Set I

Polar-Bear Pattern. This polar-bear symbol was designed by François Brisse for the Northwest Territories of Canada.*

At first glance, the outline of the bear appears to be a polygon.

1. Look carefully at the outline to tell why it is not.

It is reasonable to say that the bears in the figure below are congruent, even though they are not polygons.

2. Why?

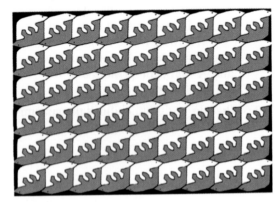

Canadian Mineralogist, vol. 19, 1981, as reported in *Symmetry: A Unifying Concept,* by István Hargittai and Magdolna Hargittai (Shelter Publications, 1994).

3. What is unusual about the arrangement of the bears?

Turkish Geometry. The following figures appear in a Turkish geometry book.

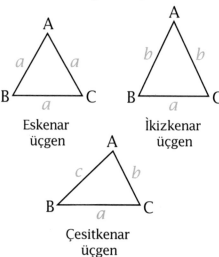

Eskenar
üçgen

İkizkenar
üçgen

Çesitkenar
üçgen

What do you know about the angles of

4. an eskenar üçgen?

5. an ikizkenar üçgen, assuming that $a \neq b$?

6. a çesitkenar üçgen?

From Euclid. Among the statements near the beginning of Euclid's *Elements* are the following ones:

(1) Things that are equal to the same thing are also equal to each other.

(2) Things that coincide with one another are equal to each other.

(3) A scalene triangle is that which has its three sides unequal.

(4) If in a triangle two angles are equal, the sides that are opposite the equal angles will also be equal.

7. Which one of these statements is a definition?

8. Which statement is one of our theorems?

9. What is the difference between a postulate and a theorem?

The first statement might be written in symbols as "If $a = b$ and $c = b$, then $a = c$."

10. From which property of equality can we draw the same conclusion?

11. In which statement does the word "equal" seem to mean "congruent"?

Angles of Repose. If a grainy material is poured to form a pile, the pile forms an angle with the horizontal called the "angle of repose."

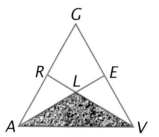

One way to construct this angle for round gravel is illustrated by the figure above, in which $\angle LAV$ is the angle of repose.

12. Use your straightedge and compass to construct the figure by first constructing equilateral $\triangle AVG$ and then bisecting $\angle GAV$ and $\angle GVA$.

13. Why is $\angle GAV = \angle GVA$?

14. Why is $\dfrac{\angle GAV}{2} = \dfrac{\angle GVA}{2}$?

15. Why is $\angle LAV = \angle LVA$?

16. Why is $LA = LV$?

Find the measure of

17. $\angle G$.

18. $\angle LAV$.

19. $\angle ALV$.

20. $\angle GRV$.

21. How large is the angle of repose for round gravel?

The figure at the right illustrates the angle of repose for a pile of coal ashes: $AS = SH$ and $AS \perp SH$.

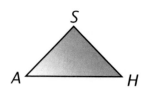

Find the measure of

22. $\angle S$.

23. $\angle A$.

24. Do you think the angles in this figure could be constructed with just a straightedge and compass? Explain why or why not.

Congruence in 3-D. A tetrahedron is a polyhedron that has four triangular faces.

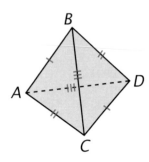

In the tetrahedron above, AB = CD, AC = BD, and AD = BC.

25. Why are the four faces congruent?

26. Why is ∠BAC = ∠BDC?

27. What other angles in the polyhedron are equal to these two angles?

28. Which angles are equal to ∠ABC?

Set II

SAT Problem. The following figure appeared in a problem on an SAT exam. Below it was a note stating that it is drawn inaccurately.

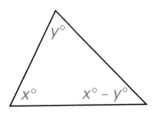

What is the value of *x* if

29. $y = 60$?

30. $y = 75$?

31. $y = 89$?

32. What is strange about this problem?

What must be the value of *y* for the triangle to be

33. isosceles?

34. equilateral?

Lines and Midpoints. The figure below shows four lines that intersect in six points.

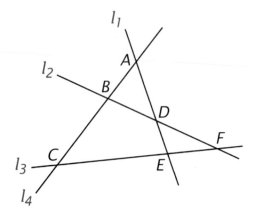

35. Use your straightedge to draw a large figure showing four lines that intersect in a similar way. Draw the line segments AF, BE, and CD and then use your straightedge and compass to construct the midpoints of these three segments.

36. What seems to be true about the three midpoints?

Ollie's Mistake. Obtuse Ollie decided to hide a bag of silver dollars by sinking it in a lake. He took it out in a rowboat and cut a notch in the boat's rim to mark the spot where the bag sank. When he went back to get the gold, Ollie discovered that, *no matter where he went,* the notch in the boat's rim told him that he had found the spot!*

37. On graph paper, draw a pair of axes extending 10 units in each direction from the origin.
     Suppose that, in looking for his money, Ollie took his boat first to A(0, 3) and then to B(−2, −1). Plot these two points.

38. How far is point B from point A?

---

*Based on a story in The Geometry Toolbox for Graphics and Modeling, by Gerald E. Farin and Dianne Hansford (A. K. Peters, 1998).

Suppose points A and B are each actually 5 units from the location of Ollie's money.

37. *(continued)* On your drawing, use your compass to draw two circles with radii of 5, one circle centered at A and the other at B.

39. How many points are 5 units from both points A and B?

Where is Ollie's money if it is in

40. the second quadrant?

41. the fourth quadrant?

Suppose the boat started from a dock located at the point (3, 8) and that Ollie's money is at the closer of the two points A and B.

42. Where is the money?

Rigid Structures. These photographs of a rock in Sweden show ancient carvings of a sled or boat.*

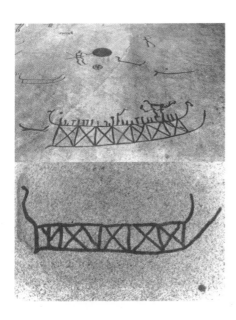

The Xs in the squares are braces added to make the structures rigid.

———————

*Cat's Paws and Catapults: Mechanical Worlds of Nature and People, by Steven Vogel (Norton, 1998).

Although a square can be made rigid with two braces, one is sufficient because one brace is *enough to form triangles.*

43. Draw a pentagon and just enough braces to make it rigid.

Make the same type of drawing for

44. a hexagon.

45. an octagon.

How many braces are enough to make

46. a decagon rigid?

47. an *n*-gon rigid?

Pool Proof. In the figure below, a pool player wants to hit a ball at A so that it banks off the cushion at B and hits the ball at C. Point D is an imaginary point outside the table at which the player aims.

48. Tell the reasons for the statements in the following proof about the path of the ball.

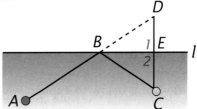

Given: A-B-D; DE = EC, and DC ⊥ *l.*
Prove: AB + BC = AD.

Proof

Statements	Reasons
1. A-B-D.	Why?
2. AB + BD = AD.	Why?
3. DE = EC and DC ⊥ *l*	Why?
4. ∠1 and ∠2 are right angles.	Why?
5. ∠1 = ∠2.	Why?
6. BE = BE.	Why?
7. △DBE ≅ △CBE.	Why?
8. BD = BC.	Why?
9. AB + BC = AD.	Why?

Masonic Tools. If asked which tool in this Masonic emblem could be used to bisect an angle, most people would probably choose the compass.

49. Use the figure below to explain how the carpenter's square could be used instead.

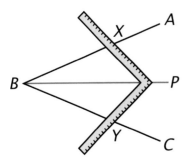

Suppose that, after the angle has been bisected, the carpenter's square is taken away. If a line is drawn through X and Y, then it must be perpendicular to BP.

50. Use the figure below to explain why.

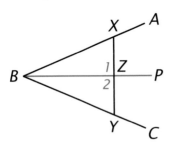

Write complete proofs for the following. In each case, copy the figure and mark the given information on it. Also copy the "given" and "prove" before writing your statements and reasons.

51.

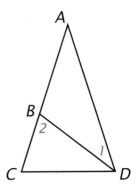

Given: ∠A = ∠1 and ∠2 = ∠C.
Prove: AB = CD.

52.

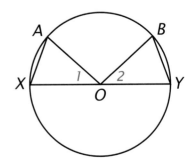

Given: O is the midpoint of XY;
       ∠1 = ∠2 and OA = OB.
Prove: ∠A = ∠B.

Factoring Polynomials

Factoring reverses the operation of multiplication. The distributive rule shows the *multiplication* of a and $b + c$.

$$a(b + c) = ab + ac.$$

Reversing this operation on $ab + ac$, we get

$$ab + ac = a(b + c).$$

We have factored a out of $ab + ac$ by using the distributive rule in reverse. Taking the greatest common factor gives the simplest remaining expression, as seen below.

Example 1: Factor $5x + 20y - 10$.
Solution: The greatest common factor of the three terms is 5.
$5x + 20y - 10 = 5(x + 4y - 2)$.

Example 2: Factor $20x^2 + 36x$.
Solution: The greatest common factor of the two terms is $4x$.
$20x^2 + 36x = 4x(5x + 9)$.

When two polynomials such as $x + 3$ and $x + 8$ are multiplied, the result is a polynomial whose terms have no common factor:

$$(x + 3)(x + 8) = x^2 + 11x + 24.$$

To see how to reverse this operation (that is, factor $x^2 + 11x + 24$), we have to find two factors of 24 whose sum is 11. The general case makes the reason for finding these numbers more obvious:

$$(x + a)(x + b) = x^2 + bx + ax + ab = x^2 + (a + b)x + ab.$$

Example 3: Factor $x^2 + 2x - 35$.
Solution: The last term, -35, can be factored into 7 and -5; $7 + -5 = 2$.
So $x^2 + 2x - 35 = (x + 7)(x - 5)$.

The next examples illustrate how to extend this process.

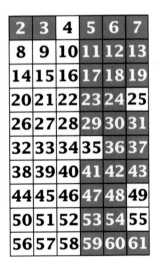

What do the numbers in the green boxes have in common? What do the numbers in the red boxes have in common? Why, except for the first two, do the red boxes appear only in the fourth and sixth columns?

Example 4:   Factor $2x^2 + 11x + 9$.
Solution: The first term, $2x^2$, can be factored into $2x$ and x; so
$$2x^2 + 11x + 9 = (2x + \quad)(x + \quad).$$
The last term can be factored into 3 and 3 or 1 and 9.
By trial and error, we write:
$(2x + 3)(x + 3) = 2x^2 + 9x + 9.$ (No.)
$(2x + 1)(x + 9) = 2x^2 + 19x + 9.$ (No.)
$(2x + 9)(x + 1) = 2x^2 + 11x + 9.$ (Yes.)
So, $2x^2 + 11x + 9 = (2x + 9)(x + 1).$

Example 5:   Factor $4x^2 - 28x - 120$.
Solution: All three terms of this polynomial have a common factor of 4, so we factor it out first:
$4(x^2 - 7x - 30).$
Factoring x^2 into x and x, we write:
$4(x\ )(x\ ).$
Looking at the factors of 30, we have 1 and 30, 2 and 15, 3 and 10, and 5 and 6.
Observing that the factors 3 and 10 have a difference of 7, we write:
$4(x + 3)(x - 10).$
So, $4x^2 - 28x - 120 = 4(x + 3)(x - 10).$

Exercises

Factor.

1. $6x - 2$
2. $6x - 3$
3. $6x - 4$
4. $4x + 12y$
5. $x^2 + 10x$
6. $3x^3 - 2x^2$
7. $15\pi - 40$
8. $8x + 2xy$
9. $ax + bx - cx$
10. $2\pi rh + 2\pi r^2$
11. $x^2 + 8x + 16$
12. $x^2 - 16$
13. $x^2 + 13x + 30$

14. $x^2 + 13x - 30$
15. $x^2 + x - 42$
16. $2x^2 - 15x + 7$
17. $3x^2 + x - 10$
18. $x^2 - 4xy$
19. $x^2 - 4xy + 4y^2$
20. $x^2 - 4y^2$
21. $\pi a^2 - \pi r^2$
22. $5x^3 - 20x$
23. $x^3 + x^2 - 12x$
24. $2xz - 3z$
25. $2x(x + 2) - 3(x + 2)$

Chapter 5

Inequalities

Which boxer is taller?

So far in our study of geometry, we have paid most of our attention to line segments and angles that are equal. The word "equal," in fact, has appeared in almost every theorem that we have proved. In this chapter, we turn to comparisons of line segments and angles that are not equal. Again, the emphasis is on the properties of triangles. Our survey concludes with one of the simplest, yet most useful, ideas of geometry, the Triangle Inequality Theorem.

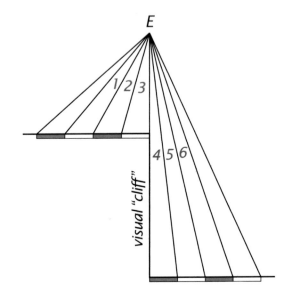

visual "cliff"

LESSON 1

Properties of Inequality

Are we born with the ability to tell which things are close and which are far away, or do we learn it? Two psychologists at Cornell University, Eleanor Gibson and Richard Walk, did an interesting experiment to answer this question. The kitten in the photograph above is sitting on a strip in the middle of a large sheet of glass. Behind the kitten is a floor directly underneath the glass; in front of it is another floor several feet below the glass. Even when a kitten is just old enough to move about, it is afraid to move off the "cliff" to the "deep" side. Chicks and baby goats just 1 day old and human infants just old enough to crawl behave exactly the same way.*

*Perception, by Irvin Rock (Scientific American Library, 1984).

The figure to the right of the photograph shows geometrically the difference in appearance between the two sides of the visual cliff. If point E represents the viewer's eye, the angles of the equal squares are unequal and there is a sudden change in their size at the edge of the cliff. This difference is a visual cue that helps give a sense of depth.

Looking at the numbered angles, we see that $\angle 3$ is larger than $\angle 4$, which we can write as $\angle 3 > \angle 4$. Or, to indicate that $\angle 4$ is less than $\angle 3$, we can write $\angle 4 < \angle 3$. Comparing the sizes of the angles on either side of the cliff, we can write $\angle 1 < \angle 2 < \angle 3$ and $\angle 4 > \angle 5 > \angle 6$.

So far in our study of geometry, we have paid a lot of attention to equalities between line segments and equalities between angles. In fact, nearly every theorem that we have proved has had the word "equal" in it. In this chapter we will consider several important theorems dealing with inequalities, including one of the most basic ideas in all of geometry, the "triangle inequality" theorem.

We begin by adding some assumptions about inequality to our list of axioms from algebra.* As before, these assumptions are stated symbolically, the letters representing real numbers. They also have names by which you may refer to them.

The "Three Possibilities" Property
Either $a > b$, $a = b$, or $a < b$.

The Transitive Property[†]
If $a > b$ and $b > c$, then $a > c$.

The Addition Property[†]
If $a > b$, then $a + c > b + c$.

The Subtraction Property[†]
If $a > b$, then $a - c > b - c$.

The Multiplication Property
If $a > b$ and $c > 0$, then $ac > bc$.

The Division Property
If $a > b$ and $c > 0$, then $\dfrac{a}{c} > \dfrac{b}{c}$.

To this list of assumptions, we add two more properties that follow from them.

The Addition Theorem of Inequality[†]
If $a > b$ and $c > d$, then $a + c > b + d$.

The "Whole Greater than Part" Theorem
If $a > 0$, $b > 0$, and $a + b = c$, then $c > a$ and $c > b$.

---

*Chapter 3, Lesson 1.
[†]This property and the others marked with a dagger are expressed in terms of the symbol $>$ but are equally valid in terms of the symbol $<$.

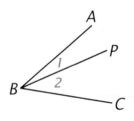

The "whole greater than part" theorem comes from Euclid. Near the beginning of the *Elements*, he states:

The whole is greater than the part.

In the figure at the left, BA-BP-BC; so ∠1 + ∠2 = ∠ABC. The measures of these angles are positive numbers; so we have the "obvious" and easily proved conclusions that ∠ABC > ∠1 and ∠ABC > ∠2. The "whole greater than part" theorem will be considered in an exercise in this lesson.

Exercises

Set I

Hat Illusion. This figure is a remarkable optical illusion.*

1. If the height of the hat is *h* and the width of its brim is *w*, how might *h* and *w* be related?

2. Which one of the properties of inequality does exercise 1 illustrate?

3. Without measuring anything, how do you think *h* and *w* compare?

4. Use your ruler to measure each distance to the nearest 0.1 cm.

Pecking Order. One chicken will peck another if both want the same grain of food.

5. If hen A always pecks hen B and hen B always pecks hen C, what conclusion might follow?

6. Which property of inequality is a "pecking order" like?

Equalities and Inequalities. Name the property of equality or inequality illustrated by each of the following statements:

7. Either $\pi > 3.14$, $\pi = 3.14$, or $\pi < 3.14$.

*From *The Snark Puzzle Book,* by Martin Gardner (Simon & Schuster, 1973).

8. Because $\pi < \dfrac{22}{7}$, $7\pi < 22$.

9. If ∠A + ∠B = 90°, then ∠B = 90° − ∠A.

10. If ∠B = 90° − ∠A and ∠A < ∠B, then ∠A < 90° − ∠A.

11. If ∠A < 90° − ∠A, then 2∠A < 90°.

12. If 2∠A < 90°, then ∠A < 45°.

Deceiving Appearances. Although the triangles below may appear to be equilateral and congruent, they are not.

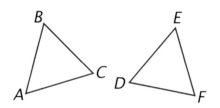

In △ABC, AB > AC and AC = BC.

13. What kind of triangle is △ABC?

14. What can you conclude about AB and BC?

15. Why?

In △DEF, DF < EF and EF < DE.

16. What kind of triangle is △DEF?

17. What can you conclude about DF and DE?

18. Why?

19. Why aren't the triangles congruent?

Perspective Inequalities. When you look up at a tall building from the ground, the floors look progressively shorter.

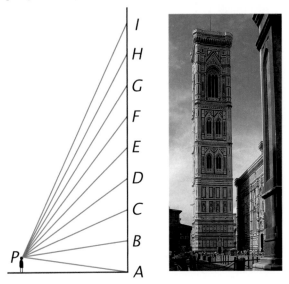

Look carefully at the figure at the left above to tell what symbol should replace the question mark in each of the following statements. (Base your answers on appearances.)

20. AB = HI but ∠APB ? ∠HPI.

21. BC = CD but ∠BPC ? ∠CPD.

22. ∠PIH ? ∠PBA.

23. ∠PHG ? ∠PGF.

24. ∠PHI ? ∠PGH and ∠PGH ? ∠PFG; so ∠PHI ? ∠PFG.

In the fourteenth century, the Italian artist and architect Giotto designed a tower, the campanile in Florence, in which the upper levels are successively taller.

25. Why do you suppose he designed the tower in this way?

Set II

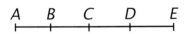

SAT Problem. The figure above appeared in a problem on an SAT exam. The points are spaced on the line so that AB < BC < CD < DE.

All of the following statements, except for one, *must* be true. Either tell why each statement must be true or identify it as the one that could be false.

26. AB < CD and BC < DE.

27. AB + BC < CD + DE.

28. AC < CE.

29. AD > DE.

30. BD > BC.

31. AB < BD.

Scalene Triangle. The following exercises are about the sides and angles of a scalene triangle.

32. Use your ruler to draw and label three line segments of the following lengths: *a* = 12 cm, *b* = 10 cm, and *c* = 8 cm.

33. Use your straightedge and compass to construct a triangle having sides of these lengths. Label the sides *a*, *b*, and *c*. Label the angles A, B, and C so that ∠A is opposite side *a*, ∠B is opposite side *b*, and ∠C is opposite side *c*.

34. Use your protractor to measure each angle as accurately as you can.

35. List the names of the angles in order of size from largest to smallest.

36. Do you think that the order of the angles could have been predicted from the order of the sides? If so, how?

Rectangle Inequalities. The figure below is a rectangle.

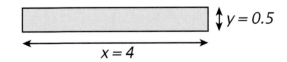

37. What is its perimeter?

38. If $x > 0$, $y > 0$, and $p = 2x + 2y$, does it follow that $p > 2x$? Why or why not?

39. What is the rectangle's area?

40. If $x > 0$, $y > 0$, and $a = xy$, does it follow that $a > x$? Explain.

PEANUTS reprinted by permission of United Feature Syndicate.

Vertical Lines and Angles. The word *vertical* is used in two different ways in geometry.

41. What does it mean to say that a line is vertical?

There are no vertical lines in the figure below and yet it seems to contain two pairs of vertical angles. The word *vertical* in "vertical angles" comes from the fact that they have the same *vertex*.

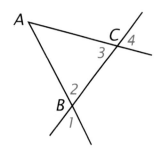

42. What else must be true for two angles to be vertical angles?

In the figure, AB = AC, $\angle 1 < \angle 3$, and $\angle 2 = \angle 4$.

43. Is it possible to draw any definite conclusion about whether $\angle 1$ and $\angle 2$ are vertical angles? Explain your reasoning.

44. Is it possible to draw any definite conclusion about whether $\angle 3$ and $\angle 4$ are vertical angles? Explain your reasoning.

Use the properties of inequality in this lesson to complete the following proofs.

45. *The Addition Theorem of Inequality.*
If $a > b$ and $c > d$, then $a + c > b + d$.

Proof

Statements	Reasons
1. $a > b$.	Why?
2. $a + c > b + c$.	Why?
3. $c > d$.	Why?
4. $b + c > b + d$.	Why?
5. $a + c > b + d$.	Why?

46. *The "Whole Greater than Part" Theorem.*
If $a > 0$, $b > 0$, and $a + b = c$, then $c > a$ and $c > b$.

Proof

Statements	Reasons
1. $a > 0$ (and $b > 0$).	Why?
2. $a + b > b$ (and $a + b > a$).	Why?
3. $a + b = c$.	Why?
4. $c > b$ (and $c > a$).	Why?

Optics Figure. In the following figure from Euclid's *Optics,* an eye at point E is looking at two equal lengths, AB and CD.

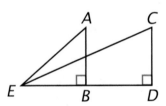

Give the reasons for the following proof that, although AB = CD, ∠AEB > ∠CED.

47. *Given:* EA-EC-ED.
    Prove: ∠AED > ∠CED.

Proof

Statements	Reasons
1. EA-EC-ED.	Why?
2. ∠AED = ∠AEC + ∠CED.	Why?
3. ∠AEC > 0.	Why?
4. ∠AED > ∠CED.	Why?

Write a complete proof for the following.

48.

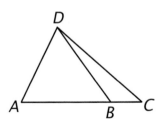

Given: A-B-C; ∠ADB = ∠DAB.
Prove: AC > DB.

Set III

The following statements appear in a book on psychology.*

(1) If A > B and B > C, then A > C.
(2) If A = B and B = C, then A = C.
(3) If A = B and C > 0, then A + C > B.

Although they appear to be about numbers, they are actually rules about making choices. In them, the symbol > means that you prefer one object over another and = means that you have no preference between them.
    Suppose A, B, and C represent the following objects respectively: an apple, a banana, and a cookie.

1. Tell what the first rule says in regard to these objects.

2. Which of our properties of inequality is represented by the same symbols?

3. Tell what the second rule says in regard to these objects.

4. Which of our properties of equality is the basis for knowing that this pattern is true for numbers?

5. Tell what the third rule says in regard to these objects.

6. Is the third rule true if A, B, and C represent numbers and = and > mean "equal" and "greater than"? If you think so, prove it. If not, give an example to show why not.

Human Information Processing: An Introduction to Psychology, by Peter H. Lindsay and Donald A. Norman (Harcourt Brace Jovanovich, 1977).

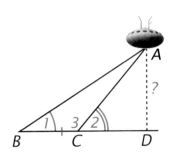

LESSON 2

The Exterior Angle Theorem

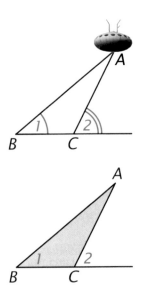

Imagine a UFO (unidentified flying object) hovering in the sky. Observers below wonder how big it is and how high it is above them. They can find its elevation by using some simple geometry. The diagram above shows how.

The observers measure the UFO's angles of elevation as seen from two positions: ∠1 and ∠2 in the diagram. If the distance between the observers is known, then in △ABC we know the measures of ∠1, BC, and ∠3 (the supplement of ∠2). The size and shape of the triangle are therefore determined by ASA. A scale drawing of the figure can be made and the distance AD can then be measured.

If the UFO moves to the position shown in the second diagram, △ABC changes in size and shape because both ∠1 and ∠2 get larger. In each figure, ∠2 seems to be larger than ∠1. Strange as it may seem, ∠2 is *always* larger, no matter where the UFO happens to be! We can prove it by using congruent triangles and inequalities.

The basic reason is that ∠1 is "in" the triangle and ∠2 is "outside" it. We will call ∠1 an *interior* angle of △ABC to distinguish it from the *exterior* angles of △ABC, of which ∠2 is an example.

Definition

An *exterior angle of a triangle* is an angle that forms a linear pair with an angle of the triangle.

In △ABC on page 190, exterior ∠2 forms a linear pair with ∠ACB. The other two angles of the triangle ∠1(∠B) and ∠A are called *remote interior angles* with respect to ∠2. Regardless of the position of point A, we can prove that ∠2 > ∠1 and ∠2 > ∠A.

Theorem 12. The Exterior Angle Theorem

An exterior angle of a triangle is greater than either remote interior angle.

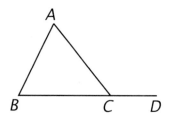

> *Given:* ∠ACD is an exterior angle of △ABC.
> *Prove:* ∠ACD > ∠A and ∠ACD > ∠B.

Our proof, that of Euclid, begins by adding some things to the figure at the right. The additions are shown here in red. In proving that the exterior angle, ∠ACD, is greater than the remote interior angle, ∠A, Euclid saw ∠3 as part of ∠ACD. He read the betweenness of rays CA-CP-CD from the figure. Look at the figure now and see if you can guess Euclid's plan of attack.

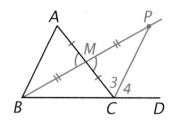

Euclid reasoned that exterior ∠ACD > ∠3 (the whole is greater than the part) and that ∠3 = ∠A because △AMB ≅ △CMP (SAS); so exterior ∠ACD > remote interior ∠A. The following proof in two-column format fills in the details.

Proof

Statements	Reasons
1. ∠ACD is an exterior angle of △ABC.	Given.
2. Let M be the midpoint of AC.	A line segment has exactly one midpoint.
3. AM = MC.	The midpoint of a line segment divides it into two equal segments.
4. Draw line BM.	Two points determine a line.
5. Choose P on line BM so that BM = MP.	The Ruler Postulate.
6. Draw CP.	Two points determine a line.
7. ∠AMB = ∠CMP.	Vertical angles are equal.
8. △AMB ≅ △CMP.	SAS.
9. ∠A = ∠3.	Corresponding parts of congruent triangles are equal.
10. ∠ACD = ∠3 + ∠4.	Betweenness of Rays Theorem.
11. ∠ACD > ∠3.	"Whole Greater than Part" Theorem.
12. ∠ACD > ∠A.	Substitution.

The other conclusion, that ∠ACD > ∠B, can be proved in a similar way by adding some more things to the figure. We will consider how in one of the exercises.

Exercises

Set I

Garage Door. One type of design for a garage door is shown in the following figures.*

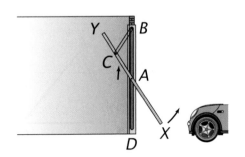

The door XY rotates as a pin at A moves up or down a vertical channel BD; CA = CB = CY.

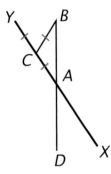

1. Name all of the angles in the figure that are exterior angles to △ABC.

What happens to the size of each of the following angles as the door is being opened?

2. ∠DAX.

3. ∠BAX.

4. ∠BCA.

5. As the door moves and △ABC changes shape, why is ∠B always equal to ∠BAY?

6. Why is ∠BCY always larger than ∠BAY?

7. Why are ∠BAY and ∠DAX always equal?

8. In what way are the measures of ∠B and ∠DAX always related? Explain.

Mathematics Meets Technology, by Brian Bolt (Cambridge University Press, 1991).

Exterior Angles. The sides of the acute triangle at the right have been extended to form its exterior angles.

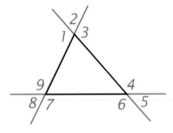

9. Which of the numbered angles in the figure are *not* exterior angles of the triangle?

How many exterior angles does a triangle have

10. at one vertex?

11. altogether?

Is it possible that all of the triangle's exterior angles could be

12. equal? Explain.

13. unequal? Explain.

14. Draw a right triangle and extend its sides to form all of its exterior angles. Mark the exterior angles with arcs.

15. Draw an obtuse triangle and do the same.

Reasoning from the figure above and the two figures that you have drawn, how many exterior angles of a triangle can be

16. acute?

17. right?

18. obtuse?

Rainbow. Aristotle used the figure below in trying to explain the rainbow.†

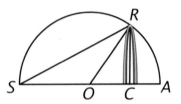

---

†*The Rainbow: From Myth to Mathematics,* by Carl B. Boyer (Princeton University Press, 1987).

The sun is on the horizon at S, a cloud is at R, and the observer is at O. The points S, O, C, and A are collinear.

19. Of which triangle is ∠ROA an exterior angle?

20. Write the two inequalities that follow from this fact.

21. Of which triangle is ∠ROS an exterior angle?

22. Write the two inequalities that follow from this fact.

23. Of which *two* triangles is ∠RCA an exterior angle?

24. Write the four inequalities that follow from this fact.

25. Is ∠ORC an exterior angle of △ROS? Explain why or why not.

Lines and Angles. The figure below shows three intersecting lines.

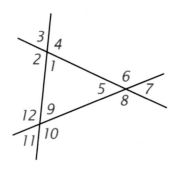

Find each of the following sums.

26. ∠1 + ∠2 + ∠3 + ∠4.

27. ∠1 + ∠2 + ∠3 + ∠4 + ∠5 + ∠6 + ∠7 + ∠8 + ∠9 + ∠10 + ∠11 + ∠12.

28. ∠1 + ∠5 + ∠9.

29. ∠3 + ∠7 + ∠11.

30. ∠2 + ∠4 + ∠6 + ∠8 + ∠10 + ∠12.

31. What does the result obtained in exercise 30 indicate about the sum of the exterior angles of a triangle?

Set II

Exterior Angle Theorem. This figure illustrates how the proof of the Exterior Angle Theorem can be completed. In it, line AC has been extended to E.

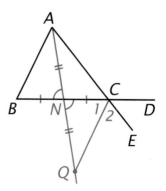

32. Why can N be chosen as the midpoint of BC?

33. Why can Q be chosen so that AN = NQ?

34. Why is △BNA ≅ △CNQ?

35. Why is ∠B = ∠1?

36. Why is ∠ACD = ∠BCE?

37. Why is ∠BCE > ∠1?

38. Why are ∠BCE > ∠B and ∠ACD > ∠B?

Angle Sum. After proving the Exterior Angle Theorem, Euclid proved that, in any triangle, the sum of any two angles is less than 180°.

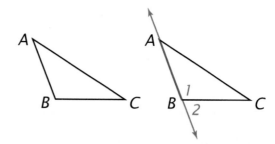

Prove that, in △ABC, ∠A + ∠B < 180° by giving a reason for each of the following statements.

39. Draw line AB.

40. ∠2 is an exterior angle of △ABC.

41. ∠1 and ∠2 are supplementary.

42. ∠1 + ∠2 = 180°.

43. ∠2 > ∠A.

44. ∠1 + ∠2 > ∠1 + ∠A.

45. 180° > ∠1 + ∠A, so ∠A + ∠1 < 180°.

Angle in a Triangle. Suppose a triangle of any shape is drawn and a point is marked inside it. If line segments are drawn from this point to two of the vertices, the angle formed always seems to be larger than the angle at the third vertex of the triangle.

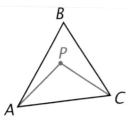

46. Copy the figure and extend the line AP to intersect side BC at point X.

47. Use the resulting figure to explain why ∠APC is larger than ∠B.

Proclus's Proof. Proclus, a Greek philosopher and mathematician of the fifth century, proved that it is impossible to draw from a point to a line more than two line segments of the same length. In other words, in the figure at the left below, it is impossible that PA = PB = PC.

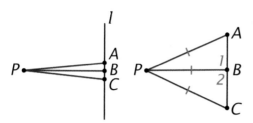

Use the second figure, which has been drawn so as to make the angles in it easier to see, to explain the following steps in Proclus's argument.

48. Suppose PA = PB = PC. Then ∠A = ∠1, ∠2 = ∠C, and ∠A = ∠C. Why?

49. What equations follow from these equations by substitution?

50. What do they contradict?

51. What kind of proof has Proclus used to show that it is impossible that PA = PB = PC?

Set III

Drumhead Geometry. Drumheads were once used to measure angles of elevation to find distances! This figure from the sixteenth century shows them being used to find the height of a tower.*

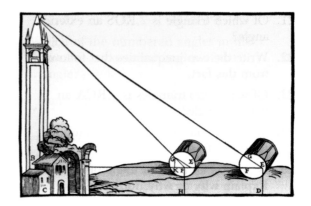

Make a scale drawing of the figure by doing the following.

1. Draw a horizontal line and mark two points 2 inches apart to represent the drumheads. Use your protractor to draw two angles of elevation measuring 45° and 34° so that their sides intersect at the point marking the top of the tower.

2. Measure the height of the tower in your drawing in inches.

3. If the two drums are 40 feet apart, how high is the tower?

_____

History of Mathematics, by David Eugene Smith (Ginn, 1923; reprint, Dover, 1958).

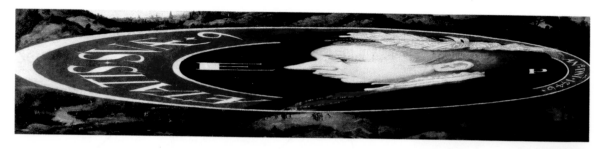

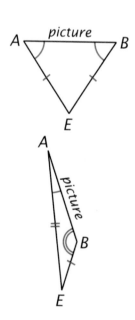

LESSON 3

Triangle Side and Angle Inequalities

As artists during the Renaissance began to master perspective, some of them began to play tricks with it. The strange-looking portrait above of Edward VI, one of the kings of England, is an example. The artist has painted it in a peculiar perspective so that it is almost unrecognizable when viewed from the front. When viewed from a certain spot in the edge of its frame, however, the perspective is such that the distortion disappears and the portrait looks normal, as seen at the right.

Artists usually paint pictures to be viewed as shown in the first diagram at the right. The diagram shows the top edge of the picture, AB, and the eyes, E, seen from overhead. If the viewer's eyes are centered with respect to the edges of the picture, EA = EB. The triangle ABE, then, is isosceles and so $\angle A = \angle B$.

The second diagram shows how the artist intended the painting of Edward VI to be viewed. The viewer has to look at the picture from a point much closer to one edge than the other: EA > EB. The angles at A and B have changed as well: now $\angle B > \angle A$. The larger angle, $\angle B$, is opposite the longer side, EA.

This relation of unequal sides and unequal angles holds true for all triangles.

Theorem 13

If two sides of a triangle are unequal, the angles opposite them are unequal in the same order.

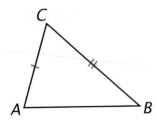 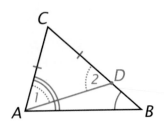

Given: △ABC with BC > AC.
Prove: ∠A > ∠B.

Like many of the proofs in this book, this one follows Euclid's. The shorter side, AC, is copied along the longer side CB as CD. AD is then drawn to form an isosceles triangle. Study the figure carefully and you may discover Euclid's plan before reading any further.

Euclid's proof is based on observing that ∠CAB > ∠1 and ∠1 = ∠2; so ∠CAB > ∠2. But ∠2 > ∠B; so ∠CAB > ∠B. Here is the proof in two-column format.

Proof

Statements	Reasons
1. △ABC with BC > AC.	Given.
2. Choose D on CB so that CD = CA.	The Ruler Postulate.
3. Draw AD.	Two points determine a line.
4. ∠1 = ∠2.	If two sides of a triangle are equal, the angles opposite them are equal.
5. ∠CAB = ∠1 + ∠DAB.	Betweenness of Rays Theorem (AC-AD-AB).
6. ∠CAB > ∠1.	"Whole Greater than Part" Theorem.
7. ∠CAB > ∠2.	Substitution.
8. ∠2 > ∠B.	An exterior angle of a triangle is greater than either remote interior angle.
9. ∠CAB > ∠B.	Transitive.

Just as the converse of the isosceles triangle theorem is true, so the converse of this theorem is true.

Theorem 14

If two angles of a triangle are unequal, the sides opposite them are unequal in the same order.

Exercises

Set I

The symbol at the right is sometimes painted on streets.*

1. What does the symbol mean?
2. Why is it painted in this way?

Theorem 13 says:

If two sides of a triangle are unequal, the angles opposite them are unequal in the same order.

Theorem 14 says:

If two angles of a triangle are unequal, the sides opposite them are unequal in the same order.

3. How are these statements related to each other?

Complete the statements and give the reasons for the following proof of Theorem 14.

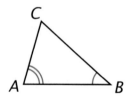

Given: △ABC with ∠A > ∠B.
Prove: BC > AC.

Proof
Suppose that BC is *not* longer than AC.

4. Then either BC = AC or ? .
5. Why?
6. If BC = AC, then ? .
7. Why?
8. This contradicts the hypothesis *(given)* that ? .
9. If BC < AC, then ? .

Can You Believe Your Eyes? by J. R. Blocker and Harold E. Yuker (Brunnel/Mazel, 1992).

10. Why?
11. This also contradicts the hypothesis that ? .
12. Therefore, what we supposed is false and ? .
13. What kind of proof is this?

Triangle Drawing 1. In △ABC (not shown), AB = 6 cm, AC = 8 cm, and BC = 4 cm.

14. Which angle of the triangle must be the largest?
15. Which angle must be the smallest?
16. Use your ruler and compass to construct △ABC.
17. What kind of triangle is it?
18. Use your protractor to measure each of its angles.

Triangle Drawing 2. In △DEF (not shown), DE = 7 cm, ∠D = 50°, ∠E = 40°, and ∠F = 90°.

19. Which side of the triangle must be the longest?
20. Which side must be the shortest?
21. Use your ruler and protractor to draw △DEF.
22. Use your ruler to measure sides DF and EF, each to the nearest 0.1 cm.

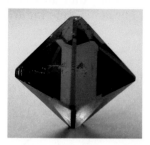

Triangle in Perspective. If a triangle is seen "in perspective," it is hard to tell what kind of triangle it is. An illustration of triangles seen in perspective is the photograph above of a chrome alum crystal, all of whose faces are equilateral triangles.

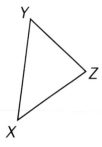

Here is another triangle shown "in perspective." Suppose YZ > XZ and ∠Z > ∠X.

23. What can you conclude about ∠X and ∠Y?

24. Why?

25. What can you conclude about ∠Y and ∠Z?

26. Why?

27. What can you conclude about XY and XZ?

28. Why?

Set II

Folding Experiment. This experiment appeared in an old book titled *First Book of Geometry.**

29. Use your ruler to draw a large triangle similar in shape to the first figure below. Cut the triangle out and then fold the shorter side AB onto the longer side BC as shown in the second figure. The figure at the top of the next column shows the result. After answering the following questions, tape the triangle to your paper.

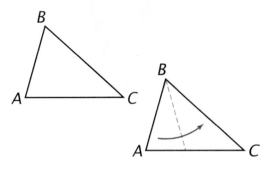

---

*Written by Grace Chisholm Young and W. H. Young and published in London in 1905.

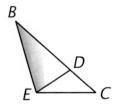

30. On what angle did ∠A fall?

31. In what way is ∠BDE related to △DEC?

32. What does this relation show about how ∠BDE compares with ∠C?

33. What theorem does this experiment illustrate?

Look at this figure.

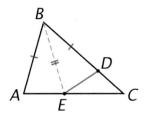

34. What does the fold line BE do to ∠ABC?

35. How can your answer to exercise 34 be used to prove that ∠BDE = ∠A?

Not Quite Equilateral. Here are some pairs of triangles that are almost equilateral but not quite.

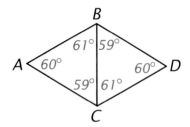

36. Are the triangles in the figure above congruent? Why or why not?

37. Which side of △ABC is longest?

38. Which side of △BCD is longest?

39. What can you conclude about these two line segments? Explain.

198   Chapter 5: Inequalities

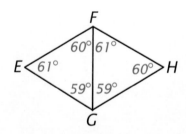

40. In the figure above, which side of △EFG is longest?

41. Which side of △FGH is longest?

42. What can you conclude about these two line segments? Explain.

43. Are these triangles congruent? Why or why not?

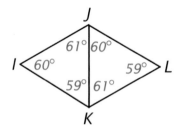

44. Is it possible to decide whether or not the triangles in the figure above are congruent? Explain your reasoning.

In the figure below, △ABC is equilateral.

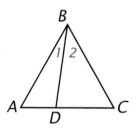

Prove that BD > DC by giving a reason for each of the following statements.

45. ∠C = ∠ABC.

46. ∠ABC = ∠1 + ∠2.

47. ∠ABC > ∠2.

48. ∠C > ∠2.

49. BD > DC.

In the puzzles of the Surfer and the Spotter in the introduction to this book, we assumed that the shortest path from the surfer's house to the beach was along a line perpendicular to the line of the beach.*

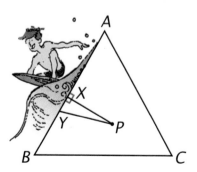

In the figure above, our assumption means that, if PX ⊥ AB, then PY > PX.

50. Explain, by using the geometry that you now know, why this is true. (Hint: Notice that ∠PXA is an exterior angle of △PXY.)

Set III

This message was created by Marvin Miller.†
What does it say?

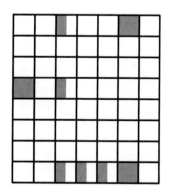

*Introduction, p. 4.
†*Riddles of the Sphinx and Other Mathematical Puzzle Tales,* by Martin Gardner (The Mathematical Association of America, 1987).

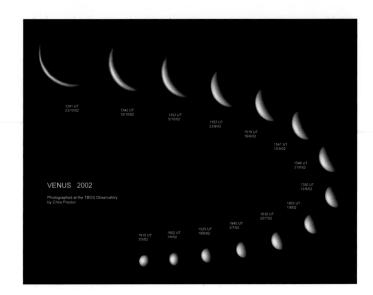

VENUS 2002

Photographed at the TBGS Observatory
by Chris Proctor

The Triangle Inequality Theorem

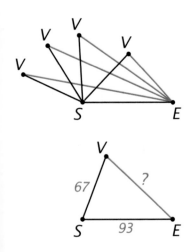

Venus is an interesting planet. Sometimes seen as the "morning star" and sometimes as the "evening star," it is often brighter than any object in the sky except the sun or moon.

The series of photographs above at the same scale show something first noticed by Galileo through his telescope. He saw that Venus has phases, like the moon. But, unlike the moon, Venus at its full phase appears only about a sixth as large as it does at its new phase. Galileo reasoned that, when Venus is in its full phase, it must be much farther from Earth than when it is in its new phase. Let's see how this could be so.

In the figure at the left, points S and E represent the sun and Earth, and the points labeled V represent some positions of Venus. In each sun-Earth-Venus triangle, SE and SV stay about the same, but the length VE changes a lot.

The average distance from the sun to Earth, SE, is 93 million miles; the average distance from the sun to Venus, SV, is 67 million miles. In the sun-Earth-Venus triangle at the left, what can we conclude about the length VE? The Triangle Inequality Theorem tells us that the sum of the lengths of any two sides of a triangle is greater than the length of the third side. From this theorem, we can write the inequalities

$$67 + 93 > VE, \quad 67 + VE > 93, \quad \text{and} \quad 93 + VE > 67.$$

The last of these inequalities doesn't tell us anything about VE, because $93 > 67$. From the other two, we can conclude that

$$160 > VE \quad \text{and} \quad VE > 26.$$

At its farthest, Venus is 160 million miles from Earth, more than six times the distance at its nearest, 26 million miles. This fact explains why the apparent diameter of Venus in its full phase is about a sixth of that in its new phase.

Our proof of the Triangle Inequality Theorem follows Euclid's. Its ingenuity helps explain why the *Elements* is such a significant book and why it is available today, not only in bookstores but also on the Internet!

Theorem 15. The Triangle Inequality Theorem
The sum of any two sides of a triangle is greater than the third side.

Given: ABC is a triangle.
Prove: AB + BC > AC.*

Before reading the proof, see if you can figure out the plan from the figures at the right.

Proof

Statements	Reasons
1. ABC is a triangle.	Given.
2. Draw line AB.	Two points determine a line.
3. Choose D beyond B on line AB so that BD = BC.	The Ruler Postulate.
4. Draw CD.	Two points determine a line.
5. ∠1 = ∠2.	If two sides of a triangle are equal, the angles opposite them are equal.
6. ∠ACD = ∠2 + ∠3.	Betweenness of Rays Theorem (CA-CB-CD).
7. ∠ACD > ∠2.	"Whole Greater than Part" Theorem.
8. ∠ACD > ∠1.	Substitution (steps 5 and 7).
9. In △ACD, AD > AC.	If two angles of a triangle are unequal, the sides opposite them are unequal in the same order.
10. AB + BD = AD.	Betweenness of Points Theorem (A-B-D).
11. AB + BD > AC.	Substitution (steps 9 and 10).
12. AB + BC > AC.	Substitution (steps 3 and 11).

———

*Also, AC + CB > AB and BA + AC > BC. These inequalities can be proved in the same way.

Exercises

Set I

Donkey Sense. Soon after the *Elements* was written, some people made fun of the Triangle Inequality Theorem, saying that it is obvious even to a donkey and needs no proof. They pointed out that, if a hungry donkey were at one corner of a triangle and some hay were put at another corner, the donkey would walk along the side between them rather than along the other two sides.

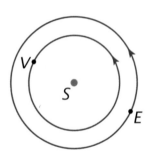

1. State the Triangle Inequality Theorem as a complete sentence.

2. Use it to write the inequality relating the sides of △DPH that the donkey knows.

3. Write the other two inequalities relating the sides of the triangle.

4. If, rather than proving it, Euclid had assumed the theorem to be true, what would it be called?

5. Does *assuming* something to be true explain *why* it is true?

Sun, Earth, and Venus. The sun, Earth, and Venus usually determine a triangle, but sometimes they do not.

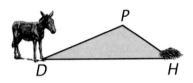

6. What relation exists between three points if they do not determine a triangle?

The average distance from the sun to Earth is 93 million miles; the average distance from the sun to Venus is 67 million miles.

Tell whether or not each of the following situations is possible. In the cases that are possible, find the distance between Earth and Venus.

7. The sun is between Earth and Venus.

8. Venus is between Earth and the sun.

9. Earth is between Venus and the sun.

Spotter Problem. In the puzzle of the Surfer and the Spotter in the introduction to this book, the spotter wanted to go to the corners of the island to look for ships. (Recall that the island is in the shape of an equilateral triangle with sides 12 km long.)

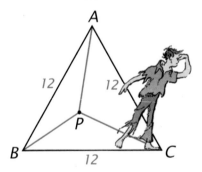

Copy and complete the following inequalities by replacing each question mark with a number.

10. PA + PB > ? , PA + PC > ? , and PB + PC > ? .

11. (PA + PB) + (PA + PC) + (PB + PC) > ? .

12. 2PA + 2PB + 2PC > ? .

13. PA + PB + PC > ? .

14. As long as the spotter builds his shelter at some point within the island, what can you conclude about the sum of the lengths of the paths from his shelter to the corners?

SAT Problem. The following problem appeared on an SAT test.

If x is an integer and $2 < x < 7$, how many different triangles are there with sides of lengths 2, 7, and x?

15. Could $x = 3$? Explain why or why not.

16. What do you think is the answer to the problem? Explain.

Distance and Collinearity. In proving our first theorem, the Betweenness of Points Theorem, we showed that, if A-B-C, then AB + BC = AC.

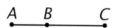

We can now prove that, if AB + BC = AC, then A, B, and C must be collinear.

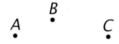

Complete the following steps in the proof.

17. Suppose ?.

If A, B, and C are not collinear, connect them to form △ABC.

18. In △ABC, AB + BC > ? . Why?

19. This contradicts the fact that ? .

20. Therefore, what we assumed is false and ? .

The Third Side. The lengths of two sides of an isosceles triangle are 4 and 9.

21. Is it possible to tell the length of the third side? Explain.

The lengths of two sides of a scalene triangle are 5 and 7.

22. Is it possible to conclude anything at all about the length of the third side? Explain.

The lengths of two sides of a right triangle are 6 and 8.

23. What could be the length of the third side? (Hint: Think of the Pythagorean Theorem.)

Set II

Heron's Proof. Heron, a Greek mathematician who lived after Euclid, created a different proof of the Triangle Inequality Theorem.

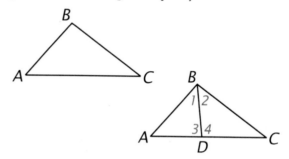

Given: ABC is a triangle.
Prove: AB + BC > AC.

Complete Heron's proof by giving a reason for each of the following statements.

24. Let line BD bisect ∠ABC.

25. ∠1 = ∠2.

26. ∠3 > ∠2 and ∠4 > ∠1.

27. ∠3 > ∠1 and ∠4 > ∠2.

28. AB > AD and BC > DC.

29. AB + BC > AD + DC.

30. AD + DC = AC.

31. AB + BC > AC.

Quadrilateral Inequality. The Triangle Inequality Theorem can be extended to polygons other than triangles.

32. Use this figure to prove that, for quadrilateral ABCD, AB + BC + CD > AD. (Hint: Draw AC.)

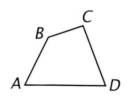

Light Path. Heron used the Triangle Inequality Theorem to show that reflected light follows shortest paths.

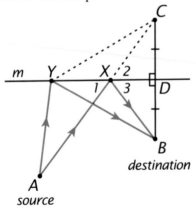

The figure above shows two possible rays of light from a source at point A being reflected by the mirror at a special point X and any other point Y. The light continues to B, its destination.

Some extra lines have been added to the figure for use in the proof: A-X-C, BC ⊥ *m*, and CD = DB. Tell why each of the following statements is true.

33. AY + YC > AC.

34. AX + XC = AC.

35. AY + YC > AX + XC.

36. △CYD ≅ △BYD and △CXD ≅ △BXD.

37. YC = YB and XC = XB.

38. AY + YB > AX + XB.

39. ∠1 = ∠2.

40. ∠2 = ∠3.

41. ∠1 = ∠3.

42. Which statement above shows that the path of the light from A to B is shortest at reflection point X?

43. Which statement shows that the angles of the path from A to X to B are equal?

Work Triangle. In the design of a kitchen, the "work triangle" (a triangle with the refrigerator, stove, and sink as its vertices) should have a perimeter between 6.5 meters and 7.0 meters. The "sink to stove" side of the triangle should be between 1.2 meters and 1.8 meters.*

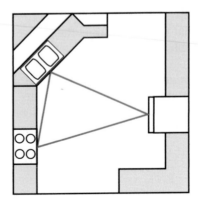

Suppose that, in this kitchen, the perimeter of the work triangle is 7 meters and the "sink to stove" side is 1.5 meters.

44. What is the sum of the other two sides?

45. If *x* represents the length of the refrigerator–sink side of the triangle, what is the length of the refrigerator–stove side in terms of *x?*

46. Draw the "work triangle" and write the three expressions for the lengths of its sides on it.

47. Write and solve the three inequalities for the triangle that follow from the Triangle Inequality Theorem.

48. What can you conclude about what the length of the refrigerator–sink side of the triangle should be?

The Shape of Space: Food Preparation Spaces, by Robin Crane and Malcolm Dixon (Van Nostrand Reinhold, 1990).

Set III

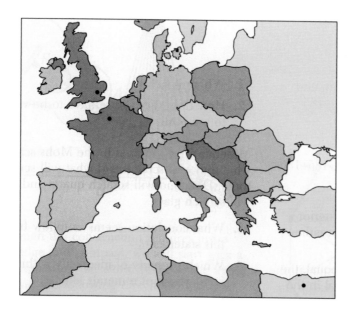

The numbers in the following chart are the distances in miles between four cities, but one of them is wrong.

	Paris	Rome	Cairo
London	214	895	2,185
Paris		590	1,998
Rome			1,326

The triangle below (not to scale) shows London, Paris, and Rome and the distances between them.

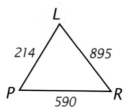

Draw and label triangles for

1. London, Paris, and Cairo.

2. London, Rome, and Cairo.

3. Paris, Rome, and Cairo.

4. Which of the four triangles contradict the Triangle Inequality Theorem? Explain.

5. Which distance in the chart do you suspect is wrong?

CHAPTER 5 Summary and Review

Basic Ideas

Addition, subtraction, multiplication, and
  division properties of inequality   185
Exterior angle of a triangle   191
"Three possibilities" property   185
Transitive property   185
"Whole greater than part" theorem   185–186

Theorems

12. *The Exterior Angle Theorem.* An exterior
    angle of a triangle is greater than either
    remote interior angle.   191

13. If two sides of a triangle are unequal, the
    angles opposite them are unequal in the
    same order.   196

14. If two angles of a triangle are unequal,
    the sides opposite them are unequal in
    the same order.   196

15. *The Triangle Inequality Theorem.* The sum
    of any two sides of a triangle is greater
    than the third side.   201

Exercises

Set I

American puzzle maker Sam Loyd drew this
picture a century ago. It shows the young
George Washington after he had cut down the
cherry tree. The puzzle is to find
Washington's face as he looked when he was
president.

1. Where is he?
2. How does the picture have to be viewed
   to see him?

Minerals are compared in the Mohs scale by
what they will scratch and what will scratch
them. Diamond will scratch quartz and quartz
will scratch glass.

3. What conclusion seems to follow from
   this statement?

4. Which property of inequality is this
   comparison of minerals like?

Gateway Arch. The Gateway Arch in St. Louis
is shown head on in this photograph.

5. Which property of inequality names the
   ways in which its height and width
   might compare?

6. Without measuring, how do you think
   the height of the arch compares with its
   width?

7. Measure its dimensions on the scale
   drawing on page 207 in inches.

8. Use the fact that 1 inch represents 252
   feet in the drawing to find the height
   and width of the Gateway Arch.

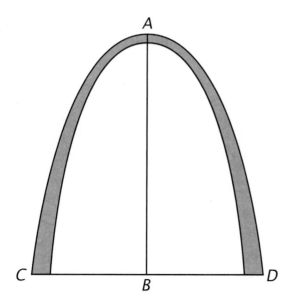

Portuguese Theorem. The following words appear in a Portuguese geometry book:

> *Teorema:* Um ângulo externo de um triângulo é maior do que qualquer dos ângulos internos não adjacentes.

9. What is our name for this theorem?

10. Write it as a complete sentence.

11. What is an "exterior angle"?

What can you conclude about the angles of a triangle if it has an exterior angle that

12. has a measure of 1°?

13. is a right angle?

14. is obtuse?

Soccer Angle. The following description of the goal keeper in soccer is from a book on the Olympics.*

> Keepers utilize their geometry skills in another tactic called "cutting the shooter's angle." The goalie imagines a straight line between himself and the ball and the middle of the goal so the shooter always has an equal amount of goal to shoot at from both sides.

―――――――――

The Science of the Summer Games, by Vincent Mallette (Charles River Media, 1996).

In the figures below, M is the midpoint of LR, and points K and S represent the positions of the keeper and the shooter.

In this figure, the shooter is "centered" so that SL = SR.

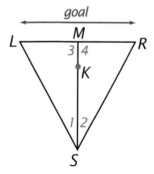

15. Draw the figure and mark it as needed to give a reason for each of the following statements.

16. LM = MR.

17. SM = SM.

18. △SML ≅ △SMR.

19. ∠1 = ∠2 and ∠3 = ∠4.

20. SM ⊥ LR.

In the figure below, the shooter is closer to the left side of the goal so that SL < SR.

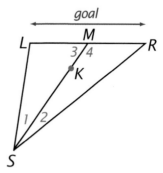

21. Draw the figure and mark it as needed to give a reason for each of the following statements.

22. ∠L > ∠R.

23. ∠4 > ∠L.

24. ∠4 > ∠R.

25. SR > SM.

Roman Column. The drawing below of an ancient Roman column was made in 1646.*

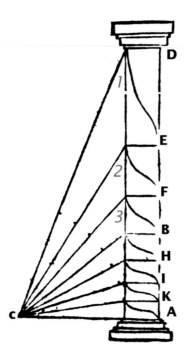

26. Center your protractor on the point at the lower left. What do you notice about the angles formed by the lines from this point?

27. What do you notice about the lengths of the sections of the column?

28. Why do you suppose the column might be designed in this way?

29. Why is ∠1 < ∠2 and ∠2 < ∠3?

30. Why is ∠1 < ∠3?

Set II

Integers and Triangles. The numbers 1, 3, and 5 are *consecutive odd integers* and the numbers 2, 4, and 6 are *consecutive even integers.*

—————————

Perspective in Perspective, by Lawrence Wright (Routledge and Kegan Paul, 1983).

The figures below show the results of trying to construct triangles with these numbers as their sides.

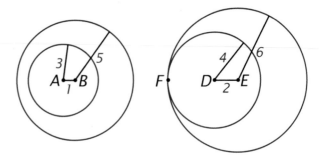

31. Explain in each case why no triangle is possible.

32. How are points D, E, and F related?

33. Try to construct a triangle GHI whose sides are the consecutive odd integers 3, 5, and 7.

In general, if *n* is an integer, then *n*, *n* + 2, and *n* + 4 are either consecutive odd integers or consecutive even integers.

From the Triangle Inequality Theorem, we know that, if *n*, *n* + 2, and *n* + 4 are the sides of a triangle, then

$$n + (n + 2) > n + 4.$$

34. Solve this inequality for *n*.

35. Do you think a triangle can have sides of 1,000,000, 1,000,002, and 1,000,004? Explain why or why not.

36. As the numbers in a set of consecutive odd or even integers get larger and larger, what does the triangle having them as sides look more and more like?

Different Definition. Near the beginning of *Euclid Simplified,* a book published in 1875, is this statement:

The base of an isosceles triangle is the unequal side.

37. If an isosceles triangle has an "unequal side," how many "unequal angles" does it have?

38. How does the statement disagree with our definition of an isosceles triangle?

39. Is an equilateral triangle isosceles?

40. If one side of an isosceles triangle has a length of 10, what possible conclusions can you draw about the lengths of its other two sides? Explain.

Screen Display. The figures below show a ball as it moves from one position to another on a stereoscopic screen display. On an actual display, the ball appears to be in front of the screen in the first figure but behind the screen in the second.*

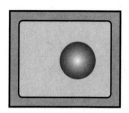

The figure below shows an overhead view of someone looking at a stereoscopic display. The stereoscopic effect works only as long as the eyes see an object as completely in the shaded region.

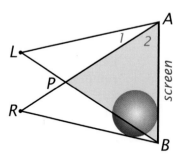

In the figure, LA = RB and LB = RA. Prove that LB > LA by giving a reason for each of the following statements.

41. △LBA ≅ △RAB.

42. ∠LBA = ∠2.

Information Visualization: Perception for Design, by Colin Ware (Morgan Kaufmann, 2000).

43. ∠LAB = ∠1 + ∠2.

44. ∠LAB > ∠2.

45. ∠LAB > ∠LBA.

46. LB > LA.

SAT Problem. The following description appeared in a problem on an SAT exam.

A triangle has sides of lengths x, $x - 2$, and $7 - x$.

47. Write the three inequalities for this triangle that follow from the Triangle Inequality Theorem.

48. From these inequalities, what can you conclude about x? Show your reasoning.

Draw the figures with appropriate markings and write complete proofs for each of the following.

49.

Given: AB > AC; ∠A and ∠B are complementary.
Prove: ∠A + ∠C > 90°.

50.

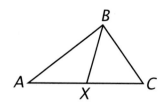

Given: Point X on side AC of △ABC such that XB = XC.
Prove: AC > AB.

Simplifying Fractions

A fraction is in "lowest terms" if its terms (its numerator and denominator) have no common factor other than 1.

In general, if $n \neq 0$,

$$\frac{a}{b} = \frac{na}{nb} \quad \text{and} \quad \frac{na}{nb} = \frac{a}{b}.$$

These equations express the fact that the terms of a fraction can be multiplied or divided by the same number without changing its value.

Example 1: Reduce $\dfrac{3x + 12}{x^2 + 7x + 12}$ to lowest terms.

Solution: $\dfrac{3x + 12}{x^2 + 7x + 12} = \dfrac{3(x + 4)}{(x + 3)(x + 4)} = \dfrac{3}{x + 3}.$

Example 2: Express $\dfrac{5}{x - 5}$ and $\dfrac{x}{2}$ as fractions with a common denominator.

Solution: $\dfrac{2(5)}{2(x - 5)} = \dfrac{10}{2(x - 5)}$ and $\dfrac{(x - 5)(x)}{(x - 5)(2)} = \dfrac{x(x - 5)}{2(x - 5)}.$

Exercises

Reduce to lowest terms.

1. $\dfrac{32}{40}$

2. $\dfrac{6x}{16}$

3. $\dfrac{x}{x^2}$

4. $\dfrac{5(x + 1)}{10}$

5. $\dfrac{4x + 4}{7x + 7}$

6. $\dfrac{x - 7}{3x - 21}$

7. $\dfrac{x + 5}{x^2 - 25}$

8. $\dfrac{x^2 - xy}{xy - y^2}$

9. $\dfrac{x^2 + 5x + 6}{10x + 20}$

10. $\dfrac{x^2 + x - 20}{x^2 - x - 30}$

Express as fractions with the indicated denominators.

11. $\dfrac{1}{x}$ with denominator $4x$.

12. $\dfrac{1}{x}$ with denominator x^4.

13. $\dfrac{3}{2 - x}$ with denominator $x - 2$.

Express as fractions with a common denominator.

14. $\dfrac{2}{3}$ and $\dfrac{3}{4}$

15. $\dfrac{4}{x}$ and $\dfrac{2}{7x}$

16. $\dfrac{1}{x}$ and $\dfrac{1}{y}$

17. $\dfrac{x}{x + 2}$ and $\dfrac{2}{3x + 6}$

18. $\dfrac{5}{x - 1}$ and $\dfrac{x}{x^2 - 1}$

19. $\dfrac{x}{yz}$ and $\dfrac{y}{xz}$

Chapter 6

Parallel Lines

The word "parallel," from the Greek word *parallelos,* meaning "side by side," suggests the idea of lines that have the same direction, something that we take for granted. In this chapter, we consider several ways to prove that lines are parallel and encounter the Parallel Postulate, an assumption that has been the subject of more controversy than everything else in Euclid's *Elements* combined! From the Parallel Postulate follow several more useful theorems about triangles.

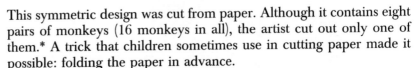

LESSON 1

Line Symmetry

This symmetric design was cut from paper. Although it contains eight pairs of monkeys (16 monkeys in all), the artist cut out only one of them.* A trick that children sometimes use in cutting paper made it possible: folding the paper in advance.

One pair of the monkeys and the fold that produced them are shown in the figure at the left. The monkeys are *symmetric* with respect to the line of the fold. The second figure at the left suggests how to define this symmetry in terms of points: A and B are symmetric with respect to *l* if they coincide when the paper is folded along *l;* they will coincide if *l* is the *perpendicular bisector* of segment AB; a point such as C on line *l* coincides with itself.

Definition
Two points are *symmetric with respect to a line* iff the line is the perpendicular bisector of the line segment connecting the two points.

Although the perpendicular bisector can be found by folding, it can also be constructed with straightedge and compass. You already know how.† The construction is based on our first postulate that *two points determine a line*–more specifically, on the fact that *two points each equidistant from the endpoints of a line segment determine a line* that is the perpendicular bisector of the line segment.

Theorem 16
In a plane, two points each equidistant from the endpoints of a line segment determine the perpendicular bisector of the line segment.

fold

The Art of Chinese Papercuts, by Zhang Daoyi (Foreign Language Press, 1989).
†Construction 1. To bisect a line segment (Chapter 1, Lesson 4, page 25).

In the first figure at the right, the two points are on opposite sides of the line segment. In the second figure, they are on the same side. Either way, the proof is the same.

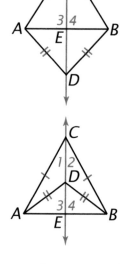

Given: CA = CB and DA = DB.
Prove: CD is the perpendicular bisector of AB.

Proof

Because CD = CD, △ACD ≅ △BCD (SSS); so ∠1 = ∠2. Also, CE = CE; so △ACE ≅ △BCE (SAS), and so ∠3 = ∠4. From the figure, ∠3 and ∠4 are also a linear pair; so their sides are perpendicular and CD ⊥ AB. Finally, AE = BE because they also are corresponding parts of △ACE and △BCE; so CD bisects AB.

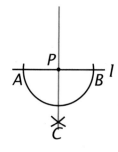

This proof provides an easy way to construct a line perpendicular to a given line and passing through any given point.

Construction 6

To construct a line perpendicular to a given line through a given point.

The following steps show that the method is the same whether or not the point is on the line.

| 1. Let *l* be the given line and P be the given point. | 2. With P as center, draw an arc that intersects *l* in two points (A and B). Note that P is equidistant from A and B. | 3. Use the compass to find another point C that is equidistant from A and B. | 4. Draw PC. |

Point on line

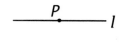

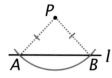

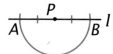

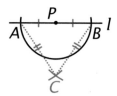

Point not on line

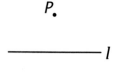

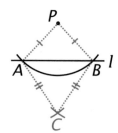

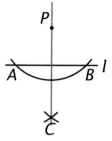

Line PC is the perpendicular bisector of segment AB according to Theorem 16, because P and C are equidistant from the endpoints A and B of the segment by construction.

Exercises

Set I

Rope Trick. An old way to make perpendicular lines on the ground is shown in the figures below.*

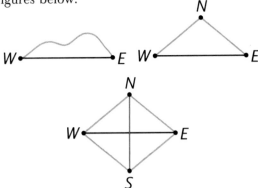

The ends of a long rope are tied to posts at W and E. Someone holding the rope at its center walks north until the rope is tight on both sides and places a post at the point N. Point S is located in a similar way by walking to the south.

1. Draw the third figure and mark the lengths on it that must be equal from this procedure.

2. Why is the line NS perpendicular to WE?

3. Does NS bisect WE?

4. Does WE necessarily bisect NS? Explain.

Lines of Symmetry. Copy each of the following figures and sketch its line(s) of symmetry.

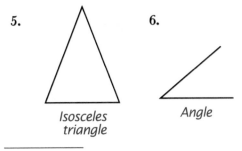

5.

6.

Isosceles triangle

Angle

Geometry Civilized, by J. L. Heilbron (Clarendon Press, 1998).

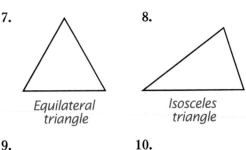

7.

8.

Equilateral triangle

Isosceles triangle

9.

10.

Rectangle

Square

Baseball Diamond. According to major league rules, a baseball diamond should be laid out so that the batter is facing east.

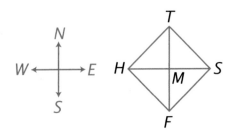

11. Use your ruler to draw line segment HS 8.5 cm long. Construct a line as its perpendicular bisector. Label the midpoint M and mark off points F and T so that MH = MS = MT = MF. Connect points H, F, S, and T to form a diamond.

12. Measure HF in centimeters.

In your drawing, 1 cm represents 15 feet. How many feet is it from home plate to

13. first base?

14. second base?

15. In what direction is the sun in the late afternoon?

16. Why are baseball diamonds laid out in the directions that they are?

17. Why is a pitcher who is left-handed called a "southpaw"?

Paper Chain. The figure below shows a paper chain. The chain was produced by cutting out just one penguin.*

18. How many times do you think the paper was folded before it was cut?

19. How many lines of symmetry between pairs of neighboring penguins are there in all?

20. How many times would a paper have to be folded to produce a chain of 16 penguins in this way?

Stealth Bomber. In this view of the B-2 Stealth Bomber, points S and T are symmetric with respect to line *l*.

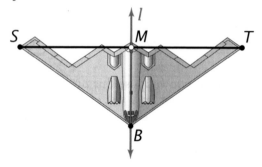

21. What can you conclude about line *l*?

Give a reason for each of the following statements.

22. SM = MT.

23. ∠BMS and ∠BMT are right angles.

24. ∠BMS = ∠BMT.

25. MB = MB.

26. △BMS ≅ △BMT.

27. BS = BT.

Wild Animal Paper Chains, by Stewart Walton and Sally Walton (Tupelo Books, 1993).

Set II

Race to the Fence. Acute Alice and Obtuse Ollie were standing on the opposite sides of a long straight fence when they decided to race to some point along it. Because Ollie was closer to the fence, Alice said it was only fair that they run to the point on the fence equidistant from both of them.[†]

Alice
•

_____ *fence*

•
Ollie

28. Draw a figure similar to but larger than the one shown above. Use your straight-edge and compass to find the point to which they ran. Also draw their paths.

Alice
•

_____ *fence*

•
Ollie

29. If Alice and Ollie were initially at equal distances from the fence, as shown in this figure, where would the point have been? Describe its location in words and draw a figure to illustrate it.

[†]Based on a problem in *You Are a Mathematician,* by David Wells (Wiley, 1995).

Clairvoyance Test. The following problem appeared in a "clairvoyance" test.*

30. Make an accurate copy of this figure by placing your paper over it and marking the five corners. Draw the figure and then choose a point anywhere inside it. Use your straightedge and compass to construct perpendicular lines from your point to each of the pentagon's five sides. (Extend the sides with your ruler if necessary.)

31. Add the lengths of the five perpendicular line segments by marking them along the edge of a sheet of paper. Measure the total length with your ruler to the nearest half inch.

32. Why do you suppose this problem might be used on a test of "supernatural power"?

Linkage Problem. Linkages are used to control motion in machines. The linkage below is made of six rods that are equal as follows: AB = AD, CB = CF = CD, and EF = ED. The rods can pivot about their ends; so the figure can change its shape.[†]

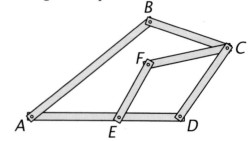

---

*The Incredible Dr. Matrix, by Martin Gardner (Scribner's, 1976).

[†]Mathematics Meets Technology, by Brian Bolt (Cambridge University Press, 1991).

Regardless of the shape of the linkage, a line through AC is always perpendicular to a line through BD.

33. Why?

34. What other pairs of points determine two lines that are always perpendicular?

35. Draw the figure by using line segments to represent the rods. Also draw AC and EC.

36. Regardless of the shape of the linkage, ∠B is always equal to ∠D. Why?

37. Is ∠B always equal to ∠F? Explain why or why not.

One Problem, Two Solutions. The figure below by Scott Kim has line symmetry, but the line is not shown.

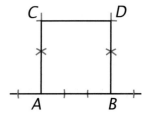

38. If the figure were folded on the symmetry line, where would the fold be?

39. To what letter on the other side of the line does the letter S correspond?

40. To what letter does U correspond?

41. What is strange about the figure?

Kepler's Diagram. The figure at the top of the next column was drawn by the astronomer Johannes Kepler in 1608.*

_____

Age of Kings, by Charles Blitzer (Time-Life Books, 1967).

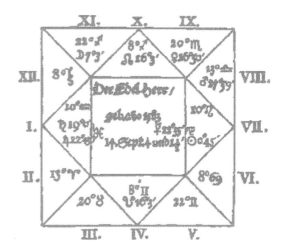

42. Draw the figure using the following procedure. Use your ruler to draw a horizontal line across your paper and mark a line segment 3 inches long on it for the base of the figure. Construct perpendicular segments at each endpoint of the base as illustrated here.

Copy AB on each perpendicular to determine C and D. Use only your straightedge and compass and what you notice about the symmetry of Kepler's figure to complete your drawing.

43. How many squares does Kepler's figure appear to contain?

44. What kind of triangle do all of the triangles in the figure appear to be?

45. How many triangles do there seem to be in all?

Set III

*An Unusual Set of Points.** Make an accurate tracing of the figure below. Choose any two points and connect them with a line segment. Construct the perpendicular bisector of the line segment. What do you notice? Do it again with several other pairs of points. What seems to always be true?

A•

•B   •C

H•

•D

G•   •F

•E

*Wheels, Life, and Other Mathematical Amusements, by Martin Gardner (W. H. Freeman and Company, 1983).

Used by permission of Johnny Hart and Creators Syndicate, Inc.

Proving Lines Parallel

So far in our study of geometry, we haven't paid much attention to parallel lines. The idea that they never meet is the basis for our definition of them, as you may recall.

Definition
Two lines are *parallel* iff they lie in the same plane and do not intersect.

B. C. and Peter's approach to trying to determine whether two lines meet illustrates the fact that, in practice, our definition of parallel lines is difficult to use. Lines are infinite in extent. We can't look everywhere along them to find out if they intersect.

The solution to this problem is to look at a third line that cuts across the two lines that we are wondering about. For example, lines l_1 and l_2 in the figure at the right appear to be parallel. The third line, t, intersects them to form a number of angles. If we know that certain of these angles are equal, such as the pair indicated, then it is easy to prove that the lines must be parallel.

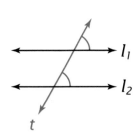

The third line is called a *transversal.* The word "transversal" comes from the Latin word *transversus,* meaning "turned across." A *transversal* is a line that "goes across"–that is, "intersects" two or more lines in different points.

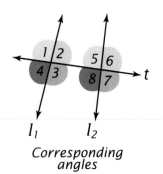

Corresponding angles

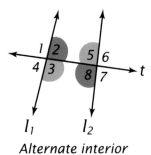

Alternate interior angles

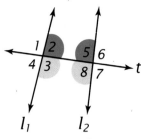

Interior angles on the same side of the transversal

When a transversal intersects two lines that lie in the same plane, it forms pairs of angles that are given special names. In the figure at the left, $\angle 1$ and $\angle 5$ are called *corresponding angles*. The other pairs of corresponding angles are $\angle 2$ and $\angle 6$, $\angle 4$ and $\angle 8$, and $\angle 3$ and $\angle 7$.

The transversal also forms two pairs of *alternate interior angles*: $\angle 2$ and $\angle 8$ are alternate interior angles, as are $\angle 3$ and $\angle 5$.

Finally, angles such as $\angle 2$ and $\angle 5$ are called *interior angles on the same side of the transversal*. So are $\angle 3$ and $\angle 8$.

All we need to know that two lines are parallel is to know that the angles in one of these pairs are related in a special way. We begin by proving that, if a pair of corresponding angles are equal, then the lines are parallel.

Theorem 17

Equal corresponding angles mean that lines are parallel.

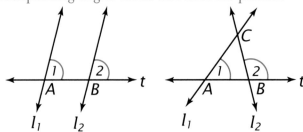

Given: Lines l_1 and l_2 with transversal t, $\angle 1 = \angle 2$.
Prove: $l_1 \parallel l_2$.

Our proof, from Euclid's *Elements*, is indirect. Look at the figure at the right above, which illustrates the possibility that the lines might intersect, and you may see the contradiction immediately.

Proof
Suppose l_1 and l_2 are *not* parallel. Then they must intersect (because they lie in the same plane). If l_1 and l_2 intersect in some point C, then they form a triangle, $\triangle ABC$. But $\angle 2$ is an exterior angle of this triangle, and $\angle 1$ is a remote interior angle; so $\angle 2 > \angle 1$, which contradicts the hypothesis that $\angle 1 = \angle 2$. So the assumption that the lines are not parallel is false, and $l_1 \parallel l_2$.

Knowing that equal corresponding angles mean that lines are parallel makes it easy to establish some other ways to prove lines parallel as well.

Corollary 1. Equal alternate interior angles mean that lines are parallel.

Corollary 2. Supplementary interior angles on the same side of a transversal mean that lines are parallel.

Corollary 3. In a plane, two lines perpendicular to a third line are parallel.

Exercises

Set I

Complete the following proofs of the corollaries of this lesson by giving the missing statements.

1. *Corollary 1.* Equal alternate interior angles mean that lines are parallel.

   Given: $\angle 1 = \angle 2$.
   Prove: $a \parallel b$.

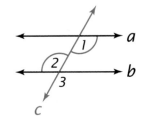

   Proof

Statements	Reasons
1. ?	Given.
2. ?	Vertical angles are equal.
3. ?	Substitution.
4. ?	Equal corresponding angles mean that lines are parallel.

2. *Corollary 2.* Supplementary interior angles on the same side of a transversal mean that lines are parallel.

   Given: $\angle 1$ and $\angle 2$ are supplementary.
   Prove: $a \parallel b$.

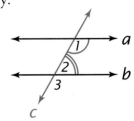

   Proof

Statements	Reasons
1. ?	Given.
2. ?	The angles in a linear pair are supplementary.
3. ?	Supplements of the same angle are equal.
4. ?	Equal corresponding angles mean that lines are parallel.

3. *Corollary 3.* In a plane, two lines perpendicular to a third line are parallel.

   Given: $a \perp c$ and $b \perp c$.
   Prove: $a \parallel b$.

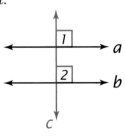

   Proof

Statements	Reasons
1. ?	Given.
2. ?	Perpendicular lines form right angles.
3. ?	All right angles are equal.
4. ?	Equal corresponding angles mean that lines are parallel.

Folded Paper. The figure below shows a sheet of paper folded into an accordion shape. The pleated edge outlined in color lies in a vertical plane.

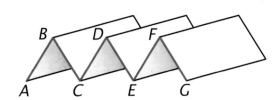

4. What are $\angle B$ and $\angle C$ called with respect to lines AB, BC, and CD?

5. If $\angle B = \angle C$, why is AB $\parallel$ CD?

6. If CD $\perp$ DE and DE $\perp$ EF, why is CD $\parallel$ EF?

Snake Track. As a sidewinding snake moves across the desert, its track appears as a series of lines, each at an angle of about 60° to the snake's line of travel.*

In the figure below, *t* is the snake's line of travel and *a, b,* and *c* are parts of its track.

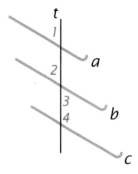

7. What are ∠1 and ∠2 called with respect to the transversal?

8. If ∠1 and ∠2 each equal 60°, what can you conclude about the lines of *a* and *b?*

9. Why?

10. What are ∠3 and ∠4 called?

11. If ∠3 = 60° and ∠4 = 120°, how are ∠3 and ∠4 related?

12. What can you conclude about the lines of *b* and *c?*

13. Why?

――――――――――

*"How Snakes Move," by Carl Gans (*Scientific American,* June 1970).

I-Beam. A shape commonly used in beams of structural steel is shown below.

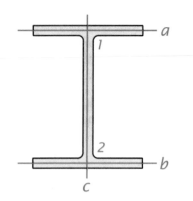

Can you conclude that *a* ‖ *b* if you know that

14. ∠1 = ∠2?

15. ∠1 and ∠2 are supplementary?

16. *a* ⊥ *c* and *b* ⊥ *c?*

Parallel Lines. Some of the line segments in the figure below appear to lie in parallel lines.

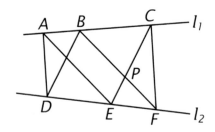

17. Copy the figure and mark its angles as needed to answer the following questions.

18. Which lines are parallel if ∠AED = ∠BFD?

19. Why?

20. Which lines are parallel if ∠DBF = ∠BPC?

21. Why?

22. Which lines are parallel if ∠DAC and ∠ACF are supplementary?

23. Why?

Set II

Drafting Triangles. Two identical drafting triangles are sometimes placed together by a navigator in plotting a chart.

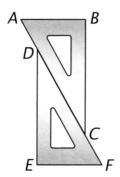

24. As long as points A, D, C, and F are lined up, AB must be parallel to EF. Why?

25. Why must BC be parallel to DE?

Optical Illusion. In the optical illusion below, two lines cross a V-shaped pattern.*

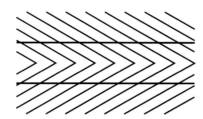

26. Draw the figure as shown below, in which all but one of the Vs have been removed.

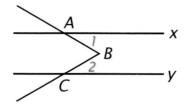

_____

*Can You Believe Your Eyes? by J. R. Block and Harold E. Yuker (Brunner/Mazel, 1992).

27. If ∠1 = ∠2, can you conclude that $x \parallel y$? Explain.

Suppose line AB is drawn to intersect y at D.

26. *(continued)* Extend line AB so that it intersects line y. Label the intersection D.

28. If ∠1 = ∠2 *and* BD = BC, can you conclude that $x \parallel y$? Explain.

Different Proofs. Here are two different proofs for the same problem. Tell the missing reasons in each proof.

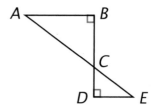

Given: ∠ABD and ∠BDE are right angles.
Prove: AB ∥ DE.

29. *Proof*

Statements	Reasons
1. ∠ABD and ∠BDE are right angles.	Given.
2. AB ⊥ BD and BD ⊥ DE.	Why?
3. AB ∥ DE.	Why?

30. *Proof*

Statements	Reasons
1. ∠ABD and ∠BDE are right angles.	Given.
2. ∠ABD = ∠BDE.	Why?
3. AB ∥ DE.	Why?

Construction Exercise. Use your construction tools to do the following construction as accurately as you can.

31. Construct △ABC with base AB = 11 cm, AC = 9 cm, and BC = 7 cm. Construct the line that bisects ∠C and let D be the point in which the line intersects AB. Construct

the perpendicular bisector of CD; let E be the point in which the bisector intersects AC, let F be the point in which it intersects CD, and let G be the point in which it intersects BC. Draw DE and DG.

Mark your figure as needed to answer the following questions.

32. How many right angles are in the figure?

33. Why is △CFE ≅ △CFG?

34. Why is EF = FG?

35. Why are all four triangles surrounding F congruent?

36. Why is CG = GD = DE = EC?

37. Why is CG ∥ DE and GD ∥ EC?

38. Is EG ∥ AB?

Write complete proofs for each of the following.

39.

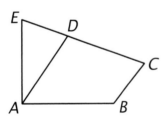

Given: AE = AD and ∠E = ∠BCE.
Prove: AD ∥ BC.

40.

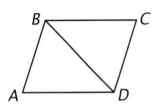

Given: AB = CD and AD = BC.
Prove: AB ∥ CD.

Set III

What Do You See? Sometimes what you *think* you see determines how you see it.*

1. Which cross bar in the figure below is perpendicular to the vertical bar?

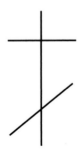

2. Which cross bar in the figure below is perpendicular to the vertical bar?

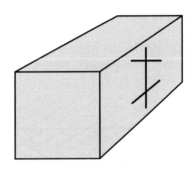

3. If you didn't give the same answer to both questions, why not? Aren't they the same figure?

4. Is it possible that *both* cross bars are perpendicular to the vertical line? Explain.

5. If they are, does it follow that they are parallel? Explain.

Human Information Processing: An Introduction to Psychology, by Peter H. Lindsay and Donald A. Norman (Harcourt Brace Jovanovich, 1977).

The Parallel Postulate

The most famous and enduring riddle of geometry arose from a construction.

Construction 7

To construct a line parallel to a given line through a given point.

The idea behind this construction is simple: equal corresponding angles mean that lines are parallel. To construct the parallel line, we draw a transversal and copy an angle.

1. Let l be the given line and P be the given point.
2. Choose any point O on line l and draw line PO. Name one of the angles formed at O ∠1 as shown in the second figure at the right.
3. Copy ∠1 at P as shown in the third figure. Name it ∠2.

Because ∠1 and ∠2 are equal corresponding angles formed by lines m and l and transversal PO, $m \parallel l$.

The *problem* is:

Is line m the *only* line that can be drawn parallel to l through point P?

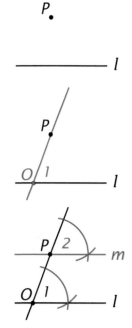

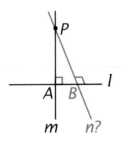

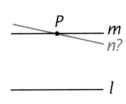

The answer surprised mathematicians when it was discovered in the 1830s, and it is not what you might expect even today. To see why, we need to take another look at what we know about perpendicular lines.

We know how to construct a line *m* perpendicular to a given line *l* through a given point P. Suppose we do so, with *l* and *m* intersecting at A as shown at the left. Could there be *another* line *n* passing through P and perpendicular to *l* with intersection point B as added in color? No, because, if there were, then the remote angle PAB of △PAB would be *equal* to the triangle's exterior angle at B. This equality would contradict the fact that an exterior angle of a triangle is *greater* than either remote interior angle and proves that

> Through a point not on a line, there is exactly one line perpendicular to the given line.

Can we use a similar proof by contradiction to show that there can't be two different lines *m* and *n* through P and *parallel* to a given line *l*? This riddle took more than 2,000 years to work out. The surprising answer came with the discovery of non-Euclidean geometries, which we will learn about in Chapter 16. There are consistent geometries that satisfy all of the postulates and theorems that we have learned so far in which *more* than one line can be parallel to a given line through a point not on it! This fact astonished people when it was discovered in the 1830s.

Euclid knew that he needed some further assumption to go forward with his development of geometry (his Fifth Postulate), and we need such a postulate, too. We call ours the Parallel Postulate.

Postulate 7.   The Parallel Postulate

Through a point not on a line, there is exactly one line parallel to the given line.

With this postulate, it is easy to prove the following theorem.

Theorem 18

In a plane, two lines parallel to a third line are parallel to each other.

Exercises

Set I

Optical Illusion.
Every pair of lines in this optical illusion appears to be either perpendicular or parallel.

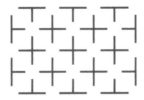

1. How many lines does the figure appear to have?

What determines whether or not two lines are

2. perpendicular?

3. parallel?

4. What do you see in the figure that "isn't there"?

Windshield Wipers. One type of windshield wipers has two blades that remain parallel as they move back and forth.

In the figure below, the lines of the wipers, *a* and *b*, form angles with the transversal *c*.

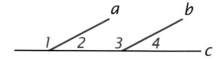

5. Which angle corresponds to ∠1?

6. If these two angles are always equal, why do the wipers always stay parallel?

7. What are ∠2 and ∠3 called with respect to lines *a*, *b*, and *c?*

8. If these two angles are always supplementary, why are the wipers always parallel?

9. Name another pair of angles that, if they were equal, would ensure that the wipers are parallel.

10. If ∠1 and ∠4 are supplementary, does it follow that the wipers are parallel? Why or why not?

Exactly One. The words "exactly one" have a twofold meaning: that there is *at least one* and that there is *no more than one.*

11. Which would be easier to prove: that a cat has at least one flea or that it has no more than one flea?

Tell whether one or more of the following expressions could correctly replace the question mark in each of the following statements: "at least," "no more than," "exactly."

12. A line segment has ? one midpoint.

13. An angle has ? one ray that bisects it.

14. A triangle contains ? one right angle.

15. Two lines intersect in ? one point.

16. Lines are perpendicular if they form ? one right angle.

17. Through a point on a line, there is ? one line perpendicular to the line.

18. Through a point not on a line, there is ? one line perpendicular to the line.

Parallelogram. The figure below shows a method for constructing a *parallelogram,* a quadrilateral with two pairs of parallel sides.

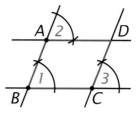

19. Draw two intersecting lines and mark points A, B, and C on them as shown in the figure. Use your straightedge and compass to construct parallelogram ABCD by copying ∠1 as illustrated.

20. Why is AD ∥ BC and CD ∥ BA?

21. What else seems to be true about segments AD and BC as well as about segments CD and BA?

What relation seems to exist between

22. ∠1 and ∠BCD?

23. ∠1 and ∠ADC?

24. Does parallelogram ABCD appear to have line symmetry? Explain why or why not.

Euclid's Assumption. Euclid made the following assumption:

If two lines form interior angles on the same side of a transversal whose sum is less than 180°, then the two lines meet on that side of the transversal.

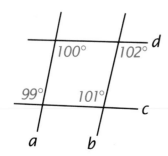

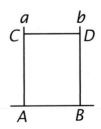

The figure above shows four lines intersecting at four points.

25. How many of these lines can be considered to be transversals?

26. Copy the figure and write the measures of the other angles surrounding each of the four points.

In what direction (left, right, up, or down) do lines

27. *a* and *b* intersect?

28. *c* and *d* intersect?

Set II

Gateway. Architect Francis Ching wrote:

Two points can denote a gateway signifying passage from one place to another. Extended vertically, the two points define both a plane of entry and an approach perpendicular to it.*

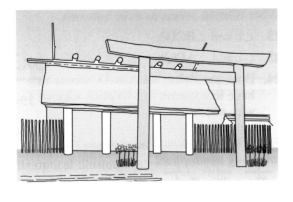

———————
Architecture: Form, Space, and Order, by Francis D. K. Ching (Wiley, 1996).

29. Draw the gateway described by doing the following.

(1) Mark two points 4 cm apart and label them A and B.

(2) Draw line AB and construct two lines, *a* and *b*, perpendicular to it at points A and B.

(3) Mark point C on line *a* and point D on line *b* so that AC = BD = 5 cm.

(4) Draw CD.

In the plane of the gateway (that is, the plane of your paper), how many lines can be drawn that are perpendicular to AB

30. through point A?

31. through point D?

32. What relation do lines *a* and *b* have?

33. Why?

34. What relation do lines AB and CD seem to have?

35. How many lines can be drawn that are parallel to AB through point C?

36. Why?

29. *(continued)* Draw line segments AD and BC.

Tell whether you think we have enough information to be able to prove each of the following statements.

37. △ADB ≅ △BCA.

38. AD = BC.

39. △ADC ≅ △BCD.

40. ∠ACD = ∠BDC.

41. △ABC ≅ △CDA.

Theorem 18. Complete the following indirect proof of Theorem 18.

In a plane, two lines parallel to a third line are parallel to each other.

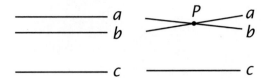

Given: Lines *a, b,* and *c* lie in a plane; $a \parallel c$ and $b \parallel c$.
Prove: $a \parallel b$.

Proof

42. Suppose ? .

If *a* and *b* are not parallel, then they intersect in some point P.

43. But $a \parallel c$ and $b \parallel c$. Why?

44. This contradicts the fact that ? .

45. Therefore, what we assumed is false and ? .

Proclus's Claim. The Greek geometer Proclus said, "In a plane, if a line intersects one of two parallels, it will intersect the other also."

In the figure at the right, $a \parallel b$ and line *c* intersects line *a* at P.

46. Does it follow that line *c* must also intersect line *b*?

47. Explain why or why not.

Set III

A Dragon Curve. The figure at the right, a model of a "dragon curve," can be formed by folding paper.*

**Mathematical Magic Show,* by Martin Gardner (Knopf, 1977).

1. Cut a strip of paper $12\frac{1}{2}$ inches long and $\frac{1}{4}$ inch wide. Fold it in half by putting the narrow ends together. Fold the result in half in the same direction. Continue in this way two more times. Open the paper so that, when viewed from the edge, every fold forms a right angle.

2. On graph paper, draw a pair of axes extending 10 units in each direction from the origin. Plot the following points and connect them in alphabetical order with line segments:

A $(-4, 8)$,　G $(-2, 4)$,　M $(2, 6)$,
B $(-7, 9)$,　H $(1, 3)$,　N $(5, 5)$,
C $(-8, 6)$,　I $(0, 0)$,　O $(6, 8)$,
D $(-5, 5)$,　J $(3, -1)$,　P $(9, 7)$,
E $(-6, 2)$,　K $(4, 2)$,　Q $(8, 4)$.
F $(-3, 1)$,　L $(1, 3)$,

3. How is the figure that you have drawn related to your paper strip?

4. Which point corresponds to the position of the first fold?

5. Which points correspond to the position of the second fold?

6. In what way is the second half of the figure (from I to Q) related to the first half (from A to I)?

7. What do you notice about the coordinates of the corners of the two halves of the figure?

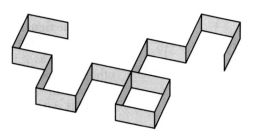

LESSON 4

Parallel Lines and Angles

Biologists see a lot of geometry when looking at a spider's web. Jean Henri Fabre, in his book *The Life of the Spider,* wrote:

> In each sector, the various chords, the elements of the spiral windings, are parallel to one another. . . . With the two radiating lines that frame them they form obtuse angles on one side and acute angles on the other; and these angles remain constant in the same sector, because the chords are parallel.

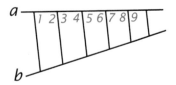

In the figure at the left, lines *a* and *b* are the "radiating lines" and the segments between them are the parallel "chords." Fabre said that angles such as ∠1 and ∠3 are equal because the chords are parallel. In other words, parallel lines form equal corresponding angles with a transversal.

This statement seems like a theorem that we have already proved, but it is not. Look at the two statements written in if-then form:

> *Theorem 17.* If two lines form equal corresponding angles, then the lines are parallel.

> *Statement about spider web.* If two lines are parallel, then they form equal corresponding angles.

It is tempting to assume that these two statements say the same thing, but they do not: one is the *converse* of the other. Remember that the converse of a true statement may be false. Here is another pair of statements about parallel lines that obviously do *not* say the same thing:

> *Statement.* If two lines are parallel, then they lie in the same plane. (True.)

> *Converse.* If two lines lie in the same plane, then they are parallel. (False.)

This is a reminder that, even though we may think that the converse of a theorem that we have already proved is true, to add it to our deductive system we must either assume it as a postulate or prove it as a new theorem. In regard to Fabre's statement about the spider web, we can easily prove it by using the Parallel Postulate.

Theorem 19
Parallel lines form equal corresponding angles.

Given: Lines l_1 and l_2 with transversal t, $l_1 \parallel l_2$.
Prove: $\angle 1 = \angle 2$.

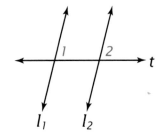

Proof
  Suppose that $\angle 1 \neq \angle 2$. Draw a line l_3 through point P so that $\angle 3 = \angle 1$ (the Protractor Postulate). Equal corresponding angles mean that lines are parallel; so $l_1 \parallel l_3$. But $l_1 \parallel l_2$ (given); so, through point P, we have two lines parallel to l_1. This contradicts the Parallel Postulate, which says that, through a point not on a line, there is exactly *one* line parallel to the line. So our assumption that $\angle 1 \neq \angle 2$ is false, and hence $\angle 1 = \angle 2$.

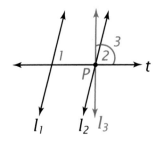

Now that we have proved the converse of Theorem 17, it is easy to prove the converses of its corollaries as well.

Corollary 1. Parallel lines form equal alternate interior angles.

Corollary 2. Parallel lines form supplementary interior angles on the same side of a transversal.

Corollary 3. In a plane, a line perpendicular to one of two parallel lines is also perpendicular to the other.

Exercises

Set I

Which Fishpole? The figure below appeared in a book of puzzles.* The four lines labeled A, B, C, and D are parallel.

1. What can you conclude about the acute angles at A, B, C, and D?

2. Why?

3. Which fishpole caught the fish?

4. What is "puzzling" about this puzzle?

Corollary Proofs. Complete the following proofs of the corollaries of this lesson by giving the missing reasons.

5. *Corollary 1.* Parallel lines form equal alternate interior angles.

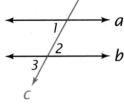

Given: $a \parallel b$.
Prove: $\angle 1 = \angle 2$.

Proof

Statements	Reasons
1. $a \parallel b$.	?
2. $\angle 1 = \angle 3$.	?
3. $\angle 2 = \angle 3$.	?
4. $\angle 1 = \angle 2$.	?

Challenge! by Charlie Rice (Hallmark Editions, 1968).

6. *Corollary 2.* Parallel lines form supplementary interior angles on the same side of a transversal.

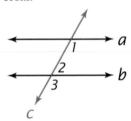

Given: $a \parallel b$.
Prove: $\angle 1$ and $\angle 2$ are supplementary.

Proof

Statements	Reasons
1. $a \parallel b$.	?
2. $\angle 1 = \angle 3$.	?
3. $\angle 2$ and $\angle 3$ are supplementary.	?
4. $\angle 2 + \angle 3 = 180°$.	?
5. $\angle 2 + \angle 1 = 180°$.	?
6. $\angle 1$ and $\angle 2$ are supplementary.	?

7. *Corollary 3.* In a plane, if a line is perpendicular to one of two parallel lines, it is also perpendicular to the other.

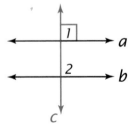

Given: $c \perp a$ and $a \parallel b$.
Prove: $c \perp b$.

Proof

Statements	Reasons
1. $c \perp a$.	?
2. $\angle 1$ is a right angle.	?
3. $\angle 1 = 90°$.	?
4. $a \parallel b$.	?
5. $\angle 1 = \angle 2$.	?
6. $\angle 2 = 90°$.	?
7. $\angle 2$ is a right angle.	?
8. $c \perp b$.	?

Bent Pencil. The pencil in this cup appears to be bent because light rays are bent when they go from air into water.

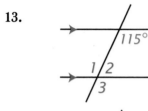

In the figure below, PE ∥ CI and ∠PEN = ∠CIL.

8. Why is ∠1 = ∠3?

9. Why is ∠PEN = ∠1 + ∠2 and ∠CIL = ∠3 + ∠4?

10. Why is ∠1 + ∠2 = ∠3 + ∠4?

11. Why is ∠2 = ∠4?

12. Why is EN ∥ IL?

Find the Angles. In each of the following figures, the arrowheads indicate parallel lines. Find the measures of the indicated angles.

13.

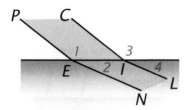

14.

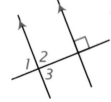

15.

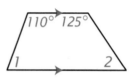

16.

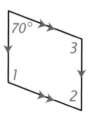

City Streets. This map shows some of the streets in New York City. The streets running from left to right on the map are parallel.

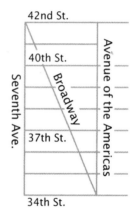

Seventh Ave. and Avenue of the Americas are perpendicular to 34th St.

17. What relation must Seventh Ave. have to 42nd St.? Why?

18. What relation must Seventh Ave. and Avenue of the Americas have? Why?

One of the acute angles at the intersection of Broadway and 37th St. is 67°.

19. How large are the other three angles at that intersection?

20. How large are the angles at the intersection of Broadway and 40th St.?

21. How do you know?

Lesson 4: Parallel Lines and Angles   **233**

T Puzzle. This four-piece puzzle in the shape of the letter T was once used to advertise sausage! Its edges are parallel and perpendicular, and the two slanted cuts are parallel.

Tell in what way each of the following pairs of angles is related and *why*.

22. ∠1 and ∠2.

23. ∠2 and ∠3.

24. ∠3 and ∠4.

25. ∠2 and ∠4.

26. ∠4 and ∠5.

27. ∠5 and ∠6.

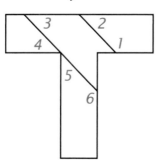

Set II

Parallel Construction. In the figure below, line *l* has been constructed through point C by copying ∠A of △ABC as ∠1.

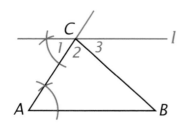

28. Draw a figure similar to this one and do the construction.

29. Why is *l* ∥ AB?

30. Why is line *l* the *only* line that can be constructed parallel to AB through point C?

31. Why is ∠3 = ∠B?

32. What is ∠1 + ∠2 + ∠3?

33. What is ∠A + ∠2 + ∠B?

Overlapping Angles.

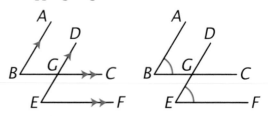

In the figure at the left above, BA ∥ ED and BC ∥ EF. It looks as if ∠B = ∠E.

34. Is this necessarily true? Explain why or why not.

In the figure at the right above, ∠B = ∠E. It looks as if BA ∥ ED and BC ∥ EF.

35. Is this necessarily true? Explain why or why not.

Sand Dune Lines. When desert sand dunes are seen from a high altitude, they often seem to form parallel lines.*

One way to describe parallel lines is to say that they are "everywhere equidistant." This description suggests that, if *x* ∥ *y* in the figure below and AB and CD are both perpendicular to *y*, then AB = CD.

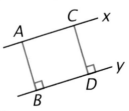

---

*The Flying Circus of Physics, by Jearl Walker (Wiley, 1977).

36. Copy the figure and add to it as needed to answer each of the following questions.

37. We can add line AD to the figure. Why?

38. Why is ∠CAD = ∠BDA?

39. Why is AB ∥ CD?

40. Why is ∠BAD = ∠CDA?

41. Why is AD = AD?

42. Why is △ABD ≅ △DCA?

43. Why is AB = CD?

44. In general, what would you measure to find the distance between two parallel lines?

SAT Problem. In the figure below, *a* ∥ *b*.

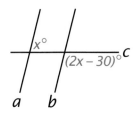

45. Write an equation relating the measures of the two indicated angles.

Find the measure of

46. the acute angle.

47. the obtuse angle.

Construction Problem. In the figure below, line *b* has been drawn parallel to line *a* through P. Also PA = PB.

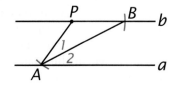

48. Draw line *a* and point P. Use your straightedge and compass to construct *b* ∥ *a* and PA = PB.

49. What seems to be true about ∠1 and ∠2?

50. Use what you know about angles and parallel lines to prove it.

MAGYAR POSTA

Johannes Kepler 1571-1630

Set III

Astronomer Johannes Kepler was the first to figure out the orbits of the planets.

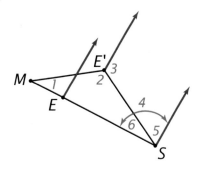

He used diagrams like the one above to calculate the shape of Earth's orbit.* The points M and S represent Mars and the sun and E and E' represent two positions of Earth. The three lines in blue are parallel and everything lies in the same plane. The angles numbered 1, 2, and 3 can be measured from Earth. From these angles, Kepler was able to figure out the measures of the angles numbered 4, 5, and 6 and the angle at M.

How did he figure out the measure of

1. ∠4? **3.** ∠6?

2. ∠5? **4.** ∠M?

Starting with SM as one side, Kepler was then able to draw △MSE and hence determine the position of Earth at E'.

5. Suppose that ∠1 = 84°, ∠2 = 124°, and ∠3 = 122°. Find ∠4, ∠5, ∠6, and ∠M.

6. Show how Kepler drew △MSE' by using your ruler and protractor to draw it. Let MS = 10 cm.

Constructing the Universe, by David Layzer (Scientific American Library, 1984).

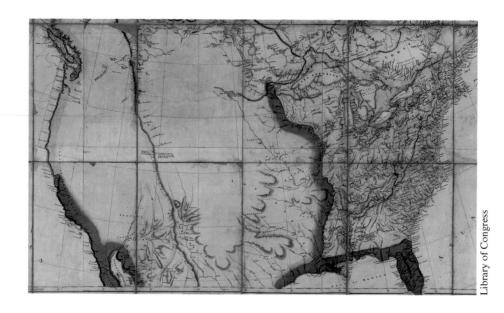

Library of Congress

The Angles of a Triangle

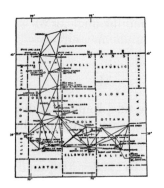

When Lewis and Clark set out on their historic expedition across America, most of the land west of the Mississippi was unknown territory. The map that they used, shown above, had been drawn in 1802. It would be many years before the entire country was surveyed.

To map the United States, surveyors used a method called *triangulation*–so named because it locates points by means of a network of triangles. The entire country is now "criss crossed with an elaborate network of many thousands of triangles, measured by surveyors' transits, and the corners of all of them are marked by permanent stones called 'bench marks.' "* The initial point from which the triangulation began was in a pasture in Meades Ranch, Kansas. Part of the network of triangles starting from this point is shown in the map at the left. Meades Ranch is marked with an arrow.

Surveyors check their accuracy over short distances by measuring the angles of the triangles in their network. That the sum of the angles of a triangle is 180° is a famous theorem of plane geometry.† Now that we have the Parallel Postulate, we can prove it.

Triangles, by Henry M. Neely (Crowell, 1962).
†Chapter 2, Lesson 6.

Theorem 20. The Angle Sum Theorem
The sum of the angles of a triangle is 180°.

> *Given:* △ABC.
> *Prove:* ∠A + ∠B + ∠C = 180°.

Proof

Statements	*Reasons*
1. △ABC.	Given.
2. Through point B, draw line DE ∥ AC.	Through a point not on a line, there is exactly one line parallel to the line.
3. ∠1 = ∠A and ∠3 = ∠C.	Parallel lines form equal alternate interior angles.
4. ∠1 + ∠2 = ∠DBC.	Betweenness of Rays Theorem (BD-BA-BC).
5. ∠DBC and ∠3 are supplementary.	The angles in a linear pair are supplementary.
6. ∠DBC + ∠3 = 180°.	The sum of two supplementary angles is 180°.
7. ∠1 + ∠2 + ∠3 = 180°.	Substitution (steps 4 and 6).
8. ∠A + ∠B + ∠C = 180°.	Substitution (steps 3 and 7).

This theorem has some useful corollaries.

Corollary 1. If two angles of one triangle are equal to two angles of another triangle, the third angles are equal.

Corollary 2. The acute angles of a right triangle are complementary.

Corollary 3. Each angle of an equilateral triangle is 60°.

A fourth immediate consequence of Theorem 20 concerns the measure of an exterior angle of a triangle. We already know that an exterior angle of a triangle is greater than either remote interior angle. Now we can prove that it is equal to their sum.

Theorem 21
An exterior angle of a triangle is equal to the sum of the remote interior angles.

Several proofs of this theorem have been discovered. We will consider one of them in the exercises.

Exercises

Set I

Corollary Proofs. Complete the following proofs of the corollaries of this lesson by giving the reasons. The proofs are written in paragraph form.

Corollary 1. If two angles of one triangle are equal to two angles of another triangle, the third angles are equal.

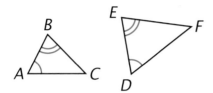

Given: In △ABC and △DEF, ∠A = ∠D and ∠B = ∠E.
Prove: ∠C = ∠F.

Proof

1. ∠A + ∠B + ∠C = 180° and ∠D + ∠E + ∠F = 180°. Why?

2. It follows that ∠A + ∠B + ∠C = ∠D + ∠E + ∠F. Why?

3. Because ∠A = ∠D and ∠B = ∠E, it follows that ∠D + ∠E + ∠C = ∠D + ∠E + ∠F. Why?

4. Therefore, ∠C = ∠F. Why?

Corollary 2. The acute angles of a right triangle are complementary.

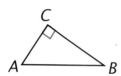

Given: △ABC is a right triangle with right ∠C.
Prove: ∠A and ∠B are complementary.

Proof

5. △ABC is a right triangle with right ∠C; so ∠C = 90°. Why?

6. Because ∠A + ∠B + ∠C = 180°, it follows that ∠A + ∠B + 90° = 180°. Why?

7. So ∠A + ∠B = 90°. Why?

8. Therefore, ∠A and ∠B are complementary. Why?

Corollary 3. Each angle of an equilateral triangle is 60°.

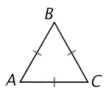

Given: △ABC is equilateral.
Prove: ∠A = 60°, ∠B = 60°, ∠C = 60°.

Proof

9. △ABC is equilateral; so it is also equiangular. Why?

10. Because △ABC is equiangular, ∠A = ∠B = ∠C. Why?

11. Because ∠A + ∠B + ∠C = 180°, it follows that ∠A + ∠A + ∠A = 3∠A = 180°. Why?

12. So ∠A = 60°. Why?

13. It follows that ∠B = 60° and ∠C = 60°. Why?

Exterior Angle Theorem. One way to prove Theorem 21 is given here. Complete the proof by giving the reasons.

Theorem 21. An exterior angle of a triangle is equal to the sum of the remote interior angles.

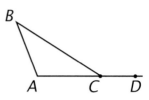

Given: ∠BCD is an exterior angle of △ABC.
Prove: ∠BCD = ∠A + ∠B.

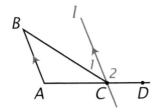

Proof

14. Through point C, draw line *l* parallel to AB. Why is this possible?

15. ∠1 = ∠B. Why?

16. ∠2 = ∠A. Why?

17. ∠BCD = ∠1 + ∠2. Why?

18. Therefore, ∠BCD = ∠A + ∠B. Why?

UFO Angles. The angles of elevation of a UFO at A are measured from two positions, B and C.

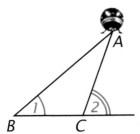

19. Write the two inequalities that follow from the Exterior Angle Theorem.

20. Write the equation relating the measures of ∠1, ∠2, and ∠A.

21. Find ∠A if ∠1 = 42° and ∠2 = 70°.

Right and Wrong. Obtuse Ollie told Acute Alice that, because ∠C is the right angle of the triangle below, ∠A and ∠B must be the wrong angles.*

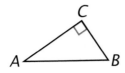

---

*From an idea in *The Heart of Mathematics,* by Edward B. Burger and Michael Starbird (Key College Publishing, 2000).

22. What kind of angles must they actually be?

Alice told Ollie that, if he is correct, then "two wrongs make a right."

23. What does she mean?

Another Kind of Triangle. The triangle in this picture is made of steel.

24. What kind of geometric triangle has a similar shape?

25. What is the triangle in the picture used for?

26. How large are its "angles"?

Economics Graph. The following words from an economics book describe the graph of the "consumption" function.†

At any point on the 45° line, the distance up from the horizontal axis (which is consumption) exactly equals the distance across from the vertical axis (which is income).

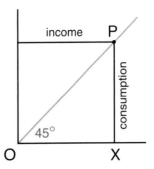

27. From the fact that XP ⊥ OX, what kind of triangle is △OPX?

28. What is the relation of ∠OPX to ∠POX?

29. What is the measure of ∠OPX?

30. Why is XP = OX?

---

†*Economics,* by Paul A. Samuelson and William D. Nordhaus (McGraw-Hill, 1989).

Set II

North Star and Latitude. In Peculiar, Missouri, the North Star is always 38° above the horizon. The angle between Peculiar and the equator also is 38°, which isn't really peculiar, because we can prove it.*

In the figure at the right, the angle of elevation of the North Star at P is ∠1; the latitude of P is ∠2. Also, OA ∥ PC, OA ⊥ OB, and OP ⊥ PA.
Explain why ∠1 = ∠2 by answering each of the following questions.

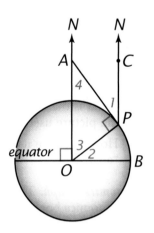

31. Why is ∠1 = ∠4?

32. What relation does ∠4 have to ∠3?

33. Why?

34. What relation does ∠2 have to ∠3?

35. What relation does ∠4 have to ∠2?

36. Why?

37. Why is ∠1 = ∠2?

Angle Bisectors. In the figure below, the bisectors of an interior and an exterior angle of △ABC meet at E.

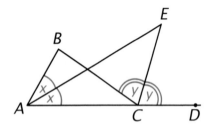

---

38. Draw a larger △ABC with exterior ∠BCD. Use your straightedge and compass to bisect ∠BAC and ∠BCD. Label the point in which the bisectors meet E.

39. Use your protractor to measure ∠B and ∠E. How do they seem to compare in size?

Tell why each of the following equations is true.

40. ∠BCD = ∠BAC + ∠B and ∠ECD = ∠EAC + ∠E.

41. 2y = 2x + ∠B and y = x + ∠E.

42. 2y = 2x + 2∠E.

43. 2x + ∠B = 2x + 2∠E.

44. ∠B = 2∠E.

Write proofs for the following.

45.

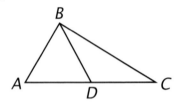

Given: In △ABC and △ADE, ∠ADE = ∠B.
Prove: ∠AED = ∠C.

46.

Given: △ABC is a right triangle with right ∠ABC; ∠ABD and ∠C are complementary.
Prove: △ABD is isosceles.

Catch Question. This problem appeared in a collection of "catch" questions.*

This proof appeared in a book of proofs without words.†

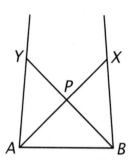

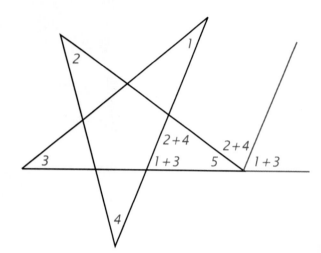

Suppose lines AX and BY bisect two of the angles of a triangle whose third vertex is out of view. If AX ⊥ BY and the base AB of the triangle is 10 inches long, how tall is the triangle?

47. Draw the figure and mark this information on it.

48. Reasoning from your figure, explain why this is a "catch" question.

1. What do you think is being proved?

2. Briefly explain in words how the proof works.

The Unexpected Hanging and Other Mathematical Diversions, by Martin Gardner (Simon & Schuster, 1969).

†Proof by Fouad Nakhli in *Proofs Without Words: Exercises in Visual Thinking,* by Roger B. Nelsen (Mathematical Association of America, 1993).

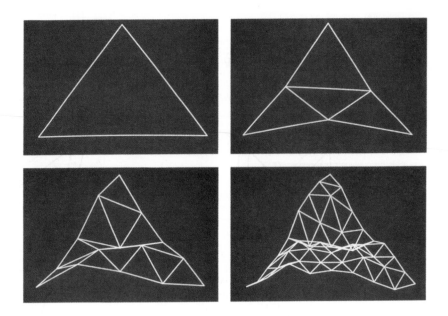

AAS and HL Congruence

Surveyors have been using triangulations—networks of triangles some-times numbering in the thousands—for centuries. Triangulations of *millions* of triangles are now used in computer programming.

The images above show how the image of a mountain can be gener-ated from repeated divisions of triangles.* The sequence, *Fractal Demo,* by Alvy Ray Smith, begins with a single triangle in "three-dimensional space." The triangle is divided into 4 triangles by connecting the midpoints of its sides. The figure is then "bent" at the midpoints to give it the impression of being three-dimensional. Each of the 4 triangles is then transformed in the same way, resulting in 16 triangles. This process is repeated as shown, and the triangles are eventually filled in to create the picture of the mountain.

Consider a pair of triangles formed by this process, as shown at the left. Are they congruent? Although it is hard to tell from their ap-pearance, we know several sets of conditions that are sufficient to prove triangles congruent. In fact, we have given them names: ASA, SAS, and SSS.

Are there any other sets of parts that can be used to prove tri-angles congruent? Yes; we will consider two of them in this lesson.

Visualization: The Second Computer Revolution, by Richard Mark Friedhoff and William Benzon (Abrams, 1989).

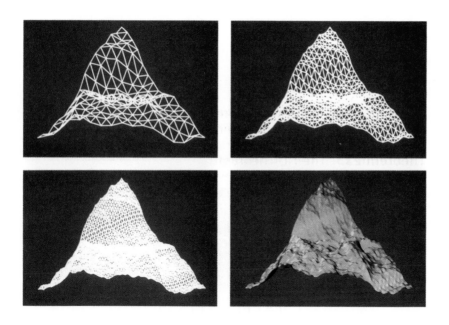

Theorem 22. The AAS Theorem

If two angles and the side opposite one of them in one triangle are equal to the corresponding parts of another triangle, the triangles are congruent.

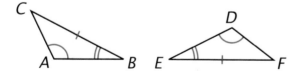

Given: △ABC and △DEF with ∠A = ∠D, ∠B = ∠E, and BC = EF.
Prove: △ABC ≅ △DEF.

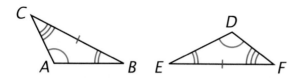

Take a good look at the figures above and you may see the proof. If two angles of one triangle are equal to two angles of another triangle, the third pair of angles also are equal. Consequently, AAS follows from ASA.

Proof
    In △ABC and △DEF, ∠A = ∠D and ∠B = ∠E. Therefore, ∠C = ∠F, and so, with BC = EF, △ABC ≅ △DEF by ASA.

As the name of the next theorem, HL for "hypotenuse–leg," implies, the theorem applies only to right triangles.

Theorem 23.   The HL Theorem

If the hypotenuse and a leg of one right triangle are equal to the corresponding parts of another right triangle, the triangles are congruent.

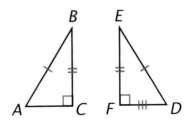

Given: △ABC and △DEF are right triangles (with right angles C and F); AB = DE and BC = EF.
Prove: △ABC ≅ △DEF.

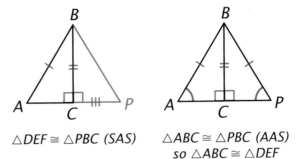

△DEF ≅ △PBC (SAS)   △ABC ≅ △PBC (AAS)
                                   so △ABC ≅ △DEF

Again, a careful look at the figures above may reveal the proof.

Proof
   Extend line AC (two points determine a line) and choose point P on it so that PC = DF (the Ruler Postulate); also, draw BP.
   △PBC ≅ △DEF (SAS); so PB = DE (corresponding parts of congruent triangles are equal). Because AB = DE (given), AB = PB (substitution).
   AB and PB are equal sides of △ABP; so ∠A = ∠BPC (if two sides of a triangle are equal, the angles opposite them are equal).
   △ABC ≅ △PBC (AAS); so △ABC ≅ △DEF (two triangles congruent to a third triangle are congruent to each other).

Exercises

Set I

Hang Glider. A popular type of hang glider is the Rogallo.

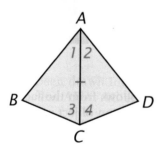

The design of its sail consists of two triangles: △ABC and △ADC. They share a common side; so AC = AC.*

Name the way of knowing that △ABC ≅ △ADC if

1. ∠1 = ∠2 and ∠3 = ∠4.
2. AB = AD and BC = CD.
3. ∠1 = ∠2 and AB = AD.
4. ∠B = ∠D and ∠3 = ∠4.
5. ∠B = ∠D = 90° and BC = CD.

Congruent or Not? SSS names a way to prove triangles congruent. Does AAA name another way?

Hang Gliding and Soaring, by James E. Mrazek (St. Martin's Press, 1976).

AAA?

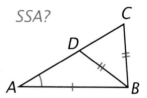

In △ABC, DE ∥ AB.

6. Why is ∠1 = ∠A and ∠2 = ∠B?
7. How many pairs of angles in △DEC and △ABC are equal?
8. Is △DEC ≅ △ABC?

AAS names a way to prove triangles congruent. Does SSA name another way?

SSA?

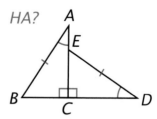

In △ABC, DB = CB.

9. How many pairs of parts in △ABC and △ABD are equal?
10. Is △ABC ≅ △ABD?

HL names a way to prove triangles congruent. Does HA name another way?

HA?

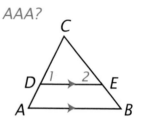

In this figure, AC ⊥ BD, AB = DE, and ∠A = ∠D.

11. How many pairs of parts in △ABC and △DEC are equal?
12. Is △ABC ≅ △DEC?
13. Explain why or why not.

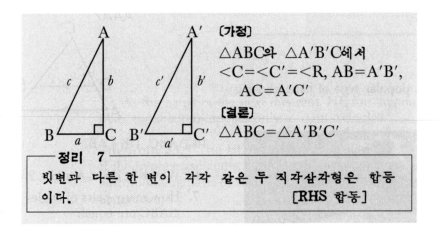

[가정]

△ABC와 △A′B′C에서
<C=<C′=<R, AB=A′B′,
AC=A′C′

[결론]

△ABC≡△A′B′C′

정리 7

빗변과 다른 한 변이 각각 같은 두 직각삼각형은 합동
이다.   [RHS 합동]

Korean Theorem. A theorem from a Korean geometry book is shown above.

14. What do you think ∠C = ∠C′ = ∠R means?

15. What do you think △ABC ≡ △A′B′C′ means?

16. What theorem do you think is illustrated? State it as a complete sentence.

The Korean name for the theorem, RHS, is remarkable in that it is an abbreviation of three words in *English* rather than Korean.

17. What do you think the three words identifying this theorem are?

Triangle Problem. In △ABC, AD ⊥ BC, BE ⊥ AC, and AD = BE.

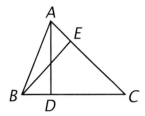

18. Copy the figure above and mark it as needed to answer the following questions.

19. Why is △BAE ≅ △ABD?

20. Why is ∠BAE = ∠ABD?

21. Why is BC = AC?

22. What kind of triangle is △ABC?

Set II

Mirror Distances. A wall mirror is sometimes used to create the illusion that the space of a room is twice as large as it actually is.

This illusion follows from the fact that, when we see light from an object reflected in a mirror, the object and its reflection seem to be at the same distance from the mirror.

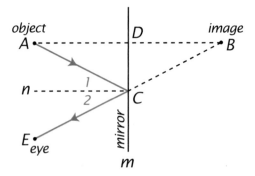

In the figure above, line *m* represents the mirror. Both AB and *n* are perpendicular to *m,* and the angle of incidence, ∠1, is equal to the angle of reflection, ∠2.

23. Copy the figure and mark it as needed to answer each of the following questions.

24. Because AB ⊥ m and n ⊥ m, AB ∥ n. Why?

25. ∠1 = ∠A. Why?

26. ∠2 = ∠B. Why?

27. Because ∠1 = ∠2, ∠A = ∠B. Why?

28. DC = DC. Why?

29. △BDC ≅ △ADC. Why?

30. Therefore, BD = AD. Why?

Angle Bisection. The figure below illustrates the first steps in a different way to bisect an angle.

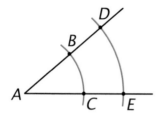

Two arcs have been drawn intersecting the sides of ∠A so that AB = AC and AD = AE.

31. Use your straightedge and compass to make a large copy of the figure. Draw BE and CD.

32. Which parts of △ADC and △AEB can be used to prove them congruent?

33. Why is △ADC ≅ △AEB?

34. Why is ∠ADC = ∠AEB?

31. *(continued)* Label the point in which BE and CD intersect P. Draw AP.

35. Which parts of △BDP and △CEP can be used to prove them congruent?

36. Why is △BDP ≅ △CEP?

37. Why is DP = PE?

38. Which parts of △ADP and △AEP can be used to prove them congruent?

39. Why is △ADP ≅ △AEP?

40. Why does AP bisect ∠DAE?

Origami Frog. The origami pattern for the Japanese jumping frog begins with a square sheet of paper and the two folds shown below.*

 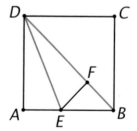

First, corner C is folded onto corner A. Then, side DA is folded onto the fold DB.

41. Copy the figure and mark the following information on it: AB = BC = CD = DA = DF. DA ⊥ AB, EF ⊥ DB, and AB ⊥ BC.

42. Why is △ABD ≅ △CBD?

43. Why is ∠ABD = ∠CBD?

What is the measure of

44. ∠ABD?

45. ∠FEB?

46. Why is EF = FB?

47. What kind of triangles are △ADE and △FDE?

48. Why is △ADE ≅ △FDE?

49. Why is AE = EF?

50. Why is AE = FB?

More on Equal Parts. Each of our methods for proving triangles congruent requires showing that three pairs of parts are equal. Can two triangles have more than three pairs of equal parts but not be congruent?

Consider, for example, one pair of equal angles and three pairs of equal sides.

51. Do you think it is possible that two triangles could have these equal parts and yet not be congruent? Explain why or why not.

―――――――――
Folding the Universe, by Peter Engel (Vintage, 1989).

Consider two pairs of equal sides and three pairs of equal angles.

52. Use your ruler and protractor to draw, as accurately as you can, △ABC with AB = 7.2 cm, ∠A = 21°, AC = 10.8 cm, ∠B = 127°, and ∠C = 32° and △DEF with DE = 10.8 cm, ∠D = 21°, ∠E = 127°, EF = 7.2 cm, and ∠F = 32°.

53. Do you think two triangles can have five pairs of equal parts and not be congruent?

54. Do you think two triangles can have six pairs of equal parts and not be congruent? Explain.

Set III

Is Every Triangle Isosceles? Here is a proof originally published in 1892 that is so strange that it has since become famous.*

The proof supposedly shows that *every* triangle is isosceles and is based on the figure below.

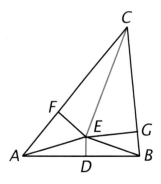

△ABC represents any triangle. The bisector of ∠ACB, CE, and the perpendicular bisector of AB, DE, intersect at E. Lines EF and EG are drawn from E so that EF ⊥ AC and EG ⊥ BC. Finally, lines EA and EB are drawn.

1. Copy the figure and mark it as necessary to explain each of the following statements.

Mathematical Recreations and Essays, by W. W. Rouse Ball (Macmillan, 1892).

2. △CEF ≅ △CEG. Why?

3. EF = EG. Why?

4. △EAD ≅ △EBD. Why?

5. EA = EB. Why?

6. △AFE ≅ △BGE. Why?

7. AF = BG. Why?

8. AF + FC = BG + GC. Why?

9. AF + FC = AC and BG + GC = BC. Why?

10. AC = BC. Why?

Although it seems as if our reasoning is correct, something is obviously very wrong. All triangles are *not* isosceles. The problem with the proof is that we have assumed something from the figure that isn't really true. Here is the same triangle with the lines accurately drawn. Compare the steps of the proof with it.

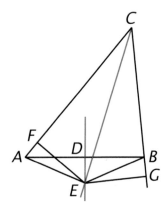

11. Which statements in the proof are actually false?

Basic Ideas

Angles formed by a transversal   220
Line symmetry   212
Parallel lines   219
Transversal   219

Postulate

7. *The Parallel Postulate.* Through a point not on a line, there is exactly one line parallel to the line.   226

Theorems

16. In a plane, two points each equidistant from the endpoints of a line segment determine the perpendicular bisector of the line segment.   212

17. Equal corresponding angles mean that lines are parallel.   220

Corollary 1. Equal alternate interior angles mean that lines are parallel.   220

Corollary 2. Supplementary interior angles on the same side of a transversal mean that lines are parallel.   220

Corollary 3. In a plane, two lines perpendicular to a third line are parallel.   220

18. In a plane, two lines parallel to a third line are parallel to each other.   226

19. Parallel lines form equal corresponding angles.   231

Corollary 1. Parallel lines form equal alternate interior angles.   231

Corollary 2. Parallel lines form supplementary interior angles on the same side of a transversal.   231

Corollary 3. In a plane, a line perpendicular to one of two parallel lines is also perpendicular to the other.   231

20. *The Angle Sum Theorem.* The sum of the angles of a triangle is 180°.   237

Corollary 1. If two angles of one triangle are equal to two angles of another triangle, the third angles are equal.   237

Corollary 2. The acute angles of a right triangle are complementary.   237

Corollary 3. Each angle of an equilateral triangle is 60°.   237

21. An exterior angle of a triangle is equal to the sum of the remote interior angles. 237

22. *The AAS Theorem.* If two angles and the side opposite one of them in one triangle are equal to the corresponding parts of another triangle, the triangles are congruent.   243

23. *The HL Theorem.* If the hypotenuse and a leg of one right triangle are equal to the corresponding parts of another right triangle, the triangles are congruent.   244

Constructions

6. To construct a line perpendicular to a given line through a given point.   213

7. To construct a line parallel to a given line through a given point.   225

Exercises

Set I

Flag Symmetries. At first glance, the flags below all appear to have line symmetry, but one does not.

Algeria

Barbados

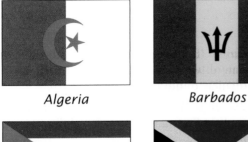

Cuba   Jamaica

1. What is a simple test to determine whether such figures have line symmetry?

2. Which flag does not have line symmetry? Explain.

3. Describe the line (or lines) of symmetry of the other three flags.

Draw two points A and B on your paper as shown in the figure below.

A.

.B

4. Use your straightedge and compass to construct the line such that A and B are symmetric with respect to it.

5. What relation does the line have to line segment AB?

Lot of Lines. A common occurrence of parallel lines and transversals is shown in this photograph.

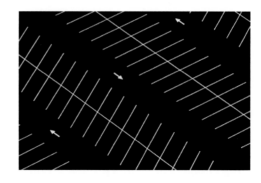

6. What does the photograph show?

The figure below illustrates one method by which the lines might have been made parallel.

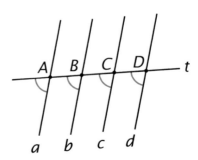

7. What is it?

Construct the figure by doing the following.

8. Draw a line to show the transversal in the figure and use your compass to mark points A, B, C, and D equally spaced along it.
   Without using your protractor, construct a line through A that makes a 60° angle with the transversal.
   Finally, construct lines *b*, *c*, and *d* parallel to line *a*.

Alphabet. The shapes of some of the letters of the alphabet illustrate some of the definitions and theorems of geometry. Complete the definition or theorem suggested by each of the following figures.

9.

An exterior angle of a triangle is equal . . .

10.

Parallel lines . . .

11.

In a plane, two lines . . .

12.

If two lines form a right angle . . .

13.

Equal alternate . . .

14.

If the angles in a linear pair . . .

15.

Vertical angles . . .

Ollie's Mistakes. In their big review for the geometry test, Obtuse Ollie misstated four theorems. Acute Alice drew a figure for each one to show him that something was wrong. Rewrite each theorem so that it is stated correctly.

16. "In a plane, a point equidistant from the endpoints of a line segment determines the perpendicular bisector of the line segment."

17. "If two angles and a side of one triangle are equal to two angles and a side of another triangle, the triangles are congruent."

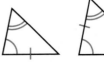

18. "If two sides of one triangle are equal to two sides of another triangle, the third sides are equal."

19. "A line perpendicular to one of two parallel lines is also perpendicular to the other."

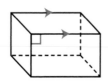

Triangle Division. Each of the equilateral triangles below is divided into five triangular pieces.* Make a large copy of each figure and write in the measures of the other angles.

20.

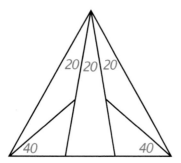

21.

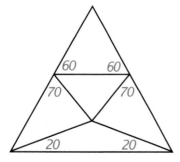

22.

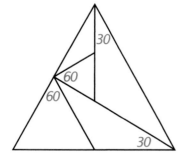

Which Way Did the Bicycle Go? by Joseph D. E. Konhauser, Dan Yelleman, and Stan Wagon (Mathematical Association of America, 1996).

23. What do all of the triangular pieces in all three figures have in common?

24. How many pieces in each figure are equilateral triangles?

Angle Trisection. Although it is impossible to trisect most angles with only a straightedge and compass, it *is* possible to trisect a right angle.

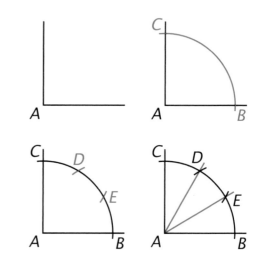

25. Use your ruler and protractor to draw right ∠A as shown in the first figure above.

    With A as center draw an arc intersecting the sides of the angle at B and C as shown in the second figure.

    With B as center, draw an arc with the same radius intersecting arc BC at D as shown in the third figure. With C as center, draw an arc with the same radius intersecting arc BC at E.

    Draw AD and AE as shown in the fourth figure.

    Finally, use your protractor to check the accuracy of your construction.

26. Draw DB and EC. What kind of triangles are △DAB and △EAC?

27. What can you conclude about ∠DAB and ∠EAC? Why?

28. What can you conclude about ∠EAB? Why?

Surveyor's Triangle. Surveyors use a right triangle in drawing perpendicular lines. If the triangle is defective, it can seem to produce two lines perpendicular to line *l* through point P as shown in the figure below.*

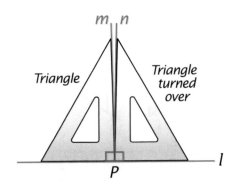

29. In a plane, through a given point, how many lines can be drawn perpendicular to a given line?

30. State the theorem that would be contradicted if lines *m* and *n* are both perpendicular to *l*.

31. What relation would the line that is actually perpendicular to line *l* at P have to the angle shown in red?

Elementary Surveying, by Paul R. Wolf and Russell C. Brinker (Harper Collins, 1989).

32. Draw line *l*, mark point P on it, and use your straightedge and compass to construct the line through P that is perpendicular to *l*.

Set II

Magnifying Glass.
A magnifying glass can be used to focus the light rays of the sun on a small spot. In this figure, AB ∥ CP ∥ EF, and CP is the perpendicular bisector of BF.

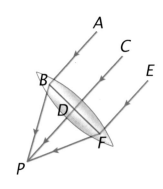

33. If all of the lines lie in the same plane, why must it be that AB ⊥ BF and EF ⊥ BF?

34. Why does it follow that ∠ABF = ∠EFB?

35. What word describes lines such as BP, CP, and FP that meet in a single point?

36. Why is △BDP ≅ △FDP?

37. Why does it follow that ∠PBF = ∠PFB?

38. What conclusion follows about ∠ABP and ∠EFP?

Measuring a Tree. The figure below appeared in an old geometry book.*

It illustrated a method for finding the height of a tree on the other side of a river. The directions said:

Find the point C directly opposite the tree where the angle of elevation ACB of the tree is 45°. Lay off from C a line CD perpendicular to AC and of such length that the angle ADC = 45°.

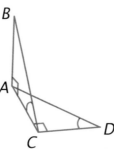

39. If this is done, what can you conclude about ∠B and ∠CAD?

40. What can you conclude about BA and AC and about AC and CD?

41. Why?

42. Why would CD have to be equal to the height of the tree?

Quadrilateral Problem. In quadrilateral ABCD, AD = BC and AB ∥ DC.

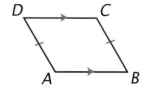

43. Name a pair of angles in the figure that must be supplementary.

---

*First Steps in Geometry, by G. A. Wentworth and G. A. Hill (Ginn, 1901).

44. How do you know?

45. Do you know that any angles in the figure are equal? If so, which ones?

Isosceles Triangle. In isosceles △ABE, AB = BC = CD = DE.

46. Draw the figure and mark it as needed to answer each of the following.

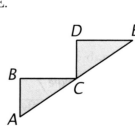

Find the measures of the following angles in terms of x.

47. ∠ECD.

48. ∠CDB.

49. ∠DBC.

50. ∠ACB.

51. ∠A.

52. ∠ABE.

53. Write an equation and solve for x to find the measure of ∠E.

Stair Steps. In the figure at the right illustrating two stair steps, △ABC and △CDE are right triangles, AB = CD, and C is the midpoint of AE.

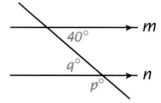

54. Copy the figure and mark it as needed to explain why BC ∥ DE.

SAT Problem. The figure at the right appeared on an SAT exam.

Three angles formed by parallel lines m and n and the transversal have been marked.

55. The problem is to find $p - q$. Explain how this can be done.

Operations with Fractions

Addition and Subtraction

Recall that division is defined in terms of multiplication:

$$\frac{a}{b} = a \cdot \frac{1}{b}.$$

For fractions having the same denominator, it follows that

$$\frac{a}{b} + \frac{c}{b} = a \cdot \frac{1}{b} + c \cdot \frac{1}{b} = (a + c) \cdot \frac{1}{b} = \frac{a + c}{b}$$

and that

$$\frac{a}{b} - \frac{c}{b} = \frac{a - c}{b}.$$

Before fractions having different denominators can be added or subtracted, they must be expressed as fractions having a common denominator.
In general,

$$\frac{a}{b} + \frac{c}{d} = \frac{ad}{bd} + \frac{bc}{bd} = \frac{ad + bc}{bd}$$

and

$$\frac{a}{b} - \frac{c}{d} = \frac{ad}{bd} - \frac{bc}{bd} = \frac{ad - bc}{bd}.$$

Example 1:

$$\frac{x}{3} + \frac{2}{y}$$

Solution:

$$\frac{xy}{3y} + \frac{6}{3y} = \frac{xy + 6}{3y}$$

Example 2:

$$\frac{x}{x - 1} - \frac{x}{x + 1}$$

Solution:

$$\frac{x(x + 1)}{(x - 1)(x + 1)} - \frac{x(x - 1)}{(x + 1)(x - 1)} =$$

$$\frac{x^2 + x - x^2 + x}{(x + 1)(x - 1)} = \frac{2x}{x^2 - 1}$$

This excerpt from a popular arithmetic book published in Germany in 1514 shows Roman numerals being used to write fractions. The first fraction is $\frac{1}{4}$. Do you recognize the others?

Multiplication

Multiplying fractions is easy. In general,

$$\frac{a}{b} \cdot \frac{c}{d} = \frac{ac}{bd}.$$

Division

The definition of division expresses division as multiplication by the reciprocal; so, in general,

$$\frac{a}{b} \div \frac{c}{d} = \frac{a}{b} \cdot \frac{d}{c} = \frac{ad}{bc}.$$

Example 3: $5x \cdot \dfrac{x}{4}$

Solution: $\dfrac{5x}{1} \cdot \dfrac{x}{4} = \dfrac{5x^2}{4}$

Example 4: $\dfrac{x}{x+6} \div \dfrac{x}{x+3}$

Solution: $\dfrac{x}{x+6} \cdot \dfrac{x+3}{x} = \dfrac{x(x+3)}{x(x+6)} = \dfrac{x+3}{x+6}$

Exercises

Do the indicated operations.
Express your answers in
lowest terms.

1. $\dfrac{1}{2} + \dfrac{2}{3}$

2. $\dfrac{x}{4} - \dfrac{x}{5}$

3. $\dfrac{x+5}{2x} + \dfrac{5}{2x}$

4. $\dfrac{4}{x^2} - \dfrac{3}{x^3}$

5. $\dfrac{3}{4} \cdot \dfrac{8}{9}$

6. $\dfrac{x^2}{2} \cdot \dfrac{x^4}{4}$

7. $\dfrac{1}{2} \div \dfrac{7}{10}$

8. $\dfrac{x+2}{x} \div \dfrac{2}{x}$

9. $\dfrac{5x}{16} + \dfrac{7x}{16}$

10. $\dfrac{x+4}{10} - \dfrac{x+2}{10}$

11. $\dfrac{x+y}{12} \cdot \dfrac{2}{x+y}$

12. $\dfrac{10}{x} \div 5$

13. $\dfrac{x}{2} + \dfrac{y}{4} - \dfrac{z}{8}$

14. $\dfrac{\pi r}{2} \cdot \dfrac{8r^2}{3}$

15. $\dfrac{x}{y} - 1$

16. $\dfrac{6}{2x-3} \cdot \dfrac{x-3}{3}$

17. $\dfrac{3x}{x^2-1} - \dfrac{2}{x+1}$

18. $\dfrac{y}{xy-y^2} + \dfrac{x}{x-y}$

19. $\dfrac{x^2+8x+15}{x^2+x-6} \div \dfrac{x+5}{x-2}$

20. $x^2 + x + 1 + \dfrac{1}{x-1}$

Chapter 7

Quadrilaterals

How many squares does this figure contain?

This page is rectangular, as are the doors that you walk through and the floors that you walk on. Rectangles, squares, parallelograms, and other quadrilaterals are found everywhere. In this chapter, you will see that what you know about triangles and parallel lines can be applied to understanding the geometry of quadrilaterals. To learn to see and identify the various types of quadrilaterals and to instinctively know their properties are the goals of this chapter.

LESSON 1

Quadrilaterals

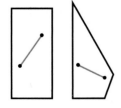

convex polygons

a concave polygon

The window in the above photograph, used in an ad for the Marvin Window and Door Company, has an unusual shape. Unlike most windows, which are rectangular in shape, it appears to have only one right angle and sides of four different lengths. It is like a rectangle, however, in that it is a *quadrilateral* and is *convex*.

A polygon is *convex* if, for each pair of points inside the polygon, the line segment connecting them lies entirely inside the polygon. Examples of such segments are shown in green in the convex polygons at the left. A polygon is *concave* if, for a pair of points inside the polygon, the line segment connecting them does *not* lie entirely inside the polygon.

Although all triangles are convex, quadrilaterals and other polygons may be convex or concave. For convenience, when we deal with any polygon having more than three sides, we will always consider it to be convex unless stated otherwise.

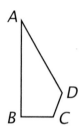 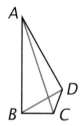

Two sides of a quadrilateral that intersect, such as AD and DC in the figure at the left above, are called *consecutive*. A pair of sides that do not intersect, such as AB and DC, are called *opposite*. The same terms are applied to the vertices and angles of a quadrilateral; ∠A and ∠D, for example, are *consecutive angles;* points A and C are *opposite vertices.*

Every quadrilateral also has two *diagonals* (AC and BD in the example at the right above).

Definition
A *diagonal* of a polygon is a line segment that connects any two nonconsecutive vertices.

All of the diagonals from one vertex of a polygon divide the polygon into a set of triangles; so we can extend our knowledge of triangles to polygons in general. For example, in regard to a quadrilateral, the diagonal from one vertex results in two triangles. Using the fact that the sum of the angles of every triangle is 180°, we can easily show that the sum of the angles of every quadrilateral is 360°.

Theorem 24
The sum of the angles of a quadrilateral is 360°.

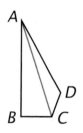

From this theorem (whose proof is considered in an exercise), it immediately follows that, if a quadrilateral is equiangular, each of its angles is a right angle. This is, in fact, how the rectangle got its name: the Latin word *rectangulum* means "right angled."

If these angles are equal, each is a right angle.   *a rectangle*

Definition
A *rectangle* is a quadrilateral each of whose angles is a right angle.

Corollary to Theorem 24
A quadrilateral is equiangular iff it is a rectangle.

Exercises

Set I

Theorem 24. Complete the following proof of Theorem 24 by giving the reasons. The proof is written in paragraph form.

The sum of the angles of a quadrilateral is 360°.

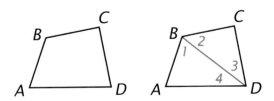

Given: ABCD is a quadrilateral.
Prove: ∠A + ∠B + ∠C + ∠D = 360°.

Proof
1. Draw BD. Why?
2. ∠A + ∠1 + ∠4 = 180° and ∠2 + ∠3 + ∠C = 180°. Why?
3. ∠A + ∠1 + ∠4 + ∠2 + ∠3 + ∠C = 360°. Why?
4. ∠1 + ∠2 = ∠ABC and ∠3 + ∠4 = ∠CDA. Why?
5. ∠A + ∠ABC + ∠C + ∠CDA = 360°. Why?

Corollary. Complete the following proof of the corollary to Theorem 24.

A quadrilateral is equiangular iff it is a rectangle.

Proof that, if a quadrilateral is equiangular, it is a rectangle.

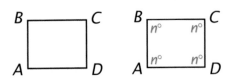

Given: ABCD with ∠A = ∠B = ∠C = ∠D.
Prove: ABCD is a rectangle.

Proof
6. If the measure of each angle is $n°$, then $4n = 360$. Why?
7. So $n = 90$. Why?
8. So ∠A, ∠B, ∠C, and ∠D are right angles. Why?
9. So ABCD is a rectangle. Why?

Proof that, if a quadrilateral is a rectangle, it is equiangular.

Given: ABCD is a rectangle.
Prove: ∠A = ∠B = ∠C = ∠D.

Proof
10. Because ABCD is a rectangle, ∠A, ∠B, ∠C, and ∠D are right angles. Why?
11. So ∠A = ∠B = ∠C = ∠D. Why?

Carpets. This photograph shows a freeway overpass under construction near Santa Barbara, California.* Old carpets were used to keep the concrete from hardening too quickly.

Carpets usually have the shape of equiangular quadrilaterals.

12. What are equiangular quadrilaterals commonly called?

Below from Above: Aerial Photography, by Georg Gerster (Abbeville Press, 1986).

ABCD is an equiangular quadrilateral.

13. What kind of angles does it have?
14. Why are AD and BC perpendicular to AB and DC?
15. Why are the opposite sides of ABCD parallel?

Rectangles. Each of the figures below is a rectangle. The diagonals are shown in blue.

16. What is always true about the angles of a rectangle?

What seems to be true about

17. the opposite sides of a rectangle?
18. the diagonals of a rectangle?

Rhombuses. Each of the figures below is a rhombus. The diagonals are shown in blue.

What seems to be true about

19. the sides of a rhombus?
20. the diagonals of a rhombus?

Squares. Each of the figures below is a *square*.

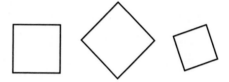

What property do you think squares have in common with

21. rectangles?
22. rhombuses?

Parallelograms. Each of the figures below is a parallelogram. The diagonals are shown in blue.

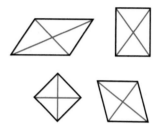

What seems to be true about

23. the opposite sides of a parallelogram?
24. the opposite angles of a parallelogram?
25. the diagonals of a parallelogram?

SAT Problem. The figure below appeared in a problem on an SAT exam.

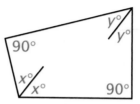

What can you conclude about

26. 2x + 2y?
27. x + y?

Set II

Penrose Tiles. "Penrose tiles," named after physicist Roger Penrose, who discovered them, can be used to tile a plane in infinitely many ways. A sample of doing so is shown above.*

The tiles have the shapes of the two quadrilaterals in the figure below.

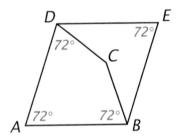

28. Which Penrose tile is convex?

29. Find the measure of ∠BCD.

30. Make a large copy of the figure and draw AC and CE.

The figure is drawn so that AB = BE = ED = DA and CB = CE = CD. Mark this information on your figure.

31. How do you know that △ADC ≅ △ABC and △EDC ≅ △EBC?

30. *(continued)* Find the measures of the rest of the angles and mark them in your figure.

32. What do all four triangles in the figure have in common?

The Penguin Dictionary of Curious and Interesting Geometry, by David Wells (Penguin, 1991).

33. What seems to be true about points A, C, and E?

34. Explain why it is true.

35. Does the figure appear to have line symmetry? Why or why not?

We have proved that, if a triangle is equilateral, it is also equiangular.

36. If a quadrilateral is equilateral, does it follow that it is also equiangular? Use the figure to explain why or why not.

Gemstone Pattern. One pattern used in cutting gemstones is the "oval cut" shown here.

37. What polygons are the shapes of its faces?

Our knowledge of the angles of triangles and quadrilaterals can be easily extended to other polygons such as the one in the center of the pattern above. To see how, look at the figure below. In it, a pentagon has been divided into triangles by the diagonals from one vertex.

38. How many sides does a pentagon have, how many diagonals were drawn, and how many triangles were formed?

39. Draw a hexagon and the diagonals from one vertex.

40. How many sides does a hexagon have, how many diagonals did you draw, and how many triangles were formed?

41. Copy the figure above, which shows the polygon at the center of the "oval cut," and draw the diagonals from one vertex.

42. How many sides does the polygon have, how many diagonals did you draw, and how many triangles were formed?

Use your observations and results to do the following exercises. In general, if a polygon has *n* sides, in terms of *n*,

43. how many diagonals can be drawn from one vertex?

44. how many triangles do these diagonals form?

45. Show that your answers are correct for a quadrilateral.

The figure below suggests that the sum of the angles of a pentagon is $3 \times 180° = 540°$.

If the pentagon is equiangular, then each angle is $\dfrac{540°}{5} = 108°$.

46. What is the sum of the angles of a hexagon?

47. If the hexagon is equiangular, how large is each angle?

48. What is the sum of the angles of an octagon?

49. If the octagon is equiangular, how large is each angle?

50. What, in terms of *n*, is the sum of the angles of an *n*-gon?

51. If the *n*-gon is equiangular, how large is each angle in terms of *n*?

Linkage Problems. The figure below shows a linkage made of four rods. The rods can pivot about their ends; so the figure can change its shape.

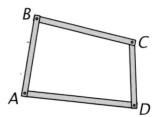

52. What can you conclude about the four angles of the linkage when it is in an arrangement such as the one shown?

Suppose the linkage is arranged so that points B, C, and D are collinear, as shown at the left below.

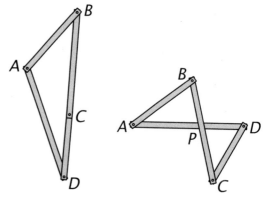

53. What can you conclude about the angles of the linkage now?

Suppose the linkage is arranged so that rods AD and BC cross in a point P as shown at the right above.

54. How do the measures of ∠A, ∠B, ∠C, and ∠D in this arrangement compare with their measures in the first arrangement?

55. Why, in this arrangement, is ∠A + ∠B = ∠C + ∠D?

Quadrilateral Angle Sum. ABCD is a quadrilateral in which a line has been drawn intersecting two opposite sides at X and Y.

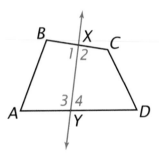

If we assume that the sum of the angles of a quadrilateral is a constant number, S, then we can use this figure to explain why S must equal 360°. Show why by giving a reason for each of the following statements.

Suppose $\angle A + \angle B + \angle C + \angle D = S$, $\angle A + \angle B + \angle 1 + \angle 3 = S$, and $\angle C + \angle D + \angle 2 + \angle 4 = S$.

56. $\angle A + \angle B + \angle C + \angle D + \angle 1 + \angle 2 + \angle 3 + \angle 4 = 2S$. Why?

57. $S + \angle 1 + \angle 2 + \angle 3 + \angle 4 = 2S$. Why?

58. $\angle 1 + \angle 2 + \angle 3 + \angle 4 = S$. Why?

59. Finish the proof by explaining why it follows that $S = 360°$.

Set III

Triangle into Square. The following figures illustrate how an equilateral triangle can be cut into four pieces that can be rearranged to form a square.

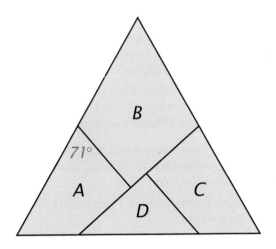

Make a large copy of the figure above, in which the measure of one of the angles of piece A has been given to the nearest degree. Find the measures of as many of the rest of the angles in the figure as you can.

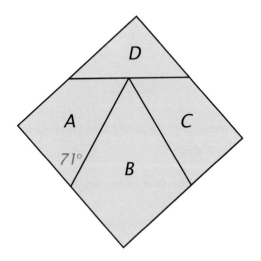

Parallelograms and Point Symmetry

An octopus sees things very differently from the way that we see them. Experiments have shown that an octopus can distinguish between certain geometric shapes but not between others.* For example, of the three figures shown above, two look alike to an octopus and one looks different. Which do you suppose looks different?

The answer is B. If an octopus recognized a geometric figure by the number of sides it has, the answer would be C. From the way in which the eyes of an octopus work, shapes A and C look alike!

This is strange because, from a geometric point of view, figures A and B are the most nearly alike. They are *parallelograms,* whereas figure C is a concave hexagon.

Definition
A *parallelogram* is a quadrilateral whose opposite sides are parallel.

Because figures A and B are parallelograms, they have several other properties in common. It is easy to prove that the opposite sides of a parallelogram are not only parallel but also equal, as are the opposite angles. Furthermore, all parallelograms have *point symmetry.*

Animal Behavior, by Niko Tinbergen (Time, Inc., 1965).

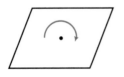

A figure has point symmetry if it looks exactly the same when it is turned upside down. For every parallelogram there is a point, called the center of symmetry, about which it can be turned 180° so that it coincides with itself. For a pair of points, we can show that this is equivalent to the following definition.

Definition

Two points are ***symmetric with respect to a point*** iff it is the midpoint of the line segment joining them.

Parallelograms have point symmetry about the point in which their diagonals intersect. This follows from the fact that the diagonals bisect each other. The properties of parallelograms mentioned in this lesson are useful to know and are stated as theorems below.

Theorem 25

The opposite sides and angles of a parallelogram are equal.

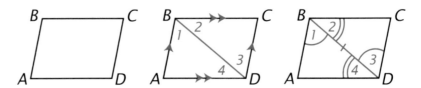

Given: ABCD is a parallelogram.
Prove: AB = DC, AD = BC, ∠A = ∠C, and ∠B = ∠D.

The three figures above suggest the proof.

Proof
Draw a diagonal of ABCD. The opposite sides of a parallelogram are parallel; so AB ∥ DC and AD ∥ BC. It follows that ∠1 = ∠3 and ∠2 = ∠4 because parallel lines form equal alternate interior angles.

Because BD = BD (reflexive), △ABD ≅ △CDB (ASA). Therefore, AB = DC, AD = BC, and ∠A = ∠C (corresponding parts of congruent triangles are equal). Because ∠1 = ∠3 and ∠2 = ∠4, ∠1 + ∠2 = ∠3 + ∠4 (addition). ∠ABC = ∠1 + ∠2 and ∠CDA = ∠3 + ∠4 (from the figure and the Betweenness of Rays Theorem); so ∠ABC = ∠CDA (substitution).

Theorem 26

The diagonals of a parallelogram bisect each other.

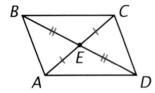

This theorem, illustrated by the figure at the left, also can be proved by using congruent triangles. A proof of it is included in the exercises.

Exercises

Set I

These cards are from a baseball card game published in Boston a century ago.*

1. Which card is symmetric?

2. What kind of symmetry does it have?

3. What is a simple test for this kind of symmetry?

Optical Illusion. The figure below, called "Sandor's parallelogram," appears in a book of optical illusions.†

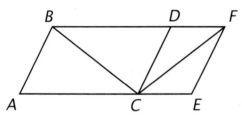

In the figure, AB ∥ CD ∥ EF and AE ∥ BF.

4. How many parallelograms does the figure contain?

It appears that AC = BD and CE = DF.

5. Is this necessarily true? Explain.

6. What do you think is the illusion in this figure?

Explain why each of the following statements must be true.

7. ∠A = ∠BDC.

8. ∠BDC > ∠BFC.

9. ∠A > ∠BFC.

_____

*Paper Toys of the World, by Blair Whitton (Hobby House Press, 1986).
†Can You Believe Your Eyes? by J. R. Block and Harold E. Yuker (Brunner/Mazel, 1992).

Theorem 26. Complete the following proof of Theorem 26 by giving the reasons. The proof is written in paragraph form.

The diagonals of a parallelogram bisect each other.

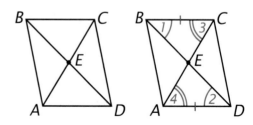

Given: ABCD is a parallelogram with diagonals AC and BD.
Prove: AC and BD bisect each other.

Proof

10. Because ABCD is a parallelogram, BC = AD. Why?

11. Also, BC ∥ AD. Why?

12. So ∠1 = ∠2 and ∠3 = ∠4. Why?

13. △BEC ≅ △DEA. Why?

14. BE = DE and EC = EA. Why?

15. AC and BD bisect each other. Why?

Point Symmetry. Every parallelogram has point symmetry. The center of symmetry is the point in which the diagonals of the parallelogram intersect.

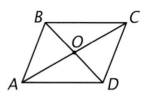

16. Copy the figure above showing parallelogram ABCD with its diagonals intersecting at O.

17. Why is OA = OC and OB = OD?

Mark your figure to show these and other equal parts as you continue.

18. Why are A and C (as well as B and D) symmetric with respect to O?

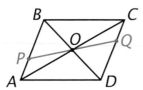

Suppose any other point, such as P in the figure above, is chosen on ABCD and line PO is drawn to intersect ABCD in Q. We can show that P and Q are symmetric with respect to O.

19. Why is ∠ABD = ∠BDC?

20. Why is ∠POB = ∠QOD?

21. Why is △POB ≅ △QOD?

22. Why is OP = OQ?

23. Why are P and Q symmetric with respect to O?

Set II

Parallelogram Rule. Isaac Newton modeled his book titled *The Mathematical Principles of Natural Philosophy* on Euclid's *Elements.*

COROL. I.

Corpus viribus conjunctis diagonalem parallelogrammi eodem tempore describere, quo latera separatis.

Si corpus dato tempore, vi sola **M** in loco *A* impreffa, ferretur uniformi cum motu ab *A* ad B; & vi fola *N* in eodem loco impreffa, ferretur ab *A* ad *C*: compleatur parallelogrammum *ABDC*; & vi utraque feretur corpus illud eodem tempore in diagonali ab *A* ad *D*. Nam quoniam vis *N* agit fecundum lineam *AC* ipfi *BD* parallelam, hæc vis per legem ɪɪ nihil

His "parallelogram rule" for the addition of forces is given above.

24. What word do you think "Corol." is an abbreviation of?

Sides AB and AC of the parallelogram represent two forces acting on point A.

25. Use your ruler and protractor to draw the part of Newton's figure shown below. Use the measurements shown. Complete the figure by drawing a line through C parallel to AB and a line through B parallel to AC. Also draw AD.

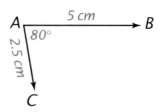

Suppose force AB is 50 pounds.

26. How many pounds does 1 cm on your figure represent?

27. How many pounds is force AC?

The diagonal AD represents the force that is equivalent to the two forces AB and AC.

28. Measure AD in centimeters.

29. How many pounds is force AD?

30. What is the measure of the angle that force AD makes with force AB?

Angle Bisectors. ABCD is a parallelogram in which BE bisects ∠ABC and CE bisects ∠BCD.

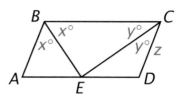

31. Copy the figure and mark this information on it.

32. Find and name another angle whose measure is $x°$ and another angle whose measure is $y°$.

33. Find and name any other line segments whose lengths are z.

34. What can you conclude about point E?

35. What can you conclude about AD and DC?

36. How are ∠ABC and ∠BCD related? Explain.

37. What is $2x + 2y$?

38. What is $x + y$?

39. What kind of triangles are △ABE and △ECD?

40. What kind of triangle is △BEC? Explain.

41. What can you conclude about BE and EC?

Two Parallelograms. In the figure below, ABDE and BCDE are parallelograms; ∠A = $x°$, ∠EBD = $y°$, and ∠C = $z°$.

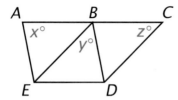

42. Copy the figure and mark any other angles whose measures are $x°$, $y°$, and $z°$.

Points A, B, and C appear to be collinear.

43. Explain, using x, y, and z, why these points are collinear.

44. Explain, using the Parallel Postulate, why A, B, and C must be collinear.

45. Which triangles in the figure are congruent?

46. Are the parallelograms congruent?

Hidden Triangles. In the figure below, ABCD is a parallelogram in which ∠BAD = 75°; △ABE and △BCF are equilateral triangles.

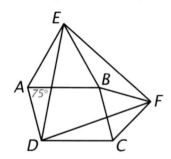

47. Copy the figure and mark it as needed to do each of the following exercises.

48. Find three triangles in the figure that are congruent.

49. How do you know that they are congruent?

50. How many equilateral triangles are in the figure? Explain.

Set III

Playing Card Symmetries. Some of the cards in a standard deck of 52 playing cards are symmetric and some are not. For example, in the old playing cards shown below, the king of clubs has point symmetry but the nine of hearts does not.

Go through a deck of cards and sort them according to their symmetry.

1. Why do so many cards have point symmetry?

2. Which cards have line symmetry?

3. Are the cards in any suit more symmetric than in the others? If so, why?

4. Can you make any general statements about the types of cards that do or do not have symmetry?

5. Could some of the cards be slightly redesigned so that they also have symmetry? If so, which ones and how?

LESSON 3

More on Parallelograms

Room as "seen"

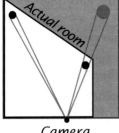

Camera

The large photographs above are of the same boy and the same dog in the same room. Neither picture has been retouched.* How can this be?

The room has been designed to fool us. Its walls and windows seem to be rectangular, but they are not. The small photograph reveals the room's actual shape. The floor and ceiling slope toward each other and, as the floor plan of the room at the left shows, the left back corner is much farther from the camera than is the corner at the right. Because we are fooled into thinking that the room is a normal one, we interpret the larger size of both the boy and the dog at the right as meaning that they are larger rather than simply closer to us.

Part of the effectiveness of the illusion is due to our taking for granted that all of the quadrilaterals in the room are *parallelograms,* which they are not. What do we need to know about a quadrilateral to be sure that it is a parallelogram?

———————

The Mind, by John Rowan Wilson (Time-Life Books, 1969).

Just knowing that its opposite sides are parallel is sufficient, because that is our definition of a parallelogram. This way and some others are listed below and illustrated at the right.

A quadrilateral is a parallelogram if
1. its opposite sides are parallel.
2. its opposite sides are equal.
3. its opposite angles are equal.
4. two opposite sides are parallel and equal.
5. its diagonals bisect each other.

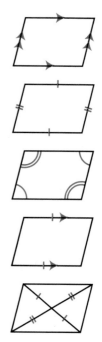

Some of these ways sound familiar because they are converses of theorems that we already know. Most of them can be proved by using congruent triangles.

Theorem 27

A quadrilateral is a parallelogram if its opposite sides are equal.

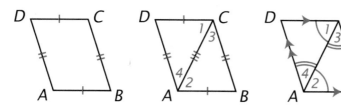

Given: In quadrilateral ABCD, AB = DC and AD = BC.
Prove: ABCD is a parallelogram.

The three figures suggest the proof.

Proof
Draw diagonal AC to form △ABC and △ADC. The triangles are congruent according to SSS. It follows that ∠1 = ∠2 and ∠3 = ∠4 because corresponding parts of congruent triangles are equal. So AB ∥ DC and AD ∥ BC (equal alternate interior angles mean that lines are parallel). Therefore ABCD is a parallelogram because its opposite sides are parallel.

The following theorems can be proved just as easily. Their proofs are included in the exercises.

Theorem 28

A quadrilateral is a parallelogram if its opposite angles are equal.

Theorem 29

A quadrilateral is a parallelogram if two opposite sides are both parallel and equal.

Theorem 30

A quadrilateral is a parallelogram if its diagonals bisect each other.

Exercises

Set I

Pop-Up Parallelogram. Pop-up books and cards operate by means of parallelograms. The pop-up parts are kept parallel to the page as it moves by means of tabs such as the one shown in the figure above.*

Each tab is constructed so that AB = DC and AD = BC.

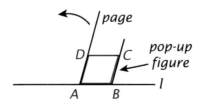

1. Why, as the tab pulls the figure up, is ABCD always a parallelogram?

2. Why is BC parallel to AD?

3. Why are the corresponding angles at A and B always equal?

4. When AD ⊥ *l*, why must BC also be perpendicular to *l*?

Theorem 28. Complete the following proof of Theorem 28 by giving the reasons.

A quadrilateral is a parallelogram if its opposite angles are equal.

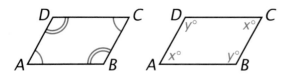

Given: In quadrilateral ABCD, ∠A = ∠C and ∠B = ∠D.
Prove: ABCD is a parallelogram.

Mathematics Meets Technology, by Brian Bolt (Cambridge University Press, 1991).

Proof
Let the measures of the angles be $x°$ and $y°$.

5. $2x + 2y = 360$. Why?

6. $x + y = 180$. Why?

7. ∠A and ∠B are supplementary and ∠A and ∠D are supplementary. Why?

8. AD ∥ BC and AB ∥ DC. Why?

9. ABCD is a parallelogram. Why?

Theorem 29. Complete the following proof of Theorem 29 by giving the reasons.

A quadrilateral is a parallelogram if two opposite sides are both parallel and equal.

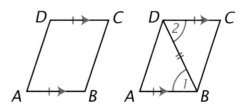

Given: In quadrilateral ABCD, AB ∥ DC and AB = DC.
Prove: ABCD is a parallelogram.

Proof
10. Draw DB. Why?

11. Because AB ∥ DC, ∠1 = ∠2. Why?

12. DB = DB. Why?

13. Because we also know that AB = DC, △ABD ≅ △CDB. Why?

14. So AD = CB. Why?

15. Therefore, ABCD is a parallelogram. Why?

Theorem 30. Complete the following proof of Theorem 30 by giving the reasons.

A quadrilateral is a parallelogram if its diagonals bisect each other.

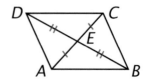

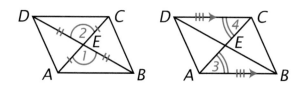

Given: In quadrilateral ABCD, AC and BD bisect each other.

Prove: ABCD is a parallelogram.

Proof

16. Because AC and BD bisect each other, AE = EC and BE = ED. Why?

17. $\angle 1 = \angle 2$. Why?

18. $\triangle AEB \cong \triangle CED$. Why?

19. AB = CD and $\angle 3 = \angle 4$. Why?

20. AB ∥ CD. Why?

21. ABCD is a parallelogram. Why?

Letter Transformations. Transformations of the first letter of the word parallelogram can be used to illustrate the two basic types of symmetry.*

Name the type of symmetry possessed by each of the following figures and briefly explain why the figure has it.

22.   **23.**   **24.**

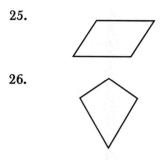

Quadrilateral Symmetries. Tell whether or not each of the following figures appears to be a parallelogram and describe the symmetry of each.

25.

26.

---

*Inversions, by Scott Kim (Byte Books, 1981).

27.

28.

Economics Graph. The figure below is part of a graph from an economics book.[†] The two segments labeled I are equal and parallel.

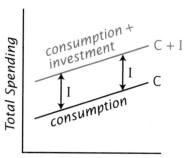

Gross National Product

29. What seems to be true about the lines labeled C and C + I?

30. Explain why it must be true.

Set II

Parallel Rulers. Parallel rulers are two rulers connected by two links so that they always remain parallel.

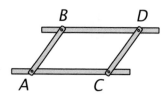

31. How do you think the parallel rulers are designed to ensure that they always remain parallel?

32. As the rulers are used, what always remain equal even though their size changes?

[†]Economics, by Paul A. Samuelson and William D. Nordhaus (McGraw-Hill, 2001).

Tent Geometry. In this drawing of a tent, ABCD and CDEF are parallelograms. It is true that, not only in a plane but also in space, two lines parallel to the same line are parallel to each other.

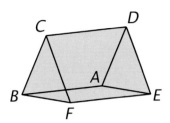

33. Copy the figure and mark it as needed to do each of the following exercises.

34. It appears that ABFE also is a parallelogram. Is this necessarily true? Explain.

35. △ADE and △BCF look as if they are congruent. Is this necessarily true? Explain.

Rope Trick. One of the methods used in Africa to construct a rectangle for the base of a house is described below.

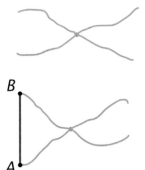

The house builders start with two ropes of equal length that are tied together at their midpoints. A bamboo stick, whose length is equal to that of the desired width of the house, is laid down on the floor and at its endpoints pins are hit into the ground. An endpoint of each of the ropes is tied to one of the pins. Then the ropes are stretched [so that each of the original ropes forms a straight segment]

and at the remaining two endpoints of the ropes, new pins are hit into the ground. These four pins determine the four vertices of the house to be built.*

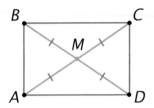

36. Draw the figure above and mark it as needed to explain why this method works by answering each of the following questions.

37. Why is ABCD a parallelogram?

38. Why is AB = DC?

39. Why is △BAD ≅ △CDA?

40. Why is ∠BAD = ∠CDA?

41. Why is ∠BAD = ∠BCD and ∠CDA = ∠ABC?

42. Why is ∠BCD = ∠ABC?

43. Why is ABCD a rectangle?

Parallel Postulate. The Parallel Postulate is one of the most famous statements of geometry.

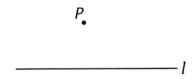

44. What does it say about the figure above?

It is possible to construct, through P, a line parallel to line *l* without ever changing the radius of the compass.

Geometry from Africa, by Paulus Gerdes (Mathematical Association of America, 1999).

The method goes back to at least 1574 and the figure below shows how to do it.*

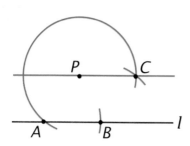

45. Use your straightedge and compass as well as the figure as a guide to do the construction.

46. Explain, by drawing PA and CB, why line PC is parallel to line *l*.

Flexible Grid. The figure at the left below shows a grid of squares whose sides are identical steel beams connected by pins at each corner. One of the squares has been braced with a longer beam.†

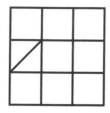 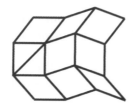

The grid is not rigid and can be flexed as shown in the figure at the right above. (Assume that the grid is still flat, so that all of the beams still lie in the same plane, and that the braced square does not turn.)

The grid contains 25 beams in all. How many of them are horizontal in the

47. first position?

48. second position?

How many of them are vertical in the

49. first position?

50. second position?

When the grid is flexed, why do the

51. two triangles remain unchanged?

52. sides of the quadrilaterals remain parallel?

Where are the beams in the second figure that remain

53. horizontal?

54. vertical?

55. Why do these beams remain horizontal and vertical?

Set III

Equilateral Triangles Mystery. Here is a remarkable result that is easier to discover than to explain.‡

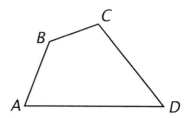

1. Draw a large quadrilateral of approximately the same shape as the one shown above. Use your straightedge and compass to construct equilateral triangles alternately inward and outward on its sides. Connect their vertices to form another quadrilateral.

2. What seems to be true?

Mathematical Circus, by Martin Gardner (Knopf, 1979).

†*Connections: The Geometric Bridge Between Art and Science,* by Jay Kappraff (McGraw-Hill, 1991).

‡*The Penguin Dictionary of Curious and Interesting Geometry,* by David Wells (Penguin, 1991).

Rectangles, Rhombuses, and Squares

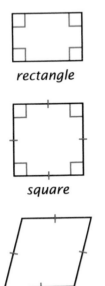

rectangle

The photograph above was taken from directly above a boxing ring. Muhammad Ali is standing at the lower-left corner after knocking Cleveland Williams flat on the floor.

The boxing ring is in the shape of the most symmetric of all quadrilaterals: the square. Every square is a *rectangle* because it is equiangular. Every square is also equilateral.

Definition

A *square* is a quadrilateral all of whose sides and angles are equal.

It is also true that every square is a *rhombus*.

square

Definition

A *rhombus* is a quadrilateral all of whose sides are equal.

It is easy to prove that all rectangles and all rhombuses, and therefore all squares, are parallelograms.

Theorem 31

All rectangles are parallelograms.

rhombus

Theorem 32

All rhombuses are parallelograms.

Consequently, every statement that is true about parallelograms is true of rectangles, rhombuses, and squares as well. For example, the diagonals of each of the following figures bisect each other.

rectangle

square

rhombus

The diagonals of a square are also equal (because it is a rectangle) and perpendicular (because it is a rhombus). These facts also are easy to prove.

Theorem 33
The diagonals of a rectangle are equal.

Theorem 34
The diagonals of a rhombus are perpendicular.

Exercises

Set I

Regular Dodecagon. The figure below shows a regular *dodecagon* divided into quadrilaterals. Every line segment in the figure has the same length.

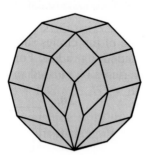

1. How many sides does a dodecagon have?

A regular polygon is one that is equilateral *and* equiangular.

2. How many regular quadrilaterals do there seem to be in the figure?

3. What is a regular quadrilateral called?

4. How many rectangles do there seem to be in the figure?

5. How many rhombuses are in the figure?

6. How many different *shapes* of rhombuses does the figure seem to contain?

Complete the proofs of the theorems of this lesson by giving the reasons.

Theorem 31. All rectangles are parallelograms.

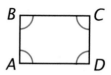

Given: ABCD is a rectangle.
Prove: ABCD is a parallelogram.

Proof
7. Because ABCD is a rectangle, ∠A = ∠C and ∠B = ∠D. Why?

8. Therefore, ABCD is a parallelogram. Why?

Theorem 32. All rhombuses are parallelograms.

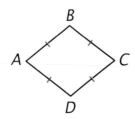

Given: ABCD is a rhombus.
Prove: ABCD is a parallelogram.

Proof
9. Because ABCD is a rhombus, AB = DC and AD = BC. Why?

10. Therefore, ABCD is a parallelogram. Why?

Theorem 33. The diagonals of a rectangle are equal.

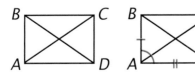

Given: ABCD is a rectangle.
Prove: AC = BD.

Proof
11. Because ABCD is a rectangle, ∠BAD = ∠CDA. Why?

12. ABCD is a parallelogram. Why?

13. AB = DC. Why?

14. AD = AD. Why?

15. △BAD ≅ △CDA. Why?

16. AC = BD. Why?

Theorem 34. The diagonals of a rhombus are perpendicular.

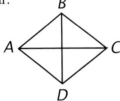

Given: ABCD is a rhombus.
Prove: AC ⊥ BD.

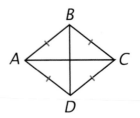

Proof
17. Because ABCD is a rhombus, AB = BC and AD = DC. Why?

18. AC ⊥ BD. Why?

Which Parts? The lines in this figure mark the boundaries of overlapping basketball and volleyball courts on a playground.

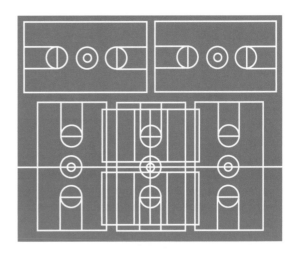

To draw one of the circles shown, only one measure is needed: its radius. For which parts would the measures be needed to draw

19.
□
a rectangle?

20.
□
a square?

21.
▱
a rhombus?

22.
▱
a parallelogram?

"Just Right." Someone once said: "A square is perfect because all of its angles are just right."

23. Why can't all of the angles of a triangle be "just right"?

24. If all of the angles of a quadrilateral are "just right," does it follow that it must be a square? Explain.

25. Can you think of any examples of other polygons all of whose angles are "just right"? If so, draw one.

Set II

Checking a Wall. Before designing built-in furniture for a wall, a carpenter measures the wall's dimensions to see if it is rectangular.

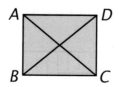

Suppose, in measuring this wall, the carpenter finds that AB = DC and AD = BC.

26. Can you conclude from these equalities that the wall is rectangular? Explain.

Suppose that the diagonals of the wall are measured instead and that AC = BD.

27. Can you conclude from this equality that the wall is rectangular? Explain.

Suppose that the wall is measured and that AB = DC, AD = BC, *and* AC = BD.

28. Draw the figure and mark it as needed to answer each of the following questions.

29. Why is △ABC ≅ △DCB?

30. Why is ∠ABC = ∠DCB?

31. Why is ABCD a parallelogram?

32. Why is ∠ABC = ∠ADC and ∠DCB = ∠DAB?

33. Why is ∠ADC = ∠DAB?

34. Why is ABCD a rectangle?

On the basis of these facts, tell whether each of the following statements is true or false.

35. If the opposite sides of a quadrilateral are equal, it is a parallelogram.

36. If the opposite sides of a quadrilateral are equal, it is a rectangle.

37. The diagonals of a rectangle are equal.

38. If the diagonals of a quadrilateral are equal, it is a rectangle.

39. If the diagonals of a parallelogram are equal, it is a rectangle.

Square Problem. ABCD is a square and M, N, O, and P are the midpoints of its sides.

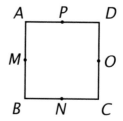

40. Use your ruler to make a large copy of this figure in which each side of the square is 2 inches long. Draw AN and CM and label the point in which they intersect X. Draw AO and CP and label the point in which they intersect Y.

41. What kind of quadrilaterals are AMCO and APCN?

42. How do you know?

43. Why does it follow that AXCY is a parallelogram?

44. What other kind of quadrilateral does AXCY appear to be?

45. What seems to be true about points B, X, Y, and D?

46. What kind(s) of symmetry does the entire figure appear to have?

Rhombus Problem. ABCD is a rhombus, AE ⊥ BC, and AF ⊥ CD.

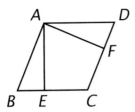

47. Copy the figure and mark it as needed to answer exercise 48.

It looks as if AE = AF.

48. Is this necessarily true? Explain why or why not.

Triangle Problem. ABDE is a parallelogram and BDCE is a rectangle.

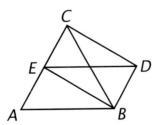

49. Copy the figure and mark it as needed to answer exercise 50.

It looks as if △ABC is equilateral.

50. What can you prove about △ABC?

Set III

Counting Squares. Acute Alice drew this figure and asked Obtuse Ollie how many squares it contains. Ollie said, "16."

Alice then shaded the one outlined in red in the figure below and asked Ollie, "Did you count this one?" To which Ollie replied, "17!"

1. How many squares does the figure actually contain? Explain.

For revenge, Ollie then drew the figure below and asked Alice how many squares it contains.* Alice said, "14."

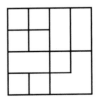

2. Do you agree? If not, what is your answer? Explain.

---

*From *Are You as Smart as You Think?* by Terry Stickels (Thomas Dunne Books, 2000).

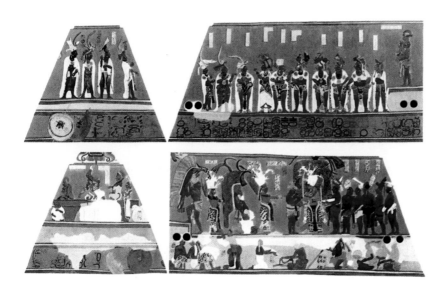

LESSON 5

Trapezoids

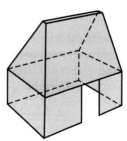

In 1946, an exciting discovery was made in a jungle in southern Mexico. Hidden by the jungle growth, it was a building whose walls were covered with murals made by a Mayan civilization in the eighth century. Four panels of one of the murals showing ancient Americans as they actually looked are shown above. The site is now called Bonampak, Mayan for "painted walls."

The unusual shape of the panels is due to the fact that they were painted on the sloping ceiling of a room whose design is shown in the first figure at the right. The panels have the shape of *trapezoids*.

Definition

A *trapezoid* is a quadrilateral that has exactly one pair of parallel sides.

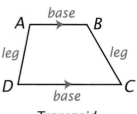

Trapezoid

The parallel sides are called the *bases* of the trapezoid, and the nonparallel sides are called its *legs*. The pairs of angles that include each base are called *base angles:* one pair of base angles in trapezoid ABCD at the right is ∠A and ∠B, and the other pair is ∠D and ∠C.

The two smaller panels in the Mayan mural are in the shape of *isosceles trapezoids*.

Definition

An *isosceles trapezoid* is a trapezoid whose legs are equal.

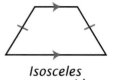

Isosceles trapezoid

Isosceles trapezoids appear to have line symmetry. If one leg is folded onto the other, the two halves of an isosceles trapezoid look as if they would coincide, which is not true for trapezoids in general. The apparent symmetry of an isosceles trapezoid suggests that its base angles are equal, something that we will prove in the exercises.

Theorem 35

The base angles of an isosceles trapezoid are equal.

A second property of isosceles trapezoids suggested by line symmetry is that their diagonals are equal. We will also prove this in the exercises.

Theorem 36

The diagonals of an isosceles trapezoid are equal.

Exercises

Set I

Quadrilaterals in Perspective. How we identify a quadrilateral depends on what we assume about it. Consider these figures from a book on architecture.*

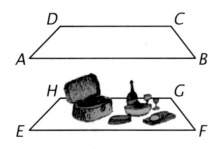

1. What kind of quadrilateral does ABCD appear to be?

2. What would you have to know to be sure that your conclusion about ABCD is correct?

Architecture: Form, Space, and Order, by Francis D. K. Ching (Wiley, 1996).

3. Does it seem reasonable to say that EFGH is probably a rectangle? Explain.

4. What would you have to know to be sure that it is?

5. Does it seem reasonable to say that EFGH is probably a parallelogram? Explain.

The figure below from the same book is another example.

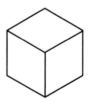

If we assume that the figure is two-dimensional (flat), it appears to contain quadrilaterals that can be named in two ways.

6. What are they?

If we assume that the figure is three-dimensional, it appears to contain quadrilaterals that can be named in four ways.

7. What are they?

Geometric Trademark. The trademark of the Chase Manhattan Bank is a simple geometric design.

8. What kind of symmetry does the figure have?

Its right angles and some of its equal lengths have been marked on the figure below.

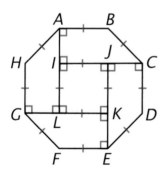

9. What kind of quadrilateral is IJKL? Explain.

10. What relation do the other four quadrilaterals in the figure seem to have to one another?

11. What kind of quadrilaterals are they?

12. Which sides of JCDE are its bases?

13. If two sides of a trapezoid are equal, does that mean that it is isosceles? Explain.

14. Are the base angles of ALGH equal? Explain.

15. What kind of polygon is ABCDEFGH?

Complete the proofs of the theorems of this lesson by giving the reasons.

Theorem 35. The base angles of an isosceles trapezoid are equal.

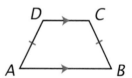

Given: ABCD is an isosceles trapezoid with bases AB and DC.
Prove: ∠A = ∠B and ∠D = ∠C.

Proof
16. Because AB and DC are the bases of trapezoid ABCD, AB ∥ DC. Why?

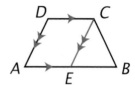

17. Through C, why can we draw CE ∥ DA?
18. AECD is a parallelogram. Why?

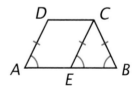

19. So DA = CE. Why?
20. Because ABCD is isosceles, DA = CB. Why?
21. So CE = CB. Why?
22. Therefore, ∠CEB = ∠B. Why?
23. Because CE ∥ DA, ∠A = ∠CEB. Why?
24. So ∠A = ∠B. Why?
25. ∠D and ∠A are supplementary and ∠C and ∠B are supplementary. Why?
26. ∠D + ∠A = 180° and ∠C + ∠B = 180°. Why?
27. ∠D + ∠A = ∠C + ∠B. Why?
28. ∠D = ∠C. Why?

Theorem 36. The diagonals of an isosceles trapezoid are equal.

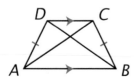

Given: ABCD is an isosceles trapezoid
with bases AB and DC.
Prove: DB = CA.

Proof

29. Because ABCD is an isosceles trapezoid, DA = CB. Why?

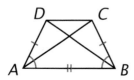

30. Also, ∠DAB = ∠CBA. Why?
31. AB = AB. Why?
32. So △DAB ≅ △CBA. Why?
33. Therefore, DB = CA. Why?

Set II

Stepladder. When a stepladder is opened for use, the tool shelf and braces should be parallel.

In this side view of the ladder, DF ∥ GH. Also, BE = BF, EG = FH, and ∠BGH = 75°.

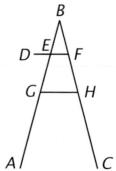

34. Copy the figure and mark it as needed to answer each of the following questions.
35. What kind of quadrilateral is EFHG?
36. How large is ∠FHG?
37. How do you know?
38. What kind of triangles are △BEF and △BGH?
39. How large is ∠BEF?
40. How do you know?
41. How large is ∠DEB?
42. How large is ∠B?

Regular Pentagon. In the *Elements*, Euclid shows how to construct a regular pentagon in a circle.*

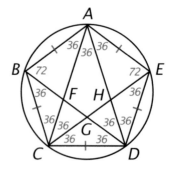

Because the pentagon is regular, AB = BC = CD = DE = EA. The measures of the angles formed by some of its diagonals also are shown.

---

*Book IV, Proposition 11.

Find an example of each of the following quadrilaterals in the figure, and in each case explain how you know that your example is correct.

43. An isosceles trapezoid.

44. A parallelogram.

45. A rhombus.

Trapezoid Diagonals. It is easy to prove that, if a quadrilateral is a trapezoid, its diagonals cannot bisect each other. Give the missing parts for the following indirect proof.

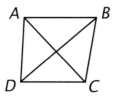

Given: ABCD is a trapezoid.
Prove: AC and DB do not bisect each other.

Proof
46. Suppose that ? .

47. Then ABCD is a parallelogram. Why?

48. If ABCD is a parallelogram, then AB ∥ DC and AD ∥ BC. Why?

49. If AB ∥ DC and AD ∥ BC, then ABCD is not a trapezoid. Why?

50. This contradicts the hypothesis that ? .

51. Therefore, what we supposed is false and ? .

We have proved that the diagonals of a trapezoid cannot bisect each other.

52. Can they be perpendicular? Explain with either a picture or words why or why not.

Set III

Congruence Puzzle. The following problem is from a popular puzzle book published in the USSR.*

An equilateral triangle can be separated into four congruent triangles as shown in the figures below.

Without the top triangle, the three remaining triangles form a trapezoid. The puzzle is to separate it into four congruent parts.

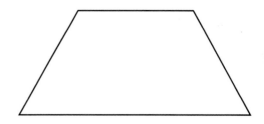

Andrew Miller, a student of Richard Brady in Washington, D.C., who became interested in this problem while studying from the first edition of this geometry book, discovered a solution different from the one thought of by the puzzle's inventor.

Trace the figure. Can you figure out a way to separate it into four congruent parts?

*An English language edition of *The Moscow Puzzles,* by Boris A. Kordemsky, was edited by Martin Gardner (Scribner's, 1972).

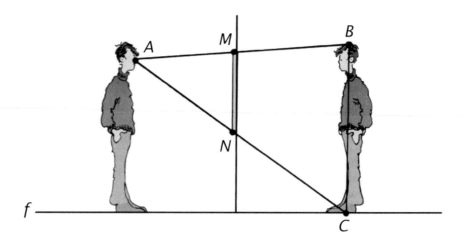

LESSON 6

The Midsegment Theorem

Imagine that you are looking at a reflection of yourself in a large mirror on a wall. How tall would the mirror have to be in order for you to see all of yourself from the top of your head to the bottom of your feet?

When you stand before a mirror, your reflection seems to be standing an equal distance behind it. In the diagram above, line *w* represents the wall with the mirror on it and line *f* represents the floor. The person looking at the mirror is shown at the left with his eyes at point A. His reflection, which seems to stand behind the mirror, is represented by BC, and the mirror itself is represented by MN. Points M and N lie on the sides of △ABC; so MN, the length of the mirror, is determined by this triangle.

It can be shown, by using the reflection properties of a mirror, that M is the midpoint of AB and that N is the midpoint of AC. For this reason, MN is called a *midsegment* of △ABC.

Definition
A *midsegment* of a triangle is a line segment that connects the midpoints of two of its sides.

We can use this definition and our knowledge of parallelograms to prove the following theorem.

Theorem 37. The Midsegment Theorem

A midsegment of a triangle is parallel to the third side and half as long.

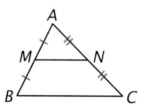

Given: MN is a midsegment of △ABC.

Prove: MN ∥ BC and MN = $\frac{1}{2}$BC.

To prove either part of the conclusion, we have to add something to the figure.

If you study the series of figures at the right carefully, you may be able to see how the proof goes before reading it.

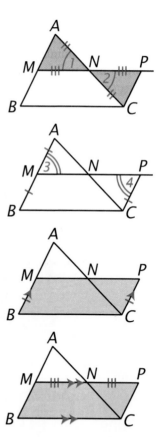

Proof

Part 1. Drawing a new triangle congruent to △AMN

Draw line MN (two points determine a line), choose point P so that NP = MN (the Ruler Postulate), and draw CP. In △AMN and △CPN, MN = NP, ∠1 = ∠2 (vertical angles are equal), and AN = NC (because MN is a midsegment of △ABC, N is the midpoint of AC). So △AMN ≅ △CPN (SAS).

Part 2. Showing that BCPM is a parallelogram

MA = CP (corresponding parts of congruent triangles are equal) and BM = MA (because M is the midpoint of BA); so BM = CP (substitution). Also ∠3 = ∠4 (corresponding parts of congruent triangles are equal); so BA ∥ CP (lines that form equal alternate interior angles are parallel). BCPM is a parallelogram because two opposite sides are parallel and equal (BM ∥ CP and BM = CP).

Part 3. Finishing the proof

MP ∥ BC and MP = BC (the opposite sides of a parallelogram are parallel and equal). Because M-N-P by construction, MP = MN + NP (the Betweenness of Points Theorem). But NP = MN; so MP = MN + MN (substitution). Because MP = 2MN, MN = $\frac{1}{2}$MP (division); so MN = $\frac{1}{2}$BC (substitution).

We can now answer the question about how long a mirror on a wall has to be in order for you to see your complete reflection. Look again at the figure at the beginning of this lesson. MN is a midsegment of △ABC; so MN = $\frac{1}{2}$BC. The segment BC, the length of your image in the mirror, is just as tall as you are. So the mirror can be half as long as you are tall.

Exercises

Set I

Portuguese Theorem. Here is the Midsegment Theorem as it appears in a Portuguese geometry book.

Teorema: O segmento de recta que une os pontos médios de dois lados de um triângulo é paralelo ao outro lado e igual à sua metade.

In the figure, points D and E illustrate the "pontos médios."

1. What do you think these words mean?

2. What do we call segment DE?

AC is the "outro lado."

3. What do you think these words mean?

4. What does the theorem say in English?

5. Write its conclusion in terms of the figure.

State Capitals Problem. The locations of four state capitals have been marked on the map below.

6. Trace the four points on your paper and draw quadrilateral SOHB. Use your straightedge and compass to bisect each of its sides. Starting with the midpoint of side SO, label the midpoints (moving clockwise around the figure) M, N, P, and Q, respectively. Draw quadrilateral MNPQ.

7. What is surprising about the result?

8. Draw SH. Why is MN ∥ SH and QP ∥ SH?

US Department of Interior

9. Why is MN ∥ QP?

10. Why is MN = $\frac{1}{2}$SH and QP = $\frac{1}{2}$SH?

11. Why is MN = QP?

12. What do these facts prove about quadrilateral MNPQ?

13. Explain why.

14. Draw MP and NQ. What seems to be true?

15. Explain why it must be true.

Midpoint Quadrilateral. E, F, G, and H are the midpoints of the sides of quadrilateral ABCD.

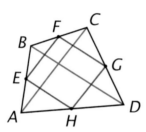

Give a reason for each statement below.

16. EF = $\frac{1}{2}$AC, FG = $\frac{1}{2}$BD, HG = $\frac{1}{2}$AC, and EH = $\frac{1}{2}$BD. Why?

17. EF + FG + HG + EH = $\frac{1}{2}$AC + $\frac{1}{2}$BD + $\frac{1}{2}$AC + $\frac{1}{2}$BD. Why?

18. EF + FG + HG + EH = AC + BD. Why?

19. What is EF + FG + HG + EH called with respect to EFGH?

20. What is AC + BD called with respect to ABCD?

21. Show how the equation proved in exercise 18 can be stated in words by completing the following sentence:

If the midpoints of the sides of a quadrilateral are connected in order by line segments to form a midpoint quadrilateral, . . .

Two Midsegments. In the figure below, DE is a midsegment of △ABC, FG is a midsegment of △DBE, and AD = CE.

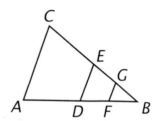

22. Copy the figure and mark it as needed to answer each of the following questions.

What can you conclude about

23. ADEC? Why?

24. ∠A and ∠C? Why?

25. △ABC? Why?

26. FG and AC? Why?

Set II

Midpoint Coordinates. On graph paper, draw a pair of axes extending 15 units to the right and 15 units up from the origin.

27. Plot the following points and connect them with line segments to form △ABC: A (3, 2), B (5, 12), C (11, 8).

Use the grid to help you in locating the midpoints of the sides of △ABC. Let M be the midpoint of AB.

28. What are its coordinates?

Let N be the midpoint of BC.

29. What are its coordinates?

Let O be the midpoint of AC.

30. What are its coordinates?

31. Is there a way to figure out the coordinates of the midpoint of a line segment from the coordinates of its endpoints? If so, how would you do it?

Draw MN.

32. Use the distance formula to find its length.

33. Use the distance formula to find AC.

34. Are the two distances related in the way that you would expect? Explain.

35. In what way should *lines* MN and AC be related?

36. Is there anything about their relation to the grid that suggests that they have this relation? If so, what is it?

Tetrahedron. An edition of Euclid's *Elements* published in London in 1570 featured little paper models attached to the pages that could be folded up to form three-dimensional figures.

One pattern consisted of a triangle and its three midsegments. It could be folded to form a tetrahedron, which is a polyhedron with four triangular faces.

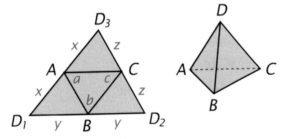

37. Copy the first figure above and label the lengths of the sides of △ABC in terms of *x*, *y*, and *z*.

38. What must be true about the four triangles in the figure? Explain.

39. Copy the second figure and label the lengths of the six edges of the tetrahedron in terms of *x*, *y*, and *z*.

Two edges of a tetrahedron that do not intersect are called *opposite edges;* for example, AC and BD are opposite edges.

40. What do you notice about the opposite edges of the tetrahedron?

In the first figure, the measures of the angles of △ABC are labeled *a*, *b*, and *c*.

37. *(continued)* Label the measures of the angles of the other triangles in terms of *a*, *b*, and *c*.

When the pattern is folded together, three angles meet at each vertex of the tetrahedron.

41. What is the sum of the three angles at each vertex?

More Midpoint Quadrilaterals. Exercises 6 through 13 of this lesson demonstrate that the midpoints of the sides of a quadrilateral are the vertices of a parallelogram.

42. Draw a large rectangle that is not a square. Find the midpoints of its sides and connect them in order with line segments to form a quadrilateral.

43. What special type of parallelogram does the quadrilateral seem to be?

44. Mark your figure and use what you know about rectangles to explain why your answer is correct.

45. Draw a large rhombus that is not a square. Find the midpoints of its sides and connect them in order with line segments to form a quadrilateral.

46. What special type of parallelogram does the quadrilateral seem to be?

47. Mark your figure and use what you know about rhombuses to explain why your answer is correct. (Hint: Draw the diagonals of the rhombus.)

48. What figure would you expect to get if you connected the midpoints of the sides of a square in order with line segments?

Base Average. M and N are the midpoints of the legs of trapezoid ABCD.

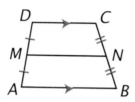

49. What seems to be true about MN?
50. Copy the figure and mark it as shown. Draw line DN and extend AB to intersect it at P.
51. Explain why △DCN ≅ △PBN.
52. Explain why MN ∥ AP.
53. Explain why MN ∥ DC.
54. Explain why MN = $\frac{1}{2}$(AB + DC).

Set III

Infinite Series. Jonathan Swift, the author of *Gulliver's Travels*, once wrote:

> So, naturalists observe, a flea
> Hath smaller fleas that on him prey;
> And these have smaller still to bite 'em;
> And so proceed ad infinitum.

The figure below represents an infinite series, not of fleas, but of equilateral triangles. The sides of the largest triangle are each 4 inches long. Each successive triangle is formed by the midsegments of the preceding one.

With the use of the Midsegment Theorem and a calculator, can you guess what the sum of the lengths of *all* of the sides of the triangles in this figure is? If so, show your reasoning.

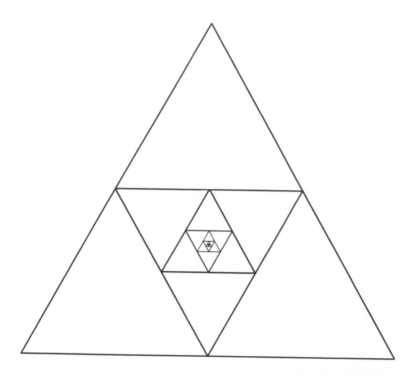

Summary and Review

Basic Ideas

Theorems

24. The sum of the angles of a quadrilateral is 360°. 259

Corollary. A quadrilateral is equiangular iff it is a rectangle. 259

25. The opposite sides and angles of a parallelogram are equal. 266

26. The diagonals of a parallelogram bisect each other. 266

27. A quadrilateral is a parallelogram if its opposite sides are equal. 271

28. A quadrilateral is a parallelogram if its opposite angles are equal. 271

29. A quadrilateral is a parallelogram if two opposite sides are both parallel and equal. 271

30. A quadrilateral is a parallelogram if its diagonals bisect each other. 271

31. All rectangles are parallelograms. 276

32. All rhombuses are parallelograms. 276

33. The diagonals of a rectangle are equal. 277

34. The diagonals of a rhombus are perpendicular. 277

35. The base angles of an isosceles trapezoid are equal. 282

36. The diagonals of an isosceles trapezoid are equal. 282

37. *The Midsegment Theorem.* A midsegment of a triangle is parallel to the third side and half as long. 287

Exercises

Set I

Palm Strand Rhombus. The figure below from a book on African geometry shows palm strands woven together to form the wall of a bag. The accompanying description states that "two crossing strips of equal width determine a rhombus."*

———————
*Geometry from Africa, by Paulus Gerdes (The Mathematical Association of America, 1999).

In the figure below, the edges of each strip are parallel; so AB ∥ DC and AD ∥ BC. The equal widths of the two strips are labeled *w*.

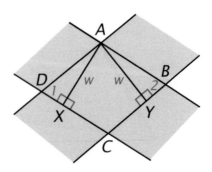

1. Draw the figure; mark it as needed to answer each of the following questions.

2. Why is ABCD a parallelogram?

3. Why is ∠1 = ∠2?

4. Why is △ADX ≅ △ABY?

5. Why is AD = AB?

6. AD = BC and AB = DC. Why?

7. Why is BC = DC?

8. Why is ABCD a rhombus?

Floating Bar. The figures below show two possible ways in which a long square bar might float on a liquid.*

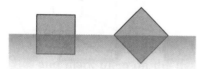

In both figures, the surface of the liquid appears to be a line of symmetry of the square.

9. How many lines of symmetry does a square have?

10. Does it have point symmetry?

11. In which of the two ways illustrated (the first or the second) do you suppose a square bar floats?

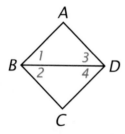

12. Copy the figure above and mark it as needed to explain each of the following statements.

13. Because ABCD is a square, AB = BC = CD = DA and ∠A = ∠C. Why?

14. △BAD ≅ △BCD. Why?

15. ∠1 = ∠2 and ∠3 = ∠4. Why?

16. Diagonal BD bisects ∠ABC and ∠ADC. Why?

---

*The Flying Circus of Physics, by Jearl Walker (Wiley, 1977).

Related Statements. Compare the following statements:

(1) If a quadrilateral is a parallelogram, one of its diagonals divides it into two congruent triangles.

(2) If one of its diagonals divides it into two congruent triangles, a quadrilateral is a parallelogram.

17. How is the second statement related to the first?

18. Are they both true? Use these figures to explain your answer.

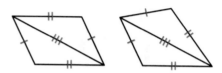

Tell whether each of the following statements is true or false. If you think a statement is false, draw a figure to illustrate why.

19. If a quadrilateral is a parallelogram, both pairs of its opposite sides are equal.

20. If both pairs of its opposite sides are equal, a quadrilateral is a parallelogram.

21. If a quadrilateral is an isosceles trapezoid, it has two pairs of equal angles.

22. If it has two pairs of equal angles, a quadrilateral is an isosceles trapezoid.

23. All parallelograms are rhombuses.

24. All rhombuses are parallelograms.

25. If a quadrilateral is a rectangle, it is equiangular.

26. If it is equiangular, a quadrilateral is a rectangle.

27. If a quadrilateral is a rhombus, its diagonals are perpendicular.

28. If its diagonals are perpendicular, a quadrilateral is a rhombus.

29. If a quadrilateral is a parallelogram, its diagonals are equal.

30. If its diagonals are equal, a quadrilateral is a parallelogram.

Jumping Frog. This jumping frog toy operates by means of a cardboard linkage. As the linkage changes shape, the marked lengths always remain equal. As a result, other things do not change.*

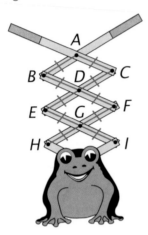

31. The sum of the angles in each quadrilateral is always the same. Why?

32. The quadrilaterals are always parallelograms. Why?

33. Pairs of opposite angles such as ∠B and ∠C always remain equal. Why?

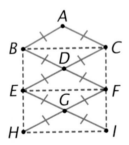

34. The quadrilaterals outlined in blue in the figure above are always parallelograms. Why?

35. BC, EF, and HI always remain parallel. Why?

Mathematics Meets Technology, by Brian Bolt (Cambridge University Press, 1991).

Set II

Dissection Puzzle. An old puzzle consists of five pieces that can be arranged in different shapes.[†]

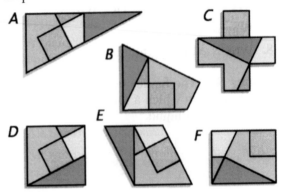

Which of the six shapes appear to be

36. parallelograms?

37. rhombuses?

38. rectangles?

39. equilateral?

40. convex?

In the drawing of shape E below, GM ∥ HP ∥ IL, the right angles have been marked, and equal lengths have been labeled with lowercase letters.

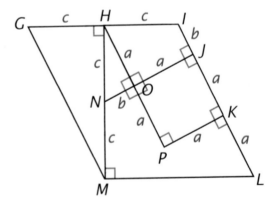

41. Make a large copy of the figure and mark it as needed to answer each of the following questions.

[†] *Creative Puzzles of the World,* by Pieter van Delft and Jack Botermans (Abrams, 1978).

42. GI ∥ ML. Why?

43. What kind of quadrilateral is GILM?

44. How do you know?

In terms of *a*, *b*, and *c*, what is the length of

45. ML?

46. GM?

47. What kind of quadrilateral is JKPO?

48. How do you know?

49. What kind of quadrilateral is HIJO?

50. How do you know?

41. *(continued)* It can be shown that, to the nearest degree, ∠G = 63°. Use this fact to find the measures of the rest of the angles and mark them on the figure.

Words from the Past. A geometry book widely used a century ago* contains the following definitions:

A *trapezium* is a quadrilateral that has no parallel sides.

A *rhomboid* is a parallelogram that has no right angles.

According to these definitions,

51. can a trapezoid be a trapezium? Explain.

52. can a rhombus be a rhomboid? Explain.

53. can a rectangle be a rhomboid? Explain.

Rectangles Not. The following quadrilaterals almost look like rectangles but, from the angles given, clearly are not. Explain what you can conclude about each one.

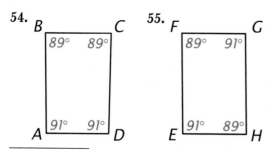

54.

55.

Plane and Solid Geometry, by G. A. Wentworth (Ginn, 1899).

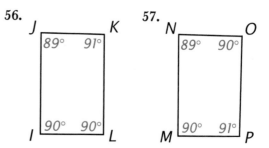

56.

57.

A magician has a deck of playing cards in which the cards are shaped like the quadrilateral in exercise 54. He asks you to take a card, look at it, and put it back into the deck. He shuffles the deck several times, holds it in front of you with one hand, and, with the other hand, slides up the card that you chose.[†]

58. How do you think the trick works?

Another Midpoint Quadrilateral. ABCD is an isosceles trapezoid with bases AB and DC; the vertices of MNOP are the midpoints of its sides.

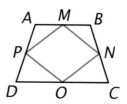

59. Copy the figure and mark it as necessary to do each of the following exercises.

60. Draw AC and use it to explain why MNOP is a parallelogram.

61. What special type of quadrilateral does MNOP appear to be? Explain why your answer is correct.

[†] *The Mammoth Book of Brain Storming Puzzles,* by David J. Bodycombe (Carroll and Graf, 1996).

Square Roots

The Square Root of a Product or Quotient

If x and y are positive,

$$\sqrt{xy} = \sqrt{x}\,\sqrt{y} \quad \text{and} \quad \sqrt{\frac{x}{y}} = \frac{\sqrt{x}}{\sqrt{y}}.$$

Simple Radical Form

An expression containing a square root is in simple radical form if the number or expression under the square root sign has no perfect square factors other than 1.

Example 1: Find the square roots of 20 to the nearest hundredth.

Solution: A calculator shows that $\sqrt{20} = 4.47213\ldots$; so $\sqrt{20} \approx 4.47$ and $-\sqrt{20} \approx -4.47$.

Example 2: Write $\sqrt{20}$ in simple radical form.

Solution: $\sqrt{20} = \sqrt{4 \cdot 5} = \sqrt{4}\,\sqrt{5} = 2\sqrt{5}.$

Example 3: Simplify $\sqrt{32} + \sqrt{18}$.

Solution: $\sqrt{32} + \sqrt{18} = \sqrt{2 \cdot 16} + \sqrt{2 \cdot 9} = 4\sqrt{2} + 3\sqrt{2} = 7\sqrt{2}.$

Exercises

Use your calculator to find each of the following square roots.

1. $\sqrt{5}$ to the nearest thousandth.
2. $\sqrt{500}$ to the nearest hundredth.
3. $\sqrt{50{,}000}$ to the nearest tenth.
4. $\sqrt{50}$ to the nearest hundredth.
5. $\sqrt{5{,}000}$ to the nearest tenth.

Write in simple radical form.

6. $\sqrt{500}$
7. $\sqrt{50{,}000}$
8. $\sqrt{50}$
9. $\sqrt{5{,}000}$

Write in simple radical form. Assume that x represents a positive number.

10. $\sqrt{25x}$
11. $\sqrt{x^5}$
12. $\sqrt{\pi x^2}$
13. $\sqrt{12x^{12}}$

Use simple radical form to show that

14. $\sqrt{147} + \sqrt{3} = 8\sqrt{3}.$
15. $\sqrt{147 + 3} = 5\sqrt{6}.$

Simplify.

16. $\sqrt{700} - \sqrt{175}$
17. $\sqrt{700 - 175}$
18. $\sqrt{20 + 20 + 20}$
19. $\sqrt{20} + \sqrt{20} + \sqrt{20}$
20. $\sqrt{6^2} + \sqrt{8^2}$
21. $\sqrt{6^2 + 8^2}$

Do as indicated and simplify.

22. $\sqrt{14}\sqrt{21}$
23. $\dfrac{\sqrt{242}}{\sqrt{2}}$
24. $(4\sqrt{5})(6\sqrt{2})$
25. $(3\sqrt{7})^2$
26. $\dfrac{12\sqrt{15}}{4\sqrt{3}}$
27. $(5 - \sqrt{2}) + (5 + \sqrt{2})$
28. $(5 - \sqrt{2})(5 + \sqrt{2})$
29. $\sqrt{3}(\sqrt{27} + 1)$
30. $\sqrt{3} + (\sqrt{27} + 1)$
31. $(\sqrt{x} + \sqrt{y}) + (\sqrt{x} + \sqrt{y})$
32. $(\sqrt{x} + \sqrt{y})^2$

Chapter 8

Transformations

How does this picture illustrate both laughing and crying?

Mathematics has been described as the "science of patterns." Geometry concerns patterns of shape and form. You are already familiar with the pattern of form called line symmetry. In this chapter, we will explore other types of symmetry and become acquainted with their relation to the subject of transformations, including reflections, translations, rotations, and glide reflections. We will also apply these ideas to widen our notion of congruence.

© 2003 Harold R. Jacobs

8. The largest of
the Rocs picks her
up by the skirt.

5.

Just as he reaches a small grassy point of land, another fish
attacks him, lashing furiously with his tail.

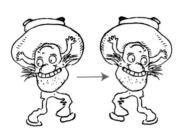

A reflection

LESSON 1

Transformations

Perhaps the most remarkable comic strip ever drawn appeared in the *New York Herald* from 1903 to 1905. A panel from one of the strips is shown above.

The other figures on this page show how several transformations important in geometry would affect one of the strip's characters, Old Man Muffaroo. The rotation is remarkable in that it turns Muffaroo into the strip's other character, Little Lady Lovekins. After the six panels of the comic strip were read in the usual way, the strip had to be turned upside down to read the rest of the story.

The word "transformation" has a special meaning in geometry. It refers to a rule for getting one set of points from another. When the rule is applied to a point in the first set, it produces exactly one point in the second set. Going backward, we find that, for each point in the second set, there corresponds exactly one point in the first set.

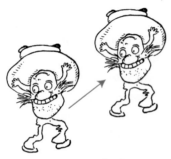

A translation

A rotation

A dilation

Definition

A *transformation* is a one-to-one correspondence between two sets of points.

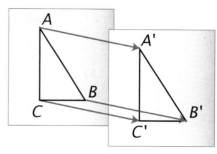

A translation

Transformations can be applied to triangles. First, imagine tracing △ABC on a sheet of transparent paper and then sliding the paper a certain distance in a given direction without turning it, as shown at the right.

The result is a *translation* of △ABC. Each point in the new figure, △A'B'C', corresponds to a point in the original figure, △ABC, and is called its *image*. Point A' (read as "A prime"), for example, is the image of point A.

Next, imagine taking the sheet of paper with the drawing of △ABC, folding the paper, tracing △ABC to produce △A'B'C', and then unfolding the paper, as shown in the three figures below.

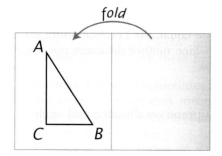

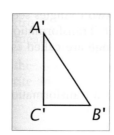

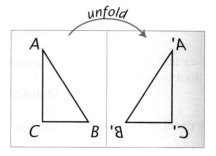

A reflection

The result is a *reflection* of △ABC, and the line along which the paper is folded is called the *mirror* of the reflection.

Now imagine taking the paper with the tracing of △ABC and rotating it a certain number of degrees about a fixed point, P, as shown below.

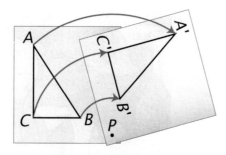

A rotation

This time the result is a *rotation* of △ABC. The fixed point, P, about which the figure is rotated is called the *center* of the rotation.

Finally, imagine taking the paper with the drawing of △ABC and making a photocopy of it by either enlarging it or reducing it, as shown below.

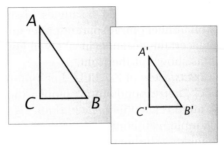

A dilation

The result is a *dilation* of △ABC. An obvious but significant difference between this transformation and the preceding ones is that △ABC and its image, △A'B'C', are not congruent. Although the corresponding angles of the two triangles seem to be equal, the corresponding sides clearly are not. Transformations in which neither distances nor angle measures change are called *isometries*.

Definition
An *isometry* is a transformation that preserves distance and angle measure.

From our descriptions, it is evident that the transformations called *translations, reflections,* and *rotations* are examples of isometries. Dilations are not.

Exercises

Set I

Transformations in Art. The figure by Maurits Escher at the right consists of fish of four colors swimming in four directions.

What type of transformation seems to relate

1. two fish of the same color?

2. a pair of red and white fish?

3. a pair of blue and white fish?

Are there any pairs of fish in the figure for which one fish of the pair seems to be

4. a dilation of the other?

5. a reflection of the other?

Mirror Molecules. The two hands in the figure below are shown holding models of a pair of amino acid molecules. Of the two molecules, L-alanine and D-alanine, only the one on the left is present in natural protein.*

6. Under what transformation is the one hand the image of the other?

7. L and D stand for "levo-" and "dextro-." What do you think these prefixes mean?

Reflections. Children sometimes write the mirror image Я when they mean to write an R. This mistake has been used in the trademark of a toy store.

The figure below shows an R and its reflection through a mirror line.

On your paper, copy and complete each of the following figures by including the reflection image of the object on the left through the mirror line.

8.

N |

9.

A |

10.

◺ |

11.

△ |

12.

E |

13.

Z |

14.

▭ |

15.

▱ |

16. In which of exercises 8 through 15 do the figure and its mirror image look the same?

17. What is it about these figures that causes them and their mirror images to look the same?

Down the Stairs. The figure below illustrates a transformation.†

18. What transformation is it?

19. What does the word "transformation" mean in geometry?

20. Is this transformation an example of an isometry?

21. What does the word "isometry" mean?

*The Galactic Club, by Ronald N. Bracewell (W. H. Freeman and Company, 1975).

†Mind Sights, by Roger N. Shepard (W. H. Freeman and Company, 1990).

Peter Jones. In this remarkable design by Douglas Hofstadter, the part shown in red is the image of the part shown in blue.

22. What transformation does the figure illustrate?

23. Describe how the image is produced from the original figure.

24. What letter is the image of P?

Set II

Escalator Transformations. The diagram below illustrates how an escalator works.*

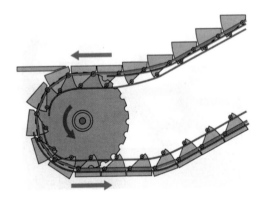

What type of transformation is illustrated by the steps as

25. they descend?

26. they move around the return wheel?

---

*Scientific American: How Things Work Today, edited by Michael Wright and M. N. Patel (Crown, 2000).

The figure below represents a translation of one step of an escalator; AA′ ∥ BB′ ∥ CC′ and AA′ = BB′ = CC′.

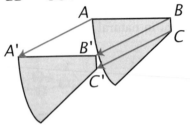

Let's see how this transformation affects distances and angles.

27. Copy the figure and mark it as needed to do each of the following exercises.

28. What can you conclude about quadrilaterals AA′B′B and BB′C′C? Why?

29. Why is A′B′ ∥ AB?

27. *(continued)* Draw AC and A′C′.

30. What can you conclude about quadrilateral AA′C′C?

31. Why is AB = A′B′, BC = B′C′, and AC = A′C′?

32. Why is △ABC ≅ △A′B′C′?

33. Why is ∠ABC = ∠A′B′C′?

The answers to exercises 31 and 33 establish that the translation part of the escalator motion is an isometry.

34. What is an isometry?

The figure below represents the rotation of one step; PA = PA′, PB = PB′, and ∠APA′ = ∠BPB′.

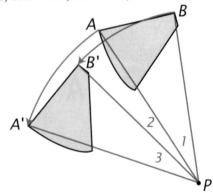

Let's see how this transformation affects distances.

35. Copy the figure and mark it as needed to answer each of the following questions.

36. Why is $\angle APA' = \angle 2 + \angle 3$ and $\angle BPB' = \angle 1 + \angle 2$?

37. Why is $\angle 2 + \angle 3 = \angle 1 + \angle 2$?

38. Why is $\angle 3 = \angle 1$?

39. Why is $\triangle ABP \cong \triangle A'B'P$?

40. Why is $AB = A'B'$?

41. What have we shown to be preserved by this rotation?

Triangle Construction. The figure below can be used to construct a transformation of $\triangle ABC$.

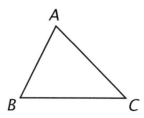

•
P

42. Make a large copy of the figure. Draw ray PA. Use your compass to mark a point A′ on PA such that AA′ = PA. Draw ray PB and find point B′ on it so that BB′ = PB. Draw ray PC and find point C′ on it so that CC′ = PC. Draw $\triangle A'B'C'$.

43. What type of transformation does your drawing seem to illustrate?

44. How do the sides of $\triangle A'B'C'$ seem to compare in length with the sides of $\triangle ABC$?

45. How do the angles of $\triangle A'B'C'$ seem to compare in size with the angles of $\triangle ABC$?

46. Is this transformation an isometry? Explain.

Computer Geometry. Transformations are used in computer drawing programs. The following figures appear in the Adobe Illustrator User Guide.* Name the transformation illustrated in each figure.

47.

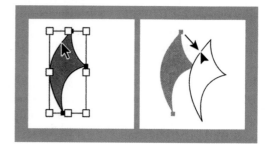

48.

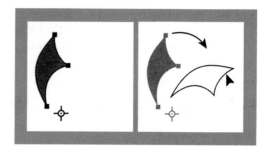

49.

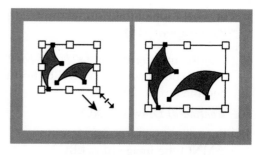

(In this figure, the drawing on the right is the transformation image of the drawing on the left.)

Adobe Illustrator 9.0 User Guide (Adobe Systems, 2000).

Computer drawing programs transform objects by changing their coordinates. To show, for example, that the coordinates of each point of an object are to be reversed to get the coordinates of each point of its image, we can write $(a, b) \rightarrow (b, a)$.

50. On graph paper, draw a pair of axes extending 10 units in each direction from the origin. Plot the following points and connect them to form △ABC: A(3, 1), B(5, 2), C(2, 6).

51. Use the transformation $(a, b) \rightarrow (a + 2, b - 7)$ on the coordinates of △ABC to find the coordinates of △DEF. For example, A(3, 1) → D(3 + 2, 1 − 7), or D(5, −6).

50. *(continued)* Draw △DEF.

52. For what type of transformation is △DEF the image of △ABC?

53. Use the transformation $(a, b) \rightarrow (-a, b)$ on the coordinates of △ABC to find the coordinates of △GHI. For example, A(3, 1) → G(−3, 1).

50. *(continued)* Draw △GHI.

54. For what type of transformation is △GHI the image of △ABC?

55. Use the transformation $(a, b) \rightarrow (-a, -b)$ on the coordinates of △ABC to find the coordinates of △JKL.

50. *(continued)* Draw △JKL.

56. For what type of transformation is △JKL the image of △ABC?

57. Use the transformation $(a, b) \rightarrow (2a, 2b)$ on the coordinates of △ABC to find the coordinates of △MNO.

50. *(continued)* Draw △MNO.

58. For what type of transformation is △MNO the image of △ABC?

Set III

Toothpick Puzzle. A puzzle thought to have originated in Japan uses eight toothpicks and a matchhead.*

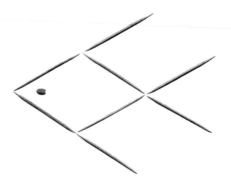

The challenge is to move just three toothpicks and the matchhead to make the fish swim in the opposite direction.

1. Can you do it? If so, make a drawing illustrating the original fish and what you did to get your answer.

2. Can the solution be regarded as the result of one of the transformations considered in this lesson? If so, which one? Explain.

---

*The Next Book of Omni Games, by Scott Morris (New American Library, 1988).

LESSON 2

Reflections

Some barber shops have mirrors on the walls that face each other, giving a series of reflections as seen above.

You already know that a reflection is a special type of transformation. The figure at the right shows how to find the points corresponding to A and B when an object is reflected in a mirror, line l. Find the perpendicular to l through the point, go to the mirror, and continue an equal distance on the other side. The distance from any point *on l to l* is 0; so the reflection of such a point through the line is the point itself.

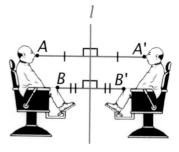

A reflection

Definition

The ***reflection*** of point P through line l is P itself if P lies on l. Otherwise, it is the point P′ such that l is the perpendicular bisector of PP′.

The reflection of a point through a line can be found by using a mirror or by folding. It can also be found by construction.

Construction 8

To reflect a point through a line.

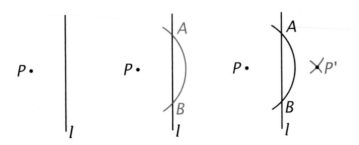

Let the point be P and the line be l. With P as center, draw an arc that intersects l in two points, A and B. With A and B as centers, draw two more arcs with the same radius as the first arc. The point in which they intersect, P′, is the reflection of P through l.

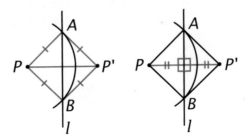

These figures show why this method works. Because PA = PB = AP′ = BP′, points A and B are equidistant from P and P′. In a plane, two points each equidistant from the endpoints of a line segment determine the perpendicular bisector of the line segment; so l is the perpendicular bisector of PP′. It follows from the definition of the reflection of a point through a line that P′ is the reflection of P through l.

In the cartoon by Charles Addams at the beginning of this lesson, not all of the successive images produced by the parallel mirrors are alike. Some of the images of the man in the barber chair face in the same direction and some face in the opposite direction. The second image, which faces in the same direction as the man in the chair, is the result of another special transformation, a *translation*. It's as if the man in the chair could be pushed through two "walls" to coincide with his translation image. We have already described a translation as sliding without turning. The figure suggests that a translation can be produced by two successive reflections in parallel mirrors.

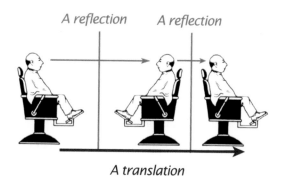

A reflection   *A reflection*

A translation

We will call a transformation that is the result of two or more successive transformations their *composite* and define translation in the following way.

Definition

A *translation* is the composite of two successive reflections through parallel lines.

The distance between a point of the original figure and its translation image is called the *magnitude* of the translation. The length of the blue arrow in the figure above illustrates the magnitude of the translation.

A translation is the composite of two reflections through *parallel* lines. What would the composite of two reflections through *intersecting* lines be?

The figure at the right suggests that it would be a rotation. If the mirrors in the barbershop were not parallel, the customer might get the impression that the barber was trying to tip him out of the chair!

Definition

A *rotation* is the composite of two successive reflections through intersecting lines.

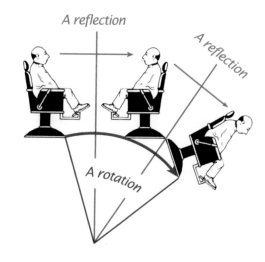

A reflection

A reflection

A rotation

The point in which the lines intersect is the *center* of the rotation, and the measure of the angle through which a point of the original figure turns to coincide with its rotation image is called the *magnitude* of the rotation. The green angle in this figure illustrates the magnitude of the rotation.

Exercises

Set I

A Suspicious Cow. Take a good look at this photograph of a cow and barn.

1. What is the "mirror" that causes the reflection?

2. What is misleading about the photograph?

3. Make a large copy of the figure below. Use your straightedge and compass to construct the reflections of points A and B through line *l*.

A.

——————————————— *l*

·
B

4. If a point is *x* units from a mirror in which it is reflected, how far is it from its image?

5. What relation does the mirror have to the line segment that connects a point and its image?

Double Reflections. It is fairly easy to imagine a reflection through a vertical or horizontal line because mirrors are usually vertical or horizontal.

The figure at the right shows two successive reflections of the flag at the upper left.

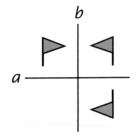

6. Through which line was the flag reflected first?

7. Through what transformation is the flag at the lower right the image of the original flag?

8. What does the measure of the angles formed by the two lines appear to be?

9. What does the magnitude of the transformation from the first flag to the last flag appear to be?

Copy the following figures on your paper. Sketch the reflection of each letter through line *a* (a vertical line) and then sketch the reflection of the image that results through line *b* (a horizontal line).

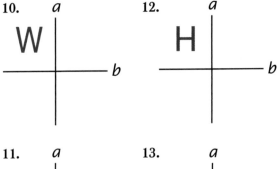

10.

11.

12.

13.

Look at your drawings for exercises 10 through 13 to answer the following questions.

What happens when a figure with

14. a vertical line of symmetry is reflected through a vertical line?

15. a horizontal line of symmetry is reflected through a horizontal line?

16. point symmetry is reflected through both a vertical and a horizontal line?

17. In which exercise do all three figures look alike? Why?

SAT Problem. The following figure appeared in a problem on an SAT exam.

All of the boxes in the strip are the same size.

18. When the strip is folded together along the dashed line, which point is most likely to coincide with point P?

19. What transformation does this problem illustrate?

20. How could you use a ruler to check your answer?

Can You Read Chinese? The figure in green below was designed by David Moser when he was a graduate student in Chinese.*

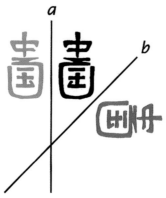

Through what transformation is

21. the figure in black the image of the figure in green?

22. the figure in red the image of the figure in black?

23. the figure in red the image of the figure in green?

_____

Can You Believe Your Eyes? by J. R. Block and Harold E. Yuker (Brunner/Mazel, 1992).

A reader of Chinese would read the figure in green as the word "China."

24. Would it be correct to say that the figure in red is a rotation of the figure in green? Explain.

25. In what sense would it be correct to say that the figure in red is a translation of the figure in green?

Set II

Kaleidoscope Patterns. A kaleidoscope uses mirrors to produce symmetric patterns. The photograph below shows the face of a toy monkey and five of its images in a kaleidoscope with two mirrors that meet at a 60° angle.

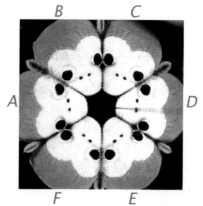

The monkey's face is at A. Which of the five images are

26. reflections of it?

27. rotations of it?

28. What is the magnitude of each rotation?

29. How many lines of symmetry does the pattern of monkey faces seem to have? Where are they?

30. Does the pattern of faces seem to have point symmetry? Explain why or why not.

Scaring Chickens. Experimental findings have shown that, if chickens see this shape flying overhead in the direction of its long end, they ignore it. If they see it flying in the direction of its short end, they run for cover.*

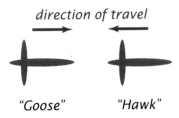

In the figure below, $a \parallel b$ and birds A, B, D, and E are reflection images of bird C through either or both of the lines.

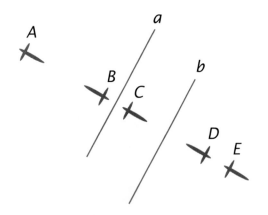

Which bird is the reflection image of

31. bird C through *a?*

32. bird B through *b?*

33. bird C through *b?*

34. bird D through *a?*

Which bird is the image of bird C as a result of successive reflections through

35. *a* and *b?*

36. *b* and *a?*

37. What transformation do exercises 35 and 36 illustrate?

_____

Visual Intelligence: How We Create What We See, by Donald D. Hoffman (Norton, 1998).

38. Use the definition of that transformation to explain why.

39. Which would scare chickens: seeing the bird at C flying to A or seeing it fly to E?

Boomerang. The figure below shows a boomerang flying overhead.

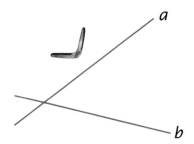

40. Draw a large copy of the figure and sketch the reflection of the boomerang through line *a*. Then sketch the reflection of the resulting image through line *b*. (Doing so will be easier if you turn your paper so that each line is vertical as you reflect through it.)

41. Under what transformation is the final image the image of the original figure?

42. Use the definition of that transformation to explain why.

43. Where is the center of the transformation?

4.

Triangle Reflections. In the figure below, △A′B′C′ is the reflection of △ABC through l_1 and △A″B″C″ is the reflection of △A′B′C′ through l_2; $l_1 \parallel l_2$.

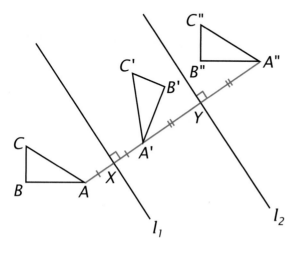

44. Why is AX = XA′ and A′Y = YA″?

45. Through what transformation is △A″B″C″ the image of △ABC?

46. What is the length of AA″ called with respect to this transformation?

47. How does the length of AA″ compare with that of XY, the distance between l_1 and l_2?

In the figure at the right, △A′B′C′ is the reflection of △ABC through l_1 and △A″B″C″ is the reflection of △A′B′C′ through l_2; l_1 and l_2 intersect at point O.

48. Why is △AOX ≅ △A′OX and △A′OY ≅ △A″OY?

49. Why is OA = OA′ and OA′ = OA″?

50. Through what transformation is △A″B″C″ the image of △ABC?

51. What is the measure of ∠AOA″ called with respect to this transformation?

52. How does the measure of ∠AOA″ compare with that of ∠XOY, the angle between l_1 and l_2?

Set III

What Time Was It? In the murder mystery titled *The House of the Arrow* by A. E. W. Mason, the solution depends on a clock:

The three witnesses advanced into the room, and as they looked again, from close at hand and with a longer gaze, a cry of surprise broke from all of them.

There was no clock upon the marquetry cabinet at all.

But high above it in the long mirror before which it stood there was a reflection of a clock, its white face so clear and bright that even now it was difficult to disbelieve that this was the clock itself. And the position of the hands gave the hour as precisely half-past ten.

"Now turn about and see!" said Hanard.

The clock itself stood upon the shelf of the Adam mantelpiece and there staring at them, the true hour was marked. It was exactly. . . .

1. Exactly what time was it? Make some drawings to support your answer.

2. Are there any other times when the reflection would also look like an actual time? Explain.

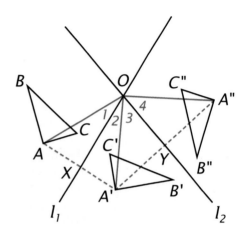

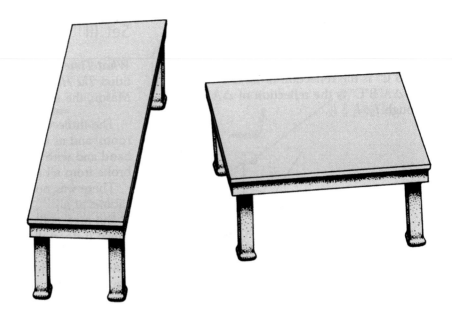

LESSON 3

Isometries and Congruence

Here is an amazing illusion by psychologist Roger Shepard. How does the shape of the table on the left above compare with the shape of the table on the right? If you trace the outline of the top of one of the tables on a thin sheet of paper and place it on the other table, you will find that it fits exactly. In other words, the tabletops are congruent!*

When this method is used to test for congruence, the tracing of the tabletop is *translated* and *rotated* to see if it can be made to coincide with the other tabletop. Because translations and rotations are isometries, this procedure suggests that congruence can be defined as an isometry. This definition agrees with our earlier definition of congruence for triangles, and it extends the idea so that it can be applied to any pair of figures having the same size and shape.

Definition
Two figures are *congruent* if there is an isometry such that one figure is the image of the other.

Mind Sights, by Roger N. Shepard (W. H. Freeman and Company, 1990).

Look at the figure at the right showing the tabletops at a smaller scale. The definition of congruence in relation to isometry says that ABCD ≅ EFGH if there is an isometry such that EFGH is the image of ABCD. Translations and rotations are composites of reflections. Is it possible to find a composite of *just reflections* in which EFGH is the image of ABCD?

Notice that E appears to be the image of A. Imagine that the figures are printed on a transparent sheet of paper and that we fold the paper so that A fits on E. The second figure shows what happens. Tracing the reflection image of ABCD through the fold line, l_1, produces EB′C′D′.

Next, since F appears to be the image of B, and hence B′, imagine folding the paper so that B′ fits on F. The third figure shows what happens. The reflection image of EB′C′D′ through the fold line, l_2, is EFGH. The composite of the two reflections through l_1 and l_2 is an isometry in which EFGH is the image of ABCD, so ABCD ≅ EFGH.

Just two reflections were needed to show that the tabletops are congruent. Is it always possible to get a pair of congruent figures to coincide with two reflections? The figure at the bottom left showing the footprints of successive steps taken by someone walking forward suggests an answer to this question.

Suppose the four steps are congruent. Step C is a translation image of step A, as is step D of step B. Under what transformation is step B an image of step A? It looks like a combination of a translation and a reflection. Such a transformation is called a *glide reflection*.

Definition

A *glide reflection* is the composite of a translation and a reflection in a line parallel to the direction of the translation.

Because a translation is the composite of *two* reflections, a glide reflection is the composite of *three* reflections. Getting step A to coincide with step B is an example of an isometry that requires three reflections. Notice that the left and right steps look different. Each is a *mirror image* of the other because it takes an odd number of reflections to carry either onto the other. We will explore congruence and isometries further in the exercises of this lesson.

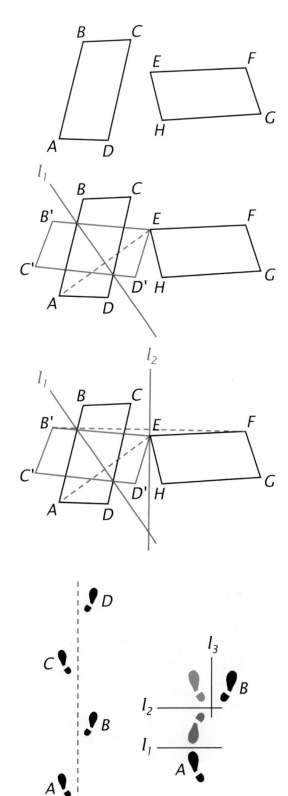

Exercises

Set I

Prevaricator. The four figures at the right by graphic artist Paul Agule are congruent.*

The artist asks: "Can you trust this man?"

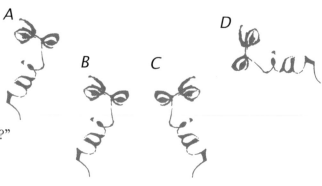

1. What do you think?

Name the isometry through which

2. figure B appears to be the image of figure A.

3. figure C appears to be the image of figure B.

4. figure D appears to be the image of figure C.

5. figure C appears to be the image of figure A.

6. Is there an isometry through which D is the image of figure B?

7. Use the definition of congruent figures in this lesson to explain why or why not.

Synchronized Oars. For maximum speed, rowers have to keep their oars synchronized. The oars along each side of the boat are synchronized if they are always parallel.

___
Can You Believe Your Eyes? by J. R. Block and Harold E. Yuker (Brunner/Mazel, 1992).

8. Name the two angles in the figure below that *must* be equal if AB ∥ CD.

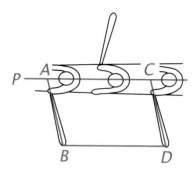

9. If AB ∥ CD, why is it reasonable to think that ABDC is a parallelogram?

10. Why does it follow that the distance between the tips of the oars, BD, is equal to the distance between the rowers, AC?

What transformation relates the positions of two oars

11. on the same side of the boat?

12. on opposite sides of the boat?

Synchronization is also important in another water sport.

13. What sport is it?

Swing Isometries. Little children like being rotated in a swing.

The figure below illustrates the composite of two isometries.

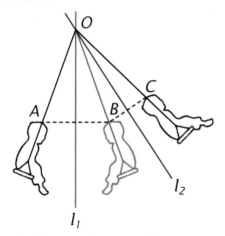

Through what transformation is

14. B the image of A and C the image of B?

15. C the image of A?

16. What is point O called with respect to this transformation?

17. What is the measure of ∠AOC called?

What relation do l_1 and l_2 have to

18. ∠AOB and ∠BOC?

19. AB and BC?

20. How does ∠AOC compare in measure with that of the acute angle formed by l_1 and l_2?

Quadrilateral Reflections. In the figure below, EFGH and EIJK are successive reflection images of ABCD. Lines *a* and *b* and line segments AE and FI have been added to the figure to show that ABCD and EIJK are related by a certain isometry.

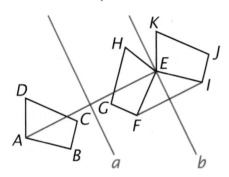

21. What postulate permits us to draw AE and FI?

22. What relation does line *a* appear to have to AE and line *b* to FI?

23. What relation do lines *a* and *b* appear to have?

24. If your observations are true, through what transformation is EIJK the image of ABCD?

25. How would this transformation show that ABCD ≅ EIJK?

Set II

Moving a Piano. A heavy piano is to be moved from one wall of a room to another. To do so, the piano is turned on its casters, which are at its corners.*

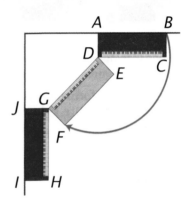

26. What type of transformation is illustrated?

27. What point is its center?

What point on DEFG is the image of

28. point A?

29. point C?

30. point D?

31. What transformation is needed to finish moving the piano? Describe it.

32. Through how many degrees do you think the piano is turned altogether?

---

*Adapted from a problem in *The School Mathematics Project, Book 4* (Cambridge University Press, 1969).

Bulldogs. All of the bulldogs in this mosaic by Escher are congruent.

33. What does it mean in relation to isometry to say that two figures are congruent?

34. Through what transformation is one of the bulldogs in the figure below the image of the other?

Is it possible that one of these bulldogs could be the image of the other

35. by a single reflection? Explain.

36. by the composite of two reflections? Explain.

37. by the composite of three reflections? Explain.

38. Through what transformation is one of the bulldogs in the figure at the top of the next column the image of the other?

39. Of what *two* transformations is this transformation a composite?

40. Of what *three* transformations is it a composite?

Grid Problem. On graph paper, draw a pair of axes extending 20 units to the right and 15 units up from the origin.

41. Plot the following points and connect them with line segments to form △ABC: A(5, 4), B(8, 3), C(3, 0).

41. *(continued)* Plot point A′(11, 10) and draw AA′. Draw △A′B′C′ so that it is the translation image of △ABC.

42. What are the coordinates of points B′ and C′?

43. Find the magnitude of the translation.

41. *(continued)* Draw the line determined by the points (7, 0) and (20, 13) and label it *l*.

44. What relation does AA′ appear to have to line *l*?

41. *(continued)* Draw △A″B″C″ so that it is the reflection image of △A′B′C′ through line *l*.

45. If your observation in exercise 44 is true, through what transformation is △A″B″C″ the image of △ABC? Explain.

41. *(continued)* Draw AA″, BB″, and CC″ and use the grid to help in finding their midpoints. Label them M, N, and P, respectively.

46. What are the coordinates of M, N, and P?

47. Exactly how is the *y*-coordinate of each of these three points related to the *x*-coordinate?

48. What is interesting about the three points?

Set III

Stamp Tricks. Obtuse Ollie found a rubber stamp and stamped it twice on a sheet of tracing paper as shown in figure 1 below.

Surprised, Ollie stamped another sheet of tracing paper twice as shown in figure 3 below.

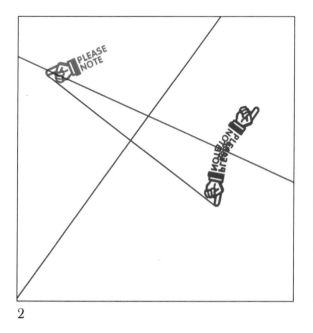

1

3

Acute Alice folded the paper to reflect one of the figures twice, getting the result shown in figure 2 below.

Again, Alice managed to fold the paper just twice, getting the result shown in figure 4 below.

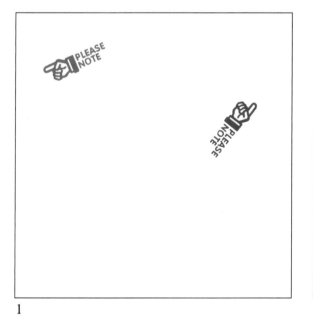

2

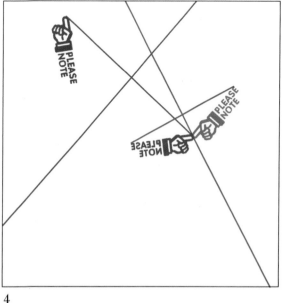

4

Ollie couldn't believe it. He decided to try to trick Alice and stamped a third sheet of tracing paper as shown below.

This time, Alice had to fold the paper more than two times to get the images to coincide.

1. How did Ollie try to trick Alice?

2. How did his "trick" prevent Alice from being able to get the images to coincide with just two folds?

3. Trace the two figures on a sheet of tracing paper. Can you get them to coincide with three folds?

Transformations and Symmetry

How many horses are pictured on the plate shown above? Counting the heads gives a different number from that obtained by counting the bodies.

The creator of the plate, who lived in Persia in the seventeenth century, made use of symmetry in its design. Each time the plate is rotated 90°, as the figures below show, it looks almost the same.

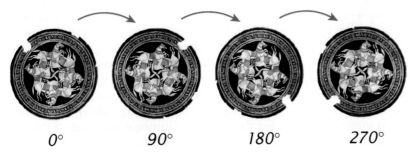

| *0°* | *90°* | *180°* | *270°* |

A figure that looks *exactly* the same after being rotated less than one full turn about its center is said to have *rotation symmetry*.

Definition
A figure has ***rotation symmetry*** with respect to a point iff it coincides with its rotation image through less than 360° about the point.

The point, which is the center of the rotation, is called the *center* of the symmetry.

The Persian plate can be rotated so that it looks the same in four positions. For this reason, it has *4-fold rotation symmetry*. Each position corresponds to a turn of 90°: $\frac{360°}{4} = 90°$. In general, a figure has *n-fold rotation symmetry* iff the smallest angle through which it can be turned to look exactly the same is $\frac{360°}{n}$.

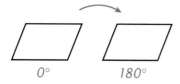

0°   180°

Recall that a figure that has *point symmetry* looks exactly the same when it is turned upside down. A parallelogram has point symmetry. The figure at the left shows that it also has 2-fold rotation symmetry. So point symmetry is symmetry by a rotation of 180°.

Just as rotation symmetry and hence point symmetry are related to the rotation transformation, *line symmetry* is related to the reflection transformation. For this reason, line symmetry is also called *reflection symmetry*.

An isosceles trapezoid has reflection symmetry. If the trapezoid is folded along the line shown in the figure at the left, the two halves coincide. Or, if a two-sided mirror is placed on the line, each half of the trapezoid is reflected onto the other half.

We can define reflection (line) symmetry in relation to the reflection transformation.

Definition

A figure has *reflection (line) symmetry* with respect to a line iff it coincides with its reflection image through the line.

The line is sometimes called the *axis* of the symmetry.

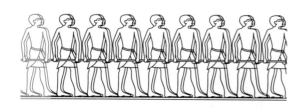

The translation transformation also is related to symmetry. The figure at the left from ancient Egypt is an example. The part of the drawing shown in red does not have any symmetry of its own but, like the repeating pattern of the horses around the plate, the repeating pattern of the people illustrates a type of symmetry. Rather than repeating around a circle, this pattern repeats along a line. The part of the drawing shown in red is translated a certain distance in the same direction again and again. The resulting pattern has *translation* symmetry. In defining this type of symmetry, we think of the pattern as continuing in both directions endlessly.

Definition

A pattern has *translation symmetry* iff it coincides with a translation image.

Because rotations, reflections, and translations are isometries, we know that corresponding distances and angles in symmetric figures are equal.

Exercises

Set I

Ambigrams. The figures below are examples of "ambigrams," words that can be read in more than one way.*

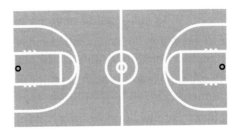

1. What type of symmetry does the first figure have?

2. What is a simple test for this type of symmetry?

3. What type of symmetry does the second figure have?

4. What is a simple test for this type of symmetry?

Sport Symmetry. The fields and courts on which most sports are played are symmetric.

5. What sport is played on the field above?

6. Describe its symmetry.

7. What sport is played on the court above?

8. Describe its symmetry.

9. What type of symmetry do you think most sport fields and courts have?

10. Why do you think they have it?

Mount Vernon. George Washington's home, Mount Vernon, has a fake window. It is the second upstairs window from the left.

11. Why do you suppose Washington had this window painted on the outside wall?

Symmetries of Basic Figures. Some geometric figures are so simple that we tend to ignore their symmetry.
 A point has rotation symmetry.

12. Where is its center of symmetry?

13. Does a point have line symmetry? If so, where is the line?

---

*"Algebra" is from *Wordplay*, by John Langdon (Harcourt Brace Jovanovich, 1992).

Euclid defined a "straight line" as "a line that lies symmetrically with the points on itself."

14. A line has rotation symmetry. Explain.

15. What points can serve as its center of symmetry?

16. A line has reflection symmetry. Explain.

17. How many lines of symmetry does a line have? Where are they?

18. Does a line have translation symmetry? Explain.

We defined "vertical angles" with reference to opposite rays.

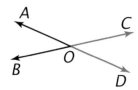

19. Explain what this definition says about ∠COD and ∠BOA, given that they are vertical angles.

20. ∠COD can be thought of as a rotation image of ∠BOA. Explain.

21. What theorem about vertical angles is suggested by the fact that rotations are isometries?

△ABC is an isosceles triangle with AB = AC.

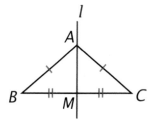

22. If a mirror line *l* is drawn through A and M, the midpoint of BC, *l* ⊥ BC. Why?

23. What are the images of A and B reflected through *l?*

24. What theorem about isosceles triangles is suggested by the fact that reflections are isometries?

ABCD is a parallelogram with diagonals AC and BD.

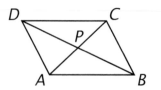

25. What must be true about AC and BD?

26. If ABCD is rotated 180° about point P as center, what is the image of AB?

27. What theorem about the sides of a parallelogram is suggested by the fact that rotations are isometries?

28. Does BD appear to be a rotation image of AC? Explain.

Set II

Piano Keyboard. Imagine that the keyboard of a piano extends endlessly in both directions.

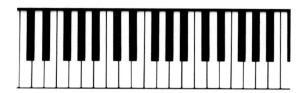

29. Draw a picture of the part of the keyboard that repeats.

30. What type of symmetry does the "endless" keyboard have because of this repeating pattern?

29. *(continued)* Draw the lines on your figure through which the "endless" keyboard could be reflected so that it coincides with itself.

31. Is there any point about which the "endless" keyboard can be rotated less than 360° so that it coincides with itself? If so, where is it?

Water Wheel. The design of an old type of water wheel is shown here.*

32. What types of symmetry does it have?

33. What is the measure of the smallest angle through which it can be turned to look exactly the same?

Would the wheel look exactly the same if it were turned

34. 125°?

35. 225°?

36. To say that the wheel has "*n*-fold" symmetry, what number should *n* be?

37. Does it have reflection symmetry?

Wave Functions. Elementary particles such as electrons and photons are associated with "wave functions." The two figures below are graphs of wave functions.[†]

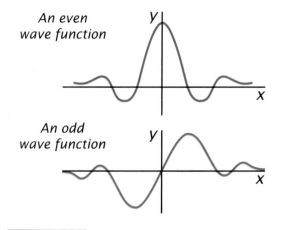

An even wave function

An odd wave function

Cats' Paws and Catapults: Mechanical Worlds of Nature and People, by Steven Vogel (Norton, 1998).
[†]*Reality's Mirror: Exploring the Mathematics of Symmetry,* by Bryan Bunch (Wiley, 1989).

38. What is the axis of symmetry of the graph of the even function?

39. What type of symmetry does the graph of an even function have?

40. What is the center of symmetry of the graph of the odd function?

41. What type of symmetry does the graph of an odd function have?

What type of function–even, odd, or neither–is described by each of these statements?

42. If the point (a, b) is on its graph, then so is the point $(-a, b)$.

43. If the point (a, b) is on its graph, then so is the point $(a, -b)$.

44. If the point (a, b) is on its graph, then so is the point $(-a, -b)$.

Cherry Orchard. Imagine that this orchard of cherry trees extends endlessly without any boundaries.[‡]

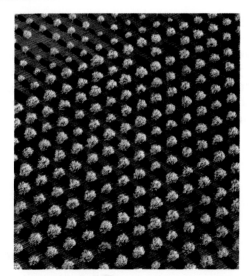

45. Why does the "infinite" orchard have translation symmetry?

46. What is the shortest distance related to the trees that the orchard can be translated and coincide with itself?

[‡]*Below from Above,* by Georg Gerster (Abbeville Press, 1986).

47.

Copy the figure above illustrating one tree and its six closest neighbors. Draw all of its lines of symmetry.

48. Why does the orchard have reflection symmetry?

49. Why does the orchard have rotation symmetry?

50. What points could serve as centers of symmetry?

51. What is the smallest angle through which the orchard can be turned to coincide with itself?

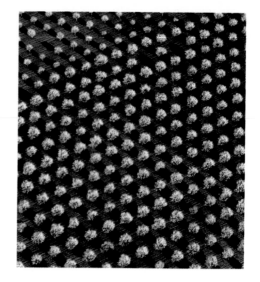

Set III

Short Story. In the following very short story by Scott Kim, some of the words have missing parts. In each case, the missing part is congruent to the part shown but rotated 180°. For example,

əɲ → *annie*

Scott Kim also created this figure.

КIΠ

2. What is unusual about it?

1. Copy the story and fill in the missing parts.

ù the summer, *Sí*   goes to the beach

and *Su*   herself, adds up *Suɯ*

of numbers, does *Sɟu*   and collects

ti   cans. The ride home is *hj l*   , and

that makes her head feel *fiz*   .

Basic Ideas

Summary of Key Ideas

Every isometry of the plane can be identified as a single reflection (a mirror image), as two reflections (a translation or rotation), or as three reflections (a glide reflection).

An isometry of the plane that changes a figure into its mirror image is either a reflection or a glide reflection. An isometry that does *not* change a figure into its mirror image is either a translation or a rotation.

Construction

8. To reflect a point through a line.   306

Exercises

Set I

Amazing Vase. This vase was created for Queen Elizabeth's Silver Jubilee in 1977.

1. Does this photograph appear to have reflection symmetry? Explain.
2. What is unusual about the vase?

Double Meanings. To an electrician, a *transformer* is a device used to transfer electric energy from one circuit to another.

3. What does the word *transformation* mean in geometry?

To an athlete, the word *isometric* refers to an exercise in which a muscle is tensed without changing its length.

4. What does the word *isometry* mean in geometry?

To an eye doctor, the word *dilation* refers to enlarging the pupil of the eye.

5. What does the word *dilation* mean in geometry?
6. Is a dilation an isometry?

Monkey Rug. This tapestry was woven in Peru sometime between 1000 and 1500 A.D.

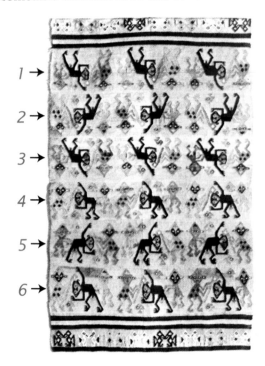

The following questions refer to the rows (numbered in red) of dark brown monkeys. Name the transformation through which the

7. third row appears to be the image of the first row.

8. second row appears to be the image of the first row.

9. fourth row appears to be the image of the third row.

10. sixth row appears to be the image of the second row.

Clover Leaves. An ordinary clover leaf has 3-fold rotation symmetry.

11. What does "3-fold" mean?

12. What is the smallest angle through which the leaf can be turned to look the same?

13. Does an ordinary clover leaf have point symmetry? Explain.

14. Sketch the leaf and draw its lines of symmetry.

15. Sketch a clover leaf with four "leaves" and draw its lines of symmetry.

16. What is the smallest angle through which it can be turned to look the same?

17. Does this kind of clover leaf have point symmetry?

18. What kind of luck is associated with the clover leaf that you drew in exercise 15?

Musical Transformations. The first measure of a piece of music by Bach is shown here.*

19. What transformation appears in it?

Another composer, Arnold Schoenberg, wrote about taking a sequence of musical notes and transforming it in different ways.†
    What geometric transformation corresponds to each of the following musical transformations?

20. Retrogression (playing a sequence of notes backward).

21. Transposition (moving a sequence of notes up or down).

22. Inversion (turning a sequence of notes upside down).

---

*First Prelude (BWV 846) from *The Well-Tempered Clavier,* Vol. 1.
†*Emblems of Mind: The Inner Life of Music and Mathematics,* by Edward Rothstein (Times Books, 1995).

Fish Design. This is one of Escher's mosaics based on fish.

23. Do all of the fish in the figure appear to be congruent? Explain.

24. Define congruence with respect to isometry.

25.

Through what transformation is one of the fish in this part of the mosaic the image of the other?

26.

Through what transformation is one of the fish in this part of the mosaic the image of the other?

27. Do any other types of transformation appear in Escher's mosaic? If so, draw a figure to illustrate an example.

Set II

Batter's Swing. The swing of a baseball bat includes two types of motion.*

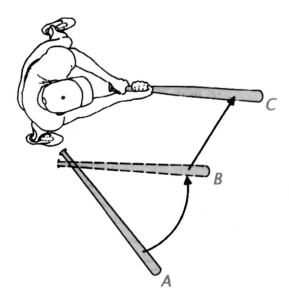

In the figure above, under what transformation is the bat

28. at B the image of the bat at A?

29. at C the image of the bat at B?

Each of these transformations can be considered the composite of two reflections.

30. What is the difference in the way that the lines of reflection are related?

31. Use your protractor to estimate the magnitude of the rotation.

32. Given that the length of the bat is 42 inches, use the figure to estimate the magnitude of the translation. (Hint: *Measure everything in millimeters.*)

Keep Your Eye on the Ball: The Science and Folklore of Baseball, by Robert G. Watts and A. Terry Bahill (W. H. Freeman and Company, 1990).

33. Trace the figure below of the bats in positions B and C and show, by an accurate drawing, one way in which the transformation can be obtained geometrically as the composite of two reflections.

C

B

Construction Problem. △ABC has no special symmetry.

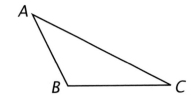

34. Draw a large copy of it on your paper. Use your straightedge and compass to construct the reflection of point B through line AC. Label its image D. Draw AD and CD.

35. What are the images of AB and BC through line AC?

36. Why is △ABC ≅ △ADC?

37. Describe the symmetry of quadrilateral ABCD.

34. *(continued)* Construct the reflection of point A through line DC. Label its image E. Draw DE and CE.

38. For what type of transformation is △EDC the image of △ABC?

From N to Z. Make an accurate copy of the following figure.

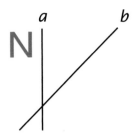

39. Sketch the reflection of the letter N through line *a*, and then sketch the reflection of the image that results through line *b*.

40. What transformation is the composite of these two reflections?

41. What does the measure of the acute angle formed by lines *a* and *b* appear to be?

42. What does the magnitude of the composite transformation appear to be?

43. Is there any other letter of the alphabet whose final image from reflections through these two lines is another letter of the alphabet? Explain.

Past and Future. The following figures are by graphic designer John Langdon.*

iTPAST PAST PAST PAS

rUREFUTUREFUTUREI

Think of each pattern in the figures as repeating endlessly in both directions.

44. Draw a picture of the part of each pattern that repeats.

45. What type of symmetry does each figure have owing to this repeating pattern?

44. *(continued)* Draw the lines on your figures through which the "endless" patterns could be reflected so that each coincides with itself.

46. Why have no vertical bars been drawn on the Es?

47. Does either pattern have rotation symmetry?

48. Which letters in the patterns have been drawn so that they have reflection symmetry?

49. Have any letters been drawn so that they have rotation symmetry? If so, which one(s)?

Dice Symmetries. The six faces of a die do not all have the same symmetry.

50. Sort them into groups in which the faces of each group have the same symmetry and describe the symmetries of each group.

Wordplay, by John Langdon (Harcourt Brace Jovanovich, 1992).

Midterm Review

Set I

Chill Factor. A 3-year-old child can understand the statement "You can't go outside if you don't put your coat on."*

1. What type of statement is it?
2. What is its hypothesis?

Losers, Sleepers. The following questions are about the diagram at the right.

3. What is a diagram of this type called?
4. Write the statement represented by the diagram.
5. What is its conclusion?

Marine Logic. Sea lions that have been taught with symbols that $a \to b$ and $b \to c$ seem to realize that $a \to c$.†

6. What is an argument of the form

$$a \to b$$
$$b \to c$$
$$\text{Therefore, } a \to c$$

called?

7. What could cause the conclusion of such an argument to be false?

Finding Truth. G. K. Chesterton once wrote: "You can only find truth with logic if you have already found truth without it."
   What are the statements called that we

8. prove to be true by using logic?
9. assume to be true without proof?

---

*Why Do Buses Come in Threes? The Hidden Mathematics of Everyday Life, by Rob Eastaway and Jeremy Wyndham (Wiley, 1998).
†*The Animal Mind,* by James L. Gould and Carol Grant Gould (Scientific American Library, 1994).

Only in Geometry. Each of the following words is an important term used *only* in geometry. Briefly explain what each word means.

10. Collinear.
11. Hypotenuse.
12. Isosceles.
13. Rhombus.

Why Three? Most insects walk on three of their six legs at a time.

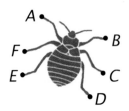

14. What postulate tells you that the insect in the figure above won't tip over when legs A, C, and E touch the ground?
15. Which geometric terms in this postulate are undefined?

What Follows? Complete the statements of the following postulates and theorems.

16. Two points determine . . .
17. The sum of the angles of a triangle is . . .
18. An angle has exactly one ray that . . .
19. Complements of the same angle . . .
20. An equilateral triangle is . . .
21. An exterior angle of a triangle is greater than . . .
22. In a plane, two points each equidistant from the endpoints of a line segment determine . . .
23. Equal corresponding angles mean that lines . . .
24. In a plane, two lines perpendicular to a third line . . .
25. In a plane, a line perpendicular to one of two parallel lines is . . .

26. An exterior angle of a triangle is equal to the sum of . . .

27. A quadrilateral is a parallelogram if its opposite angles are . . .

28. The diagonals of an isosceles trapezoid . . .

Formulas. Explain what each of the following formulas means.

29. $A = \pi r^2$.

30. $A = lw$.

31. $d = \sqrt{(x_2 - x_1)^2 + (y_2 - y_1)^2}$.

32. $p = a + b + c$.

33. $p = 2l + 2w$.

Protractor Problems. The figure below shows a protractor placed on $\angle$AOB so that the coordinates of its sides are 123 and 39.

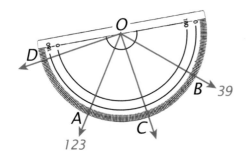

123

34. Find the measure of $\angle$AOB.

35. Find the measures of $\angle$AOC and $\angle$COB, given that ray OC bisects $\angle$AOB.

36. Find the coordinate of ray OC.

37. Find the measure of $\angle$AOD, given that $\angle$AOD and $\angle$AOC are complementary.

38. Find the coordinate of ray OD.

39. Would it be correct to say that ray OC is between ray OD and ray OB? Explain why or why not.

Metric Angles. As part of the metric system adopted at the time of the French revolution, right angles were defined to have a measure of 100 "grades."

Write each of the following definitions or theorems in terms of "grades."

40. The definition of supplementary angles.

41. The definition of an obtuse angle.

42. The theorem about the sum of the angles of a quadrilateral.

43. The theorem that each angle of an equilateral triangle is 60°.

Linear Pair. The figure below appeared on the opening page of the first printed edition of the *Elements* (1482).

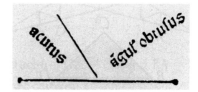

44. What do you need to know about this figure to know that it contains a linear pair?

45. If two angles form a linear pair, does it follow that one is acute and the other is obtuse? Explain.

46. In what way are the measures of the angles of every linear pair related?

47. If the angles in a linear pair are equal, what can you conclude about each angle?

Polygons. In each of the following exercises, the measure of one or more parts of a polygon is given. Tell what the measures of the indicated parts must be.

48. A right triangle. The other side if the two shorter sides are 15 and 30.

49. An isosceles triangle. The third side if two sides are 15 and 30.

50. A rhombus. The other angles if one angle is 30°.

51. An isosceles trapezoid. The other angles if one angle is 30°.

Bent Pyramid. The Bent Pyramid at Dahshur in Egypt is shown in the photograph below.

In the following side view of it, ABDE is an isosceles trapezoid and △BCD is an isosceles triangle.

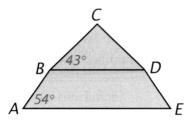

Use the facts that ∠A = 54° and ∠CBD = 43° to find

52. ∠ABD.

53. ∠C.

54. ∠E.

55. ∠CDE.

Six Triangles. Three triangles in the following figure are right triangles, and the other three are isosceles.

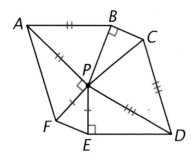

56. Two triangles look as if they might be congruent. Which two are they?

57. If you knew that AB = ED, you could prove these triangles congruent. How?

58. You could also prove them congruent if you knew that AF = CD. How?

Italian Theorem. The following theorem appears in an Italian geometry book.

Teorema. Se due lati di un triangolo sono disegauli, l'angolo opposto al lato maggiore è maggiore di quello opposto al lato minore.

In terms of the figure above, the hypothesis of this theorem might be stated as: "In △ABC, CA > CB."

59. State the conclusion in terms of the figure.

60. State the theorem as a complete sentence in English.

61. What English words are related in meaning to "maggiore" and "minore"?

Impossibly Obtuse. Recalling that an acute triangle has three acute angles, Obtuse Ollie concluded that an obtuse triangle has three obtuse angles.

The beginning of a proof that such a triangle is impossible follows.

Proof

Suppose that △ABC has three obtuse angles.

Then ∠A > 90°, ∠B > 90°, and ∠C > 90°.

62. What follows from adding these inequalities?

63. What does this result contradict?

64. What does the contradiction show about what we supposed?

65. What kind of proof is this proof?

Converses. Write the converses of the following statements and tell whether the converses are true or false.

66. If two angles are the acute angles of a right triangle, then they are complementary.

67. If a quadrilateral is a parallelogram, then the diagonals of the quadrilateral bisect each other.

Construction Exercises.

68. First, use your ruler to draw a line segment 8 cm long. Label its endpoints A and B and mark the points X and Y on it that are 3 cm and 6 cm from point A.

Use your straightedge and compass to construct △ABC with AC = AY and BC = BX.

Construct the line that bisects ∠A.

69. Does this line also bisect BC?

68. *(continued)* Check your answer by constructing a line that bisects BC.

68. *(continued)* Through C, construct a line perpendicular to AB. Let P be the point in which this line intersects AB.

70. What point on line AB is closest to point C?

71. Which three lines in the figure are concurrent?

Set II

Grid Exercise. On graph paper, draw a pair of axes extending 20 units to the right and 10 units up from the origin.

72. Plot the following points and connect them with line segments to form quadrilateral ABCD: A(0, 2), B(12, 2), C(16, 8), D(4, 8).

73. What kind of quadrilateral does ABCD appear to be?

74. Find the lengths of its sides to check your answer.

72. *(continued)* Plot P(10, 2) and draw PD and PC.

75. Which segment looks longer: PD or PC?

76. Use the distance formula to check your answer.

Roof Truss. The figure below from a book on architecture illustrates one type of truss, a structure used to support a roof.

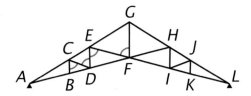

In the structure, GA = GL and FA = FL.

77. What can you conclude about ∠A and ∠L? Explain.

Also, ∠BCD = ∠CDE = ∠DEF = ∠EFG.

78. What can you conclude about BC and FG? Explain.

It appears as if CD ∥ EF.

79. Is this necessarily true? Explain.

∠AGF is acute and ∠GFA is obtuse.

80. Can these two angles be supplementary? Explain.

Angles Problem 1. In the figure at the right, △ABC is equilateral and its vertices lie on the sides of △DEF, AB ∥ DE, ∠D = 65°, and ∠F = 50°.

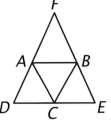

81. Make a large copy of the figure and write the given information on it. Find the measures of the other angles and write them on the figure.

82. What can you conclude about △ACD and △BCE? Explain.

Irregular Star. The five angles at the points of the star below, formed from five intersecting line segments, are equal.

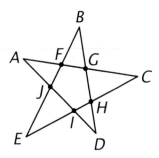

83. Copy the figure and mark it as needed to help in deciding whether each of the following statements is true. *If you think a statement is true, explain why.*

84. △EFC is isosceles.

85. Pentagon FGHIJ is equiangular.

86. Pentagon FGHIJ is equilateral.

87. Every triangle in the figure is isosceles.

Angle Trisector. The linkage below can be used to trisect an angle.

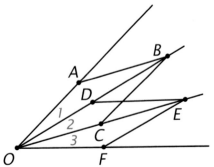

It is designed so that OA = AB = BC = CO = OD = DE = EF = FO.

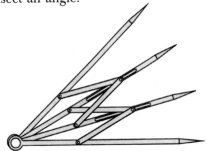

Explain why each of the following statements is always true, no matter how the linkage is moved.

88. △OAB ≅ △OCB, and △ODE ≅ △OFE.

89. ∠1 = ∠2 = ∠3.

Quadrilateral Problem. The measures of the angles of quadrilateral ABCD are multiples of *x*.

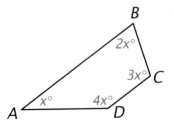

90. Write an appropriate equation and solve for *x*.

91. What is the measure of the largest angle of ABCD?

92. What other conclusions can you make about this figure?

Angles Problem 2. In the figure below, $l_1 \parallel l_2$ and AC bisects ∠BAD.

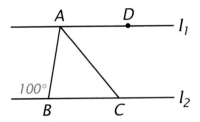

93. Make a large copy of the figure and write in the measure of the 100° angle. Find the measures of the other angles and write them on the figure.

94. What can you conclude about △ABC? Explain.

A, B, C. Suppose that the legs of a right triangle have lengths *a* and *b* and the hypotenuse has length *c*.

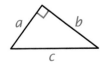

95. Write an equation relating a, b, and c.

96. Write three inequalities relating a, b, and c.

97. Could a triangle have sides of lengths a^2, b^2, and c^2? Explain.

Midsegments. In the figure below, D and E are the midpoints of AC and BC, AE and BD intersect at F, and G and H are the midpoints of AF and BF.

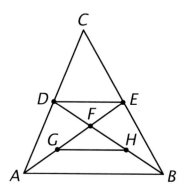

98. Copy the figure and mark it as needed to explain why each of the following statements is true.

99. DE = GH.

100. DE ∥ GH.

98. *(continued)* Draw DG and EH.

101. DEHG is a parallelogram.

102. AG = GF = FE and BH = HF = FD.

On the Level. The plank of this swing always stays level with the ground as the plank moves back and forth.*

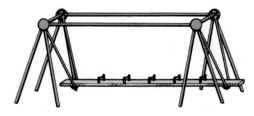

103. What is it about the design of the swing that makes the plank stay level?

Mathematics Meets Technology, by Brian Bolt (Cambridge University Press, 1991).

Folding Experiment.
Mark a point on a sheet of paper and label the point A. Choose a corner of the paper, label it B, and draw segment AB. Fold the paper so that B falls on A, and make a sharp crease. Unfold the paper so that it is flat.

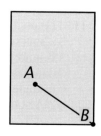

104. Draw a sketch of the result.

105. What relation does the crease line seem to have to AB?

106. Add some extra line segments as needed to help in explaining why.

Earth Measurement. In the ninth century, a team of surveyors working near Baghdad found that 1 degree at the center of the earth corresponded to about 57 miles on the surface.

With the use of this information, what did they estimate for

107. the circumference of the earth?

108. the distance from the surface of the earth to its center?

Not a Square. Although parallelogram ABCD looks like a square, it is not because ∠DAB ≠ ∠ABC.

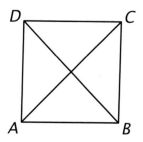

On the basis of this information, *could* it be that

109. ABCD is a rhombus? Explain.

110. AC ⊥ DB? Explain.

111. AC and BD bisect each other? Explain.

112. ABCD is a rectangle? Explain.

113. AC = DB? Explain.

Construction Exercise.

114. Draw a scalene triangle in the center of a sheet of paper and label its vertices A, B, and C. Use your straightedge and compass to construct three equilateral triangles outwardly on the sides of △ABC. Label the equilateral triangles △ABZ, △BCX, and △ACY.

115. Draw AX, BY, and CZ. What seems to be true about these three line segments?

SAT Problem. The figures below appeared in a problem on an SAT test.

The first figure shows a rectangular sheet of paper being folded in half. The second figure shows the result of cutting off two opposite corners of the folded paper.

In figure A below, the lower half is the image of the upper half by a reflection.

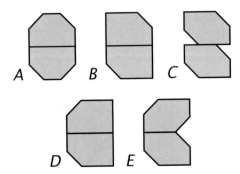

Name the transformation(s) through which the lower half is the image of the upper half in

116. figure B.

117. figure C.

118. figure D.

119. figure E.

120. Which one of the five figures represents the paper when it is unfolded?

Quilt Patterns. Three patterns used in making quilts are shown below.* Describe the symmetries of each pattern.

121.

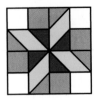

122.

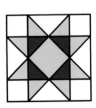

123.

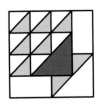

Dividing a Lot. A real estate developer[†] is planning to subdivide a vacant lot into congruent parcels (the ' stands for feet).

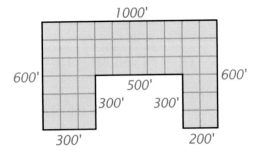

Make a sketch to illustrate each of the following divisions.

124. A way to divide the lot into three congruent parcels.

125. A way to divide it into five congruent parcels.

Designing Tessellations, by Jinny Beyer (Contemporary Books, 1999).
†Solomon Golomb.

Chapter 9

Area

Formulas for the areas of various geometric figures are so useful that they are commonly learned and used by people who never take a course in geometry. In this chapter, you will see not only how these formulas can be derived as part of our deductive system but also how they can be used to solve a wide variety of practical problems. You will also see how these area theorems can be used to prove the Pythagorean Theorem.

© 2003 Harold R. Jacobs

Area

Alaska hasn't always been the largest state. Before Alaska, it was Texas. In fact, in the history of our country, four states have had the distinction of being the largest. Georgia was the largest of the original 13 states. Then Missouri (1821–1845), followed by Texas (1845–1959), followed by Alaska.

To compare their sizes, we use numbers. For example, the area of Alaska is about 591,000 square miles, and the area of Texas is about 267,000 square miles. Without numbers, such comparisons aren't always as easy. Look, for example, at the map above. Can you name the three largest states following Texas? The areas of all 50 states can be found in reference books.

It is easy to see how we could work out the areas of states such as Utah and Colorado on this map. Their shapes seem to be simple polygons. On the other hand, the area of Florida on this map would be more difficult to figure out. Even so, it is reasonable to assume that, no matter what shape a closed figure might have, it has an area.

In this chapter, we will review some of the formulas for the areas of various geometric figures. In doing so, we will begin with some basic definitions and assumptions, and from them we will develop the area formulas as a logical sequence of theorems.

We start by making a simple observation. When we refer to the *area of a polygon*, we mean a number that is the measure of the region bounded by it. The figures below illustrate the distinction.

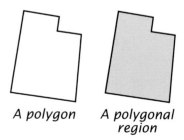

A polygon   *A polygonal region*

By a *polygonal region*, we mean the union of a polygon and its interior.

We can always divide a polygonal region into triangular regions by drawing some of its diagonals, which is how we relate the formulas for basic geometric figures to each other. Consider a parallelogram, for example. Drawing one of its diagonals forms two congruent triangles. It is reasonable to assume that these congruent triangles have equal areas and that the area of the parallelogram is equal to their sum. We summarize these observations as the following postulate.

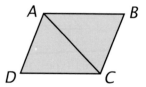

Postulate 8. The Area Postulate

Every polygonal region has a positive number called its area such that
(1) congruent triangles have equal areas and
(2) the area of a polygonal region is equal to the sum of the areas of its nonoverlapping parts.

Although the Area Postulate is stated in relation to polygonal regions, it can be extended to other closed figures. For example, the figure at the right is a map of the smallest state, Rhode Island, and its five counties. The area of Rhode Island is equal to the sum of the areas of the five counties. If two of the counties were congruent (which they are not), then we could conclude that they have equal areas.

We will represent the words "the area of" by α (alpha), the first letter of the Greek alphabet. For example, for the parallelogram at the right above, we can write that

$$\alpha\triangle ABC = \alpha\triangle CDA \text{ and}$$

$$\alpha ABCD = \alpha\triangle ABC + \alpha\triangle CDA.$$

Rhode Island

Exercises

Set I

Train Logo. The Amtrak symbol, shown below, consists of three hexagonal regions.

1. Copy the version of the figure below and show a way to divide it into six quadrilaterals.

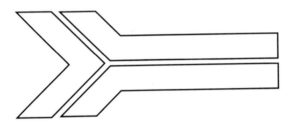

2. What types of quadrilaterals are they?

3. What does the Area Postulate say about the area of the Amtrak symbol?

Star in Square. The figure below shows a "star" drawn inside a square.

4. Which has the greater perimeter, the "star" or the square? Why?

5. Which has the greater area? Why?

6. If one region has a greater perimeter than another, does it follow that it has a greater area?

Area Relations. ABCD is a parallelogram with diagonal AC; EF and GH have been drawn parallel to its sides.

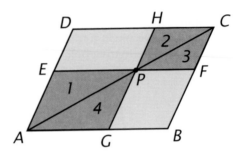

Tell whether you think each of the following statements is true or false. Indicate your reasoning.

7. $\alpha \triangle ADC = \alpha \triangle ABC$.

8. $\alpha \triangle 1 = \alpha \triangle 4$ and $\alpha \triangle 2 = \alpha \triangle 3$.

9. $\alpha EPHD = \alpha GBFP$.

10. $\alpha AGHD = \alpha ABFE$.

11. $\alpha EFCD = \alpha GBCH$.

12. $\alpha AGPE = \alpha PFCH$.

Flag Geometry. The flag of the United States is not the only one that is red, white, and blue.

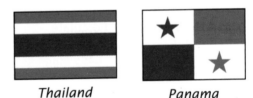

Thailand   Panama

Suppose that the three colors in the flag of Thailand cover equal areas and that the area of one of the red stripes is x square units.

Write an expression for the area of

13. one of the white stripes.

14. the blue stripe.

15. the entire flag.

The flag of Panama contains four congruent rectangles. Suppose that the flag has an area of $4x$ square units and that the area of each star is y square units.

Write an expression for

16. the red area.

17. the white area.

18. the blue area.

19. If you add these three expressions, do you get the area of the entire flag? Show why or why not.

Drum Polygons. You might expect identical drums to sound alike. Surprisingly, mathematicians Carolyn Gordon and David Webb have discovered that drumheads with these two shapes sound alike.*

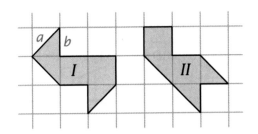

(For convenience, the shapes have been drawn on a square grid.)

20. What kind of polygon is each shape?

21. How do the polygons compare in area?

22. How do their perimeters compare?

23. Write an expression in terms of *a* and *b* for each perimeter.

24. Are the polygons congruent?

Set II

Midsegment Triangle. The sides of △MNO are the midsegments of △ABC.

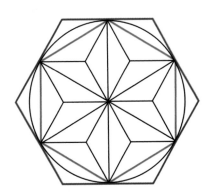

25. Copy the figure and mark the segments that are equal.

The Jungles of Randomness, by Ivars Peterson (Wiley, 1998).

26. What two conclusions follow about △MNO, △AMO, △BMN, and △CNO?

27. What conclusion follows about the areas of △MNO and △ABC?

28. What kind of quadrilaterals are AMNO, BNOM, and COMN?

29. How do you know?

30. Are they congruent?

31. Do they have equal areas? Explain why or why not.

32. What kind of quadrilaterals are AMNC, BNOA, and COMB?

33. Are they congruent?

34. Do they have equal areas? Explain why or why not.

Circle Area. All of the small triangles in the figure below are congruent.†

Given that the area of the red hexagon is 3 square units, find

35. the area of one of the small triangles.

36. the area of one of the equilateral triangles.

37. the area of the star.

38. the area of the blue hexagon.

39. Use your results to guess the approximate area of the circle.

---

† *Wheels, Life, and Other Mathematical Amusements,* by Martin Gardner (W. H. Freeman and Company, 1983).

Doubling a Square. In one of his books, the Greek philosopher Plato explores how it is possible to prove that one square has twice the area of another. His method is based on these figures.

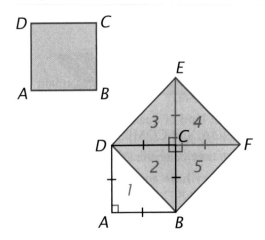

Explain Plato's argument by giving a reason for each of the following statements.

40. The five numbered triangles are congruent. Why?

41. They are equal in area. Why?

42. BFED is a square. Why?

43. αBFED = 2αABCD. Why?

SAT Problem. The figure below appeared in a problem on an SAT exam.

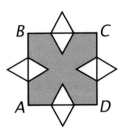

All of the triangles are congruent, the area of the shaded region is 84, and the area of square ABCD is 100.

44. What is the area of one of the triangles?

45. What is the total area of the entire figure?

Comparing Parallelograms. Which one of the parallelograms below, ABCD or ABEF, do you think has the greater area?

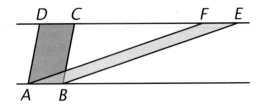

Euclid proved that their areas are equal. Show how he did so by answering each of the following questions.

> *Given:* ABCD and ABEF are parallelograms as shown.
> *Prove:* αABCD = αABEF.

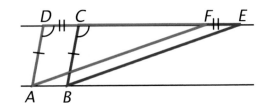

46. Why is AD = BC?

47. Why is AD ∥ BC?

48. Why is ∠ADF = ∠BCE?

49. Why is DC = FE?

50. Why is DF = CE?

51. Why is △ADF ≅ △BCE?

52. Why is α△ADF = α△BCE?

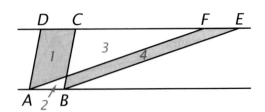

53. Why is α1 + α3 = α3 + α4?

54. Why is α1 = α4?

55. Why is αABCD = αABEF?

Set III

Magic Playing Card. Here is a baffling puzzle. A "magic" playing card has been cut into four pieces. When the pieces are put together face up, they look like the figure at the left below. If the pieces are turned over and put together, part of the back of the card is missing!

Carefully compare the front and back of the card. The area of each piece is the same regardless of whether it is face up or face down.

1. Can the borders of the playing card face up and face down be congruent? Explain.

2. What can you conclude about the dimensions of the card in each position?

3. What does your conclusion have to do with how the puzzle works?

 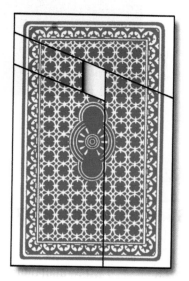

New Book of Puzzles, by Jerry Slocum and Jack Botermans (W. H. Freeman and Company, 1992).

LESSON 2

Squares and Rectangles

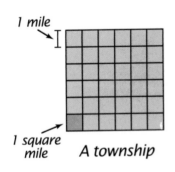

1 mile

1 square mile

A township

More than that of any other country, the American landscape has been influenced by geometry. The word "geometry," in fact, comes from the Greek word *geometrein*, which means "to measure land." The pattern established by the Land Ordinance of 1785 was that the country west of the Alleghenies was to be divided up into squares 6 miles on a side called "townships," which were in turn divided into even smaller squares. The influence of this system is evident even in the shape of individual homesteads, as the photograph above of a homestead on a square lot in North Dakota illustrates.*

Because a township was a square of land 6 miles on a side, it had an area of 36 square miles. Area is normally measured in *square units* that are derived from *linear units*, or units of length. The numbers known as "squares" get their name from this connection. We call 6^2 "six *squared*" because a square 6 units on a side contains 6^2, or 6×6, unit *squares*.

***Taking Measures: Across the American Landscape*, by James Corner and Alex S. MacLean (Yale University Press, 1996).

660 ft

One acre

Another unit commonly used in the United States for measuring land is the "acre." The acre originally was considered to be the amount of land that could be plowed with oxen in 1 day and was a rectangle 660 feet long and 66 feet wide. The length 660 feet was roughly the distance that a team of oxen could plow before needing to rest.

Ruling a 660-ft by 66-ft rectangle into 1-ft by 1-ft squares gives its area in square feet:

$$660 \text{ feet} \times 66 \text{ feet} =$$
$$43{,}560 \text{ square feet.}$$

The dimensions of a rectangle are sometimes called its length and width. They are also called its *base* and *altitude*. The words *base* and *altitude* can also refer to two consecutive sides of the rectangle. (Any side can be considered the base, and a side perpendicular to the base can be considered the altitude, or "height"–another word for "altitude.") The letters *b* and *h* are usually used to represent the base and altitude.

We have seen that the area of a 1-acre rectangle in square feet is the product of its dimensions. We will assume that the area of any rectangle can be found by multiplying its dimensions, even rectangles whose dimensions are not integers.

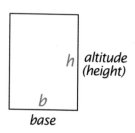

Postulate 9

The area of a rectangle is the product of its base and altitude.

A square is a rectangle whose base and altitude are equal, and so the special case of finding the area of a square follows as a corollary to this postulate.

Corollary to Postulate 9

The area of a square is the square of its side.

Exercises

Set I

Abstract Art. One of the strangest pieces of modern art is an oil painting by Ad Reinhardt. It belongs to the New York Museum of Modern Art and consists of a solid black square measuring 5 feet on each side.

*Abstract Painting
1960–61*

Find its perimeter

1. in feet.

2. in inches.

Find its area

3. in square feet.

4. in square inches.

Tile Pattern. Each of the smallest squares in the figure below has an area of 1 square unit.

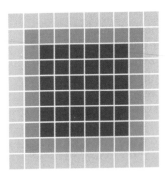

5. Which of the three colored regions do you think has the largest area?

6. Find the area of each region.

Fishing Nets. The mesh in fishing nets is measured in relation to the square inch.

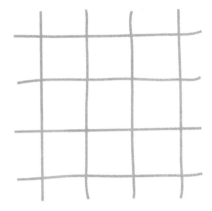

The net above has a "half inch" mesh.

7. Use your ruler to explain why.

8. How many small squares are there per square inch?

9. How many small squares per square inch would you expect in quarter-inch mesh?

10. Why do you suppose there are laws regarding the size of mesh used in fishing?

Distributive Property. The rectangular figure below is sometimes used in algebra books to illustrate the distributive property.

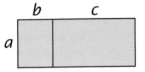

11. What is the area of the entire figure in terms of the lengths of its sides?

12. What are the areas of the two parts of the figure?

13. Copy and complete the distributive property:
$$a(b + c) = \ ?$$

Binomial Square. The figure at the right is used in algebra books to illustrate the square of a binomial.

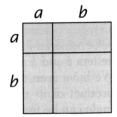

14. What is the area of the entire figure in terms of the lengths of its sides?

15. What are the areas of the four parts of the figure?

16. Copy and complete the formula for the square of a binomial:
$$(a + b)^2 = \ ?$$

Difference of Two Squares.

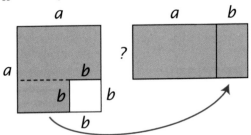

17. Use the figure above as a guide to writing the formula for the difference of two squares.
$$a^2 - b^2 = \ ?$$

Area Connection. The figure below suggests a connection between the area of a right triangle and the area of a rectangle.

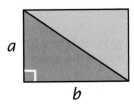

18. Write a formula for the area, *A*, of the rectangle in terms of its sides, *a* and *b*.

19. Into what does the diagonal of the rectangle divide it?

20. Why do the two triangles have equal areas?

21. Write a formula for the area, *A*, of a right triangle in terms of its legs, *a* and *b*.

Two Squares. The two squares below have areas of 25 and 26.

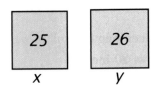

Because the area of the first square is 25, $x^2 = 25$; so $x = \sqrt{25} = 5$.

22. How long is each side of the second square?

Use a calculator to help in answering each of the following questions.

23. Is the length of each side of the second square 5.099?

24. What is the *exact* area of a square whose sides are 5.099?

25. Is the length of each side of the second square 5.0990195?

26. Do you think you could write the exact length of each side of the second square in decimal form?

27. What kind of number is the length of each side of the second square?

Set II

Bed of Nails. An old trick is to lie on a bed of nails. For it to be comfortable, the bed should have one nail per square inch.*

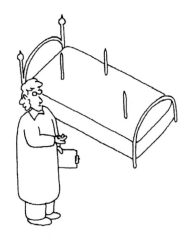

Dr. Jones rechecks his calculations on proper nail spacing before lying down on the bed of nails.

28. To construct a bed of nails 6 feet long and 3 feet wide, how many nails would you need?

29. Which do you think would hurt the most: to lie on a bed of nails, to sit on it, or to stand on it?

Surveyor's Chain. The tool used by early American surveyors to measure distances was a chain of 100 links, each 7.92 inches long.

30. What was the total length of the chain in feet?

The Cosmological Milkshake: A Semi-Serious Look at the Size of Things, by Robert Ehrlich (Rutgers University Press, 1994).

66 ft

660 ft

One acre

31. What are the dimensions of the above rectangular acre in "chains"?

32. What is its area in "square chains"?

A mile is a distance of 80 chains.

33. Use your answer to exercise 30 to find the number of feet in a mile.

34. How many "square chains" are in 1 square mile?

35. How many acres are in 1 square mile?

Map Reading. Figuring out how to get somewhere from a map book can be awkward if a road or your destination is too close to the edge of the page.*

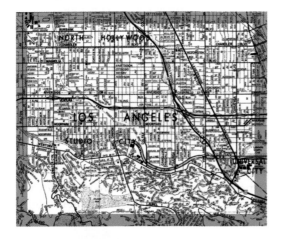

Suppose the map pages are 24 cm by 20 cm and that the awkward region is 1 cm into the page along each edge.

36. What is the total area of the map page?

37. What is the area of the "awkward region"?

38. What percentage of the area of the map page is the awkward region?

Suppose the awkward region is 2 cm into the page instead.

39. Now what percentage of the area of the map page would the awkward region be?

Wallpaper Geometry. Wallpaper is sold in 36-square-foot rolls. The most common widths are 20 inches (20") and 27 inches.†

20" or 27"

How many feet long is a roll of wallpaper with

40. a width of 20 inches?

41. a width of 27 inches?

The rule for estimating the number of rolls needed to paper a room is to *assume that each roll will cover 30 square feet.*

42. Why not 36 square feet, given that it is the area of a roll?

The rule continues: *Multiply the room's perimeter by its height, divide by 30, and round up.*

43. What does multiplying the room's perimeter by its height give?

44. After dividing by 30, why not just round the answer to the nearest number?

45. There is one more part to the rule. What do you suppose it is about?

46. What effect would it have on the number of rolls needed?

Why Do Buses Come in Threes? The Hidden Mathematics of Everyday Life, by Rob Eastaway and Jeremy Wyndham (Wiley, 1998).

---

†*Sizes,* by John Lord (Harper Perennial, 1995).

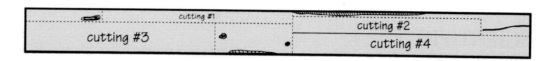

Cutting a Board. The figure above from the *Wood Handbook* shows how four smaller boards can be cut from a board so as to avoid knots and cracks in the boards produced.*

The original board is 12 *inches* wide and 12 *feet* long.

47. Find its area in square inches.

Use the following dimensions to find the areas of the four smaller boards in square inches.

48. Cutting #1: $3\frac{1}{2}$ in by $4\frac{1}{2}$ ft.

49. Cutting #2: $4\frac{1}{2}$ in by $4\frac{1}{2}$ ft.

50. Cutting #3: $8\frac{1}{2}$ in by $4\frac{1}{2}$ ft.

51. Cutting #4: 6 in by $5\frac{2}{3}$ ft.

To be graded as a high-quality board, the four boards cut from it must use at least two-thirds of the board.

52. Do they? Explain.

The Number 17. The Greek historian Plutarch said that "the followers of Pythagoras have a horror for the number 17. For 17 lies exactly halfway between 16, which is a square, and the number 18, which is the double of a square."[†]

53. Draw figures to show why 16 is a square and 18 is the double of a square.

Plutarch also mentioned something unusual about the perimeters and areas of these two figures.

54. What is it?

55. Can you find any other square or rectangle for which it is true? (Hint: The dimensions need not be integers.)

---

*Wood Handbook, Forest Products Laboratory (U.S. Department of Agriculture, 1974).

[†]*Science Awakening,* by B. L. van der Waerden (Oxford University Press, 1961).

Total Living Area. Realtors use the total living area to help calculate the market value of a house.

The figure below shows the "living area" part of the house. Its dimensions have been rounded to the nearest foot.[‡]

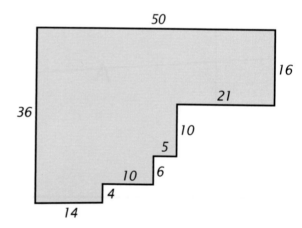

56. Sketch the figure and mark it as needed to calculate the total living area of the house.

57. Sketch the figure again, divide it into pieces in a different way, and check your answer to exercise 56 by calculating the total living area again.

[‡]*The Best of Better Homes and Gardens Home Plans,* Fall 1997.

SCIENTIFIC
AMERICAN

"PERFECT" RECTANGLE   FIFTY CENTS

November 1958

Set III

Dividing into Squares. To divide a square into smaller squares each having a different area was once thought to be impossible. The figure below, which once appeared on the cover of *Scientific American* magazine, seems to show a solution.

1. Trace the figure on your paper.

The areas of squares C and D are 64 and 81 square units, respectively.

2. Find the areas of the other squares.

3. Is the figure containing the nine squares a square? Explain why or why not.

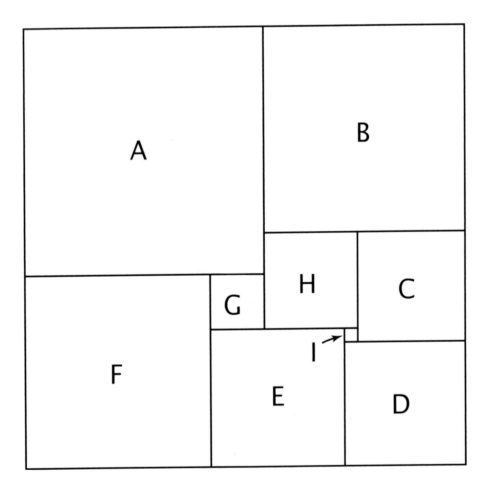

LESSON 3

Triangles

In 1858, an English tourist purchased an old scroll when visiting Egypt. Now in the British Museum, it is known as the Rhind Papyrus and is our main source of information about mathematics in ancient Egypt. It was written in about 1650 B.C. by a scribe named Ahmose, who gave it the title "The correct method of reckoning, for grasping the meaning of things and knowing everything that is."*

Rather than explaining "everything that is," the papyrus simply contains a series of mathematics problems and their solutions. Problem 51, shown above, was titled "Example of making a triangle in land." Ahmes wrote:

> If it is said to you, a triangle of 10 khet on the side of it, 4 khet on the base of it, what is the area of it?
> Make you half of 4, namely 2, to cause that it become rectangular. Make you the multiplication: 10 times 2; the area of it is this.

Ahmose's solution is correct only if the triangle is a right triangle. The figures at the right show where the "rectangular" part comes in and suggest why the method works.

Although we could write a proof based on these figures to explain why the area of a right triangle is half the product of its legs, it is easier to base the proof on a rectangle enclosing the entire triangle.

---

*The Rhind Mathematical Papyrus, by Arnold Buffum Chace (The Mathematical Association of America, 1927).

Lesson 3: Triangles   **351**

Triangles

In 1858, an English tourist purchased an old scroll when visiting Egypt. Now in the British Museum, it is known as the Rhind Papyrus and is our main source of information about mathematics in ancient Egypt. It was written in about 1650 B.C. by a scribe named Ahmose, who gave it the title "The correct method of reckoning, for grasping the meaning of things and knowing everything that is."*

Rather than explaining "everything that is," the papyrus simply contains a series of mathematics problems and their solutions. Problem 51, shown above, was titled "Example of making a triangle in land." Ahmes wrote:

> If it is said to you, a triangle of 10 khet on the side of it, 4 khet on the base of it, what is the area of it?
>
> Make you half of 4, namely 2, to cause that it become rectangular. Make you the multiplication: 10 times 2; the area of it is this.

Ahmose's solution is correct only if the triangle is a right triangle. The figures at the right show where the "rectangular" part comes in and suggest why the method works.

Although we could write a proof based on these figures to explain why the area of a right triangle is half the product of its legs, it is easier to base the proof on a rectangle enclosing the entire triangle.

---

*The Rhind Mathematical Papyrus, by Arnold Buffum Chace (The Mathematical Association of America, 1927).

Theorem 38

The area of a right triangle is half the product of its legs.

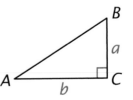

Given: Right △ABC with legs *a* and *b*.

Prove: $\alpha\triangle ABC = \frac{1}{2}ba.$

The following figures show the plan of the proof, whose main ideas are outlined below.

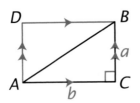 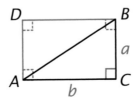 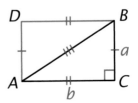

Proof

Through A and B, draw lines parallel to the legs of the triangle to form parallelogram ACBD. ACBD is also a rectangle; so $\alpha ACBD = ba.$

$\triangle ABC \cong \triangle BAD$; so $\alpha\triangle ABC = \alpha\triangle BAD.$ Therefore, $\alpha\triangle ABC = \frac{1}{2}\alpha ACBD$ and so $\alpha\triangle ABC = \frac{1}{2}ba.$

Knowing this formula for right triangles, we can derive a comparable formula for the area of *any* triangle. Look again at right △ABC: if leg AC is the *base* of the triangle, it seems reasonable to call the length of leg BC the *height,* or *altitude,* of the triangle. In general, we think of an *altitude* of a triangle as the *distance* from a vertex to the line of the opposite side. The distance from a point to a line is measured along the perpendicular from the point to the line. Consequently, the word *altitude* is also used to refer to a *perpendicular line segment* from a vertex to the line of the opposite side.

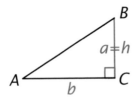 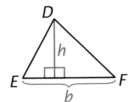 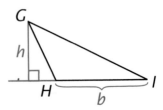

As the figures above show, an altitude of a triangle may lie on a side of the triangle, inside the triangle, or outside it. Regardless of where the altitude may be, by using the information in these figures it is easy to show how the area of a triangle can be found if the lengths of one side and the corresponding altitude are known.

Theorem 39

The area of a triangle is half the product of any base and corresponding altitude.

An immediate consequence of this theorem is the following corollary.

Corollary to Theorem 39

Triangles with equal bases and equal altitudes have equal areas.

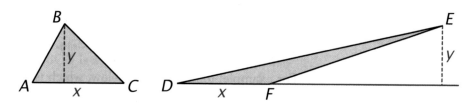

Our reasoning shows that this corollary is true, but its application sometimes leads to surprises. For example, from it we can conclude that the acute and the obtuse triangles shown above must have equal areas.

Exercises

Set I

Match Puzzle. An old puzzle begins with 12 matches arranged to form a right triangle. The puzzle is to rearrange the matches to form a figure with half its area.

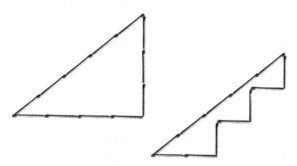

1. Given that each match is 1 unit long, what is the area of the triangle?

2. Does the arrangement of the matches shown in the second figure solve the puzzle? Explain.

3. How do the perimeters of the two figures compare?

Isosceles Right Triangle. The figures below illustrate two ways to find the area of an isosceles right triangle.

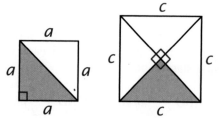

Write an expression for the area of the triangle in terms of

4. the length of one of its legs, *a.*

5. the length of its hypotenuse, *c.*

Theorem 39. Complete the following proof of Theorem 39 by giving the reasons.

The area of a triangle is half the product of any base and corresponding altitude.

Given: △ABC with base *b* and altitude *h*.

Prove: α△ABC = $\frac{1}{2}$*bh.*

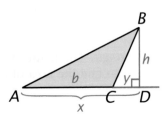

Proof

6. α△ABD = $\frac{1}{2}$*xh* and α△CBD = $\frac{1}{2}$*yh.*

 Why?

7. α△ABC = α△ABD + α△CBD. Why?

8. α△ABC = $\frac{1}{2}$*xh* + $\frac{1}{2}$*yh* = $\frac{1}{2}$*h*(*x* + *y*). Why?

9. Since *b* = *x* + *y*, α△ABC = $\frac{1}{2}$*bh.* Why?

In the proof above, the altitude was assumed to be *inside* the triangle. The figure below illustrates the case in which the altitude is *outside* the triangle.

The proof for this case is almost the same, as you will see in giving a reason for each of the following statements.

10. α△ABD = $\frac{1}{2}$*xh* and α△CBD = $\frac{1}{2}$*yh.* Why?

11. α△ABD = α△ABC + α△CBD. Why?

12. α△ABC = α△ABD − α△CBD. Why?

13. α△ABC = $\frac{1}{2}$*xh* − $\frac{1}{2}$*yh* = $\frac{1}{2}$*h*(*x* − *y*). Why?

14. Since *b* = *x* − *y*, α△ABC = $\frac{1}{2}$*bh.* Why?

Enlargement. When something is enlarged, everything does not change in the same way.

For example, look at △DEF below, which is an enlargement of △ABC.

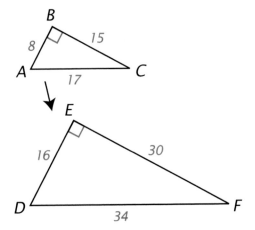

15. How do the angles of △DEF seem to compare in measure with the angles of △ABC?

16. How do the sides of △DEF compare in length with the sides of △ABC?

17. Find the perimeter of each triangle.

18. How does the perimeter of △DEF compare with the perimeter of △ABC?

19. Find the area of each triangle.

20. How does the area of △DEF compare with the area of △ABC?

21. If the sides of a triangle are doubled, what seems to happen to the measures of its angles?

22. What happens to its perimeter?

23. What happens to its area?

Chinese Parallelogram. The Chinese practice of coloring the parts of geometric figures makes it easier to discover some of their properties.

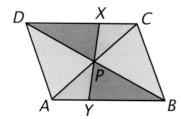

ABCD is a parallelogram with its diagonals intersecting at P. XY is any line through P.

24. Copy the figure and mark it as needed to do each of the following exercises.

25. The triangular regions shaded the same color seem to have the same area. Do they? Explain.

26. What can you conclude about quadrilaterals XYAD and XYBC?

Four-Sided Field. This problem is from an old geometry book.*

To survey the four-sided field ABCD, begin by measuring the diagonal BD. Then determine the points E, F on BD, where perpendiculars from the points A and C meet BD. Then measure the lengths of AE and CF.

The book gives the measurements in "chains":
BD = 14.36 chains,
AE = 8.17 chains,
and
CF = 5.74 chains.

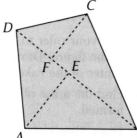

27. Use this information to find the area of the field in "square chains."

28. Given that 1 acre is equal to 10 square chains, find the area of the field in acres.

First Steps in Geometry, by G. A. Wentworth and G. A. Hill (Ginn, 1901).

Set II

Surfer Puzzle. In the puzzle of the surfer, the sum of the lengths of the perpendicular paths from every point on the island to the beaches seemed to be the same.[†]

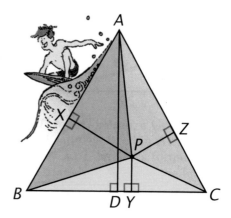

The island was in the shape of an equilateral triangle; so AB = BC = CA. Use the figure above to give a reason for each of the following statements.

29. $\alpha\triangle ABC = \frac{1}{2}BC \cdot AD$, $\alpha\triangle APB = \frac{1}{2}AB \cdot PX$,

   $\alpha\triangle BPC = \frac{1}{2}BC \cdot PY$, and

   $\alpha\triangle CPA = \frac{1}{2}CA \cdot PZ$.

30. $\alpha\triangle ABC = \alpha\triangle APB + \alpha\triangle BPC + \alpha\triangle CPA$.

31. $\frac{1}{2}BC \cdot AD = \frac{1}{2}AB \cdot PX + \frac{1}{2}BC \cdot PY + \frac{1}{2}CA \cdot PZ$.

32. $\frac{1}{2}BC \cdot AD = \frac{1}{2}BC \cdot PX + \frac{1}{2}BC \cdot PY + \frac{1}{2}BC \cdot PZ$.

33. AD = PX + PY + PZ.

34. How does this result prove that the sum of the lengths of the three paths from every point on the island to the beaches is the same?

[†]Page 5.

Three Equal Triangles. All of the triangles below have the same area.

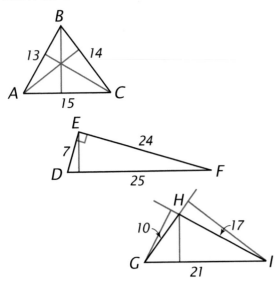

35. What is it?

What is the length of the shortest altitude of

36. △ABC?

37. △DEF?

What is the length of the longest altitude of

38. △DEF?

39. △GHI?

Kite Geometry. In the kite pictured at the right, two wooden cross pieces, AC and BD, are lashed together at E. The area of the material needed to cover the kite can be found from the lengths of the two cross pieces.

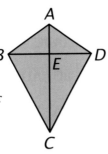

Complete the following proof.

Given: Kite ABCD with AB = AD and BC = DC.

Prove: αABCD = $\frac{1}{2}$AC · BD.

40. Copy the figure. Mark it as needed to explain the following statements.

41. AC ⊥ BD and BE = ED. Why?

42. BE + ED = BD. Why?

43. α△ABC = $\frac{1}{2}$AC · BE and

α△ADC = $\frac{1}{2}$AC · ED. Why?

44. αABCD = α△ABC + α△ADC. Why?

45. αABCD = $\frac{1}{2}$AC · BE + $\frac{1}{2}$AC · ED =

$\frac{1}{2}$AC(BE + ED) = $\frac{1}{2}$AC · BD. Why?

Dividing a Cake. For Acute Alice's birthday, Obtuse Ollie bought a square cake, 9 inches on each side. They wanted to cut it into three equal pieces.*

Ollie was going to cut the cake as shown at the left below, but Alice said she wouldn't want the piece in the middle.

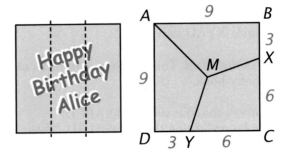

46. Why not?

Alice did some figuring and cut the cake as shown at the right above.

47. Use your ruler to make an accurate copy of the figure. Draw lines from M, the center of the cake, to B, C, and D.

48. Find the areas of the six triangles formed.

49. Does Alice's plan produce three "equal" pieces? Explain.

50. Can you figure out a way to cut the cake into five "equal" pieces? If so, show how you would do it.

_____

Why Do Buses Come in Threes? The Hidden Mathematics of Everyday Life, by Rob Eastaway and Jeremy Windham (Wiley, 1998).

Shingle Roof. A general rule for a wood-shingle roof is to "estimate 4 bundles (1,000 shingles) for every 100 square feet of roof and 3 pounds of nails for 100 square feet."*

Several sections of the roof of the house shown above have the shape of isosceles triangles. In the scale drawing of one section below, 1 inch represents 8 feet.

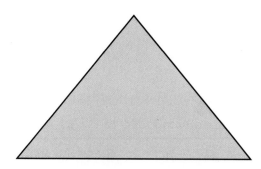

51. Measure the drawing with your ruler so that you can calculate the area of this section in square feet. Describe your method.

52. About how many shingles are needed for this section?

53. About how many bundles of shingles are needed?

54. What weight of nails is needed?

Grid Exercise. On graph paper, draw a pair of axes extending 20 units to the right and 20 units up from the origin.

55. Plot the following points and connect them with line segments to form △ABC: A(1, 2), B(16, 6), C(5, 17).

How to Design and Build Your Own Home, by Lupe DiDonno and Phyllis Sperling (Knopf, 1981).

56. Is △ABC equilateral, isosceles, or scalene? Explain.

57. Add some extra lines to enclose △ABC in a rectangle so that you can find its *exact* area in terms of the unit squares of the graph paper.

58. What kind of numbers are the lengths of the sides of △ABC?

59. What kind of number is the area of △ABC?

Set III

Heron's Theorem. Heron, a Greek mathematician who lived in Alexandria in the first century A.D., derived a formula for the area of a triangle in terms of the lengths of its sides.

His formula, sometimes called Heron's Theorem, says that the area of a triangle with sides a, b, and c is $\sqrt{s(s-a)(s-b)(s-c)}$, where s is half of the triangle's perimeter. Before you try the formula out, suppose that there are three triangles with the following sides.

Triangle 1: 5, 5, and 6.
Triangle 2: 5, 5, and 8.
Triangle 3: 5, 5, and 10.

1. Which triangle do you think has the greatest area?

2. Use Heron's Theorem to find the area of each triangle.

3. One of the "triangles" isn't really a triangle. Which one and why not?

Now try this. Suppose there are two triangles with the following sides.[†]

Triangle 4: 4, 6, and 8.
Triangle 5: 400, 600, and 1000.

4. Which do you think has the greater area?

5. Use Heron's Theorem to find it.

[†]*Riddles of the Sphinx*, by Martin Gardner (Mathematical Association of America, 1987).

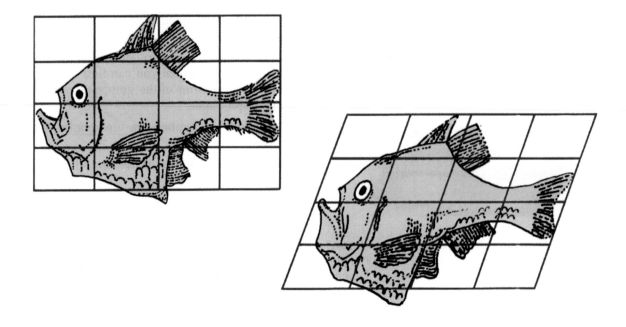

LESSON 4

Parallelograms and Trapezoids

Galileo once said that the book of nature is written in characters of geometry, "without which it is humanly impossible to understand a single word."* A remarkable application of geometry to the study of biological shapes was made by the great British scientist D'Arcy Thompson. In his book *On Growth and Form*, he showed many examples of how one species of animal can be considered to be a geometric transformation of another.† For example, the fish shown on the rectangular grid at the left above is of the species *Argyropelecus olfersi*. If the rectangles are transformed into the parallelograms shown at the right above, the shape of the fish becomes that of a species of an entirely different genus and has the name *Sternoptyx diaphana*.

How do you think the pictures of the two fish compare in size? The answer to this question depends on how the rectangles in the first grid compare in area with the parallelograms in the second. In this lesson, we will prove that the formulas for the areas of these two figures are the same.

---

*Il Saggiatore, 1623.
†D'Arcy Thompson, "On the Theory of Transformations, or the Comparison of Related Forms," *On Growth and Form*, edited by J. T. Bonner (Cambridge University Press, 1961).

Altitudes

 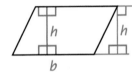 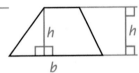

A rectangle   A parallelogram   A trapezoid

Before we do so, it is convenient to extend the idea of *altitude* from triangles and rectangles to parallelograms and trapezoids. As in our previous use of the word *altitude*, we will use it to refer to either a *number* or a *line segment*. An **altitude** of any quadrilateral that has parallel sides is the *distance* between them. Altitude can also refer to any *perpendicular line segment* that connects points on the lines of the parallel sides.

Theorem 40
The area of a parallelogram is the product of any base and corresponding altitude.

> *Given:* ABCD is a parallelogram with base b and altitude h.
> *Prove:* $\alpha ABCD = bh$.

Proof
Draw diagonal BD to divide ABCD into two triangles.

$\triangle CDB \cong \triangle ABD$ by SSS. Because $\alpha \triangle ABD = \frac{1}{2}bh$ and

$\alpha \triangle CDB = \alpha \triangle ABD$, $\alpha \triangle CDB = \frac{1}{2}bh$.

$\alpha ABCD = \alpha \triangle CDB + \alpha \triangle ABD$; so $\alpha ABCD = \frac{1}{2}bh + \frac{1}{2}bh = bh$.

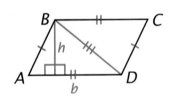

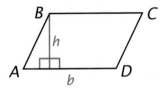

Although the area of a trapezoid cannot be found quite as easily, the formula for it can be derived by similar reasoning.

Theorem 41
The area of a trapezoid is half the product of its altitude and the sum of its bases.

> *Given:* ABCD is a trapezoid with bases a and b and altitude h.
> *Prove:* $\alpha ABCD = \frac{1}{2}h(a + b)$.

Proof
Draw diagonal BD to divide ABCD into two triangles.

$\alpha \triangle CDB = \frac{1}{2}ah$ and $\alpha \triangle ABD = \frac{1}{2}bh$.

$\alpha ABCD = \alpha \triangle CDB + \alpha \triangle ABD$;

so $\alpha ABCD = \frac{1}{2}ah + \frac{1}{2}bh = \frac{1}{2}h(a + b)$.

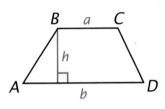

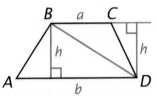

Exercises

Set I

From Above. The photograph below shows an automobile loading area in Belgium.*

1. What fact about the areas of two parallelograms with equal bases and equal altitudes do the figures below suggest?

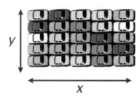

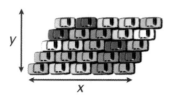

If each car occupies a space 14 feet long and 8 feet wide,

2. what is the approximate area of each figure?

3. what is the perimeter of the first figure?

4. How do the perimeters of the two figures compare?

---

5. If two parallelograms have the same area, does it follow that they have the same perimeter?

Tax Assessor Formula. You may recall that the tax assessors in ancient Egypt used the formula

$$A = \frac{1}{4}(a + c)(b + d)$$

to find the areas of fields in the shape of quadrilaterals.[†]

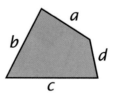

The letters *a*, *b*, *c*, and *d* represent the lengths of the consecutive sides.

6. Show that this formula gives the correct area for a square.

7. Does it give the correct area for a rectangle? Explain.

8. Use the Egyptian formula to find the area of the parallelogram below.

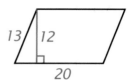

9. Is the result correct? Explain.

10. Use the Egyptian formula to find the area of the trapezoid below.

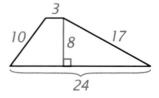

11. Is the result correct? Explain.

---

12. Use the Egyptian formula to find the area of the quadrilateral below.

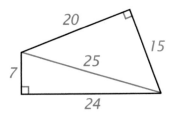

13. Is the result correct? Explain.

14. Use the Egyptian formula to find the area of the rhombus below.

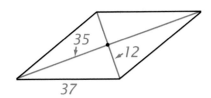

15. Is the result correct? Explain.

16. Why do you think the tax assessors continued to use their formula even if they knew it didn't always give the correct answer?

Pegboard Quadrilaterals. The figure below shows pegs and rubber bands on a pegboard.* The red rubber band around the four pegs in the corner forms a square with an area of 1 unit.

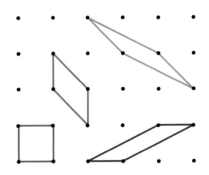

Geometry and the Imagination, by David Hilbert and Stefan Cohn-Vossen (reprint, American Mathematical Society, 1999).

17. What kind of figure does the blue rubber band form?

18. What is its area? Explain.

19. What kind of figure does the green rubber band form?

20. What is its area?

21. What kind of figure does the orange rubber band form?

22. What is its area? Explain.

John Hancock Tower

Skyscraper Design. The John Hancock Tower in Boston has an unusual design. Its floor plan, shown below, is in the shape of a parallelogram from which two right triangles have been removed.

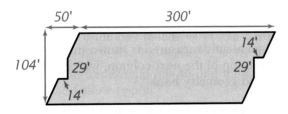

23. Find the area of its base in square feet.

The building is 790 feet tall.

24. Find the area of one of its larger sides.

Shuffleboard Court. The figure below shows the design of one end of an outdoor shuffleboard court.

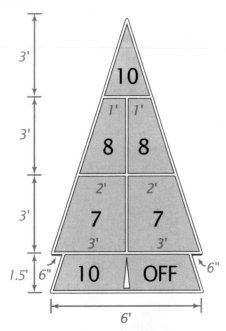

Find the areas of the following regions (zones) in square feet.

25. Zone "10" at the top.

26. One of the "8" zones.

27. One of the "7" zones.

28. The "10 OFF" penalty zone including the triangular wedge in its center.

29. The total area of all six zones.

Set II

Inaccessible Field. A way to find the area of a field when its diagonals cannot be conveniently measured is shown in the figure at the top of the next column, which is from an old geometry book.*

30. Describe how the area of the field, ABCD, can be found from the areas of other regions in the figure.

_____

First Steps in Geometry, by G. A. Wentworth and G. A. Hill (Ginn, 1901).

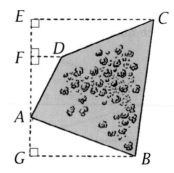

31. Copy the figure and mark the following distances on it: EC = 60 m, FD = 15 m, GB = 52 m, EF = 18 m, FA = 30 m, AG = 18 m.

Use these distances to find the following areas in square meters.

32. αECDF.

33. $\alpha\triangle$FDA.

34. $\alpha\triangle$ABG.

35. αECBG.

36. αABCD.

A Fold-and-Cut Experiment.

37. Refer to the figure below as a guide in beginning the following experiment.

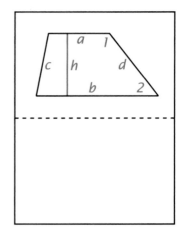

(1) Draw a large trapezoid on the upper half of a sheet of lined paper; use the lines on the paper to ensure that its bases are parallel.

(2) Write the letters *a*, *b*, *c*, *d*, and *h* to represent the lengths of the bases, legs, and altitude inside the trapezoid as shown in the figure. Label the two indicated angles 1 and 2.

(3) Fold the paper in half so that, when you cut out your trapezoid, you get a second one identical with it.

(4) Label the second trapezoid in the same way that you labeled the first.

(5) Place the two trapezoids side by side to form a single quadrilateral and so that the legs labeled *d* coincide.

(6) Tape the trapezoids on your paper.

38. The bases of the two trapezoids seem to line up with each other. Explain why they do.

39. What kind of quadrilateral do the trapezoids form when arranged in this way?

40. How do you know?

41. Express the area of the quadrilateral in terms of letters on the two pieces.

42. How does your result lead to the formula for the area of a trapezoid?

Trapezoidal Rule. The "trapezoidal rule" is one of the methods used in calculus to estimate the area under a curve.

   For example, to estimate the area of the yellow region in the figure below, we can add the areas of the three trapezoids.

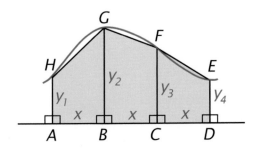

43. How do you know from the figure that these quadrilaterals are trapezoids?

44. Write expressions in terms of x, y_1, y_2, y_3, and y_4 for their areas.

45. Show that the sum of the areas of the three trapezoids is $\frac{1}{2}x(y_1 + 2y_2 + 2y_3 + y_4)$.

46. Use this expression to estimate the area of the yellow region if $x = 5$, $y_1 = 8$, $y_2 = 15$, $y_3 = 11$, and $y_4 = 6$.

The curve below, called a parabola, has the equation $y = \dfrac{x^2}{2}$.

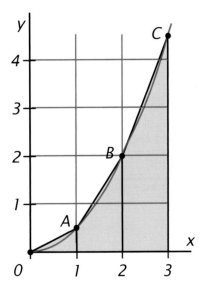

The *x*-coordinate of point A is 1; so its *y*-coordinate is $\dfrac{1^2}{2} = \dfrac{1}{2}$.

47. What are the coordinates of points B and C?

48. Use the trapezoidal rule to find the area of the yellow region.

Your answer is the approximate area of the region between the parabola and the *x*-axis from 0 to 3.

49. Is your answer larger or smaller than the area under the parabola?

SAT Problem. The figure below appeared in a problem on an SAT exam. The problem was to find the area of the unshaded region.

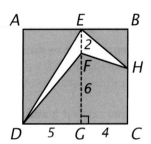

Although the figure was described as a rectangle, there is not enough information given to make it possible to find the areas of some of the regions in it.

50. Which regions are they?

51. Explain.

Nevertheless, it *is* possible to find the area of the unshaded region.

52. What is it?

53. Explain how you found it.

Set III

Chessboard Mystery. This puzzle about a chessboard appeared in the *Brooklyn Daily Eagle* on February 14, 1897.

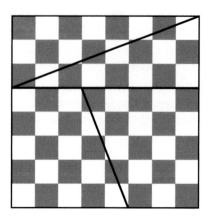

The board is divided into two right triangles and two trapezoids.

1. Taking the area of one of the small squares of the board as 1 unit, find the area of each of the four pieces. Do the areas add up to the number that you would expect? Explain.

2. Draw a large copy of the board, letting each side be 8 inches. Cut out the four pieces and try to rearrange them to form a rectangle having a different shape. If you succeed, make a drawing of your solution.

3. What is the area of the rectangle?

4. The result seems to contradict the Area Postulate. Why?

The Pythagorean Theorem

At the beginning of the twentieth century, some scientists believed that intelligent creatures might live on Mars. Among them was the American astronomer Percival Lowell, whose work led to the discovery of Pluto. Lowell thought that he could see canals on the surfaces of Mars through his telescope and speculated that they might have been dug by a Martian civilization to irrigate their dry land with water melted from polar ice caps.

To let the Martians know that there was also intelligent life on Earth in a time long before any kind of space travel was possible, it was proposed that gigantic geometric figures be used to convey a message. For example, broad lanes of trees might be planted in Siberia to form a huge right triangle. Or canals might be dug in the Sahara desert to do the same thing; kerosene could be poured on the water in them and set on fire at night for the Martians to see through their telescopes. A geometric figure thought to be especially appropriate for this purpose is shown at the right. You probably recognize it as illustrating what is perhaps the most famous theorem in all of geometry.

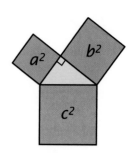

Theorem 42 (The Pythagorean Theorem)

The square of the hypotenuse of a right triangle is equal to the sum of the squares of its legs.

Many different proofs have been developed for the Pythagorean Theorem—more, in fact, than for any other theorem of geometry. Our proof, based on area, is the one to which you were introduced in Chapter 2.

Given: Right $\triangle ABC$ with legs a and b and hypotenuse c.
Prove: $c^2 = a^2 + b^2$.

Proof

Construct a square DEFG with sides of length $a + b$. Draw lines to divide the square into four right triangles and a quadrilateral as shown in the figure at the left. The four triangles are congruent to $\triangle ABC$ (SAS); so the length of each side of the quadrilateral HIJK is c.

If x and y are the measures of the acute angles of $\triangle ABC$, then $x + y = 90°$ because the acute angles of a right triangle are complementary. Numbering the angles of quadrilateral HIJK as shown in the next figure at the left, we have

$$x + \angle 1 + y = x + \angle 2 + y = x + \angle 3 + y = x + \angle 4 + y = 180°;$$

so $\angle 1 = \angle 2 = \angle 3 = \angle 4 = 90°$. Because HIJK is equilateral and equiangular, it is a square.

According to the Area Postulate, the area of the entire figure is the sum of the areas of its parts; so

$$(a + b)^2 = 4\left(\frac{1}{2}ab\right) + c^2.$$

Doing the algebra, we get

$$a^2 + 2ab + b^2 = 2ab + c^2; \text{ so}$$
$$c^2 = a^2 + b^2.$$

Now that we have proved the Pythagorean Theorem, look at the figure at the left. The lengths of the sides of $\triangle ABC$ are 20, 21, and 29. Is it a right triangle? If it is, then $20^2 + 21^2$ must be equal to 29^2. Doing the arithmetic gives $20^2 = 400$, $21^2 = 441$, and $29^2 = 841$. Since $400 + 441 = 841$, $20^2 + 21^2 = 29^2$. Can we now conclude that $\triangle ABC$ must be a right triangle? Surprisingly, the answer is not yet!

To conclude that a triangle with sides a, b, and c is a right triangle because $c^2 = a^2 + b^2$ would be to assume that the *converse* of the Pythagorean Theorem is true. Remember that, even though a statement is true, its converse may be false. Conveniently, the converse of the Pythagorean Theorem is true. It is stated below, and its proof is included in the exercises.

Theorem 43. Converse of the Pythagorean Theorem

If the square of one side of a triangle is equal to the sum of the squares of the other two sides, the triangle is a right triangle.

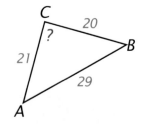

Exercises

Set I

Batik Design. A special case of the Pythagorean Theorem is illustrated in this Javanese batik design.*

1. Draw one of the triangles and the squares on its sides.

2. If the area of the triangle is 1 unit, what are the areas of the three squares on its sides?

3. How does the way in which these areas are related illustrate the Pythagorean Theorem?

Theorem 43. Complete the following proof of Theorem 43 (the converse of the Pythagorean Theorem) by giving the missing reasons.

If the square of one side of a triangle is equal to the sum of the squares of the other two sides, the triangle is a right triangle.

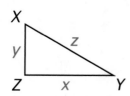

Given: $\triangle XYZ$ with $z^2 = x^2 + y^2$.
Prove: $\triangle XYZ$ is a right triangle.

Symmetry: A Unifying Concept, by István Hargittai and Magdolna Hargittai (Shelter Publications, 1994).

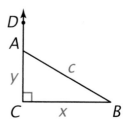

Proof

4. Draw CB so that $CB = x$.

5. Draw ray CD so that $\angle C = 90°$.

6. Choose point A on ray CD so that $CA = y$.

7. Draw AB.

8. Letting $AB = c$, $c^2 = x^2 + y^2$.

9. Since $z^2 = x^2 + y^2$, $c^2 = z^2$; so $c = z$.

10. $\triangle XYZ \cong \triangle ABC$.

11. $\angle Z = \angle C$.

12. $\angle Z = 90°$.

13. $\angle Z$ is a right angle.

14. $\triangle XYZ$ is a right triangle.

Squares on the Sides. In each of the following figures, squares have been drawn on the sides of the triangles.

In the figure below, the area of the yellow square is 144 and the length of each side of the blue square is 35.

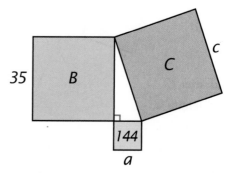

15. Find length a.

16. Find area B.

17. Find area C.

18. Find length c.

In the figure below, the areas of the green and orange squares are 100 and 676, respectively.

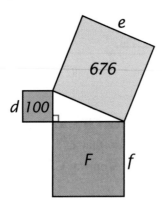

19. Find length *d*.
20. Find length *e*.
21. Find area *F*.
22. Find length *f*.

In the figure below, the length of each side of the brown square is 22 and the areas of the yellow and pink squares are 256 and 225, respectively.

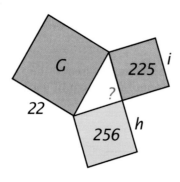

23. Find area *G*.
24. Find length *h*.
25. Find length *i*.
26. Is the triangle a right triangle? Explain.

In the figure at the top of the next column, the lengths of the sides of the purple and blue squares are 48 and 55, respectively, and the area of the orange square is 5329.

27. Find the area *K*.

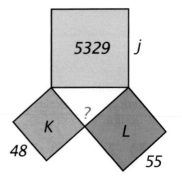

28. Find area *L*.
29. Find length *j*.
30. Is the triangle a right triangle? Explain.

Ollie's Triangles. Obtuse Ollie drew two triangles and told Alice that they were examples of "$a^2 = b^2 + c^2$" and "$c^2 > a^2 + b^2$." Alice told him that he must be wrong but, after seeing the triangles, she had to admit that both Ollie and one of the triangles were right.
    Draw a triangle for which it is true that

31. $a^2 = b^2 + c^2$.
32. $c^2 > a^2 + b^2$.

Set II

Was Pythagoras Chinese? The figure below appears in the *Chou Pei Suan Ching*, the oldest Chinese mathematics text known.* (The letters have been added for reference.)

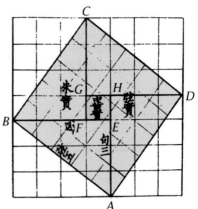

_____

Was Pythagoras Chinese?, by Frank J. Swetz and T. I. Kao (Pennsylvania State University Press, 1977).

If the area of square EFGH is 1 unit, what is the area of

33. △ABE?

34. the yellow region?

35. square ABCD?

In the version of the Chinese figure below, the sides of the eight right triangles are *a*, *b*, and *c*.

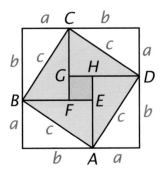

In terms of *a* and *b*, what is the area of

36. △ABE?

37. the yellow region?

38. square EFGH?

39. Write two expressions for the area of square ABCD, one in terms of *a* and *b* and the other in terms of *c*.

40. Use these two expressions to derive the Pythagorean Theorem.

Garfield's Proof. President Garfield invented an original proof for the Pythagorean Theorem in 1876 when he was a member of the House of Representatives.

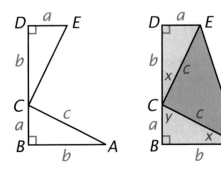

Starting with right △ABC, he extended side BC upward and constructed right △CDE so that its legs were equal to the legs of △ABC.

41. Why is △CDE ≅ △ABC?

42. Why are the two angles labeled *x* in the second figure equal?

43. In △ABC, why is $x + y = 90°$?

44. What kind of angle is ∠ECA?

45. What kind of quadrilateral is ABDE?

46. Write two different expressions for the area of ABDE.

47. Use these two expressions to finish Garfield's proof.

Angle-Bisector Surprise. In this figure, ABDE is the square on the hypotenuse of right △ABC.

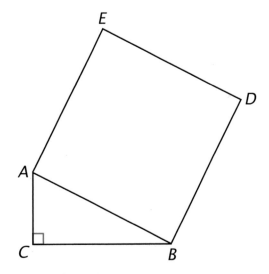

48. Trace the figure and then use your straightedge and compass to bisect ∠C.

49. What does the line appear to do to ABDE?

In the figure below, three more triangles congruent to △ABC have been drawn on the other sides of ABDE to form a larger square, CFGH.*

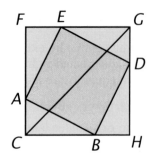

50. What relation does CG have to ∠ACB? Explain.

51. What does CG do to square ABDE?

Set III

Twenty Triangles. A puzzle sold in toy or game stores consists of 20 identical pieces. Each has the shape of a right triangle in which one leg is twice as long as the other.

Make the puzzle by cutting 20 triangles like the one shown below from heavy paper.

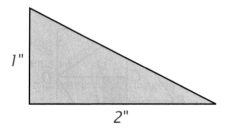

The figure below shows a convenient way to draw them on a 4-inch by 6-inch file card.

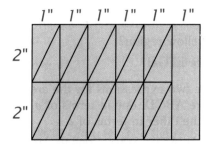

The easy part of the puzzle is to arrange the pieces to form two solid squares. The hard part is to then rearrange the pieces to form a single solid square.

1. If you are able to solve the hard part, make a drawing to illustrate your solution. (Hint: It may help to think about the areas of the three squares and how they are related to the lengths of the sides of the triangles.)

2. What is it about this puzzle that makes it so tricky to construct the third square?

---

*Proofs Without Words: Exercises in Visual Thinking, by Roger B. Nelsen (The Mathematical Association of America, 1993).

Basic Ideas

Postulates

8. *The Area Postulate.* Every polygonal region has a positive number called its area such that
   (1) congruent triangles have equal areas and
   (2) the area of a polygonal region is equal to the sum of the areas of its nonoverlapping parts.   339
9. The area of a rectangle is the product of its base and altitude.   345

Theorems

Corollary to Postulate 9. The area of a square is the square of its side.   345

38. The area of a right triangle is half the product of its legs.   352
39. The area of a triangle is half the product of any base and corresponding altitude. 353

Corollary. Triangles with equal bases and equal altitudes have equal areas.   353

40. The area of a parallelogram is the product of any base and corresponding altitude. 359
41. The area of a trapezoid is half the product of its altitude and the sum of its bases. 359
42. *The Pythagorean Theorem.* The square of the hypotenuse of a right triangle is equal to the sum of the squares of its legs.   366
43. If the square of one side of a triangle is equal to the sum of the squares of the other two sides, the triangle is a right triangle.   366

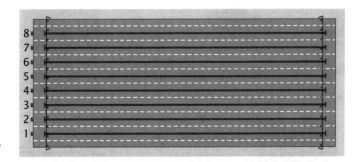

Exercises

Set I

Olympic Pools. Olympic pools are 50 meters long and 21 meters wide.
   For the Olympic games, the pool is divided into eight lanes, each 2.5 meters wide.

1. What is the area of each lane?
2. Do the eight lanes fill the pool? Explain.

For leisure use, at least 2 square meters are needed per swimmer.*

3. How many swimmers can use an Olympic pool at one time?

_____

Indoor Sports Spaces, by Robin Crane and Malcolm Dixon (Van Nostrand Reinhold, 1991).

Enemy Camps. In the ancient world, army commanders estimated the number of soldiers in an enemy camp according to its perimeter.*

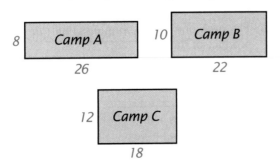

The rectangles above represent three enemy camps. The lengths of their sides are given in Roman paces.

4. What is the perimeter of each camp?

5. What is the area of each camp?

6. Which camp would a commander think contained the most soldiers? Explain.

7. Do you think the commander's choice is reasonable? Explain.

Tangrams. The figures below were made from tangrams, Chinese puzzles made by dividing a square into seven pieces.†

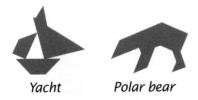

Yacht   Polar bear

The pieces are shown in the figure below.

_____
*The History of Mathematics, by David M. Burton (Allyn & Bacon, 1985).
†Time Travel and Other Mathematical Bewilderments, by Martin Gardner (W. H. Freeman and Company, 1988).

Given that the area of one of the small squares is 1 unit, find the area of

8. one of the large triangles.

9. one of the smallest triangles.

10. each of the other pieces.

This vulture was made by fitting together, without overlapping, all seven pieces.

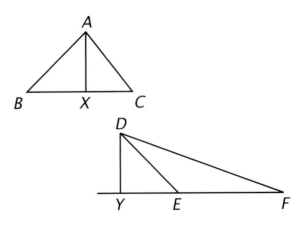

11. What is its area?

12. State the part of the Area Postulate that you used in finding it.

Altitudes and Triangles. In the following figures, AX and DY are altitudes of △ABC and △DEF, respectively, AB = DE, BC = EF, and ∠B and ∠DEF are supplementary.

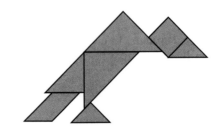

13. Copy the figures and mark them as needed to do each of the following exercises.

14. Find an angle equal in measure to ∠B.

15. Find a pair of triangles that are congruent.

16. Why are they congruent?

17. Why must they have equal areas?

18. Why is AX = DY?

19. Find a pair of triangles with equal areas that are not congruent.

20. Why do they have equal areas?

Suriname Stamp. The stamp at the right was issued by Suriname, a country in South America.

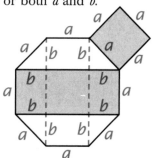

21. State the theorem it illustrates. Answer with a complete sentence.

22. State the converse theorem.

In the figure below, the area of the blue square is 121 and the lengths of the sides of the other squares are 7 and 13.

23. Find length *a*.

24. Find area *B*.

25. Find area *C*.

26. Is the triangle a right triangle? Explain.

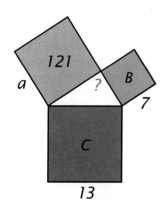

Moroccan Mosaic. The mosaic below was created in the fourteenth century for a wall in Morocco.

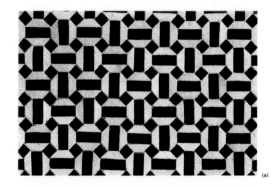

Write an expression for each of the following parts of it shown in the detail below in terms of *a* or *b* or both *a* and *b*.

27. The perimeter of the square.

28. Its area.

29. The perimeter of the other rectangle.

30. Its area.

31. The perimeter of one of the trapezoids.

32. Its area.

Set II

Courtyard Design. In the Middle Ages, it was customary in designing a courtyard to make the central garden equal in area to the path surrounding it.*

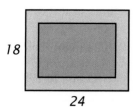

In the figure above, the courtyard is 18 feet by 24 feet, and the path around the garden is 3 feet wide.

33. Copy the figure and mark it as needed to answer each of the following questions.

34. What is the area of the garden?

35. What is the area of the path?

36. Does the design fit the description above?

Geometry Civilized, by J. L. Heilbron (Clarendon Press, 1998).

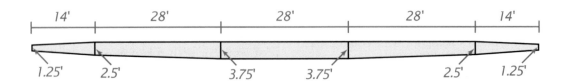

Daedalus Wing. The Daedalus, a human-powered plane, is shown below on a NASA test flight.

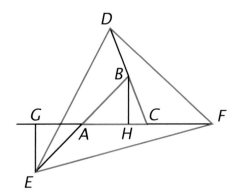

The design of its wing is shown at the top of this page.

37. What is the length of its wingspan?

38. What is the area of the wing?

Crack Formation. The figure below shows a crack forming in a bar of brittle material that is being pulled in opposite directions.*

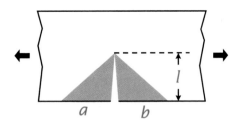

The colored area around the crack can be used to find the amount of energy that is released.

_____

*The New Science of Strong Materials, by J. E. Gordon (Princeton University Press, 1976).

Engineers calculate this area to be approximately l^2, where l is the length of the crack.

39. If the shaded area is l^2, what can you conclude about $a + b$? Explain.

If the length of the crack were twice as great, then the area would become $(2l)^2$.

40. How would this area compare with the area shown in the figure?

Triangle Comparisons. In the figure below, the sides of $\triangle ABC$ have been extended so that BA = AE, AC = CF, and CB = BD. Also, both BH and EG are perpendicular to line AF.

41. Copy the figure and mark it as needed to do the following exercises.

42. Why is $\triangle EGA \cong \triangle BHA$?

43. Why is EG = BH?

44. Given that $\alpha\triangle ABC = x$, express $\alpha\triangle AEF$ in terms of x.

45. On the basis of this result, how do you think $\alpha\triangle DEF$ compares with $\alpha\triangle ABC$?

SAT Problem. The figure below appeared in a problem on an SAT exam. It is a square whose area is $4x^2$.

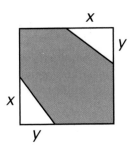

Write expressions for the following in terms of x or y or both x and y.

46. The area of the purple region.

47. The length of a rectangle R whose width is x and whose area is equal to that of the purple region.

48. The perimeter of the square.

49. The perimeter of the rectangle R.

Surveying Rule. Surveyors sometimes use the following rule: "Irregular tracts can be reduced to a series of trapezoids by right-angle offsets from points at regular intervals along a measured straight line."*

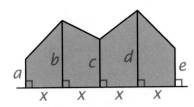

50. Write an expression for the area of the tract shown above in terms of a, b, c, d, e, and x.

Suppose that $a = b = c = d = e$.

51. If this equality were true, what shape would the tract have?

52. What would your expression for its area become in terms of x and a?

Elementary Surveying, by Paul R. Wolf and Russell C. Brinker (Harper Collins, 1989).

Pythagorean Proof. George Airy, a British astronomer, discovered the following "dissection proof" of the Pythagorean Theorem in 1855.

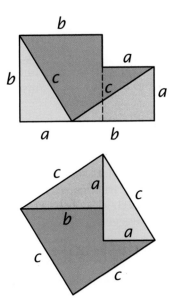

The two figures show the same three pieces arranged in different ways.

53. Explain how the two arrangements illustrate the Pythagorean Theorem.

In announcing his discovery of this proof, Airy wrote the following poem:

> Here I am, as you may see,
> $a^2 + b^2 - ab.$
> When two Triangles on me stand,
> Square of hypotenuse is plann'd;
> But if I stand on them instead
> The squares of both the sides are read.

54. To what does "$a^2 + b^2 - ab$" refer?

Fractional Equations

An equation that contains fractions can be solved by first multiplying both sides by a number that will clear the equation of all of the fractions. The simplest way to do so is to multiply by the least common denominator of the fractions.

Example 1: $\dfrac{x}{4} + \dfrac{x-1}{3} = 2$

Solution: The least common denominator of the fractions is 12. Multiplying both sides of the equation by 12, we get

$$12\left(\frac{x}{4}\right) + 12\left(\frac{x-1}{3}\right) = 12(2)$$

$$\frac{12x}{4} + \frac{12(x-1)}{3} = 24$$

$$3x + \quad 4(x-1) = 24$$

$$3x + \quad 4x - 4 = 24$$

$$7x = 28$$

$$x = 4$$

Checking this result in the original equation, we get

$$\frac{4}{4} + \frac{4-1}{3} = 1 + 1 = 2.$$

Example 2: $\dfrac{1}{6} = \dfrac{10}{x} - \dfrac{1}{2}.$

Solution: The least common denominator of the fractions is $6x$. Multiplying both sides by $6x$, we get

$$6x\left(\frac{1}{6}\right) = 6x\left(\frac{10}{x}\right) - 6x\left(\frac{1}{2}\right)$$

$$\frac{6x}{6} = \frac{60x}{x} \quad - \frac{6x}{2}$$

$$x = \quad 60 \quad - 3x$$

$$4x = \quad 60$$

$$x = 15$$

Checking this result by substituting it in the right-hand side of the original equation, we get

$$\frac{10}{15} - \frac{1}{2} = \frac{2}{3} - \frac{1}{2}$$

$$= \frac{4}{6} - \frac{3}{6} = \frac{1}{6}.$$

Exercises

Solve the following equations. Check your answers.

1. $\dfrac{x}{10} = 50$

2. $\dfrac{3}{x} = 15$

3. $\dfrac{6}{x-1} = 4$

4. $\dfrac{4}{x} = \dfrac{x}{25}$

5. $\dfrac{11}{x} + 2 = \dfrac{5}{x}$

6. $\dfrac{x}{3} = \dfrac{x}{2} - 7$

7. $\dfrac{1}{3} - \dfrac{4}{x} = \dfrac{1}{x}$

8. $\dfrac{x}{4} = \dfrac{x}{5} + 1$

9. $\dfrac{x+5}{2} = \dfrac{4x-3}{7}$

10. $\dfrac{10}{x-3} - \dfrac{6}{x-3} = 8$

11. $\dfrac{5}{x+3} - \dfrac{2}{3} = 1$

12. $\dfrac{7x-2}{x} + \dfrac{x+2}{x} = x$

13. $\dfrac{15}{x+4} + \dfrac{1}{3} = 2$

14. $\dfrac{3x+1}{4} - \dfrac{x}{5} = x - 2$

15. $\dfrac{x+8}{2} - \dfrac{x-4}{8} = \dfrac{x}{4}$

Similarity

In this chapter, we explore the properties of similar figures—figures that have "the same shape." Because the corresponding sides of similar polygons are proportional, we begin with a lesson on ratio and proportion. Strange as it may seem, the existence of similar figures is connected to the Parallel Postulate; so the proofs of the theorems on similarity depend on the properties of parallel lines. Many practical problems have solutions based on similarity.

Ratio and Proportion

If you saw just the photograph on the left of Roy Lichtenstein's painting *Mural with Blue Brushstroke*, you would never guess how large it is. The photograph on the right, showing the artist standing on a ladder below the mural, gives a clue to its true scale.

On this page, the photograph is 2 inches wide and 4.25 inches high. The mural itself is actually *32 feet* wide. How high is it?

One way to answer this question is to write and solve a proportion:

$$\frac{2''}{4.25''} = \frac{32'}{x\,'}$$

This proportion is based on the fact that, because the photograph on the facing page and the actual mural have the *same shape*, their dimensions have the *same ratio*. In geometry, figures that have the same shape are said to be *similar* to one another.

Before studying the properties of similar figures, we will review the meaning of *ratio* and *proportion*.

Definitions

The *ratio* of the number a to the number b is the number $\dfrac{a}{b}$.*

A *proportion* is an equality between two ratios.

We can represent a proportion symbolically as

$$\frac{a}{b} = \frac{c}{d}.$$

The numbers a, b, c, and d are called the *first, second, third,* and *fourth terms* of the proportion, respectively. The second and third terms, b and c, are also called the *means*, and the first and fourth terms, a and d, are called the *extremes*.

Proportions have many useful properties. For example, you may remember from your study of algebra that, in a proportion, the product of the means is equal to the product of the extremes. This property is easy to prove.

$$\textit{Given: } \frac{a}{b} = \frac{c}{d}.$$
$$\textit{Prove: } ad = bc.$$

Proof

1. $\dfrac{a}{b} = \dfrac{c}{d}$ (Given.)

2. $bd\left(\dfrac{a}{b}\right) = bd\left(\dfrac{c}{d}\right)$ (Multiplication.)

3. $\dfrac{abd}{b} = \dfrac{bcd}{d}$; so $ad = bc$.   (Substitution.)

To solve the proportion

$$\frac{2}{4.25} = \frac{32}{x}$$

we can cross multiply to get

$$2x = (4.25)(32)$$
$$2x = 136$$
$$x = 68$$

Lichtenstein's painting *Mural with Blue Brushstroke* is 68 feet tall!

---

*Note that b cannot be 0, because division by 0 is undefined.

In some proportions, the means are the same number. For example, in the proportion

$$\frac{4}{10} = \frac{10}{25}$$

both means are 10. For this reason, the number 10 is called the *geometric mean* between 4 and 25.

Definition.
The number b is the *geometric mean* between the numbers a and c if a, b, and c are positive and

$$\frac{a}{b} = \frac{b}{c}.$$

Exercises

Set I

Parthenon Architecture. The Parthenon in Athens was completed in 432 B.C. Its architects used the numbers 81, 36, and 16 in determining its dimensions.

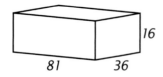

1. Express the ratio $\frac{81}{36}$ in decimal form.

2. Express the ratio $\frac{36}{16}$ in decimal form.

3. Show that, in the proportion $\frac{81}{36} = \frac{36}{16}$, the product of the means is equal to the product of the extremes.

4. What is the number 36 called with respect to 81 and 16?

5. Write the proportion that follows from taking the square root of each side of $\frac{81}{36} = \frac{36}{16}$.

6. Express each of the ratios in your proportion in decimal form.

There is an exact replica of the Parthenon in Nashville, Tennessee. It is 228 feet long.

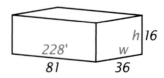

7. Solve the proportion $\frac{228}{w} = \frac{81}{36}$ to find its width in feet.

8. Write and solve a proportion to find its height in feet.

The dimensions of the columns in the Parthenon are related to their diameters as shown in the figure at the right.*

Find the following ratios.

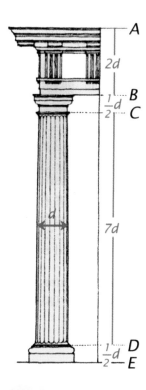

9. $\dfrac{AB}{CD}$.

10. $\dfrac{BE}{AE}$.

11. $\dfrac{AE}{d}$.

Turtles Forever. The picture below by Belgian artist Peter Raedschelders is titled *Turtles Forever.*

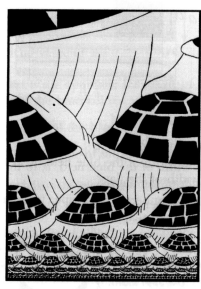

Each successive row has twice as many turtles as the row above it:

    1 2 4 8 16 32 64 128 . . .

Architecture: Form, Space, and Order, by Francis D. K. Ching (Wiley, 1996).

Copy and complete the following proportions:

12. $\dfrac{16}{32} = \dfrac{32}{?}$.

13. $\dfrac{2}{16} = \dfrac{16}{?}$.

14. Find three different pairs of numbers for which 8 is their geometric mean.

Ratio. Euclid defined a ratio as "a sort of relation in respect of size between two magnitudes of the same kind."

15. In saying "a sort of relation in respect of size," to what operation with numbers was Euclid referring?

16. Which of the following expressions does not fit Euclid's definition of a ratio?

$$\frac{2 \text{ square meters}}{4.5 \text{ square meters}}$$

$$\frac{45 \text{ degrees}}{2 \text{ feet}}$$

17. Explain.

Four Rectangles. The four numbered parts of the figure below are rectangles, and $\dfrac{b}{a} = \dfrac{d}{c}$.

	b	
a	1	2
	4	3

d

c

18. Write expressions for the areas of the rectangles in terms of *a*, *b*, *c*, and *d*.

19. Which two rectangles have the same area?

20. For which two rectangles are their corresponding sides proportional?

21. Which two rectangles have the same shape?

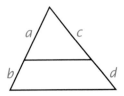

We can show why it follows that $\dfrac{a}{c} = \dfrac{b}{d}$.

49. If $\dfrac{a}{b} = \dfrac{c}{d}$, then $ad = bc$. Why?

50. If $ad = bc$, then $\dfrac{ad}{cd} = \dfrac{bc}{cd}$; so $\dfrac{a}{c} = \dfrac{b}{d}$. Why?

It also follows that $\dfrac{a+b}{b} = \dfrac{c+d}{d}$.

51. If $\dfrac{a}{b} = \dfrac{c}{d}$, then $\dfrac{a}{b} + 1 = \dfrac{c}{d} + 1$. Why?

52. If $\dfrac{a}{b} + 1 = \dfrac{c}{d} + 1$, then $\dfrac{a}{b} + \dfrac{b}{b} = \dfrac{c}{d} + \dfrac{d}{d}$; so

$\dfrac{a+b}{b} = \dfrac{c+d}{d}$. Why?

Sinker or Floater. To a swimming teacher, you are either a "sinker" or a "floater." If your density is less than that of water, you will float. If your density is greater than that of water, you will sink.*

Sport Science: Physical Laws and Optimum Performance, by Peter J. Brancazio (Simon & Schuster, 1984).

The density of water is 62.4 pounds per cubic foot.

53. Acute Alice weighs 120 pounds and has a volume of 1.95 cubic feet. Is she a "sinker" or a "floater"? Explain.

54. Obtuse Ollie's volume is 2.3 cubic feet and he is a "sinker." What can you conclude about his weight? Explain.

Set III

The White Horse. A mysterious figure from the past is the White Horse of Uffington. Located on the hills of southern England, it is thought to have been created in about 1000 B.C.

The horse is 28 meters tall (measured from the top of its head to the bottom of its front legs).

1. Use your ruler, the photograph at the top of this page, and an appropriate proportion to figure out how long the horse is. (It is convenient to use millimeters in measuring the picture.)

The scale of the photograph is the ratio of the lengths in it to the corresponding lengths in the actual horse.

2. Express the scale of the photograph as a fraction in the form $\dfrac{1}{n}$.

9

16

9

12

LESSON 2

Similar Figures

When you watch a movie on television, you are probably not seeing as much of it as you would have seen in a theater. The reason is that television and movie theater screens are shaped differently.

The shape of a screen is given by its "aspect ratio," the ratio of its width to its height. Most movies are now filmed in

a $\frac{16}{9}$ aspect ratio, whereas most television sets produce pic-

tures with a $\frac{4}{3}$ aspect ratio. Because these ratios are different,

these movies are the wrong shape for the television screen. One way to deal with this problem is to cut off the sides of the picture (sometimes called "pan and scan"). The other way is to reduce the picture so that its width fits the screen (called "letter box").

The movie industry would like to make the $\frac{16}{9}$ aspect ratio

standard for television pictures. If it succeeds, you may be able to see all of a movie image even on a wristwatch size screen as shown at the right, one-third the size of the image at the top left on this page.

Pan and scan

Letter box

Wristwatch size image

At the top of the photograph: *D* (top left), *C* (top right), *A* (bottom left), *B* (bottom right).

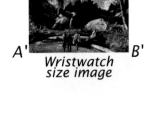

Wristwatch size image

Labels around the small image: *D'* (top left), *C'* (top right), *A'* (bottom left), *B'* (bottom right).

If rectangle ABCD above is matched with the one-third scale rectangle A′B′C′D′ at the left, *corresponding sides are proportional,*

$$\frac{A'B'}{AB} = \frac{B'C'}{BC} = \frac{C'D'}{CD} = \frac{D'A'}{DA} = \frac{1}{3},$$

and *corresponding angles are equal,*

$$\angle A' = \angle A, \ \angle B' = \angle B, \ \angle C' = \angle C, \text{ and } \angle D' = \angle D.$$

If the dinosaur's head were at X and its tail at Y in the image above, then it would also be true that $\frac{X'Y'}{XY} = \frac{1}{3}$, with X′ and Y′ being the

positions of the head and tail in the scale image at the left.

Because the original image and the scale image have the same shape, their corresponding segments are proportional. Such figures are *similar* and a correspondence between their points such that corresponding segments are proportional is a *similarity*.

We begin with similar triangles.

Definition

Two triangles are *similar* iff there is a correspondence between their vertices such that their corresponding sides are proportional and their corresponding angles are equal.

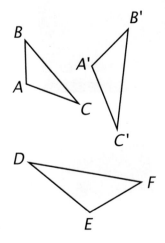

If △ABC and △A′B′C′ are similar, we write △ABC ∼ △A′B′C′. As with the congruence correspondence, the order of the vertices in the similarity correspondence tells you which points correspond and hence which sides are proportional and which angles are equal. For example, given that △ABC ∼ △EFD, we can write

$$\frac{EF}{AB} = \frac{FD}{BC} = \frac{DE}{CA} \text{ and } \angle E = \angle A, \ \angle F = \angle B, \text{ and } \angle D = \angle C$$

without even looking at the figures.

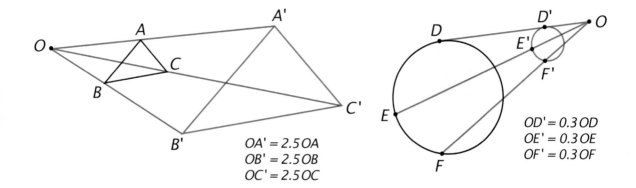

OA' = 2.5 OA
OB' = 2.5 OB
OC' = 2.5 OC

OD' = 0.3 OD
OE' = 0.3 OE
OF' = 0.3 OF

Understanding reflections was a key to understanding isometries and congruence of figures in general. The key to understanding similarity is the dilation transformation. The idea of a dilation comes from the way in which a movie projector works. Light from a bulb is sent through the frame on the film, enlarging it to form the image on the screen. The figures above illustrate how this idea works in geometry—first for two triangles and then for two circles. Point O, chosen as the *center* of the dilation, corresponds to the source of light. A positive number *r*, called the *magnitude* of the dilation, gives the relative size of the image compared with the original. This *r* is the ratio of the corresponding lengths. Rays drawn from O through points of the figure correspond to the rays of light from the projector. On each ray, a point is chosen so that, for every point P on the figure, there is a corresponding point P' on its image such that OP' = *r*OP. As the figures illustrate, the image can be larger than, smaller than, or even equal to the figure, depending on whether $r > 1$, $r < 1$, or $r = 1$.

Exercises

Set I

The Pyramids and Orion. The three pyramids at Giza lie at the corners of a long narrow triangle that appears to be similar to the triangle formed by the three stars in Orion's belt.*

Given that the two triangles are similar, what can you conclude about

1. their corresponding sides?

2. their corresponding angles?

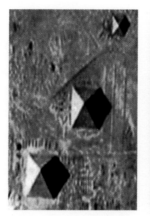

The Orion Mystery, by Robert Bauval and Adrian Gilbert (Crown, 1994).

Plane Table. Surveyors used to make maps by using a "plane table." The figure below shows the table in two successive positions as a map is constructed on it.* Points D and E represent distant points and points F and G are their images on the map.

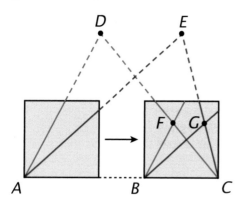

In the figure, △ADC ~ △BFC and △AEC ~ △BGC. Copy and complete the following equations.

3. ∠DAC = ∠?.

4. ∠AEC = ∠?.

5. ∠GCB = ∠?.

6. $\dfrac{AD}{BF} = \dfrac{DC}{?}$.

7. $\dfrac{GC}{EC} = \dfrac{BC}{?}$.

8. $\dfrac{BC}{AC} = \dfrac{BG}{?}$.

Geometry Civilized: History, Culture, and Technique, by J. L. Heilbron (Clarendon Press, 1998).

Kempe's Linkage. In 1875, Alfred Kempe, a young London lawyer, invented the linkage shown in the figure below. The linkage is constructed so that $\dfrac{OA}{OC} = \dfrac{OC}{OE} = \dfrac{OE}{OG}$.

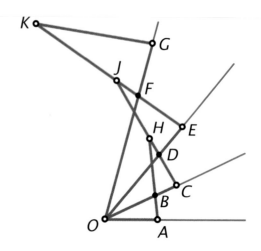

9. Find OE and OG if OA = 1 and OC = 2.

As the linkage changes shape, the following three triangles are always similar: △OAB ~ △OCD ~ △OEF.

10. What can you conclude about ∠AOB, ∠COD, and ∠EOF? Explain.

11. What does the linkage do to ∠AOG?

Billboards. "Poster panel" billboards come in two sizes.

12. Show why they are almost, but not quite, similar.

13. To what number could 23 be changed to make the two sizes similar?

14. To what number could 5 be changed to make them similar?

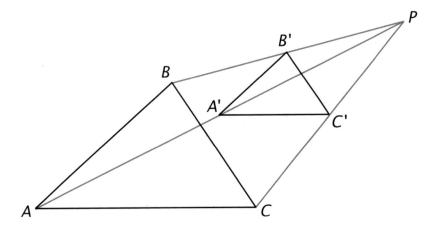

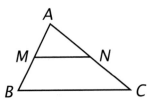

Dilation Problem. In the figure above, △A'B'C' is a dilation image of △ABC.

15. What is point P called?

16. Measure the lengths of the sides of △ABC and △A'B'C' in centimeters.

17. Exactly how do the sides of △A'B'C' compare in length with the corresponding sides of △ABC?

18. What is the magnitude of the transformation from △ABC into △A'B'C'?

19. How are points A', B', and C' related to line segments PA, PB, and PC?

Quadrilateral Conclusions. All of the quadrilaterals in the figure below are rectangles, and ABCD ~ EFGD.

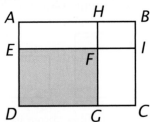

20. $\dfrac{AD}{ED} = \dfrac{CD}{GD}$. Why?

21. AD × GD = ED × CD. Why?

22. What can you conclude about ADGH and EDCI?

23. What can you conclude about AEFH and FGCI? Explain.

Set II

Similar-Triangles Proof. In the figure below, MN is a midsegment of △ABC. △AMN appears to be similar to △ABC.

Prove that the triangles are similar by giving a reason for each of the following statements.

24. MN ∥ BC.

25. ∠AMN = ∠B and ∠ANM = ∠C.

26. ∠A = ∠A.

27. MN = $\dfrac{1}{2}$BC.

28. $\dfrac{MN}{BC} = \dfrac{1}{2}$.

29. AM = MB and AN = NC.

30. AM + MB = AB and AN + NC = AC.

31. 2AM = AB and 2AN = AC.

32. $\dfrac{AM}{AB} = \dfrac{1}{2}$ and $\dfrac{AN}{AC} = \dfrac{1}{2}$.

33. $\dfrac{AM}{AB} = \dfrac{AN}{AC} = \dfrac{MN}{BC}$.

34. △AMN ~ △ABC.

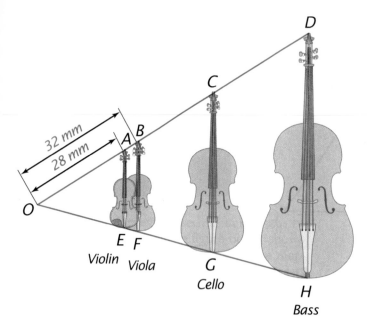

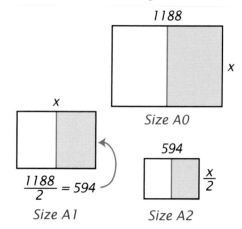

Paper Sizes. The International Standard for paper sizes is set up so that a sheet of a given size can be cut in half to produce two sheets of the next size that are similar to it, to within a millimeter. Size A0 has length 1188 mm.*

Violin Family. The figure above shows the viola, cello, and bass as three dilations of the violin.

The magnitude of a dilation can be found from a scale drawing by using any units. For example, letting the magnitude of the viola dilation be r_1, we can write $OB = r_1 OA$, or

$$r_1 = \frac{OB}{OA} = \frac{32 \text{ mm}}{28 \text{ mm}} \approx 1.1.$$

35. Find the magnitude, r_2, of the cello dilation by measuring OC in millimeters and solving $OC = r_2 OA$ for r_2.

36. Find the magnitude, r_3, of the bass dilation.

37. AE = 21 mm. Check this length with your ruler, and measure BF in millimeters. Find the ratio of the lengths of the viola and the violin, $\dfrac{BF}{AE}$.

38. Measure CG and find the ratio of the lengths of the cello and the violin, $\dfrac{CG}{AE}$.

39. Do the same for the bass and violin.

A violin is about 24 inches long.

40. Find the approximate lengths of the viola, cello, and bass.

41. Refer to the figures above to write a proportion for the corresponding dimensions of sizes A0 and A1.

42. Solve the proportion to find x, the width of size A0.

43. What is x called with respect to the numbers 1188 and 594?

44. What is the approximate area of a sheet of size A0 in square meters?

45. What is the width of a sheet of size A2?

When this system of paper sizes was established, the dimensions were rounded off.

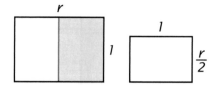

46. Refer to the figures above to write a proportion for the corresponding dimensions of two successive sizes.

47. Solve the proportion to find the *exact* ratio of the length to width of each size.

———————

*Some of the dimensions in these exercises have been slightly altered to make the calculations easier.

Picture Frames. A rectangular picture 28 inches by 20 inches is surrounded by a frame of constant width.

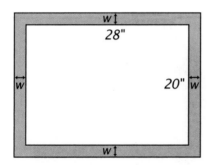

48. Write a proportion based on the assumption that the outer edge of the frame has the same shape as the picture.

49. Solve the proportion for w.

50. Repeat exercises 48 and 49 for the figure below.

51. If there is a solution for $w \neq 0$, what shape is the picture?

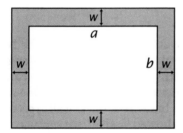

Set III

Similar Rectangles. Andrea Palladio was perhaps the most influential architect of the Italian Renaissance. His floor plan for the

Villa Foscari

Villa Foscari built in 1558 is filled with similar rectangles.*

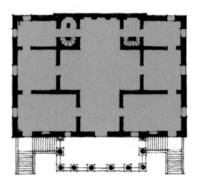

For example, the rectangles GHNM, IJPO, KLRQ, MNTS, OPVU, and QRXW in the figure below have dimensions 2×2 and the rectangle HKWT has dimensions 4×4. They are similar because

$$\frac{2}{2} = \frac{4}{4} = 1.$$

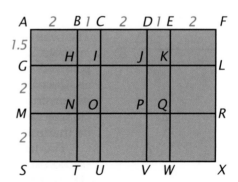

How many sets of similar rectangles of different sizes can you find whose dimensions have each of the following ratios? Name the rectangles in each set and their dimensions.

1. $\frac{1}{2}$.

2. $\frac{1}{4}$.

3. $\frac{2}{3}$.

4. $\frac{3}{4}$.

Architecture: Form, Space, and Order, by Francis D. K. Ching (Wiley, 1996).

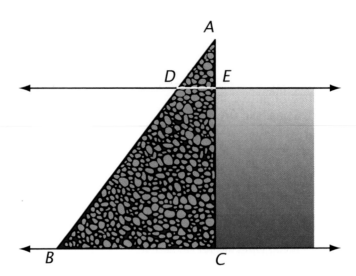

The Side-Splitter Theorem

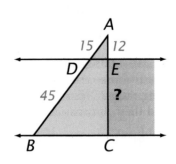

The oldest dam on record was built by the Egyptians on the Nile River in about 2900 B.C. It was washed away in a flood not long after its completion. Built without modern anchoring and reinforcing materials, this dam had to be held in place by its own weight. One mistake in its construction was that it was built as a thick wall, rectangular in cross section. A French engineer showed in 1850 that such a dam should be triangular so as to be thickest where the pressure is greatest.

The figure above is a side view of a triangular dam. The cross section of the dam is △ABC; the line of the water level behind the dam, DE, is parallel to the line of the ground, BC.

The amount of force of the water against the dam depends on several factors; one of them is the length of EC, the segment that represents the surface of contact. Can the length of EC be determined from the lengths of the other segments in the figure? For example, suppose that AD = 15 meters, DB = 45 meters, and AE = 12 meters. Can we find EC from these numbers?

We will show that, if DE ∥ AB, then

$$\frac{AD}{DB} = \frac{AE}{EC}.$$

By substituting into this equation, we have

$$\frac{15}{45} = \frac{12}{EC}.$$

Solving for EC,

$$15 \cdot EC = 45 \cdot 12,$$

$$EC = \frac{45 \cdot 12}{15} = 36,$$

we find that EC is 36 meters long.

This method depends on the following theorem.

Theorem 44. The Side-Splitter Theorem

If a line parallel to one side of a triangle intersects the other two sides in different points, it divides the sides in the same ratio.

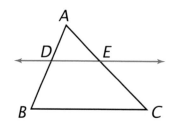

Given: △ABC with DE ∥ BC.

Prove: $\dfrac{AD}{DB} = \dfrac{AE}{EC}$.

Our proof, based on area, is that of Euclid. Two line segments are added to the figure to form some triangles whose bases are the four segments in the theorem's conclusion.

Proof

The first part: Draw BE and draw EF ⊥ AB. EF is an altitude of both △AED and △DEB; so

$$\alpha\triangle AED = \frac{1}{2} AD \cdot EF \quad \text{and} \quad \alpha\triangle DEB = \frac{1}{2} DB \cdot EF.$$

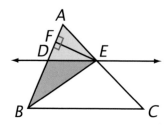

Dividing, we get

$$\frac{\alpha\triangle AED}{\alpha\triangle DEB} = \frac{\frac{1}{2} AD \cdot EF}{\frac{1}{2} DB \cdot EF} = \frac{AD}{DB}. \tag{1}$$

The second part: Draw DC, and draw DG ⊥ AC. DG is an altitude of both △AED and △DEC; so

$$\alpha\triangle AED = \frac{1}{2} AE \cdot DG \quad \text{and} \quad \alpha\triangle DEC = \frac{1}{2} EC \cdot DG.$$

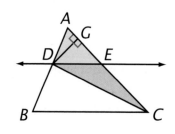

Dividing, we get

$$\frac{\alpha\triangle AED}{\alpha\triangle DEC} = \frac{\frac{1}{2} AE \cdot DG}{\frac{1}{2} EC \cdot DG} = \frac{AE}{EC}. \tag{2}$$

The third part: Locate points H and I on line DE so that BH ⊥ DE and CI ⊥ DE. Because HI ∥ BC and BH ∥ CI (in a plane, two lines perpendicular to a third line are parallel), HICB is a parallelogram. △DEB and △DEC have equal bases (DE = DE) and equal altitudes (BH = CI because the opposite sides of a parallelogram are equal); so

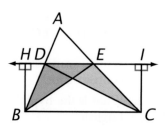

$$\alpha\triangle DEB = \alpha\triangle DEC.$$

Substituting this result in equation 2, we have

$$\frac{\alpha\triangle AED}{\alpha\triangle DEB} = \frac{AE}{EC}.$$ (3)

We know from equation 1 that

$$\frac{\alpha\triangle AED}{\alpha\triangle DEB} = \frac{AD}{DB},$$

so we can substitute in equation 3 to get

$$\frac{AD}{DB} = \frac{AE}{EC}.$$

A useful corollary to the Side-Splitter Theorem is:

Corollary to the Side-Splitter Theorem
If a line parallel to one side of a triangle intersects the other two sides in different points, it cuts off segments proportional to the sides.

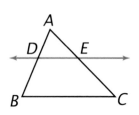

This corollary permits us to conclude that, if DE ∥ BC in the figure at the left, then

$$\frac{AD}{AB} = \frac{AE}{AC} \text{ and } \frac{DB}{AB} = \frac{EC}{AC}.$$

Exercises

Set I

Turkish Theorem. Here is the Side-Splitter Theorem as it appears in a Turkish geometry book.

Teorem. Bir üçgenin bir kenarina çizilen paralel dogru, diger iki kenari içten yahut distan ayni oranda böler.

Hipotez: **DE // BC.**

Hüküm: $\dfrac{DA}{DB} = \dfrac{EA}{EC}.$

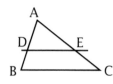

1. Which words other than "teorem" do you recognize?

2. What is the hypothesis of the theorem in English?

3. What is the conclusion of the theorem in English?

Errors of Omission. Leaving out some of the words of a true statement may result in a statement that is false. Draw figures to show why the following statements are false.

4. If a line is parallel to one side of a triangle, it divides the other two sides in the same ratio.

5. If a line intersects two sides of a triangle in different points, it divides the sides in the same ratio.

6. If a line parallel to one side of a triangle intersects the other two sides, it divides them in the same ratio.

Picturing Products. In mathematics at the time of Euclid, the product of two numbers was represented as shown in the figure below.

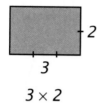

3×2

7. What represents 6 in the figure?

René Descartes, a French mathematician of the seventeenth century, thought of a way to represent a product by using parallel lines.

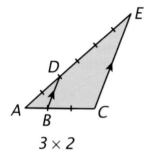

3×2

8. How are 3, 2, and 6 represented in the figure above?

9. Write a proportion whose first term is 1 for the figure below.

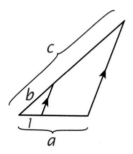

10. Show why Descartes's method works by solving this proportion for c.

11. Draw a figure that illustrates the square of 3 as an area.

12. Draw a figure like that of Descartes that illustrates the square of 3 as a length.

Supply and Demand. The greater the supply of a product, the lower the price it will bring, as shown in the figure below, based on a graph in an economics book.*

In the figure, CP ∥ OB and PD ∥ AO.

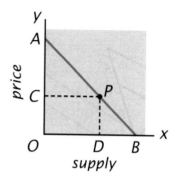

Copy and complete the following proportions in terms of other lengths in the figure.

13. $\dfrac{AC}{CO} = \dfrac{?}{?}.$

14. $\dfrac{CO}{AO} = \dfrac{?}{?}.$

15. $\dfrac{OD}{DB} = \dfrac{?}{?}.$

16. $\dfrac{OD}{OB} = \dfrac{?}{?}.$

17. Why is $\dfrac{AC}{CO} = \dfrac{OD}{DB}$?

Side-Splitter Practice. Write a proportion for each of the following figures, and solve each proportion for x.

18.

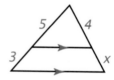

---

*Economics, by Paul A. Samuelson and William D. Nordhaus (McGraw-Hill, 1989).

19.

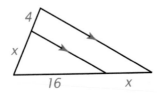

20.

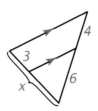

21.

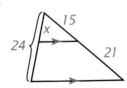

Two-Point Perspective. The figure below is a two-dimensional picture of a cube drawn in "two-point perspective."*

In the figure, BC = CD, EF = FG, and BE ∥ CF ∥ DG.

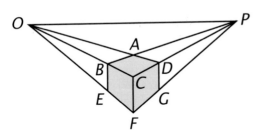

Tell whether each of the following conclusions seems reasonable. In each case, explain why or why not.

22. $\dfrac{OB}{BC} = \dfrac{OE}{EF}.$

23. $\dfrac{PA}{AB} = \dfrac{PD}{DC}.$

24. $\dfrac{BC}{EF} = \dfrac{CD}{FG}.$

25. $\dfrac{PD}{PC} = \dfrac{PG}{PF}.$

---

*Perspective in Perspective, by Lawrence Wright (Routledge and Kegan Paul, 1983).

Set II

Parallelogram Exercise. ABCD is a parallelogram, and E and F are the midpoints of its opposite sides; DE and BF intersect AC at X and Y.

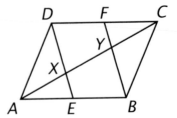

26. What can you conclude about EBFD? Explain.

27. Why is $\dfrac{AE}{EB} = \dfrac{AX}{XY}$ and $\dfrac{XY}{YC} = \dfrac{DF}{FC}$?

28. What can you conclude about AX, XY, and YC? Explain.

Corollary to Theorem 44. Complete the following proof of the corollary to the Side-Splitter Theorem by giving the reasons.

Given: △ABC with DE ∥ BC.

Prove: $\dfrac{AD}{AB} = \dfrac{AE}{AC}.$

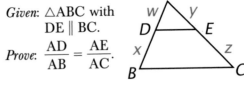

Because the proof is algebraic, it is convenient to express the lengths in the figure in terms of w, x, y, and z and show that $\dfrac{w}{w+x} = \dfrac{y}{y+z}$.

29. Because DE ∥ BC, $\dfrac{w}{x} = \dfrac{y}{z}$. Why?

30. $wz = xy$. Why?

31. $wy + wz = wy + xy$. Why?

32. $w(y + z) = y(w + x)$. Why?

33. $\dfrac{w(y + z)}{(y + z)(w + x)} = \dfrac{y(w + x)}{(y + z)(w + x)}$; so

$\dfrac{w}{w + x} = \dfrac{y}{y + z}$. Why?

Parallels Path. In the figure below, a path has been drawn starting at point A on side MN of △MNO so that each part of the path is parallel to one of the sides of the triangle. G is the name of the point in which the path intersects MN on its return.

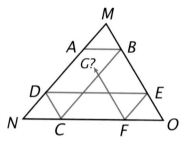

34. Why is $\dfrac{AM}{MN} = \dfrac{BM}{MO}$?

35. Follow the path to copy and complete the following statement:

$$\dfrac{AM}{MN} = \dfrac{BM}{MO} = \dfrac{CN}{?} = \dfrac{?}{?} = \dfrac{?}{?} = \dfrac{?}{?} = \dfrac{GM}{?}$$

Use your result to answer the following questions.

36. To what segment is BM equal?

37. To what segment is CN equal?

38. Why is AM = GM?

39. What does this equality indicate about point G?

40. How would the path look if it were continued past point G?

Bridge Cables. The Dames Point Bridge in Jacksonville, Florida, is supported by parallel cables.

In the figure below showing three of its cables, the tower, AD, is perpendicular to the deck, DG. The cables are arranged so that AG ∥ BF ∥ CE and EF = FG. To find out how AB and BC are related, an extra line, IE, has been drawn perpendicularly to DG.

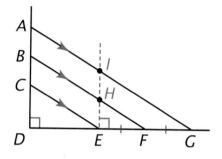

41. Why is $\dfrac{EF}{FG} = 1$?

42. What can you conclude about $\dfrac{EH}{HI}$? Explain.

43. Why is IE ∥ AD?

44. What can you conclude about ABHI and BCEH?

45. Why is BC = EH and AB = HI?

46. What can you conclude about $\dfrac{BC}{AB}$? Explain.

47. What can you conclude about AB and BC? Explain.

Original Proofs. Write proofs for the following exercises.

48.

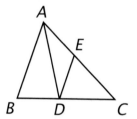

Given: In △ABC, AD bisects ∠BAC; AE = ED.

Prove: $\dfrac{AE}{EC} = \dfrac{BD}{DC}$.

49.

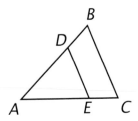

Given: In △ABC, AB = AC and DE ∥ BC.
Prove: AD = AE.

Set III

Pantograph. A pantograph is an instrument used by artists to copy a figure to any desired scale.

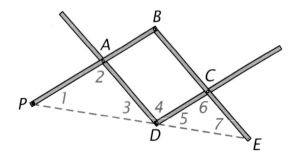

It consists of four bars hinged together as shown in the figure below and is attached to the drawing board at point P. As a stylus at point D traces the figure, a pencil at point E draws a larger copy of it. The bars are connected so that AB = DC = CE and PA = AD = BC.

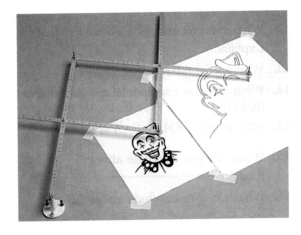

1. Copy the figure and mark it as needed to answer the following questions.

2. As the pantograph is being used, PB always stays parallel to DC and BE always stays parallel to AD. Why?

3. Which of the numbered angles always stay equal to ∠B?

4. If ∠B = $x°$, what is the measure of each of the following angles in terms of x: ∠1, ∠3, ∠5, and ∠7?

As the pantograph is being used,

5. to what number is ∠1 + ∠2 + ∠3 always equal?

6. to what number is ∠3 + ∠4 + ∠5 always equal?

7. what is always true about ∠PDE?

8. what is always true about points P, D, and E?

As the pantograph is being used, PD and DE continually change in length, but $\dfrac{PD}{DE}$ always stays the same.

9. Why?

The "scale factor" of the pantograph is the numerical value of $\dfrac{PE}{PD}$.

10. If the pantograph is set up so that PA = 20 cm and AB = 15 cm, what is its "scale factor"? Explain.

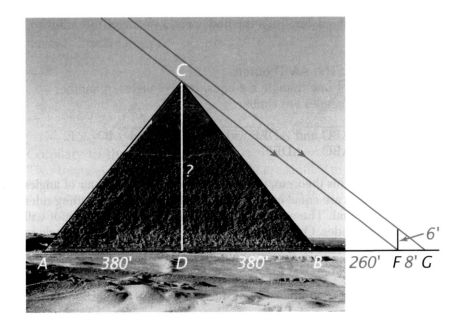

The AA Similarity Theorem

According to the ancient Greek historian Plutarch, Thales, a mathematician who lived several centuries before Euclid, used shadows to find the height of the Great Pyramid. Plutarch wrote:

> The king of Egypt particularly liked the manner by which you [Thales] measured the height of the pyramid without any trouble or instrument; for, by merely placing your staff at the extremity of the shadow which the pyramid casts, you formed, by the impact of the sun's rays, two triangles and so showed that the height of the pyramid was to the length of the staff in the same ratio as their respective shadows.*

The figure above illustrates what Thales may have done. △ABC represents the pyramid, CD its height, and BF its shadow. EF represents Thales' staff and FG its shadow. Reasoning that CF ∥ EG and that △CDF ~ △EFG, Thales wrote and solved a proportion for the corresponding sides of the triangles from which he found the height of the pyramid:

$$\frac{CD}{EF} = \frac{DF}{FG}, \quad \frac{h}{380 + 260} = \frac{6}{8}, \quad 8h = 6(640), \quad h = 480.$$

The height is 480 feet.

---

*The History of Mathematics, by David M. Burton (Allyn & Bacon, 1985).

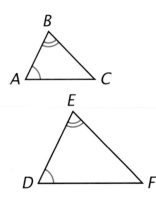

To understand how this method works, we need the following theorem.

Theorem 45. The AA Theorem
If two angles of one triangle are equal to two angles of another triangle, the triangles are similar.

> *Given:* △ABC and △DEF with ∠A = ∠D and ∠B = ∠E.
> *Prove:* △ABC ~ △DEF.

To prove this theorem, we must show that the third pair of angles in the triangles are equal and that all three pairs of corresponding sides are proportional. The angles are easy, and so most of the proof will deal with the sides. Our method will be to copy the smaller triangle in one corner of the larger one as shown in the second pair of triangles at the left. We then have a triangle with a line segment parallel to one side, which lets us apply the corollary to the Side-Splitter Theorem to show that corresponding sides of the triangles are proportional.

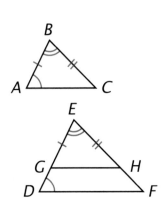

Proof
Choose G and H on ED and EF so that EG = BA and EH = BC. Draw GH. Because ∠B = ∠E, △GEH ≅ △ABC (SAS). Therefore, ∠EGH = ∠A. Because ∠A = ∠D, ∠EGH = ∠D. So GH ∥ DF.

From the fact that a line parallel to one side of a triangle cuts off segments on the other two sides that are proportional to those sides, we have

$$\frac{EG}{ED} = \frac{EH}{EF}.$$

Because EG = BA and EH = BC,

$$\frac{BA}{ED} = \frac{BC}{EF}$$

by substitution.

By constructing △DIJ ≅ △ABC as shown in the third pair of triangles and by using the same reasoning, we can show that

$$\frac{BA}{ED} = \frac{AC}{DF}.$$

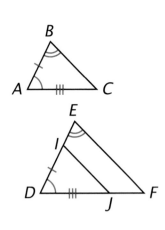

Hence, $\frac{BA}{ED} = \frac{BC}{EF} = \frac{AC}{DF}$, and so we have shown that all three pairs of corresponding sides of the triangles are proportional.

Because all three pairs of corresponding angles in the triangles are equal (∠C = ∠F because, if two angles of one triangle are equal to two angles of another, the third pair of angles are equal), the triangles are similar by definition.

Although we could prove the following theorem directly from the definition of similar triangles, the AA Theorem makes its proof especially easy. All we have to do is show that two pairs of angles in the triangles are equal.

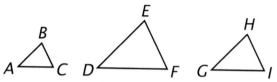

Corollary to the AA Theorem
Two triangles similar to a third triangle are similar to each other.

> *Given:* △ABC ~ △GHI and △DEF ~ △GHI.
> *Prove:* △ABC ~ △DEF.

Proof
Because △ABC ~ △GHI, ∠A = ∠G and ∠B = ∠H; and, because △DEF ~ △GHI, ∠D = ∠G and ∠E = ∠H. Therefore, ∠A = ∠D and ∠B = ∠E (substitution). It follows from the AA Theorem that △ABC ~ △DEF.

Exercises

Set I

Thales' Method. In the figure below illustrating Thales' method for measuring the height of the Great Pyramid, CF and EG represent rays of the sun. Because the sun is so far away, Thales assumed that the rays were parallel.

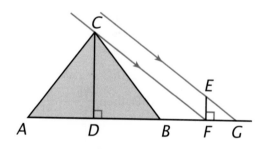

Show how Thales drew the following conclusions by giving a reason for each.

1. ∠CFD = ∠G.

2. ∠CDF = ∠EFG.

3. △CDF ~ △EFG.

4. $\dfrac{CD}{EF} = \dfrac{DF}{FG}$.

Triangle Average. Here is a strange fact.* In the figure below, △ABC ~ △DEF and line segments have been drawn between their corresponding vertices.

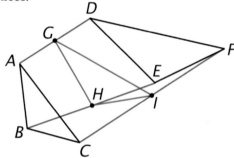

5. What relation do points G, H, and I appear to have to these line segments?

If this relation is true, then △GHI is similar to △ABC.

6. Does it follow that △GHI must also be similar to △DEF? Explain why or why not.

The Penguin Dictionary of Curious and Interesting Geometry, by David Wells (Penguin, 1991).

Chessboard Puzzle. In the chessboard puzzle, the board is cut into four pieces that, when rearranged, seem to form a rectangle having a different shape.

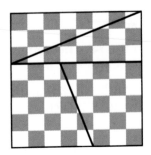

Newton's Figure. The figure below appeared on the British postage stamp shown above honoring Sir Isaac Newton.

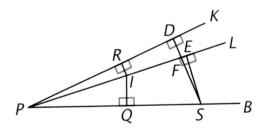

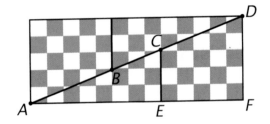

7. Find two different pairs of similar triangles in the figure.

8. Tell how you know that the triangles are similar.

Nine Triangles. The figure below contains six similar isosceles triangles.

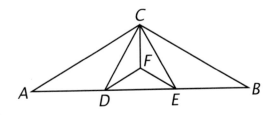

9. Name them.

10. What are the measures of the angles of these triangles?

11. What conclusions can you make about the other triangles in the figure?

12. If the area of one of the small squares of the board is taken as 1 unit, what seems to be the area of each arrangement?

In the second arrangement, points A, B, C, and D appear to be collinear.

13. If they are, then △AEC ~ △AFD. Why?

14. If △AEC ~ △AFD, then $\dfrac{AE}{AF} = \dfrac{EC}{FD}$. Why?

From the figure, AE = 8 and AF = 13.

15. What are the lengths of EC and FD?

16. Does $\dfrac{AE}{AF} = \dfrac{EC}{FD}$? Explain why or why not.

17. What does your answer to exercise 16 indicate about points A, B, C, and D?

18. What kind of proof is a proof in which an assumption leads to a contradiction?

402   Chapter 10: Similarity

Detail from *The Ideal City*
Piero della Francesca (1420–1492)

Piero's Theorem. Piero della Francesca, an important painter of the fifteenth century, was also a mathematician. In his book *On Perspective for Painting,* he proved the following theorem:

> If above a line divided into several parts a line be drawn parallel to it and from the points dividing the first line there be drawn lines which are concurrent, they will divide the parallel line in the same proportion as the given line.*

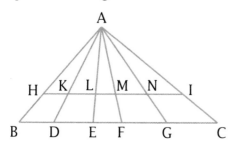

19. What does this theorem say about lines BC and HI?

20. What does the word "concurrent" mean?

21. Copy and complete the following similarity correspondences:
$\triangle AHK \sim \triangle$? and $\triangle AKL \sim \triangle$?.

22. Use your similarity correspondences to copy and complete the following proportions: $\dfrac{HK}{?} = \dfrac{AK}{?}$ and $\dfrac{AK}{?} = \dfrac{KL}{?}$.

---

*The Invention of Infinity: Mathematics and Art in the Renaissance, by J. V. Field (Oxford University Press, 1997).

23. What proportion follows directly from these two proportions?

Piero completed his proof by showing that three more ratios are equal to the two in your last proportion.

24. What are they?

Set II

Electrician's Formula. Electricians know that, if two resistances R_1 and R_2 are "in parallel," they are equivalent to a single resistance R, where $R = \dfrac{R_1 R_2}{R_1 + R_2}$.†

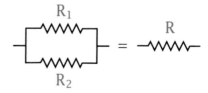

Prove that the figure below illustrates this equation by giving a reason for each of the following statements.

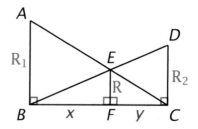

25. $\triangle EFC \sim \triangle ABC$ and $\triangle EFB \sim \triangle DCB$.

26. $\dfrac{R}{R_1} = \dfrac{y}{x+y}$ and $\dfrac{R}{R_2} = \dfrac{x}{x+y}$.

27. $\dfrac{R}{R_1} + \dfrac{R}{R_2} = \dfrac{y}{x+y} + \dfrac{x}{x+y} = \dfrac{y+x}{x+y} = 1$.

28. $RR_2 + RR_1 = R_1 R_2$.

29. $R(R_2 + R_1) = R_1 R_2$.

30. $R = \dfrac{R_1 R_2}{R_1 + R_2}$.

---

†Graphics, by A. S. Levens (Wiley, 1962).

Sides and Angles. In △ABC, AB = 12, BC = 18, AC = 15, and ∠1 = ∠C.

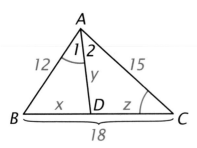

Copy and complete the following statements.

31. △ABD ~ △?.

32. $\dfrac{AB}{?} = \dfrac{BD}{?} = \dfrac{AD}{?}$.

33. $\dfrac{12}{?} = \dfrac{x}{?} = \dfrac{y}{?}$.

34. Find x, y, and z

What can you conclude about

35. ∠2 and ∠C?

36. ∠BAC and ∠C?

Mascheroni Construction. Lorenzo Mascheroni, an eighteenth-century Italian mathematician, discovered a way of using just a compass to find a point midway between two given points.*

37. Do the construction by carrying out the following steps.

(1) First, use your ruler to mark two points, A and B, 2 inches apart.

(2) Draw two circles with centers at A and B and with radius AB. Label the upper point in which they intersect C.

_____

Mathematical Circus, by Martin Gardner (Knopf, 1979).

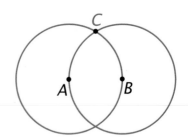

(3) With the same radius AB and C as center, mark point D; then, with D as center, mark point E.

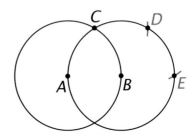

(4) Open the compass to radius EA and, with E as center, draw an arc intersecting the circle on the left at points F and G.

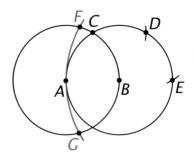

(5) With F and G as centers and radius FA, draw two arcs that intersect at H. Point H is midway between points A and B. (Check this with your ruler.)

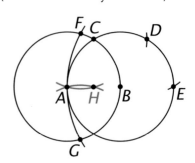

To show why this construction works, draw FA, FH, FE, and AE, as shown in the figure below.

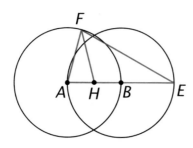

38. What kind of triangles are △FAH and △EFA?

39. Why is △FAH ~ △EFA?

40. Why is $\dfrac{AH}{FA} = \dfrac{FH}{EA}$?

41. To what number is $\dfrac{FH}{EA}$ equal? Explain.

42. Why is $AH = \dfrac{1}{2} AB$?

Deja Vu. △ABC is a right triangle, and CDEF is a square.

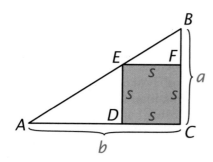

43. Why is △ABC ~ △AED?

44. Copy and complete the following proportion: $\dfrac{BC}{?} = \dfrac{AC}{?}$.

45. Rewrite the proportion in terms of *a*, *b*, and *s*.

46. Solve the proportion for *s* in terms of *a* and *b*.

Compare your answer with the electrical-resistance formula derived in exercises 25 through 30.

47. If *a* and *b* in your answer represent two resistances in parallel, what does *s* represent?

Original Proofs. Write proofs for the following exercises.

48.

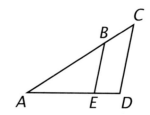

Given: △ACD with BE ∥ CD.
Prove: △ABE ~ △ACD.

49.

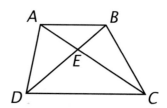

Given: Trapezoid ABCD with bases AB and DC and diagonals AC and BD meeting at E.
Prove: AE × ED = BE × EC.

50.

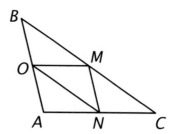

Given: △ABC with midsegments MN, MO, and NO.
Prove: △MNO ~ △ABC.

Set III

Dividing Line.
Puzzle: To draw a line through point P that divides the figure of nine squares below into two parts of equal area.*

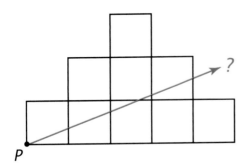

In the figure below, an extra square has been added, and lines AB (intersecting DE at Q) and PQ have been drawn.

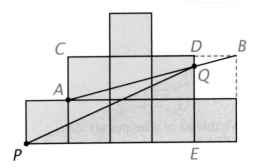

1. If the sides of the nine squares are each 1 unit, what are the areas of the two parts?

The figure below shows a way of dividing the region that doesn't quite work.

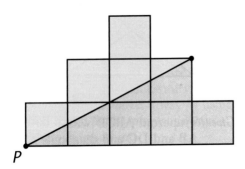

2. What are the areas of its two parts?

3. Why is △QDB ~ △ACB?

4. Why is $\dfrac{QD}{AC} = \dfrac{DB}{CD}$?

5. To what number is QD equal? Explain.

6. What is the area of the blue region?

7. Does this figure solve the puzzle?

Penrose Tiles to Trapdoor Ciphers, by Martin Gardner (W. H. Freeman and Company, 1989).

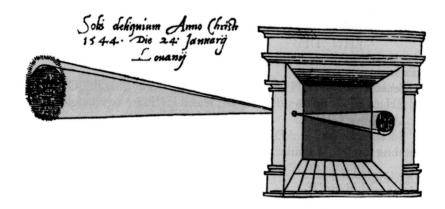

Soli deliquium Anno Christi
1544. Die 24: Januarij
L ouanij

Proportions and Dilations

Strange as it may seem, cameras were used long before photography. Their earliest form was the *camera obscura,* a Latin name meaning "dark room." The camera obscura, popular in the Middle Ages, was simply a dark room into which light was admitted through a tiny hole. The figure above shows the image of a solar eclipse being formed inside such a camera in 1544. Film for recording the images as photographs was not invented until almost three centuries later.

As you can see in the figure, the camera produces an image that is upside down with respect to the object that it pictures. The size of the image depends on the distance of the object from the pinhole. In the figure at the right, AB represents the object, CD represents the image, and P represents the hole in the wall. If AB ∥ DC, it is easy to show that △APB ~ △CPD.

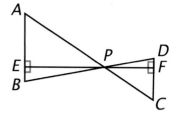

The distances of the object and image from P are the lengths of PE and PF. Altitudes in two triangles such as these are called *corresponding altitudes* because they are drawn from corresponding vertices of the triangles. It is easy to prove that these altitudes have the same ratio as that of the corresponding sides:

$$\frac{PE}{PF} = \frac{AB}{CD}.$$

Theorem 46

Corresponding altitudes of similar triangles have the same ratio as that of the corresponding sides.

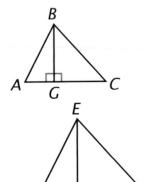

Given: △ABC ~ △DEF; BG and EH are corresponding altitudes.

Prove: $\dfrac{BG}{EH} = \dfrac{AC}{DF}$.

Proof*

Because BG and EH are altitudes of △ABC and △DEF, BG ⊥ AC and EH ⊥ DF. It follows that ∠AGB and ∠DHE are right angles, and so ∠AGB = ∠DHE.

Because △ABC ~ △DEF, we know that ∠A = ∠D (corresponding angles of similar triangles are equal). So △ABG ~ △DEH (AA), and $\dfrac{BG}{EH} = \dfrac{AB}{DE}$.

Because △ABC ~ △DEF, $\dfrac{AB}{DE} = \dfrac{AC}{DF}$. So $\dfrac{BG}{EH} = \dfrac{AC}{DF}$ by substitution.

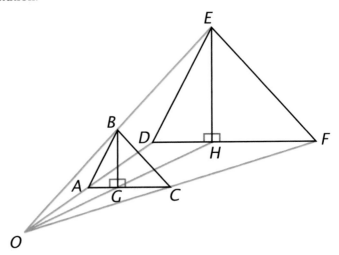

In Lesson 2, we considered the idea of the *dilation* transformation. This transformation also suggests why the theorem about corresponding altitudes is true. In the figure above, point O is the center of dilation in which △DEF and its altitude EH are the dilation images of △ABC and its altitude BG. On every ray from point O through a point P on △ABC and BG, a point P′ is chosen so that OP′ = rOP. In this case, $r = 2$; so OD = 2OA, OE = 2OB, OF = 2OC, and OH = 2OG. As the dilation approach to similarity tells us, when a figure is enlarged or reduced, the distances between all pairs of corresponding points in the figure are changed in the same ratio.

---

*Our proof is based on figures in which the altitudes are inside the triangles. Similar proofs can be written for the cases in which they are not.

Exercises

Set I

Fish Story. How big is the fish? Its apparent size depends on whether you cover the hand or cover the fisherman.*

In the figure below, C represents the camera lens, DE the fish, and AB the man.

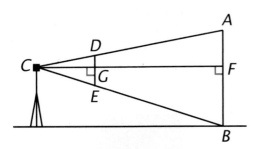

1. Which line segments represent the relative distances of the fish and the man from the camera?

2. Given that DE ⊥ CF and AB ⊥ CF, how do you know that DE ∥ AB?

3. What can you conclude about △CDE and △CAB? Explain.

4. What are CG and CF called with respect to these triangles?

*Perception, by Irvin Rock (Scientific American Library, 1984).

5. Copy and complete the following proportion:
$$\frac{CG}{?} = \frac{DE}{?}.$$

6. State the theorem on which your proportion is based.

7. If the man is 6 feet tall and is 12 feet from the camera, what other distance would you need to know to be able to figure out the length of the fish?

8. If that distance is 2 feet, how big is the fish?

In the figure below, either fish can be considered to be the dilation image of the other.

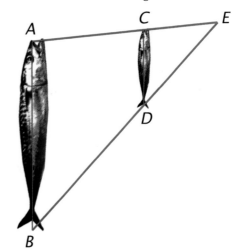

9. What is point E called with respect to the dilation?

Measure the following distances in centimeters.

10. BE.

11. DE.

If AB is the image of CD and r_1 is the magnitude of the dilation, then BE = r_1DE.

12. Find r_1.

13. What does this number indicate about the relative lengths of the two fish?

14. Measure AB and CD in centimeters and find $\frac{AB}{CD}$.

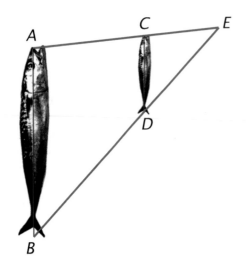

If CD is the image of AB and r_2 is the magnitude of the dilation, then DE = r_2BE.

15. Find r_2.

16. What does this number indicate about the relative lengths of the two fish?

17. Use your measurements of AB and CD to find $\dfrac{CD}{AB}$.

18. How is the number r_2 related to the number r_1?

Drawing Conclusions. In the figure below, AB ∥ ED, AD ⊥ BE, and AGEF and BGDC are parallelograms.

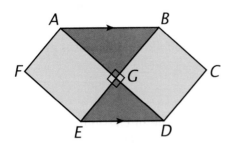

Tell whether or not you think each of the following statements is a reasonable conclusion. In each case, explain why or why not.

19. △AGB ≅ △DGE.
20. △AGB ~ △DGE.

21. $\dfrac{AG}{DG} = \dfrac{GB}{GE}$.

22. αAGEF = αBGDC.

23. α△AGB = α△DGE.

24. αADEF = αBEDC.

Grid Exercise. On graph paper, draw a pair of axes extending 20 units to the right and 20 units up from the origin.

25. Plot the following points and connect them to form △ABC: A(4, 8), B(5, 3), C(10, 6).

26. Use the transformation $(a, b) \rightarrow (2a - 3, 2b - 4)$ on the coordinates of △ABC to find the coordinates of △A′B′C′. For example, A(4, 8) → A′(2 · 4 − 3, 2 · 8 − 4), or A′(5, 12).

25. *(continued)* Draw △A′B′C′.

27. How does △A′B′C′ appear to be related to △ABC?

25. *(continued)* Draw lines through the corresponding vertices of the two triangles and extend them across the graph.

28. For what type of transformation is △A′B′C′ the image of △ABC?

29. Where is its center?

30. What is its magnitude?

Set II

Washington Monument. The tallest structure in our nation's capital is the Washington Monument.

It is a tapered column topped with a small pyramid. The figure below (which is not to scale) shows its dimensions in feet.*

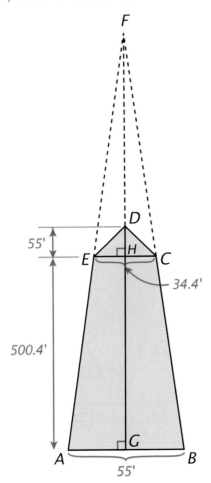

31. How tall is the Washington Monument?

The dotted lines show what the monument would look like if its sides did not change direction at E and C.

32. Name the pairs of similar triangles in the figure.

33. Letting FG = x, write and solve a proportion to find out how tall the Washington Monument would be if its sides did not change direction.

***

*Slicing Pizzas, Racing Turtles, and Further Adventures in Applied Mathematics, by Robert B. Banks (Princeton University Press, 1999).

34. State the theorem on which your proportion is based.

Congruence and Similarity. Although you know several ways to prove triangles congruent, we have considered only one way to prove them similar.

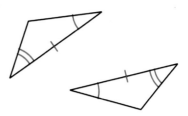

How do you know that the triangles above are

35. congruent?

36. similar?

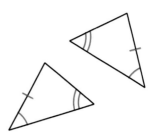

How do you know that the triangles above are

37. congruent?

38. similar?

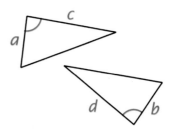

Suppose that, for the triangles above, $\frac{a}{b} = \frac{c}{d}$.

39. Would you know that they are congruent if these ratios were equal to 1? Explain.

Complete the following proofs by giving the reasons.

SAS Similarity Theorem.
If an angle of one triangle is equal to an angle of another triangle and the sides including these angles are proportional, then the triangles are similar.

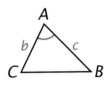

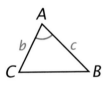

Given: △ABC and △A′B′C′ with

$$\angle A = \angle A' \text{ and } \frac{b}{b'} = \frac{c}{c'}.$$

Prove: △ABC ~ △A′B′C′.

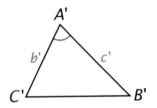

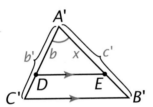

Proof

40. Choose point D on A′C′ so that A′D = AC = b. Why?

41. Through D, draw DE ∥ C′B′. Why?

42. In △A′B′C′, $\frac{b}{b'} = \frac{x}{c'}$. Why?

43. Because $\frac{b}{b'} = \frac{c}{c'}$ (given), it follows that

    $\frac{x}{c'} = \frac{c}{c'}$. Why?

44. So $x = c$. Why?

45. Therefore, △ABC ≅ △A′ED. Why?

46. So ∠C = ∠A′DE. Why?

47. Because DE ∥ C′B′, ∠A′DE = ∠C′. Why?

48. So ∠C = ∠C′. Why?

49. Therefore, △ABC ~ △A′B′C′. Why?

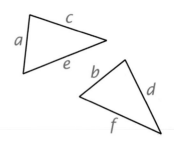

Suppose that, for the triangles above,

$$\frac{a}{b} = \frac{c}{d} = \frac{e}{f}.$$

50. Would you know that they are congruent if these ratios were equal to 1? Explain.

SSS Similarity Theorem.
If the sides of one triangle are proportional to the sides of another triangle, then the triangles are similar.

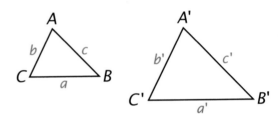

Given: △ABC and △A′B′C′ with

$$\frac{a}{b} = \frac{b}{b'} = \frac{c}{c'}.$$

Prove: △ABC ~ △A′B′C′.

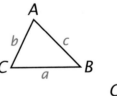

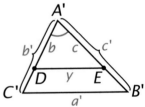

Proof

51. Choose point D on A′C′ so that A′D = AC = b, and choose point E on A′B′ so that A′E = AB = c. Why?

52. Draw DE. Why?

53. ∠DA′E = ∠C′A′B′. Why?

It follows that $\triangle A'ED \sim \triangle A'B'C'$ by the SAS Similarity Theorem.

54. State this theorem as a complete sentence.

55. Because $\triangle A'ED \sim \triangle A'B'C'$, it follows that $\dfrac{y}{a'} = \dfrac{b}{b'}$. Why?

56. Because $\dfrac{a}{a'} = \dfrac{b}{b'}$ (given), it follows that

$\dfrac{y}{a'} = \dfrac{a}{a'}$. Why?

57. So $y = a$. Why?

58. It follows that $\triangle A'ED \cong \triangle ABC$. Why?

59. Therefore, $\angle A'ED = \angle B$ and $\angle A' = \angle A$. Why?

60. So $\triangle A'ED \sim \triangle ABC$. Why?

61. Because we have already proved that $\triangle A'ED \sim \triangle A'B'C'$, it follows that $\triangle ABC \sim \triangle A'B'C'$. Why?

Set III

Camera Experiment. You can see how a camera obscura works by doing the following experiment. All that you need is a stiff card (a file card is convenient), a candle, and a dark room.

1. Poke a hole through the center of the card with your compass point. The hole should have a diameter of about $\dfrac{1}{16}$ inch. Light the candle and hold it about 6 inches from a wall. Hold the card midway between the candle and the wall with your other hand so that the hole, flame, and wall are in line. You should observe an upside-down image of the flame on the wall.

Hold the card close to the wall and move it toward the candle. What happens to the size of the flame's image?

In the figure below, AB represents the candle flame, H represents the hole in the card, and CD represents the flame's image on the wall.

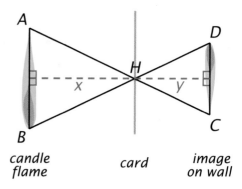

candle flame   card   image on wall

Explain what you observed by doing each of the following exercises.

2. Assume that $\triangle AHB \sim \triangle CHD$, and derive an equation for CD in terms of AB, x, and y.

3. When the card is moved from the wall toward the candle, what happens to y?

4. What happens to x?

5. What happens to $\dfrac{y}{x}$?

6. What happens to CD?

LESSON 6

Perimeters and Areas of Similar Figures

Ever since the rules for baseball were established in 1845, the game has been played on a diamond with bases 90 feet apart. Softball, the scaled-down version of the game first played in 1887, is played on a diamond whose bases are 60 feet apart. How far does a batter have to run to score a run in each game?

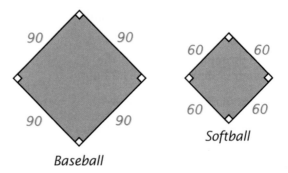

Baseball

Softball

In baseball, the distance is 360 feet; whereas, in softball, it is 240 feet. It is easy to see that these two distances, the perimeters of the diamonds, have the same ratio as that of the lengths of their sides:

$$\frac{360}{240} = \frac{4 \times 90}{4 \times 60} = \frac{90}{60} = \frac{3}{2}, \text{ or } 1.5.$$

Because each side of a baseball diamond is 1.5 times as long as each side of a softball diamond, it makes sense that a baseball player has to run 1.5 times as far as a softball player.

What about the *areas* enclosed by the two diamonds? Does the person who mows the field inside a baseball diamond have 1.5 times as much grass to mow as that inside a softball diamond? The two fields are square in shape; so their areas are $90^2 = 8,100$ square feet and $60^2 = 3,600$ square feet. Comparing the areas of the two fields gives

$$\frac{8,100}{3,600} = \frac{90^2}{60^2} = \left(\frac{90}{60}\right)^2 = \left(\frac{3}{2}\right)^2, \text{ or } 2.25;$$

so their ratio is equal to the *square* of the ratio of the lengths of their sides.

These results show that, even though the two diamonds are square in shape and therefore similar, their perimeters and areas are related in different ways.

Comparable relations are true for any pair of similar polygons. Although we will derive them for similar triangles, proofs can also be written for polygons having any number of sides. In the same way that we have been using α, the first letter of the Greek alphabet, to represent the word "area," we will use ρ (rho), another Greek letter, to represent the word "perimeter."

Theorem 47

The ratio of the perimeters of two similar polygons is equal to the ratio of the corresponding sides.

Given: $\triangle ABC \sim \triangle A'B'C'$.

Prove: $\dfrac{\rho\triangle ABC}{\rho\triangle A'B'C'} = r$, where $r = \dfrac{AB}{A'B'} = \dfrac{BC}{B'C'} = \dfrac{CA}{C'A'}$.

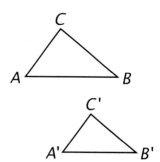

Proof

Because $r = \dfrac{AB}{A'B'} = \dfrac{BC}{B'C'} = \dfrac{CA}{C'A'}$, it follows by multiplication that

$$AB = rA'B', \quad BC = rB'C', \quad \text{and} \quad CA = rC'A'.$$

Adding these equations, we get

$$AB + BC + CA = rA'B' + rB'C' + rC'A'$$
$$= r(A'B' + B'C' + C'A').$$

Because $AB + BC + CA = \rho\triangle ABC$ and $A'B' + B'C' + C'A' = \rho\triangle A'B'C'$, we can substitute to get

$$\rho\triangle ABC = r\rho\triangle A'B'C'.$$

Dividing gives

$$\frac{\rho\triangle ABC}{\rho\triangle A'B'C'} = r.$$

Theorem 48

The ratio of the areas of two similar polygons is equal to the square of the ratio of the corresponding sides.

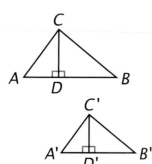

Given: $\triangle ABC \sim \triangle A'B'C'$.

Prove: $\dfrac{\alpha \triangle ABC}{\alpha \triangle A'B'C'} = r^2$, where $r = \dfrac{AB}{A'B'} = \dfrac{BC}{B'C'} = \dfrac{CA}{C'A'}$.

Proof

Through C, draw CD ⊥ AB, and through C', draw C'D' ⊥ A'B'. Because CD and C'D' are corresponding altitudes of $\triangle ABC$ and $\triangle A'B'C'$ and $\triangle ABC \sim \triangle A'B'C'$,

$$\frac{CD}{C'D'} = \frac{AB}{A'B'} = r$$

(corresponding altitudes of similar triangles have the same ratio as the corresponding sides).

Because $\alpha \triangle ABC = \dfrac{1}{2} AB \cdot CD$ and $\alpha \triangle A'B'C' = \dfrac{1}{2} A'B' \cdot C'D'$, the ratio of the areas is

$$\frac{\alpha \triangle ABC}{\alpha \triangle A'B'C'} = \frac{\dfrac{1}{2}AB \cdot CD}{\dfrac{1}{2}A'B' \cdot C'D'} = \frac{AB}{A'B'} \cdot \frac{CD}{C'D'} = r \cdot r = r^2$$

Exercises

Set I

Triangle Ratios. The figure at the right from an old geometry book shows a triangle divided into 16 congruent triangles.*

Find each of the following ratios.

1. $\dfrac{BC}{DE}$.

2. $\dfrac{\alpha \triangle ABC}{\alpha \triangle ADE}$.

3. $\dfrac{BC}{FG}$.

4. $\dfrac{\alpha \triangle ABC}{\alpha \triangle AFG}$.

5. $\dfrac{DE}{FG}$.

6. $\dfrac{\alpha \triangle ADE}{\alpha \triangle AFG}$.

7. $\dfrac{DE}{HI}$.

8. $\dfrac{\alpha \triangle ADE}{\alpha \triangle AHI}$.

9. State the theorem illustrated by exercises 1 through 8.

First Steps in Geometry, by G. A. Wentworth and G. A. Hill (Ginn, 1901).

Judo Mat. Judo contests are held on a square mat, the "contest area," measuring 8 meters on each side. This mat is surrounded by a "danger area" 1 meter wide, which is surrounded by a "safety area" 3 meters wide.*

For convenience, we will use numbers to refer to these three squares as shown in the figure below.

Find each of the following measurements.

10. side of 1.

11. $\rho 1$.

12. $\alpha 1$.

13. side of 2.

14. $\rho 2$.

15. $\alpha 2$.

16. side of 3.

17. $\rho 3$.

18. $\alpha 3$.

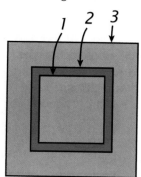

Find each of the following ratios as a common fraction in simplest terms.

19. $\dfrac{\text{side of 1}}{\text{side of 2}}$.

20. $\dfrac{\rho 1}{\rho 2}$.

21. $\dfrac{\alpha 1}{\alpha 2}$.

22. $\dfrac{\text{side of 2}}{\text{side of 3}}$.

23. $\dfrac{\rho 2}{\rho 3}$.

24. $\dfrac{\alpha 2}{\alpha 3}$.

Map Scaling. In one of his books, Lewis Carroll once described a map drawn on a scale of a mile to a mile: "It has never been spread out, yet . . . the farmers objected; they said it would cover the whole country, and shut out the sunlight! So we now use the country itself, as its own map, and I assure you it does nearly as well."

Sports: The Complete Visual Reference, by François Fortin (Firefly Books, 2000).

If a map is similar to the country that it represents, what must be true about corresponding

25. distances?

26. angles?

27. areas?

A map in which a foot represents a mile has a scale of

$$\frac{1 \text{ foot}}{5{,}280 \text{ feet}} = \frac{1}{5{,}280}$$

because 1 mile = 5,280 feet.

28. On a map of this scale, how many feet would 1 inch represent?

29. How many square feet would 1 square inch represent?

30. What is the scale of a map in which an *inch* represents a mile?

31. What is the scale of the map described by Lewis Carroll?

Set II

SAT Problem. The figure at the right appeared in a problem on an SAT exam. It was given that the area of $\triangle ABC = 54$ and that

$$AD = \frac{1}{3} AB.$$

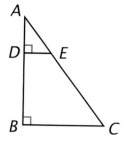

The answers to some SAT problems cannot be determined from the information given.

32. Can any conclusion be drawn about $\triangle ADE$ and $\triangle ABC$? Explain.

33. Is it correct to assume that $DE = \frac{1}{3} BC$? Why or why not?

34. Is it possible to figure out the lengths of AB and BC?

35. Is it possible to figure out the lengths of AD and DE?

36. Is it possible to figure out the area of $\triangle ADE$? Explain.

Quilt Pattern. The quilt pictured above, made by Barbara Dean, is based on the pattern of squares shown below.*

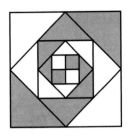

37. How many different sizes of squares does the pattern contain?

What is the ratio of

38. the area of one of the smallest squares to the area of the next larger square?

39. their corresponding sides?

40. their perimeters?

What is the ratio of

41. the area of the largest square to the area of the next largest square?

42. their corresponding sides?

43. their perimeters?

Cranberry Circles. This photograph shows cranberries being gathered into a circle on the surface of a bog in Plymouth, Massachusetts.†

Imagine that the circles below have diameters of 90 feet and 120 feet and that each is filled with a layer of cranberries.

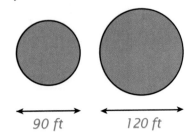

90 ft   *120 ft*

44. Why is it reasonable to say that all circles are similar?

45. What are the radii of the two circles?

46. What are their exact and approximate circumferences?

47. What are their exact and approximate areas?

Compare the first circle with the second and find each of the following ratios both as a common and as a decimal fraction.

48. The ratio of their diameters.

49. The ratio of their radii.

50. The ratio of their circumferences.

51. The ratio of their areas.

Designing Tessellations: The Secrets of Interlocking Patterns, by Jinny Beyer (Contemporary Books, 1999).

†*Look at the Land: Aerial Reflections on America,* by Alex MacLean and Bill McKibben (Rizzoli, 1993).

Pentagon Measurements. The Pentagon, home of the United States Department of Defense in Arlington, Virginia, is named for its shape.

In the scale drawing of the Pentagon below, each side is 1 inch long and each angle is 108°. The area covered by the Pentagon (the blue region in the drawing) is about 1.5 square inches.

The scale used is $\dfrac{1}{11,052}$.

Also, 1 acre = 43,560 square feet.

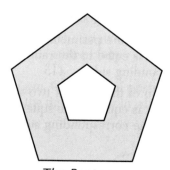

The Pentagon

Find each of the following measurements.

52. The measure of each angle of the Pentagon.

53. The length of each side of the Pentagon in feet.

54. The perimeter of the Pentagon.

55. The area covered by the Pentagon in acres.

Set III

Pythagoras on the Sides. According to Pythagoras, the area of the square on the hypotenuse of a right triangle is equal to the sum of the areas of the squares on the two legs.

Would this still be true if pictures of Pythagoras himself were placed on the three sides of a right triangle? Would the Pythagoras on the hypotenuse be equal to the sum of the Pythagorases on the two legs?

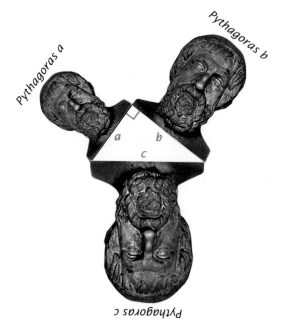

Suppose that, in the figure above, a, b, and c are the lengths of the sides of the right triangle and that the three pictures of Pythagoras (Py.) are similar; that is,

$$\text{Py.}a \sim \text{Py.}b \sim \text{Py.}c.$$

If this is the case, then it seems reasonable to conclude that

$$\frac{\alpha\text{Py.}a}{\alpha\text{Py.}c} = \left(\frac{a}{c}\right)^2 \quad \text{and} \quad \frac{\alpha\text{Py.}b}{\alpha\text{Py.}c} = \left(\frac{b}{c}\right)^2.$$

1. Why?

2. Can you reason from the equations above to show that

$$\alpha\text{Py.}a + \alpha\text{Py.}b = \alpha\text{Py.}c?$$

Used by permission of Johnny Hart and Creators Syndicate, Inc.

CHAPTER 10 Summary and Review

Basic Ideas

Dilation: center, magnitude   386
Geometric mean   380
Proportion   379
Ratio   379
Similar figures   386–387
Similar triangles   386

Theorems

44. *The Side-Splitter Theorem.* If a line parallel
to one side of a triangle intersects the
other two sides in different points, it
divides the sides in the same ratio.   393

Corollary. If a line parallel to one side of a
triangle intersects the other two sides in
different points, it cuts off segments
proportional to the sides.   394

45. *The AA Theorem.* If two angles of one
triangle are equal to two angles of another triangle, the triangles are similar.
400

Corollary . Two triangles similar to a third
triangle are similar to each other.   401

46. Corresponding altitudes of similar
triangles have the same ratio as that of
the corresponding sides.   408

47. The ratio of the perimeters of two similar
polygons is equal to the ratio of the
corresponding sides.   415

48. The ratio of the areas of two similar
polygons is equal to the square of the
ratio of the corresponding sides.   416

Additional Results

The SAS Similarity Theorem. If an angle of
one triangle is equal to an angle of
another triangle and the sides including
these angles are proportional, then the
triangles are similar.   412

The SSS Similarity Theorem. If the sides of
one triangle are proportional to the sides
of another triangle, then the triangles are
similar.   412

420   Chapter 10: Similarity

Exercises

Set I

Body Ratios. The figures below show a 5-month-old infant and an adult drawn as if both were 6 feet tall.*

Write each of the following ratios as a simple fraction.

1. The length of the infant's head to the length of the rest of his body.
2. The length of the adult's head to the length of the rest of his body.
3. The length of the infant's arms to the length of his entire body.
4. The length of the adult's arms to the length of his entire body.

Perspective Law. One "law of perspective" is illustrated by the figure below in which DE ∥ BC.

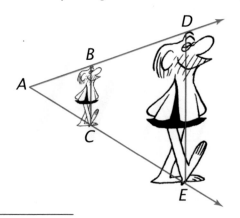

_____

Cats' Paws and Catapults, by Steven Vogel (Norton, 1998).

5. Why is $\dfrac{AB}{AD} = \dfrac{AC}{AE}$?

6. Why is △ABC ~ △ADE?

7. Measure each of the following lengths in centimeters: AC, AE, and DE.

8. Write and solve a proportion in terms of these lengths to find BC. Then measure BC in centimeters to see if your answer is reasonable.

9. How many times as tall as the figure at BC is the figure at DE?

10. How does the area of the figure at DE compare with the area of the figure at BC?

Proportion Practice. Find the length marked x in each of the following figures.

11.

12.

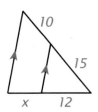

13.

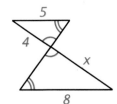

The triangles are similar

14.

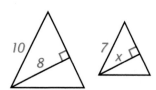

The parallelograms are similar

Similar Triangles. The triangles below are similar, and the sides of the larger triangle are 3 times as long as the corresponding sides of the smaller triangle.

15. How many smaller triangles could be packed into the larger?

16. Draw a figure to illustrate your answer.

Reptiles. The figure below shows four congruent tiles that have been put together to form a figure that is similar to them.

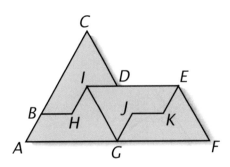

17. Exactly what kind of polygons are they?

Copy and complete these correspondences.

18. ABHIG ≅ E????.

19. AFEDC ~ G????.

20. What can you conclude about GFEI? Explain.

21. Express the area of AFEDC as a multiple of the area of ABHIG.

22. Express their perimeters in the same way.

23. What is the ratio $\dfrac{AC}{IG}$?

Free Fall. Galileo used the figure below in his study of the behavior of objects in free fall.*

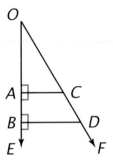

In the figure above, ray OE represents time, and the lengths of AC and BD represent the speed of the falling object at instants A and B; AC ⊥ OE and BD ⊥ OE.

24. Why is AC ∥ BD?

25. What happens to the speed of the object as it falls?

26. Why is △OAC ~ △OBD?

27. Why is $\dfrac{OA}{OB} = \dfrac{AC}{BD}$?

28. Why is $\dfrac{\alpha \triangle OAC}{\alpha \triangle OBD} = \left(\dfrac{OA}{OB}\right)^2$?

Type Transformations. The figure below shows several transformations of the letter A into type of different sizes. The sizes are given in "points" (pt).

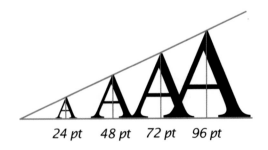

24 pt   48 pt   72 pt   96 pt

29. What are these transformations called?

───────────

Geometry Civilized: History, Culture, and Technique, by J. L. Heilbron (Clarendon Press, 1998).

What is the magnitude of the transformation in which

30. the 48-point A is the image of the 24-point A?

31. the 72-point A is the image of the 96-point A?

As the 24-point A is transformed into the 72-point A, what happens to

32. the distances from the center of the transformation to all of its points?

33. the angles within the letter?

Set II

Trick Card. The figure below shows the front and back of a trick playing card that seems to get smaller and smaller. A magician secretly folds it in half each time while turning it over to show another card half as large.*

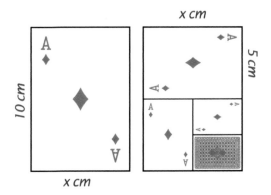

The card is designed so that all four "cards" are similar.

34. Use this fact to write and solve a proportion to find *x*, the width of the original card.

35. Find the area of the original card.

36. Find the ratio of the longer dimensions of the second card and the original card.

_____
The Unexpected Hanging and Other Mathematical Diversions, by Martin Gardner (Simon & Schuster, 1969).

37. Use this ratio to find the ratio of the areas of the second card and the original card.

38. Does your answer seem reasonable? Explain.

Catapult. The Roman general Marcellus is attacking the city of Syracuse.[†] In the overhead view shown below, Archimedes is standing at point A by the city wall and has placed a catapult at point C. A ditch, DE, is parallel to the city wall, CA, and the headquarters of the enemy camp at point B is directly across from Archimedes so that BA ⊥ CA; also DF ⊥ CA.

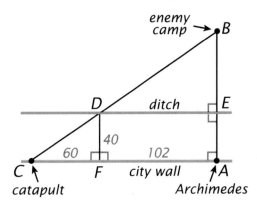

39. Given the distances marked on the map, find the distance of the enemy camp from Archimedes.

Leg Splitter. ABCD is a trapezoid with bases AD and BC; EF ∥ BC.

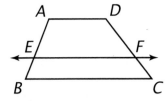

40. Copy the figure and mark it as needed to do each of the following exercises.

41. EF ∥ AD. Why?

_____
[†]This problem is based on one that appeared in the 1725 edition of the *Ladies Diary*, a book of puzzles and mathematical problems published yearly in London.

40. *(continued)* Draw diagonal AC. Let G be the point in which the diagonal intersects EF.

42. $\dfrac{AE}{EB} = \dfrac{AG}{GC}$ and $\dfrac{AG}{GC} = \dfrac{DF}{FC}$. Why?

43. $\dfrac{AE}{EB} = \dfrac{DF}{FC}$. Why?

44. What do exercises 40 through 43 prove about a line that intersects the legs of a trapezoid and is parallel to its bases?

Crossed Ladders. Two long ladders, AB and CD, lean against two buildings as shown below.*

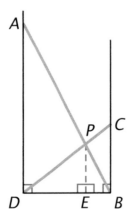

The shorter ladder reaches a point 42 feet above the ground.

45. Copy the figure and mark the following distances on it: CB = 42, DE = 40, and EB = 16.

Find each of the following distances.

46. PE, the distance of the point in which the ladders cross above the ground.

47. AD, the distance that the longer ladder reaches above the ground.

48. CD, the length of the shorter ladder.

49. AB, the length of the longer ladder.

50. The remaining four distances, PA, PB, PC, and PD.

Seven Triangles. In △ABC, BD ⊥ AC, EF ⊥ AC, and AB ∥ DE.

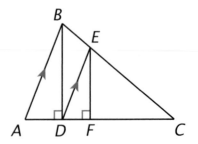

51. Find three pairs of similar triangles.

52. Copy the figure and mark the following lengths on it: BD = 20, AD = 8, and DF = 6.

Write and solve a proportion to find

53. EF.

54. FC.

Find each of the following numbers.

55. $\dfrac{AB}{DE}$.

56. $\alpha \triangle ABD$.

57. $\alpha \triangle DEF$.

58. $\dfrac{\alpha \triangle ABD}{\alpha \triangle DEF}$.

59. $\dfrac{BE}{EC}$.

60. $\alpha \triangle BED$.

61. $\alpha \triangle DEC$.

62. $\dfrac{\alpha \triangle BED}{\alpha \triangle DEC}$.

Mathematical Circus, by Martin Gardner (Knopf, 1979).

Quadratic Equations

A quadratic equation is an equation that can be written in the form

$$ax^2 + bx + c = 0.$$

This form is called its standard form.

Some quadratic equations can be solved by *factoring.*

Example 1:   Solve $x^2 + 5x = 14$.

Solution: Writing the equation in standard form, we get

$$x^2 + 5x - 14 = 0.$$

Factoring the left side, we get

$$(x - 2)(x + 7) = 0.$$

For a product of two factors to be equal to zero, at least one of the factors must be equal to zero, and so

$$\text{either} \quad x - 2 = 0$$
$$\text{or} \quad x + 7 = 0.$$

Solving these equations, we get

$$x = 2 \quad \text{or} \quad x = -7.$$

All quadratic equations can be solved by using the *quadratic formula:*

$$x = \frac{-b \pm \sqrt{b^2 - 4ac}}{2a}.$$

The solutions to the equation

$$ax^2 + bx + c = 0$$

can be found by substituting its values for a, b, and c in this formula and simplifying the result.

Example 2:   Solve $x(x + 2) = 9$.

Solution: To find a, b, and c, the equation must be written in standard form:

$$x^2 + 2x = 9$$
$$x^2 + 2x - 9 = 0.$$

Because $a = 1$, $b = 2$, and $c = -9$,

$$x = \frac{-(2) \pm \sqrt{(2)^2 - 4(1)(-9)}}{2(1)}$$

$$x = \frac{-2 \pm \sqrt{4 + 36}}{2} = \frac{-2 \pm \sqrt{40}}{2}$$

$$= \frac{-2 \pm 2\sqrt{10}}{2} = -1 \pm \sqrt{10}.$$

The solutions of the equation are $-1 + \sqrt{10}$ and $-1 - \sqrt{10}$.

Exercises

Solve the following equations by either factoring or using the quadratic formula.

1. $x^2 + 3x - 28 = 0$

2. $5x^2 - 4x - 1 = 0$

3. $x^2 + 5 = 8x$

4. $x^2 - 49 = 0$

5. $x(x + 4) = 20$

6. $9x^2 - 6x + 1 = 0$

7. $3x^2 = 12 - 5x$

8. $(x - 3)(x - 4) = 2$

9. $(x + 5)^2 = x + 17$

10. $5(x^2 - 1) = 2x$

ALGEBRA REVIEW

Solving Formulas

In working with formulas, it is often useful to solve for one of the variables in the formula in terms of the other variables.

Example 1: Solve the formula $F = \dfrac{mv^2}{r}$ for v, given that $v > 0$.

Solution: To do so, we want to end up with an equation beginning with $v = $.

Multiplying both sides by r gives

$$rF = mv^2$$

and dividing by m gives

$$\frac{rF}{m} = v^2, \text{ so } v^2 = \frac{rF}{m}.$$

Taking the square root of each side, we have

$$v = \sqrt{\frac{rF}{m}}.$$

(We list only the positive square root because it is given that $v > 0$.)

Example 2: Solve the formula $mv_2 - mv_1 = Ft$ for m.

Solution: Factoring the left side of the equation gives

$$m(v_2 - v_1) = Ft.$$

Dividing both sides by $v_2 - v_1$ gives

$$m = \frac{Ft}{v_2 - v_1}.$$

Exercises

Solve the following formulas from mathematics and science for the variables indicated. Assume that all of the variables represent positive numbers.

1. $c = 2\pi r$ for r.

2. $p_1v_1 = p_2v_2$ for p_1.

3. $p_1v_1 = p_2v_2$ for v_2.

4. $c^2 = a^2 + b^2$ for c.

5. $c^2 = a^2 + b^2$ for a.

6. $A = \dfrac{1}{2}bh$ for h.

7. $V = \sqrt{2gh}$ for h.

8. $A = 4\pi r^2$ for r.

9. $I = \dfrac{E}{R}$ for R.

10. $V = \dfrac{1}{3}\pi r^2 h$ for h.

11. $S = \dfrac{a}{1 - r}$ for a.

12. $S = \dfrac{a}{1 - r}$ for r.

13. $M = \dfrac{wL^2}{8}$ for w.

14. $W = \sqrt{w_1 w_2}$ for w_1.

15. $R = r(A - 150)$ for r.

16. $R = r(A - 150)$ for A.

17. $E = \dfrac{I}{d^2}$ for d.

18. $T = 2\pi\sqrt{\dfrac{l}{g}}$ for l.

19. $I_n = I_x + Ad^2$ for A.

20. $I_n = I_x + Ad^2$ for d.

21. $\dfrac{1}{R} = \dfrac{1}{r_1} + \dfrac{1}{r_2}$ for R.

22. $\dfrac{1}{R} = \dfrac{1}{r_1} + \dfrac{1}{r_2}$ for r_1.

23. $\dfrac{n}{v} + \dfrac{1}{u} = \dfrac{n - 1}{r}$ for n.

24. $F = \dfrac{9}{5}C + 32$ for C.

25. $f_0 = f_s\sqrt{\dfrac{c + v}{c - v}}$ for v.

Chapter 11

The Right Triangle

Of all geometric figures, the right triangle is perhaps the most important. The subject of trigonometry, or "triangle measurement," began with observations about the properties of similar right triangles, which led to the creation of the trigonometric ratios, three of which are named sine, cosine, and tangent. These ratios have turned out to be useful in working with triangles other than right triangles and even in problems that have no connection to triangles at all.

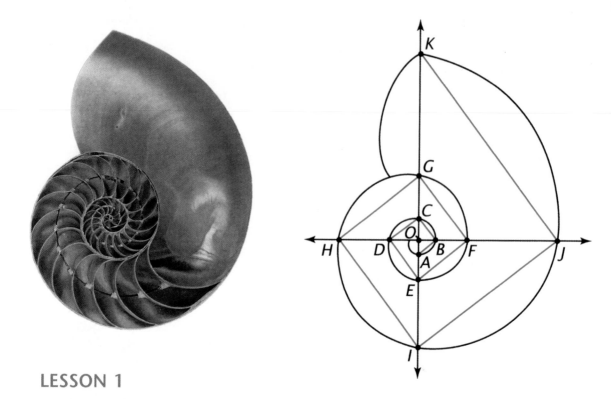

LESSON 1

Proportions in a Right Triangle

The chambered nautilus is a remarkable creature. Although the outside of its shell is attractively covered with brown stripes, it is the beautiful design inside for which the nautilus is famous. As it grows, the nautilus moves through a series of successively larger compartments that wind around a curve called a *spiral*. All the compartments are similar in shape and, as a result, their corresponding dimensions are proportional.

The photographs at the left and above are of a living nautilus and a shell that has been cut in half to reveal its internal design. In the drawing above, the beginning of the spiral is labeled point O. Two perpendicular lines have been drawn through point O and, as the spiral winds around this point, it intersects these lines in a series of points: A, B, C, and so on. If these points are connected in order by a series of line segments, AB, BC, CD, and so on, each segment is perpendicular to the next: AB ⊥ BC ⊥ CD, and so on.

For this reason, the consecutive pairs of segments are the legs of a series of progressively larger right triangles winding around point O. It is easy to prove that these triangles are similar and, as a result, that

$$\frac{OA}{OB} = \frac{OB}{OC} = \frac{OC}{OD} = \cdots$$

Each successive distance, OB, OC, OD, and so on, is the geometric mean between the distances before and after it. Each distance is the altitude to the hypotenuse of a right triangle, and the distances between which it is the geometric mean are the two segments of the hypotenuse. These relations are established by the proofs of the following theorem and the first of its corollaries.

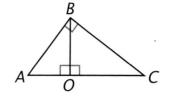

Theorem 49

The altitude to the hypotenuse of a right triangle forms two triangles similar to it and to each other.

> *Given:* Right △ABC with altitude BO to
> hypotenuse AC.
> *Prove:* △AOB ~ △BOC ~ △ABC.

The three triangles have been redrawn at the right to make the proof easier to follow.

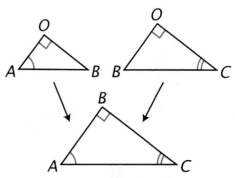

Proof
    △AOB and △ABC are right triangles with a common acute angle at A; so △AOB ~ △ABC. Also, △BOC and △ABC have a common acute angle at C; so △BOC ~ △ABC. Finally, △AOB ~ △BOC because, if two triangles are similar to a third triangle, they are similar to each other.

    Perhaps more important than this theorem are the proportions that follow from it. For example, from the fact that △AOB ~ △BOC, it follows that

$$\frac{AO}{BO} = \frac{BO}{CO}.$$

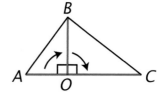

BO is the geometric mean between AO and OC

Corollary 1 to Theorem 49

The altitude to the hypotenuse of a right triangle is the geometric mean between the segments into which it divides the hypotenuse.

    From the correspondences △AOB ~ △ABC and △BOC ~ △ABC follow the proportions

$$\frac{AO}{AB} = \frac{AB}{AC} \quad \text{and} \quad \frac{OC}{BC} = \frac{BC}{AC}.$$

The first equation shows that leg AB of the triangle is the geometric mean between the hypotenuse AC and segment AO of the hypotenuse. The second equation shows that leg BC is the geometric mean between the hypotenuse AC and segment OC of the hypotenuse. We will refer to segments AO and OC as the *projections* of sides AB and BC on the hypotenuse, respectively.

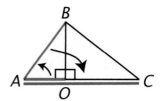

AB is the geometric mean between AO and AC

Corollary 2 to Theorem 49

Each leg of a right triangle is the geometric mean between the hypotenuse and its projection on the hypotenuse.

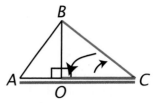

BC is the geometric mean between OC and AC

Exercises

Set I

Chameleon Tail. The tail of this West African chameleon is coiled up in a shape similar to that of a nautilus shell.

1. What is this type of curve called?

In the figure below, AC ⊥ BD and ∠ABC and ∠EFG are right angles.

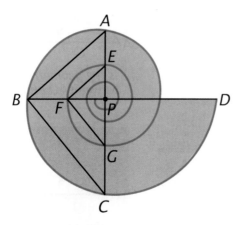

2. What is BP called with respect to △ABC?
3. Between which two segments is BP the geometric mean?
4. How do you know?
5. Which segment is the projection of EF on the hypotenuse of △EFG?
6. Between which two segments is EF the geometric mean?
7. How do you know?

Shadows. Imagine that right △ABC stands with side AB on the ground and that the sun is directly overhead.

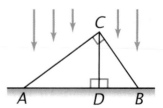

8. Which segment is the shadow of AC on the ground?
9. Which segment is the shadow of CB?
10. What are AC and CB called with respect to △ABC?
11. What are AD and DB called with respect to AC and CB?

Which line segment in the figure is the geometric mean between

12. AB and AD?
13. AD and DB?
14. AB and DB?

Find the Lengths. Solve for x in each of the following figures.

Example:

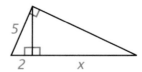

Solution:
The length of one leg is 5 and its projection on the hypotenuse is 2. Also, the length of the hypotenuse is $2 + x$. Each leg of the right triangle is the geometric mean between the hypotenuse and its projection on the hypotenuse; so

$$\frac{2 + x}{5} = \frac{5}{2}.$$

Solving for x, we have

$$2(2 + x) = 25$$
$$4 + 2x = 25$$
$$2x = 21$$
$$x = 10.5.$$

15.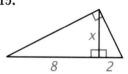

16.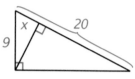

17.

18.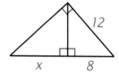

19.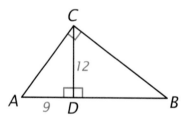

With and Without Pythagoras. In the figure below, CD is the altitude to the hypotenuse of right △ABC, AD = 9, and CD = 12.

20. Copy the figure and mark it as needed to do each of the following exercises.

21. Find DB.

22. Find AC without using the Pythagorean Theorem.

23. Find AC by using the Pythagorean Theorem.

24. Find BC without using the Pythagorean Theorem.

25. Find BC by using the Pythagorean Theorem.

26. Find $\dfrac{AD}{DB}$.

27. Find $\dfrac{AC}{CB}$.   **28.** Find $\left(\dfrac{AC}{CB}\right)^2$.

On the basis of your answers to exercises 26 through 28, tell whether each of the following statements is true or false.

29. $\dfrac{AD}{DB} = \dfrac{AC}{CB}$.

30. $\dfrac{AD}{DB} = \left(\dfrac{AC}{CB}\right)^2$.

Rectangle and Square. In the figures below, the sides of the rectangle and square are equal in length to the three labeled segments in the triangle.

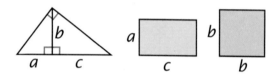

31. What can you conclude about the areas of the rectangle and square? Explain.

Set II

Strongest Beam. The figure below shows a rectangular cross section of a wooden beam cut from a circular log. For the beam to have the greatest stiffness, points E and F should trisect diameter AC.

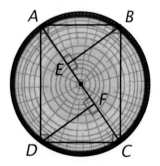

Suppose AC = 12 inches.

32. Copy the figure and mark it as needed to do each of the following exercises.

33. Find the *exact* length of BC.

34. Find the *exact* length of AB.

35. Find the *exact* value of the ratio $\dfrac{BC}{AB}$.

36. Find the area of rectangle ABCD to the nearest square inch.

37. Find the area of the circle to the nearest square inch.

Zigzag. In the figure below, segments AB, BC, CD, and so on, are alternately perpendicular to the sides of ∠O.

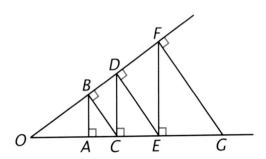

38. Copy and complete the following proportion for △OBC:

$$\frac{OA}{OB} = \frac{OB}{?}$$

39. State the theorem (corollary) that is the basis for your answer.

40. Copy and complete the following proportions for △OCD and △ODE:

$$\frac{OB}{OC} = \frac{OC}{?} \quad \text{and} \quad \frac{OC}{OD} = \frac{OD}{?}.$$

Given that OA = 1 and OB = *r*, use your proportions to find each of the following lengths in terms of *r*.

41. OC.

42. OD.

43. OE.

44. How long do you think OF and OG are in terms of *r*?

Suppose the figure were drawn so that OA = 1 inch and OB = 10 inches.

45. How long would OG be?

Plato's Proportions. The Greek philosopher Plato thought that, when God constructed the universe, He used four elements. Plato wrote:

> God placed water and air between fire and earth; and made them so far as possible proportional to each other, so that air is to water as water is to earth.*

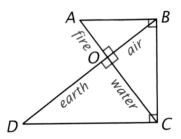

The figure above geometrically illustrates Plato's proportions.

46. Does it necessarily follow that $\dfrac{OA}{OB} = \dfrac{OC}{OD}$? Explain why or why not.

47. Does it necessarily follow that $\dfrac{AB}{BC} = \dfrac{BC}{CD}$? Explain why or why not.

SAT Problem. The figure below appeared in a problem on an SAT exam.

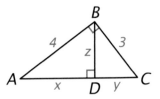

48. Find *x* + *y*.

49. Find *x*.

50. Find *y*.

51. Find *z*

Timaeus. Quoted in *Connections: The Geometric Bridge between Art and Science,* by Jay Kappraff (McGraw-Hill, 1990).

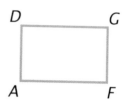

Quadrilateral AFGD is a golden rectangle. The ratio of its dimensions, $\dfrac{AF}{AD}$, is called the *golden ratio*.

The Golden Rectangle. The spiral of the chambered nautilus is closely related to a figure called the *golden rectangle* discovered by the Greeks in the fifth century B.C.

One way to construct a golden rectangle is suggested by the drawing in the cartoon above and described below.

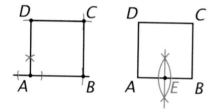

1. First, use the method illustrated by the figure at the left above to construct a square with sides 2 inches long. Label it ABCD as shown.

Bisect the base of the square and label the midpoint E as shown in the figure at the right above.

With E as center and EC as radius, draw an arc intersecting line AB in point F as shown in the figure at the left below.

Construct a line perpendicular to AB at F. Let G be the point in which it intersects line DC as shown in the figure at the right below.

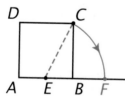
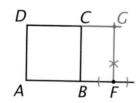

2. Find the exact value of the golden ratio by starting with AB = 2 and finding the exact values of the following lengths.

a) AD.

b) EB.

c) EC (use the Pythagorean Theorem).

d) EF.

e) AF.

f) Find $\dfrac{AF}{AD}$, the golden ratio.

3. Use your calculator to find the approximate value of the golden ratio to as many decimal places as you can.

4. Find the exact values of the following lengths.

a) GF.

b) BF.

c) Find $\dfrac{GF}{BF}$.

5. Use your calculator to find the approximate value of $\dfrac{GF}{BF}$ to as many decimal places as you can.

6. What does this result suggest about rectangle BFGC?

7. Use your calculator to find the approximate value of $\dfrac{BF}{GF}$.

8. What is surprising about the result?

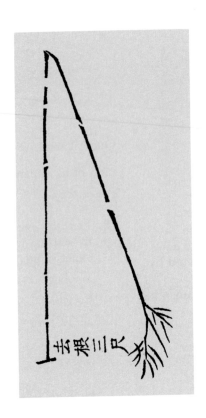

LESSON 2

The Pythagorean Theorem Revisited

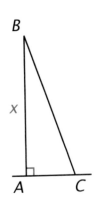

A very old problem in geometry is the puzzle of the Broken Bamboo. The earliest known book in which it appears is the *Chiu Chang Suan Shu* (Nine Chapters on the Mathematical Art), written in China at about the same time that Euclid was writing the *Elements.**

The problem as it appeared in a book published in 1261 is shown at the top of this page. It says:

A bamboo shoot is 10 ch'ih tall. It is broken and the top touches the ground 3 ch'ih from the root. What is the height of the break?

In the figure at the left, the problem is to find **AB**, given that

$$AB + BC = 10 \text{ and } AC = 3.$$

*Was Pythagoras Chinese? by Frank J. Swetz and T. I. Kao (Pennsylvania State University Press, 1977).

If we let AB = x, it follows that BC = $10 - x$. Applying the Pythagorean Theorem to right $\triangle ABC$, we have

$$AB^2 + AC^2 = BC^2, \text{ or}$$
$$x^2 + 3^2 = (10 - x)^2.$$

Solving for x, we get

$$x^2 + 9 = 100 - 20x + x^2$$
$$9 = 100 - 20x$$
$$20x = 91$$
$$x = \frac{91}{20} = 4.55.$$

The break is 4.55 ch'ih above the ground.

    The problem of the Broken Bamboo is famous as an early application of the Pythagorean Theorem. You have studied several proofs of the Pythagorean Theorem that are based on area. In this lesson, we will consider a proof based on similarity. It depends on the second corollary to Theorem 49–the fact that each leg of a right triangle is the geometric mean between the hypotenuse and its projection on the hypotenuse.

The Pythagorean Theorem

In a right triangle, the square of the hypotenuse is equal to the sum of the squares of the legs.

    Given: Right $\triangle ABC$ with legs of lengths a and b
          and hypotenuse of length c.
  Prove: $a^2 + b^2 = c^2$.

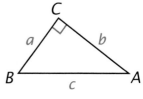

Proof
    Project the legs of $\triangle ABC$ on the hypotenuse by drawing CD $\perp$ BA; let the lengths of the two projections be called x and y.
    Because either leg of a right triangle is the geometric mean between the hypotenuse and its projection on the hypotenuse,

$$\frac{c}{a} = \frac{a}{x} \quad \text{and} \quad \frac{c}{b} = \frac{b}{y}.$$

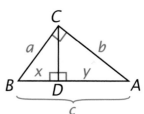

Multiplying, we get

$$a^2 = cx \quad \text{and} \quad b^2 = cy.$$

Adding these equations gives

$$a^2 + b^2 = cx + cy$$
$$= c(x + y).$$

Because $x + y = c$,

$$a^2 + b^2 = c \cdot c = c^2.$$

Exercises

Set I

Baseball Distances. A baseball diamond is a square with sides 90 feet long. A batter hits the ball and runs toward first base.

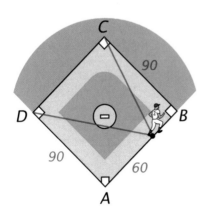

When he has run 60 feet, how far is he from

1. first base?

2. second base?

3. third base?

4. Draw a figure and mark it as needed to answer each of the following questions.

When the batter has run halfway from first base to second base, how far is he from

5. third base?

6. home plate?

Pole Problem. The following problem appears in the Cairo papyrus, written in Egypt in about 100 B.C.

A pole 10 cubits long stands along a wall. Its base is moved 6 cubits away from the wall.

7. Copy the figure at the right, in which AB represents the original position

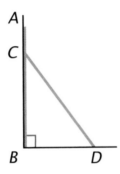

of the pole and CD represents its final position. Mark your figure as needed to answer each of the following questions.

8. How far up the wall does the pole reach in its final position?

9. How far did the top of the pole move down the wall?

Emergency Exits. If a rectangular room has two emergency exits, the distance between them must be at least one-half the length of a diagonal of the room's floor.*

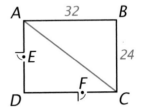

Suppose that the dimensions of the room pictured above are 32 feet by 24 feet and that one emergency exit is at E, midway between A and D, and the other exit is at F, between D and C.

10. Copy the figure and mark it as needed to answer each of the following questions.

11. What is the length of AC?

12. What is the minimum legal length of EF?

13. Would it be legal to place emergency exit F midway between D and C? Explain.

Suppose instead that emergency exit E is 6 feet from A, as shown in the scale drawing below.

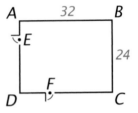

14. Copy the figure and mark it as needed to answer each of the following questions.

Uniform Building Code (International Conference of Building Officials, 1991).

15. How close to D can exit F be placed on wall DC?

16. How close to A could exit F be placed if it were on wall AB?

17. Could exit F be placed on wall BC? If so, where?

Pythagorean Triples. The set of numbers "3-4-5" is well known as the simplest *Pythagorean triple;* that is, a set of three integers that can be the lengths of the sides of a right triangle.

There are infinitely many Pythagorean triples; those in which no number is more than 50 are listed at the right below.

18. Show why the set "7-24-25" is a Pythagorean triple.

19. Can all three numbers in a Pythagorean triple be even? Explain.

20. Can all three numbers in a Pythagorean triple be odd? Explain.

Some of the Pythagorean triples in the list are related to one another.

21. How is the triple 14-48-50 related to the triple 7-24-25?

The figure below suggests why Pythagorean triples are related in the way that they are.

3-4-5
5-12-13
6-8-10
7-24-25
8-15-17
9-12-15
9-40-41
10-24-26
12-16-20
12-35-37
14-48-50
15-20-25
15-36-39
16-30-34
18-24-30
20-21-29
21-28-35
24-32-40
27-36-45
30-40-50

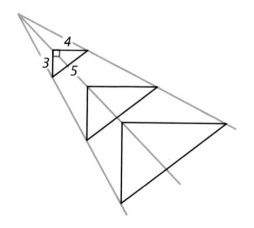

22. Under what transformation are the larger triangles images of the 3-4-5 right triangle?

23. What Pythagorean triples do they illustrate?

24. Name the other triples in the yellow list that also are part of this set.

25. Find two triples in the list that are related to 5-12-13.

Not Quite Right. The triangles below look like right triangles, but they actually are not.

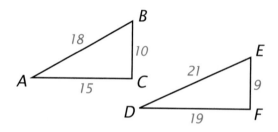

26. Use the lengths of their sides to show why each figure looks so much like a right triangle.

27. What kind of angles do you think ∠C and ∠F actually are? Explain your reasoning.

Distance Formula. The Distance Formula comes from the Pythagorean Theorem.

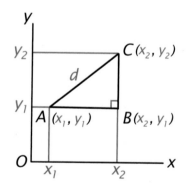

28. Which side of △ABC has length $x_2 - x_1$?

29. What is the length of side BC?

30. Why does it follow that
$d = \sqrt{(x_2 - x_1)^2 + (y_2 - y_1)^2}$?

Set II

TV Screens. Television tubes were originally round, which is why the length of a tube's diagonal (diameter) is used in giving the size of a television screen.

1946 RCA television set

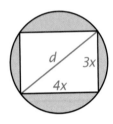

The screen is rectangular with an aspect ratio of 4 to 3.*

31. Representing the dimensions of the screen as $4x$ and $3x$ and the length of the diagonal as d, write an equation for d in terms of x.

32. Write an equation for x in terms of d.

The first television tubes were produced in 1938 and had a diameter (diagonal) of 14 inches.

33. What were the corresponding dimensions of the television screen?

The standard television set now has a diagonal of 27 inches.

34. Find its dimensions.

35. Find the ratio of the dimensions of the 27-inch screen to those of the 14-inch screen.

36. How many times as big is the area of the picture on a 27-inch screen compared with that of a 14-inch screen?

*Behind the Tube: A History of Broadcasting Technology and Business, by Andrew F. Inglis (Focal Press, 1990).

Grid Exercise. On graph paper, draw a pair of axes extending from -10 to 10 on the x-axis and from -5 to 15 on the y-axis.

37. Plot the following points: P(-1, 8), Y(1, 12), T(5, 10), H(3, 6), A(9, 3), G(6, -3), O(0, 0), R(-8, -1), and S(-9, 7). Draw the quadrilaterals PYTH, HAGO, and ORSP.

38. Use the Distance Formula to find the following lengths: OH, OP, and PH.

39. What can you conclude about △OHP? Explain.

40. What do you think is true about PYTH, HAGO, and ORSP?

41. If your answer to exercise 40 is true, what are the areas of PYTH, HAGO, and ORSP?

Rope Surveying. Following the *Sulvasutras* (Rules of the Rope), surveyors in ancient India used ropes to lay out perpendicular lines.† Starting with a west–east line, they placed three poles at W, P, and E as shown below.

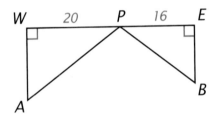

They then tied the ends of a rope 40 units long to W and P and the ends of a second rope 32 units long to P and E.

By holding each rope at a special knot tied in it and stretching the ropes tight, they formed two right triangles, △WAP and △PBE. Because the rope tied to W and P was 40 units long, WA + AP = 40.

42. If WA = x, what length does $40 - x$ represent?

43. Write an equation based on the Pythagorean Theorem for △WAP and solve it for x.

† *Geometry Civilized: History, Culture, and Technique*, by J. L. Heilbron (Clarendon Press, 1998).

Because the rope tied to P and E was 32 units long, PB + BE = 32.

44. If BE = y, how long is PB in terms of y?

45. Write an equation based on the Pythagorean Theorem for △PBE and solve it for y.

46. What theorem were the ancient Indians using when they concluded that ∠W and ∠E were right angles?

Oil Well. Here is a puzzle that can be solved in an unexpected way.*

An oil well being drilled in flat prairie country struck pay sand at a spot exactly 21,000 feet from one corner of a rectangular plot of farmland, 18,000 feet from the opposite corner, and 6,000 feet from a third corner. How far is the drilling spot from the fourth corner?

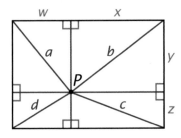

The figure above (not to scale) represents the rectangular plot, and point P represents the oil well. Notice that $a^2 = w^2 + y^2$.

47. Write similar equations for b^2, c^2, and d^2.

48. Write equations for $a^2 + c^2$ and $b^2 + d^2$.

49. What can you conclude from these equations?

50. Use your conclusion to solve the oil-well puzzle.

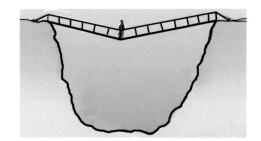

Suspension Bridge. The figure above shows someone walking across a suspension bridge made of ropes.

Suppose the bridge is 100 feet long and stretches to a length of 101 feet under your weight when you are halfway across.

51. Draw and label a figure to illustrate this description.

52. How far does the bridge sag in the middle?

Turning Radius. The figure below shows an overhead view of the wheels of a car as it turns a corner. R is the turning radius and B is the wheelbase.‡

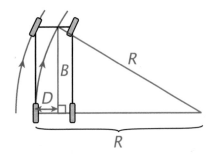

53. Find an expression in terms of R and B for D, the divergence beween the front and rear wheels.

54. If the wheelbase is 12 feet and the turning radius is 27 feet, find D.

55. Suppose the turning radius is doubled from 27 feet to 54 feet. What happens to D?

Martin Gardner's Sixth Book of Mathematical Games from Scientific American, by Martin Gardner (W. H. Freeman and Company, 1971).

---

‡ *Time-Saver Standards for Site Planning,* by Joseph De Chiara and Lee E. Koppelman (McGraw-Hill, 1984).

Rocket Car. According to the theory of relativity, the length of an object appears to get shorter as it moves at speeds near the speed of light.

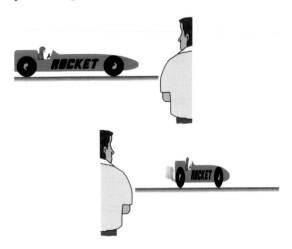

The Pythagorean Theorem is used in developing the formula for this change.

56. Show for the figure at the right why

$$\frac{A}{C} = \sqrt{1 - \left(\frac{B}{C}\right)^2}.$$

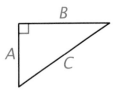

$\frac{A}{C}$ represents the ratio by which length shortens when $\frac{B}{C}$ is the ratio of the moving object's speed to the speed of light.

57. Use your calculator to find the ratio by which the length of a rocket car shortens when it is moving at 90% of the speed of light (in other words, when $\frac{B}{C} = 0.90$).

Set III

Fermat's Last Theorem. In 1637, French mathematician Pierre de Fermat wrote a note in the margin of a book that has since become one of the most famous theorems of mathematics. Now known as Fermat's Last Theorem, it says that, if *a*, *b*, *c*, and *n* are

FERMAT'S FIRST THEOREM

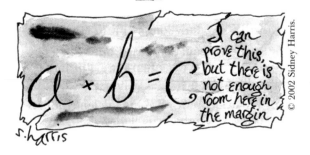

positive integers, the equation

$$a^n + b^n = c^n$$

has no solutions if *n* is larger than 2. Fermat wrote that he had discovered a proof of this hypothesis but that the margin of the page was too narrow to contain it. No one to this day has been able to figure out what Fermat's proof was. It was not, in fact, until 1995 that Andrew Wiles, a mathematician at Princeton University, succeeded in proving Fermat's Last Theorem.

1. How many solutions does the equation $a + b = c$ have if *a*, *b*, and *c* are integers?

2. How many solutions does the equation $a^2 + b^2 = c^2$ have? Explain.

3. How many solutions does the equation $a^3 + b^3 = c^3$ have if *a*, *b*, and *c* are positive integers?

An article in the March 7, 1938, issue of *Time* magazine reported that Samuel Krieger had discovered an equation that disproved the theorem.*

The equation was

$$1,324^n + 731^n = 1,961^n$$

in which *n* was an integer that Krieger refused to disclose. A reporter for the *New York Times* showed that Krieger had to be mistaken.

4. How did the reporter do it? (Hint: In what digits can each power in the equation end?)

---

*Wheels, Life, and Other Mathematical Amusements, by Martin Gardner (W. H. Freeman and Company, 1983).

Isosceles and 30°-60° Right Triangles

Archeologists digging in the land between the Tigris and Euphrates rivers in the late nineteenth century found thousands of clay tablets dating to 1700 B.C. Some of these tablets reveal what the ancient Babylonians knew about mathematics.* The one in the photograph above, for example, shows a square and its diagonals. The three wedge-shaped symbols at the upper left of the tablet represent the number 30. The symbols along the diagonal represent the number 1.41421 and the symbols below them represent the number 42.4263. These numbers are related because

$$30 \times 1.41421 = 42.4263.$$

Did the Babylonians mean by these numbers that, if 30 is the length of the side of a square, it can be multiplied by 1.41421 to get the length of a diagonal? Where did the number 1.41421 come from?

The figure at the right shows that a diagonal of a square is the hypotenuse of two isosceles right triangles. If each leg of one of these triangles is 30 units long, then from the Pythagorean Theorem we know that

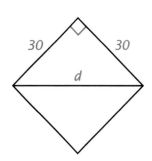

$$d^2 = 30^2 + 30^2 = 2 \cdot 30^2.$$

Solving for d gives

$$d = \sqrt{2 \cdot 30^2} = 30\sqrt{2}.$$

---

*Episodes from the Early History of Mathematics, by Asger Aaboe (Random House, 1964).

Your calculator gives $\sqrt{2} \approx 1.41421$ and $30\sqrt{2} \approx 42.4263$, which are the numbers on the tablet. The Babylonians evidently knew that the hypotenuse of an isosceles right triangle and hence the diagonal of a square can be found by multiplying a leg (side) by $\sqrt{2}$.

Theorem 50. The Isosceles Right Triangle Theorem

In an isosceles right triangle, the hypotenuse is $\sqrt{2}$ times the length of a leg.

Given: An isosceles right triangle with legs of length a and hypotenuse c.
Prove: $c = a\sqrt{2}$.

Proof

By the Pythagorean Theorem,

$$c^2 = a^2 + a^2 = 2a^2;$$

$$\text{so } c = \sqrt{2a^2} = \sqrt{2}a = a\sqrt{2}.$$

The Babylonian tablet shows how this result applies to the diagonal of a square.

Corollary to Theorem 50

Each diagonal of a square is $\sqrt{2}$ times the length of one side.

Because each acute angle of an isosceles right triangle has a measure of 45°, it is a "45°-45° right triangle." A diagonal of a square divides it into two 45°-45° right triangles. Another important triangle in geometry is the "30°-60° right triangle." An altitude of an equilateral triangle divides it into two 30°-60° right triangles.

Theorem 51. The 30°-60° Right Triangle Theorem

In a 30°-60° right triangle, the hypotenuse is twice the shorter leg and the longer leg is $\sqrt{3}$ times the shorter leg.

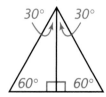

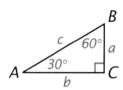

Given: $\triangle ABC$ is a 30°-60° right triangle.
Prove: $c = 2a$ and $b = a\sqrt{3}$.

Proof

Reflect point B through line AC as shown in the figure at the left, and label the reflection point D. Draw AD. $\triangle ADC \cong \triangle ABC$ (SAS); so $\angle D = \angle B = 60°$ and $\angle CAD = \angle CAB = 30°$.

From these equalities it follows that $\angle BAD = 60°$; so $\triangle ABD$ is both equiangular and equilateral. So $c = 2a$.

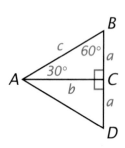

By the Pythagorean Theorem,

$$a^2 + b^2 = c^2.$$

Substituting, we get

$$a^2 + b^2 = (2a)^2,$$
$$a^2 + b^2 = 4a^2,$$
$$b^2 = 3a^2,$$
$$b = \sqrt{3}a = a\sqrt{3}.$$

The 30°-60° right triangle theorem can be used to express the altitude and area of an equilateral triangle in terms of one of its sides.

Corollary to Theorem 51

An altitude of an equilateral triangle having side s is $\dfrac{\sqrt{3}}{2}s$ and its

area is $\dfrac{\sqrt{3}}{4}s^2$.

Given: Equilateral $\triangle ABD$ with side s and altitude h.

Prove: $h = \dfrac{\sqrt{3}}{2}s$ and $\alpha\triangle ABD = \dfrac{\sqrt{3}}{4}s^2$.

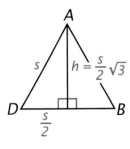

Proof
The altitude is the longer leg of each of the two 30°-60° right triangles into which it divides the equilateral triangle. Because the

shorter leg of each 30°-60° right triangle is $\dfrac{s}{2}$, the altitude is

$$\frac{s}{2}\sqrt{3} = \frac{\sqrt{3}}{2}s.$$

The area of the equilateral triangle is $\dfrac{1}{2}sh = \dfrac{1}{2}s\left(\dfrac{s}{2}\sqrt{3}\right) = \dfrac{s^2}{4}\sqrt{3} =$

$\dfrac{\sqrt{3}}{4}s^2$.

Exercises

Set I

Isosceles Right Triangles. The two isosceles right triangles below look similar.

1. Are the triangles similar? Explain.

2. Complete this proportion: $\dfrac{a}{?} = \dfrac{c}{?}$.

Use the proportion to express

3. c in terms of a.   4. a in terms of c.

5. State the theorem illustrated by the result obtained for exercise 3 as a complete sentence.

30°-60° Right Triangles. The two 30°-60° right triangles below appear to be similar.

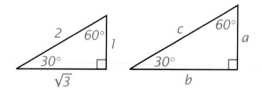

6. Are these triangles similar?

7. Complete the following ratios: $\frac{a}{?} = \frac{b}{?} = \frac{c}{?}$.

Use them to express

8. *b* in terms of *a*.

9. *c* in terms of *a*.

10. *a* in terms of *b*.

11. *c* in terms of *b*.

12. *a* in terms of *c*.

13. *b* in terms of *c*.

14. State the theorem illustrated by exercises 8 and 9 as a complete sentence.

Length Problems. Find *x* in each of the following figures.

15.

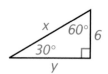

16.

Find *x* and *y* in each of the following figures.

17.

18.

19.

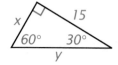

Find *x* in each of the following rectangles.

20.

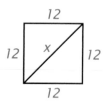

21.

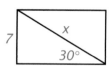

22.

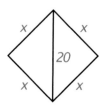

Equilateral Triangles. In the figure below, △AFG contains nine small equilateral triangles, whose sides are each 2 units long.

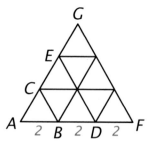

Use the formula for the area of an equilateral triangle in terms of its sides to write an *exact* expression for the area of

23. △ABC.

24. △ADE.

25. △AFG.

26. Use the figure to explain why your answers to exercises 23 through 25 are related as they are.

Line of Sight. At residential intersections, the legs of the "line of sight" triangle should be at least 90 feet long.*

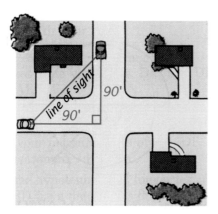

How long is the line of sight if
27. each leg is 90 feet long?
28. one leg is 90 feet and the other leg is 120 feet?
29. each leg is 120 feet long?

Cathedral Design. Michelangelo used the dimensions of an equilateral triangle in a plan for Saint Peter's Cathedral.†

30. How tall would the cathedral be if its base were 150 feet wide?
31. If a model of the cathedral were 20 inches tall, how wide would its base be?

Time-Saver Standards for Site Planning, by Joseph De Chiara and Lee E. Koppelman (McGraw-Hill, 1984).
†*Renaissance,* by John R. Hale (Time-Life Books, 1965).

Olympic Course. Part of the course for the sailing competition in the Olympics requires boats to sail around three buoys located at the corners of an isosceles right triangle.‡

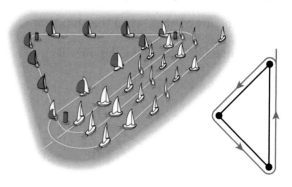

32. Given that the hypotenuse of the triangle is 3.25 nautical miles, about how long is each leg?
33. About how far does a boat sail in going around the triangle?

Set II

Not Quite Right. In a tenth-century popular French geometry book, the area of an equilateral triangle of side s was claimed to be $\frac{3}{7}s^2$.

34. Use this expression to find the area of an equilateral triangle whose sides are 7 units long.
35. What is the *correct* expression for the area of an equilateral triangle of side s?
36. Use the correct expression to find the area of the triangle pictured above to the nearest tenth.
37. Show that the two expressions would give the same answer if $\sqrt{3}$ were equal to $\frac{12}{7}$.

‡*Sports: The Complete Visual Reference,* by François Fortin (Firefly Books, 2000).

Navigator's Rule. The navigator of a ship sailing from A to B to C along line *l* observes a lighthouse at D. If the angles are as shown in the figure below, the navigator uses the "$\frac{7}{8}$ rule," which says that, when the ship is at C, its distance CD from the lighthouse is $\frac{7}{8}$ of the distance from A to B.*

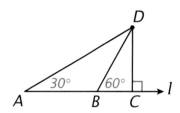

38. To what other distance in the figure is AB equal? Explain.

If AB = *x*, express

39. BC in terms of *x*.

40. CD in terms of *x*.

41. Use your answer to exercise 40 to explain where the name "$\frac{7}{8}$ rule" comes from.

Trigonometric Angles. Figures showing angles in coordinate systems are used in trigonometry.

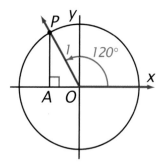

42. How large is each angle of △PAO in the figure above?

Given that OP = 1, find

43. OA and AP.

44. the coordinates of point P.

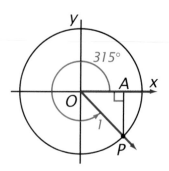

45. How large is each angle of △PAO in the figure above?

Given that OP = 1, find

46. OA and AP.

47. the coordinates of point P.

Construction Exercise. The figure below illustrates a construction that has interesting results.†

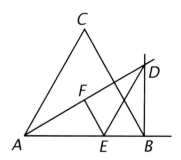

48. Construct equilateral △ABC with sides 3 inches long. Bisect ∠CAB and construct a line perpendicular to AB at B. Label the point in which the bisector and perpendicular line intersect D. Bisect ∠ADB and label the point in which the bisector and AB intersect E. Through E construct EF ⊥ AD.

---

*Dutton's Navigation and Piloting, by Elbert S. Maloney (Naval Institute Press, 1985).

†The Unexpected Hanging and Other Mathematical Diversions, by Martin Gardner (Simon & Schuster, 1969).

49. Name the 30°-60° right triangles that can be named by the letters in the figure.

If you have constructed the figure accurately, EB should be 1 inch long. Check this length with your ruler.

50. Find each of the following lengths *without* using your ruler: DE, DB, DF, EF, AE, AF.

Use your ruler to check your answers.

51. Are your measurements of DB, DF, and AF reasonable? Explain.

52. Do the hypotenuse and longer leg of △ABD have the lengths that you would predict from the length of DB? Explain.

Area Problem. The figure at the left below consists of 12 equilateral triangles and 12 isosceles right triangles.

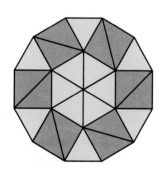

Given that the perimeter of the figure is 12 units long, find

53. the area of one of the isosceles right triangles.

54. the exact area of one of the equilateral triangles.

55. the exact area of the entire figure.

56. the area of the entire figure to the nearest tenth.

Moscow Challenge. This problem is from a geometry book published in Moscow.

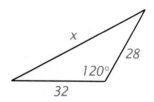

57. Find the length marked *x* in this triangle.

Set III

A Big Mistake. The illustrator of the newspaper article below telling how to cut down a tree made a big mistake.

1. What is it?

2. How do you think the article should be corrected? Explain.

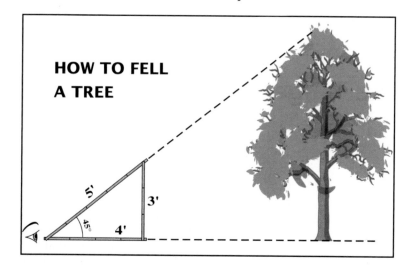

HOW TO FELL A TREE

Tree removal used to be a hard, hazardous job, one better left to tree removal companies. But along came the lightweight chain saw and now it's easy to cut a 30-foot-tall tree into neat fireplace-length logs in a few hours. There's just one problem. Felling the tree is still hazardous, although it need not be. If you have analyzed its fall correctly and have made the proper cuts, it will fall exactly where you plan. But if you haven't, no amount of guy wires or ropes can be trusted to guide its crash to the ground.

The first thing you have to do is find how much room it needs when it falls. You can do this by using the Boy Scout method of measuring heights. A triangle with sides of three, four and five feet is placed so that you sight along the five-foot side while you move the triangle to a point where the top of the tree comes into sight, as shown above. That's how far the tree will reach when it's felled.

LESSON 4

The Tangent Ratio

Mount Everest is the highest place on Earth. In Nepal, the mountain is known as "He whose head touches the sky." Named by the British for George Everest, its height was determined in 1852, a century before anyone had succeeded in climbing to its summit.

George Everest was the head of the Great Trigonometrical Survey of India, known as one of the biggest ventures in the history of science.* The survey was named after the branch of mathematics known as *trigonometry,* a word derived from two Greek words meaning "triangle" and "measurement." It was by measuring triangles that the height of Everest was discovered.

The idea is illustrated in the second figure on the facing page. In the figure (not to scale), point A represents the surveyor's position on the plains of India and point B represents the top of the mountain. To find side BC of the triangle from ∠A and side AC, the surveyors used the *tangent ratio.*

The Great Arc: The Dramatic Tale of How India Was Mapped and Everest Was Named, by John Keay (HarperCollins, 2000.)

Definition

The *tangent* of an acute angle of a right triangle is the ratio of the length of the opposite leg to the length of the adjacent leg.

In the figure at the right, the tangent of $\angle A$ is $\frac{a}{b}$ and the tangent of $\angle B$ is $\frac{b}{a}$. These relations are usually abbreviated as

$$\tan A = \frac{a}{b} \text{ and } \tan B = \frac{b}{a}.$$

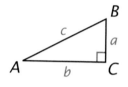

The tangent is one of the basic ratios of trigonometry. To use it, we need to know its values for various angles. The first table of tangents was constructed in the tenth century by the Arab scholar Abul-Wefa. When the height of Everest was calculated, a table of tangents was used. Now angles and their tangents are easily found by using the tangent key of a calculator.

Usually, to find the tangent of an angle, you enter the measure of the angle and then press the "tan" key. For example, to find tan 50°, enter 50 and then press "tan" to get "1.1917536."*

To find an angle when you know its tangent, you enter the value of the tangent first, and then press the "inverse" (or "second function") key, followed by the "tan" key. For example, to find the angle whose tangent is 0.123, enter .123, then "inverse," and then "tan" to get "7.0121601." The angle whose tangent is 0.123 is approximately 7°.

To find the height of Everest after the distance AC and the angle A have been worked out, we can write

$$\tan 3° = \frac{h}{104.8}.$$

Multiplying by 104.8 gives

$$h = 104.8 \tan 3°.$$

Using a calculator, we find that

$$h \approx 104.8(0.0524077)$$
$$\approx 5.4923353 \text{ miles.}$$

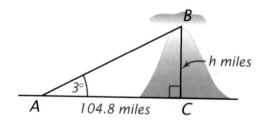

Because 1 mile = 5,280 feet,

$$h \approx 5.4923353(5,280)$$
$$\approx 29,000 \text{ feet.}$$

These measurements indicate that Mount Everest is about 29,000 feet high.

---

*Be sure that your calculator is set for angles in *degrees*.

Exercises

Set I

Tangent Practice. Express each of the following ratios in terms of the lowercase (small) letters in the figures below.

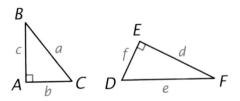

Example: tan B.

Answer: $\dfrac{b}{c}$.

1. tan C.
2. tan D.
3. tan F.

Use your calculator to find each of the following tangents to three decimal places.

Example: tan 15°.
Answer: 0.268.

4. tan 24°.
5. tan 1°.
6. tan 89°.

Given the following tangents, use your calculator to find the measure of the angle to three decimal places.

Example: tan A = 0.25.
Answer: ∠A = 14.036°.

7. tan B = 0.1.
8. tan C = 24.
9. tan D = 1,000.

Isosceles Right Triangle.
△ABC is a right triangle.
Suppose that a = b.

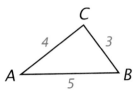

10. How large is ∠A?

11. Find the value of tan A without using your calculator.

12. Use your calculator to check your answer.

Suppose that a > b.

13. How does ∠A compare with 45°?

14. What can you conclude about tan A?

15. How does ∠B compare with 45°?

16. What can you conclude about tan B?

30°-60° Right Triangle.
△ABC is a 30°-60° right triangle.

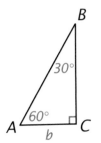

17. Use the 30°-60° Right Triangle Theorem to find the lengths of AB and BC in terms of b.

18. Find the *exact* value of tan 60° without using your calculator.

19. Check your answer with your calculator.

20. Find the *exact* value of tan 30° without using your calculator.

21. Use your calculator to check your answer.

3-4-5 Triangle. △ABC is a "3-4-5" triangle.

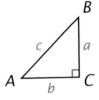

22. What kind of triangle is it? Explain.

Find each of the following measures.

23. tan A.

24. tan B.

25. ∠A to the nearest degree.

26. ∠B to the nearest degree.

In what ways are

27. ∠A and ∠B related?

28. tan A and tan B related?

Finding Lengths. Use the tangent ratio to find the length labeled *x* in each of the following figures. Express each length to the nearest tenth.

Example:

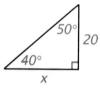

Solution:

$$\tan 50° = \frac{x}{20}$$
$$x = 20 \tan 50°$$
$$x \approx 23.8.$$

29.

6

30.

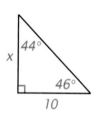

10

31.

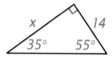

Finding Angles. Use the tangent ratio to solve for the angle marked *x* in each of the following figures. Express each angle to the nearest degree.

Example:

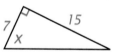

Solution:

$$\tan x = \frac{15}{7}.$$
$$x \approx 65°.$$

32.   **33.**

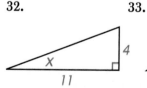

34.

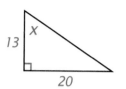

Set II

Fly Ball. The figures below are from the book *Sport Science.**

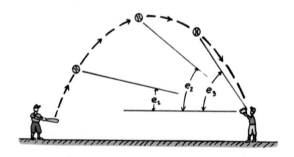

The angle of elevation increases as the fly ball approaches the fielder —

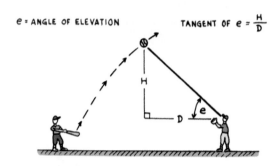

Find the angle of elevation to the nearest degree when

35. H = 80 feet and D = 50 feet.

36. H = 70 feet and D = 30 feet.

37. H = 60 feet and D = 20 feet.

38. What happens to the angle of elevation as the fly ball approaches the fielder?

_____

Sport Science: Physical Laws and Optimum Performance, by Peter J. Brancazio (Simon & Schuster, 1984).

Lighthouse. One of the seven wonders of the ancient world was the lighthouse at Alexandria. Pictured on this ancient coin, it was built at the time of Euclid and stood for more than 1,500 years until destroyed by an earthquake.*

Use the measures of the following angles at point P, 300 feet from point A on its base, to find the following distances to the nearest foot.

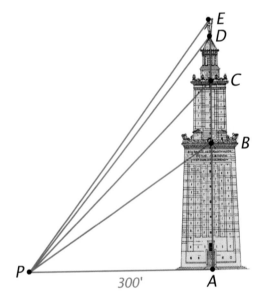

39. Find AB, given that ∠BPA = 33.3°.

40. Find AC, given that ∠CPA = 44.5°.

41. Find AD, given that ∠DPA = 51.0°.

42. Find AE, given that ∠EPA = 52.6°.

43. How tall was the statue (DE) at the top of the lighthouse?

Science Awakening, by B. L. van der Waerden (Oxford University Press, 1961).

Binoculars. The "field width" of a pair of binoculars is sometimes given as a ratio of distances such as "130 meters at 1,000 meters" and sometimes as the measure of an angle in degrees.†

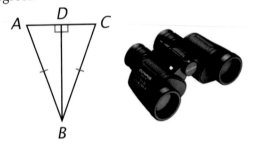

In the figure above (not to scale), point B represents the position of the binoculars, BA = BC, and BD ⊥ AC. Given that AC = 130 meters and BD = 1,000 meters, find

44. $\dfrac{AC}{BD}$.

45. AD.

46. ∠ABD to the nearest 0.1 degree.

47. ∠ABC to the nearest 0.1 degree.

Grid Triangle. The figure below is drawn on a grid of six squares, each having sides of 1 unit.‡

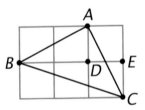

48. Find ∠ABD to six decimal places.

49. Find ∠EBC to six decimal places.

50. Find ∠ABC.

51. Find the exact lengths of AB, BC, and AC.

52. What can you conclude about △ABC? Explain.

---

† *Sizes: The Illustrated Encyclopedia,* by John Lord (Harper Perennial, 1995).
‡ *Proofs Without Words: Excursions in Visual Thinking,* by Roger B. Nelsen (Mathematical Association of America, 1993).

Diamond Cut. The cut that produces the brightest diamond is shown in the figure below, which consists of an isosceles trapezoid, a rectangle, and an isosceles triangle.*

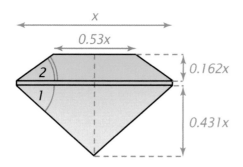

Given the lengths shown, find each of the following angles to the nearest tenth of a degree.

53. The "pavilion" angle, $\angle 1$.

54. The "bezel" angle, $\angle 2$.

Space-Flight Errors. Because of the great distances in space, small navigational errors can have serious consequences.

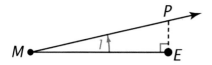

In the figure above (not to scale), ME represents the intended path of a space flight from the moon back to Earth, and ray MP represents the path resulting from an error of 1 degree; ME ≈ 239,000 miles.

55. Find PE, the distance by which path MP misses Earth.

Suppose that, instead of the moon, M represents Mars, which means that ME ≈ 49,000,000 miles, and that $\angle M = 1$ *minute*, a 60th of a degree, rather than 1 degree.

56. Find the distance PE for this situation.

Sizes: The Illustrated Encyclopedia, by John Lord (Harper Perennial, 1995).

Exam Problem. This problem is from a national exam that was given to German students at the end of the 10th grade.[†]

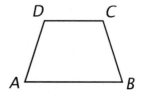

ABCD is an isosceles trapezoid in which AB = 10 and CD = 6.

57. Copy the figure and mark it as needed to explain why $\alpha ABCD = 16 \tan A$.

58. Find the value of A for which $\alpha ABCD = 40$.

Set III

What Time Is It? Suppose that the shadow cast by each camel in this caravan is three times as long as the camel's height.[‡]

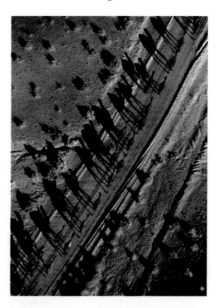

If the sun rose at 6:00 A.M. and will be directly overhead at noon, what time was the picture taken? Explain your reasoning.

[†]The 1994 Realschule Exam.
[‡]*Below from Above,* by George Gerster (Abbeville Press, 1986).

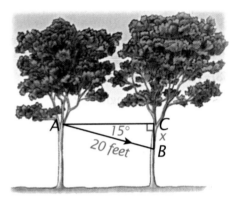

LESSON 5

The Sine and Cosine Ratios

Flying squirrels have flaps of skin between their front and back legs that they can use to glide through the air. One of these squirrels climbs to the top of a tree, jumps off and glides to a lower point on a nearby tree, climbs to the top of it, glides to another tree, and so on.*

Observations of flying squirrels show that they usually glide at an angle of 15° with the horizontal. How far does one of them fall during a flight of 20 feet?

Solving this problem is equivalent to knowing the measure of ∠A in right △ABC in the figure at the right above and trying to find the length of the opposite leg, given the length of the hypotenuse. To do so, we need another trigonometric ratio, called the *sine* ratio.

---

*Exploring Biomechanics: Animals in Motion, by R. McNeill Alexander (Scientific American Library, 1992).

Definition

The *sine* of an acute angle of a right triangle is the ratio of the length of the opposite leg to the length of the hypotenuse.

In the figure at the right, the sine of $\angle A$ is $\dfrac{a}{c}$ and the sine of $\angle B$ is $\dfrac{b}{c}$. These relations are abbreviated as

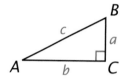

$$\sin A = \frac{a}{c} \text{ and } \sin B = \frac{b}{c}.$$

The sines of angles of different measures, like their tangents, can be found by using the sine key of a scientific calculator. To find the distance that a flying squirrel falls in gliding 20 feet at a 15° angle with the horizontal, we can write

$$\sin 15° = \frac{x}{20}.$$

Multiplying by 20, we get

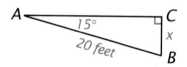

$$x = 20 \sin 15°.$$

Using a calculator, we get

$$x \approx 20(0.258819)$$
$$\approx 5.1763809 \text{ feet.}$$

A third useful trigonometric ratio is the *cosine*. It relates, for a given acute angle of a right triangle, the lengths of the adjacent leg and the hypotenuse.

Definition

The *cosine* of an acute angle of a right triangle is the ratio of the length of the adjacent leg to the length of the hypotenuse.

In the figure at the right, the cosine of $\angle A$ is $\dfrac{b}{c}$ and the cosine of $\angle B$ is $\dfrac{a}{c}$. These relations are abbreviated as

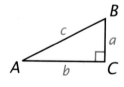

$$\cos A = \frac{b}{c} \text{ and } \cos B = \frac{a}{c}.$$

To find an angle when you know its sine or cosine, you enter the value of the sine or cosine first and then press the "inverse" (or "second function") key, followed by the "sin" or "cos" key. For example, to find the angle whose cosine is 0.747, enter .747, then "inverse," and then "cos" to get "41.668827." The angle whose cosine is 0.747 is approximately 41.7°.

Exercises

Set I

Sine and Cosine Practice. Express each of the following ratios in terms of the lowercase letters in the figure below.

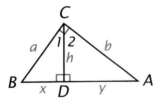

Example: sin A in two ways.

Answer: $\dfrac{h}{b}$ or $\dfrac{a}{x+y}$.

1. sin B in two ways.
2. tan A in two ways.
3. cos A in two ways.
4. cos B in two ways.
5. sin 1.
6. cos 2.

Use your calculator to find each of the following ratios to three decimal places.

Example: cos 5°.
Answer: 0.996.

7. sin 85°.
8. sin 46°.
9. cos 44°.

Given the following ratios, use your calculator to find the measure of each angle to three decimal places.

Example: sin A = 0.123.
Answer: ∠A = 7.065°.

10. cos B = 0.123.
11. sin C = 0.70711.
12. cos D = 0.70711.

Pythagorean Triangle. △ABC is a "5-12-13" triangle.

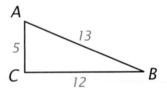

13. What kind of triangle is it? Explain.
14. Find sin A as a simple fraction.
15. Find ∠A to the nearest degree.
16. Find cos B as a simple fraction.
17. Find ∠B to the nearest degree.
18. In what ways are ∠A and ∠B related?
19. What relation does sin A have to cos B?
20. Find cos A as a simple fraction.
21. Find sin B as a simple fraction.
22. What relation does cos A have to sin B?

Finding Lengths and Angles. Solve for *x* in each of the following figures. Express each length to the nearest tenth and each angle to the nearest degree.

Example:

Solution:

$$\cos 55° = \frac{24}{x}$$

$$x \cos 55° = 24$$

$$x = \frac{24}{\cos 55°}$$

$$x \approx 41.8.$$

23.

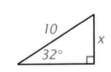

24.

25.

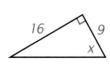

26.

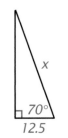

27.

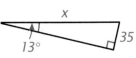

28.

Sines from a Circle. Bhaskara, a seventh-century Indian mathematician, calculated the sines of some angles by first dividing a quarter of a circle into six equal parts.*

In the figure at the bottom of the page, the circle has been drawn so that it has a radius of 10 cm.

29. Measure each of the following lengths to the nearest 0.1 cm: BH, CI, DJ, EK, and FL.

30. Use the lengths to estimate the values of sin 15°, sin 30°, sin 45°, sin 60°, and sin 75°. (For example, sin 15° ≈ $\frac{2.6}{10}$ = 0.26.)

31. Use a calculator to check your answers to exercise 30. (For example, sin 15° ≈ 0.258819 ≈ 0.26.)

32. What happens to the sine of an acute angle as the angle gets larger?

What kind of number do you think is the sine of an angle whose measure is very close to

33. 0°?

34. 90°?

35. Check your guesses by using your calculator to find sin 0° and sin 90°.

Geometry and Algebra in Ancient Civilizations, by B. L. van der Waerden (Springer, 1983).

Set II

Kite Flying. How high a kite will fly depends on both the length of its string (line) when the line is taut and on the size of its angle of elevation. In kite-flying competitions, performance is often judged by this angle.*

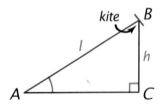

In the figure above,

36. $\sin A = \dfrac{h}{l}$. Why?

37. $h = l \sin A$. Why?

An expert on kite flying wrote:

Just like most kiters I'm obsessed with flying kites at as high an angle as possible. . . . At a line angle of 30°, the kite is half as high as it's ever going to get.†

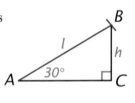

38. Use the 30°-60° Right Triangle Theorem to explain why what the expert wrote is true for a given length of line.

39. Use the sine of 30° to explain why it is true.

On August 12, 2000, the kite shown in the photograph below was flown to a record altitude.

40. Given that its angle of elevation was 42° when the line was 21,600 feet long, how high above the ground was it?

Force Components. This is a sample question from an exam for architects.‡

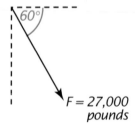

What are the horizontal and vertical components of the force shown above?

Answering the question is equivalent to finding the legs of right △ABC in the figure at the right, given that ∠CAB = 60° and AB = 27,000.

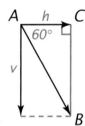

41. Use the 30°-60° Right Triangle Theorem to find h and v.

42. Check your answers by using the sine and cosine ratios to find h and v.

Flight Path. In 1992, a plane crashed into a mountain in France because the pilot apparently punched in a 3,300-feet-per-minute descent mode into the flight computer when he wanted a 3.3-degree flight path.§

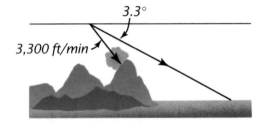

*****Kites: The Science and the Wonder,** by Toshio Ito and Hirotsugu Komura (Japan Publications, 1983).
†Richard P. Synergy, in *Kiting to Record Altitudes* (Fly Right Publications, 1994).

‡*Architectural Exam Review,* vol. 1, by David Kent Ballast (Professional Publications, 1992).
§*Invention by Design,* by Henry Petroski (Harvard University Press, 1996).

In the figure below (not to scale), AB represents the correct flight path for 1 minute of descent time.

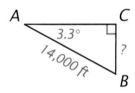

43. Find CB if AB = 14,000 feet.

In the figure at the right (not to scale), AB represents the wrong flight path for 1 minute of descent time.

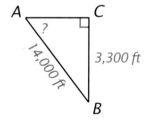

44. Find ∠A if AB = 14,000 feet and CB = 3,300 feet.

Leaning Tower. Ever since it was built, the Leaning Tower of Pisa has been leaning more and more.

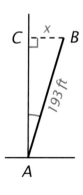

In the figure at the right above, AB represents the tower and CB represents the distance that the top leans over the base.

45. In 1400, the tower leaned 3° to one side. How long was CB at that time?

46. In 1500, the distance CB had increased to 13.5 feet. At what angle did the tower lean then?

47. Now the tower leans about 5.5°. How long is CB now?

Fiber Optics. In fiber optics, a light is reflected back and forth along a fiber.

The figure below represents a section of fiber in which $l_1 \parallel l_2$. As the light is reflected, ∠1 = ∠2, ∠3 = ∠4, ∠5 = ∠6, and so on.*

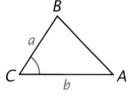

48. Why is ∠2 = ∠3, ∠4 = ∠5, ∠6 = ∠7, and so on?

49. Why are all the right triangles congruent?

50. Why are all of the segments of the light path equal?

51. In terms of *a*, how far along the fiber does the light travel in going from P to Q?

52. In terms of *d*, how far does the light travel in going from P to Q?

53. Why is the ratio of these two distances equal to the cosine of one of the numbered angles?

SAS Area. It is possible to figure out the area of a triangle if two sides and the included angle are known.

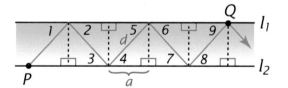

54. Copy the figure above, draw the altitude from B to CA, and label it *h*.

55. Show that $a \triangle ABC = \frac{1}{2}ab \sin C$.

---

*Optics, by Miles V. Klein and Thomas E. Furtak (Wiley, 1986).

Dominoes. One of the stunts listed in the *Guinness Book of World Records* is "toppling dominoes."

The figure below shows the first three dominoes of an evenly spaced row of dominoes standing on end. A second position of the first domino is shown as it hits the second one.*

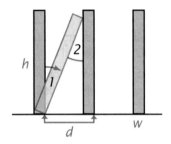

Angle 1 is the angle through which each domino turns before striking the next one.

56. Why is ∠1 = ∠2?

The height and thickness of each domino are *h* and *w*, respectively, and the spacing between each pair of dominoes is *d.*

57. Write an expression for sin ∠2.

58. Find the measure of ∠1 if $d - w = \frac{1}{2}h$.

59. Find the measure of ∠1 if $d - w = h$.

60. What might happen if $d - w = h$?

Set III

Star Distance. The distance to Proxima Centauri, the closest star beyond the sun, was determined by using the sine ratio and the diagram below.[†]

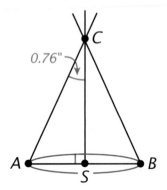

Point S represents the sun, A and B represent Earth at opposite positions in its orbit around the sun, and C represents Proxima Centauri. In right △ACS, ∠ACS was determined to have a measure of 0.76 *second* (″) and the distance from Earth to the sun, AS, was already known to be about 93,000,000 miles.

1. Find the distance, AC, from Earth to Proxima Centauri in miles.

One light-year, the distance that light travels in 1 year, is about 5,880,000,000,000 miles.

2. How many light-years is Proxima Centauri from Earth?

Towing Icebergs, Falling Dominoes, and Other Adventures in Applied Mathematics, by Robert B. Banks (Princeton University Press, 1998).

[†]*Stars,* by James B. Kaler (Scientific American Library, 1992).

Slope

The steepest streets in the United States are in San Francisco. Steepness is measured with respect to the horizontal. The steepness of a street can be measured by its *slope.*

To find the slope of a line, we choose two points on it. As we go from the left point to the right point, we move a horizontal distance, called the *run*, and a vertical distance, called the *rise*. The *slope* of the line is found by dividing the rise by the run:

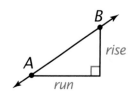

$$\text{slope} = \frac{\text{rise}}{\text{run}}.$$

Some steep streets in San Francisco *rise* 3 feet for every 10 feet that they *run* on the level; their slope is $\dfrac{\text{rise}}{\text{run}} = \dfrac{3}{10} = 0.3$.

Another way to measure the steepness of a line is to give its *angle of inclination*, the angle that it forms with the horizontal. What is the angle of inclination of a line whose slope is $\dfrac{3}{10}$? The figure at the right shows that the angle of inclination is connected to the line's slope through the tangent ratio:

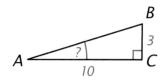

$$\tan A = \frac{3}{10}.$$

A calculator shows that $\angle A \approx 17°$; so a street with a slope of 0.3 has an angle of inclination of about 17°.

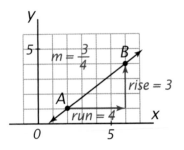

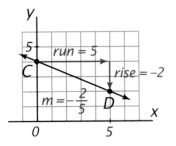

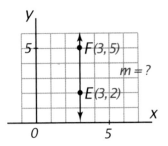

The slope of a line is easy to see in a coordinate system. In the figures at the left, the slope of line AB is $\frac{3}{4}$ and the slope of line CD is $-\frac{2}{5}$. It is customary to represent slope by the letter m.

Because two points determine a line, their coordinates can be used to find its slope. For example, in the first figure at the left, the coordinates of A and B are $(2, 1)$ and $(6, 4)$. The rise is $4 - 1 = 3$, the run is $6 - 2 = 4$, and the slope is

$$\frac{4 - 1}{6 - 2} = \frac{3}{4}.$$

In the second figure, the coordinates of C and D are $(0, 4)$ and $(5, 2)$. The rise is $2 - 4 = -2$, the run is $5 - 0 = 5$, and the slope is

$$\frac{2 - 4}{5 - 0} = -\frac{2}{5}.$$

There is one type of line, however, for which this method will not work. To see why, look at the third figure at the left. The coordinates of E and F are $(3, 2)$ and $(3, 5)$. The rise is $5 - 2 = 3$, the run is $3 - 3 = 0$, and the slope is

$$\frac{5 - 2}{3 - 3} = \frac{3}{0} = ?$$

A calculator will indicate "error" if you try to divide by zero, and so, like division by zero, *the slope of a vertical line is undefined.*

For other lines, the slope is defined in the following way.

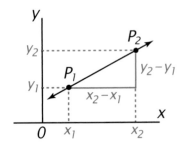

Definition

The *slope*, m, of a nonvertical line that contains points $P_1(x_1, y_1)$ and $P_2(x_2, y_2)$ is

$$m = \frac{\text{rise}}{\text{run}} = \frac{y_2 - y_1}{x_2 - x_1}.$$

This definition tells how to find the slope of a line from the coordinates of two points on it. The choice of points doesn't matter; every pair of points on a line determines the same slope.

Lines that are parallel or perpendicular have slopes that are related in very simple ways. Consider the figure at the right, in which ABCD is a rectangle. Here AB ∥ DC and the slopes of AB and DC are both $\frac{2}{3}$. Similarly, AD ∥ BC and both of these lines have slope $-\frac{3}{2}$. The sides in each pair of consecutive sides are perpendicular, and their slopes, $\frac{2}{3}$ and $-\frac{3}{2}$, are the *opposites* of the *reciprocals* of each other. Because $\left(\frac{2}{3}\right)\left(-\frac{3}{2}\right) = -1$, another way to put it is to say that the product of the slopes is -1.

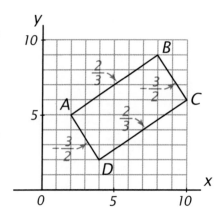

These observations suggest the following theorems, which are explored further in the exercises.

Theorem 52
Two nonvertical lines are parallel iff their slopes are equal.

Theorem 53
Two nonvertical lines are perpendicular iff the product of their slopes is -1.

Exercises

Set I

Slope Practice. All of the lines named with letters in the graph below go through the origin.

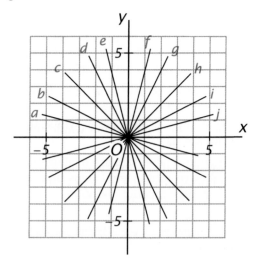

1. Which line has a slope of 1?

2. Which line has a slope of -1?

3. Which line has a slope of 0?

4. Which line has a slope that is undefined?

5. Which line appears to be perpendicular to line *j*?

6. What are the slopes of line *j* and that line?

7. Which line appears to be perpendicular to line *b*?

8. What are the slopes of it and line *b*?

9. State the theorem illustrated by your answers to exercises 5 through 8.

10. Can you find any lines named with letters in the figure that have the same slope? Explain.

Between points A and B on the "water table" line, what is the

13. rise?

14. run?

15. slope?

16. angle of inclination, $\angle 1$?

Stair Design. Vitruvius, a Roman architect of the first century B.C., wrote about the design of stairs. He said that the rise should be between 9 and 10 inches and the tread (run) should be between 18 and 24 inches.[†]

Snow Avalanches. Most snow avalanches start on slopes inclined at between 30° and 45°.

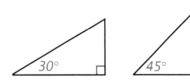

11. Use your calculator to show that snow inclined at an angle of 30° has a slope of about 0.58.

12. What is the slope of snow inclined at an angle of 45°?

Hydraulic Gradient. The figure below from a geology book illustrates the "hydraulic gradient" of a hill.[*]

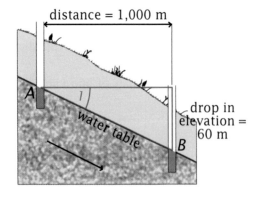

17. Draw and label a figure of stairs rising to the right showing the steepest steps that follow his recommendations.

18. What would be the slope of a staircase consisting of these steps?

19. What angle of inclination would the staircase have?

20. Draw and label a figure to illustrate the shallowest (least-steep) steps that follow Vitruvius's recommendation.

---

[*]*Environmental Geology,* by Dorothy J. Merritts, Andrew de Wet, and Kirsten Menking (W. H. Freeman and Company, 1998).

[†]*Steps and Stairways,* by Cleo Baldon and Ib Melchior (Rizzoli, 1989).

21. What would be the slope of a staircase consisting of these steps?

22. What angle of inclination would the staircase have?

Quadrilateral Problem. Find the slopes of the lines through the following pairs of points.

Example: A(−8, −5) and B(−1, 4).

Solution: $m = \dfrac{4 - -5}{-1 - -8} = \dfrac{4 + 5}{-1 + 8} = \dfrac{9}{7}.$

23. B(−1, 4) and C(10, 7).
24. C(10, 7) and D(3, −2).
25. D(3, −2) and A(−8, −5).
26. A(−8, −5) and C(10, 7).
27. B(−1, 4) and D(3, −2).

Find the distances between the following pairs of points.

Example: A(−8, −5) and B(−1, 4).

Solution: $\text{AB} = \sqrt{(-1 - -8)^2 + (4 - -5)^2}$

$\qquad\qquad = \sqrt{7^2 + 9^2} = \sqrt{130}.$

28. B(−1, 4) and C(10, 7).
29. C(10, 7) and D(3, −2).
30. D(3, −2) and A(−8, −5).

31. On graph paper, draw a pair of axes extending 10 units in each direction from the origin. Plot the four points of the examples and exercises 23 through 30; draw quadrilateral ABCD and its diagonals. Use your drawing to check your answers.

32. What kind of quadrilateral is ABCD? Explain.

33. What relation does line AC have to line BD? How do you know?

34. How are the slopes of the opposite sides of ABCD related to each other?

35. How are the slopes of the diagonals of ABCD related to each other?

Set II

Slope and x-Intercept. Sailplanes can glide on paths with slope $m = -\dfrac{1}{55}.$*

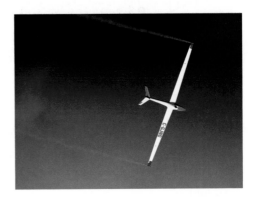

Suppose a sailplane is 300 meters above the ground as it passes overhead.

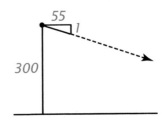

36. After the plane has glided 550 meters horizontally, what are its run and rise?

37. How high is the plane after gliding this distance?

Suppose instead that, after crossing overhead, the plane glides *x* meters horizontally.

38. What are its run and rise in terms of *x*?

39. After gliding *x* meters, how high is the plane in terms of *x*?

40. How far can the sailplane glide horizontally before it hits the ground?

41. Can it reach an airport 15 kilometers away?

On Size and Life, by Thomas A. McMahon and John Tyler Bonner (Scientific American Library, 1983).

Point–Slope Equation of a Line. If line l passes through point $P_1(x_1, y_1)$ and has slope m, we can find the height of every point $P(x, y)$ on l by using run and rise.

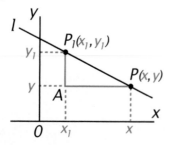

42. Express the run and rise of l from P_1 to P in terms of coordinates.

43. Solve $m = \dfrac{y - y_1}{x - x_1}$ for y in terms of m, x, x_1, and y_1.

For the sailplane described in exercises 36 through 41, P_1 has coordinates $(0, 300)$ and $m = -\dfrac{1}{55}$.

44. Write the point–slope equation for the line of the path of the sailplane.

45. Does your answer agree with your answer to exercise 39?

46. Which of the following points are on the path of the sailplane? $(5,500, 200)$, $(2,200, 250)$, $(1,100, 280)$.

100-Meter Dash. The slope of a line is the same at every point, but the slope of a curve is not. The curve below shows the speed of an athlete running the 100-meter dash with respect to time.*

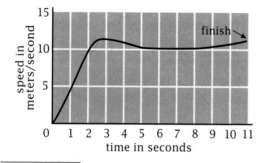

*Liberal Arts Physics, by John M. Bailey (W. H. Freeman and Company, 1974).

The slope of the curve is positive from 8 seconds to the finish.

47. Where else does it appear to be positive?

48. Over what interval does it appear to be zero?

49. Where does it appear to be negative?

What is happening to the runner's speed when the slope of the curve is

50. negative?

51. zero?

Theorem 52. Complete the following proof of part of Theorem 52 by giving the reasons.

If two nonvertical lines are parallel, their slopes are equal.

In the figure below, $l_1 \parallel l_2$ and $\triangle ABC$ and $\triangle DEF$ have been drawn so that AC and DF are perpendicular to the x-axis.

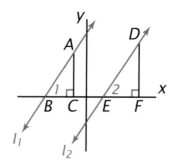

52. What is the slope of l_1?

53. What is the slope of l_2?

54. Why is $\angle 1 = \angle 2$?

55. Why is $\triangle ABC \sim \triangle DEF$?

56. Why is $\dfrac{AC}{DF} = \dfrac{BC}{EF}$?

57. Why is $AC \times EF = BC \times DF$?

58. Why is $\dfrac{AC}{BC} = \dfrac{DF}{EF}$?

59. If $\dfrac{AC}{BC} = m_1$ and $\dfrac{DF}{EF} = m_2$, why is $m_1 = m_2$?

Theorem 53. Complete the following proof of part of Theorem 53 by giving the reasons.

If two nonvertical lines are perpendicular, the product of their slopes is -1.

In the figure below, $l_1 \perp l_2$ and $\triangle ABC$ has been drawn so that AC is parallel to the y-axis and BD is parallel to the x-axis.

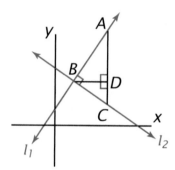

60. Which line has the slope $\dfrac{-DC}{BD}$?

61. What is the slope of the other line?

62. Why is $\dfrac{AD}{BD} = \dfrac{BD}{DC}$?

63. If $\dfrac{-DC}{BD} = m_2$, what does $\dfrac{BD}{DC}$ equal in terms of m_2?

64. If $\dfrac{AD}{BD} = m_1$, why is $m_1 = -\dfrac{1}{m_2}$?

65. Why is $m_1 m_2 = -1$?

Fire Speed. Fire spreading up a hillside "increases in proportion to the square of the slope of the terrain."*

66. Find, to the nearest hundredth, the slope of the hills represented by the two figures at the right.

67. Given similar conditions, how many times faster would you expect fire to spread up the second hill? Explain.

---

*Visual Revelations, by Howard Wainer (Copernicus, 1997).

Set III

Celsius and Fahrenheit. The graph below shows how Celsius and Fahrenheit temperatures are related. The two points that determine the line, A and B, correspond to the freezing point of water (0°C and 32°F) and its boiling point (100°C and 212°F).

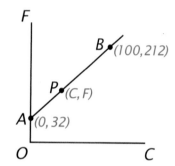

1. What is the slope of line AB?

The coordinates of point P represent any other pair of related temperatures on these two scales.

2. Write an expression for the slope of line AB in terms of the coordinates of A and P.

3. Write an equation based on the fact that your answers to exercises 1 and 2 represent the same slope.

4. Solve the equation for C in terms of F.

5. Solve the equation for F in terms of C.

6. Is there a temperature for which F = C? Show why or why not.

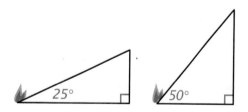

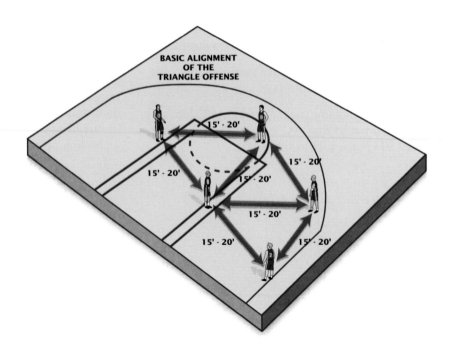

BASIC ALIGNMENT
OF THE
TRIANGLE OFFENSE

15' - 20'

15' - 20'

15' - 20'

15' - 20'

15' - 20'

15' - 20'

15' - 20'

The Laws of Sines and Cosines

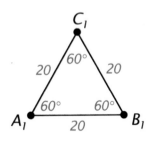

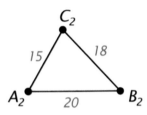

In the "triangle offense" in basketball, the players move on the floor so that they are at the corners of large triangles having sides between 15 and 20 feet in length. One coach has called it "the best offense in the N.B.A."

Suppose three players are spaced 20 feet from one another as shown in the first figure at the left so that they are at the corners of an equilateral triangle. If the triangle is equilateral, then we know that each of its angles is 60°.

Now suppose they move so that they are spaced as shown in the second figure. How large are the angles now? Because the three sides of the triangle now have different lengths, it follows that its angles have different measures.

You have seen how the trigonometric ratios can be used to find the sides and angles of right triangles, but $\triangle A_2B_2C_2$ is not a right triangle. Nevertheless, the sine and cosine can be used to find parts of triangles that are acute or even obtuse. Because we have defined these ratios in terms of acute angles, however, we will limit their use to triangles all of whose angles are acute.

The sine ratio appears in an equation relating all six parts of a triangle.

Theorem 54. The Law of Sines

If the sides opposite $\angle A$, $\angle B$, and $\angle C$ of $\triangle ABC$ have lengths a, b, and c, then $\dfrac{\sin A}{a} = \dfrac{\sin B}{b} = \dfrac{\sin C}{c}$.

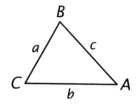

Given: $\triangle ABC$.

Prove: $\dfrac{\sin A}{a} = \dfrac{\sin B}{b} = \dfrac{\sin C}{c}$.

Proof

Draw altitude BD. In right $\triangle CBD$, $\sin C = \dfrac{BD}{a}$; so $BD = a \sin C$.

Because $\alpha\triangle ABC = \dfrac{1}{2}b(BD)$, it follows by substitution that

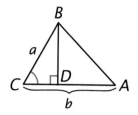

$\alpha\triangle ABC = \dfrac{1}{2}b(a \sin C) = \dfrac{1}{2}\, ab \sin C$. This equality shows that the area

of a triangle is half the product of two of its sides and the sine of the included angle.

Extending this reasoning to the other angles and the sides that include them, we have

$$\alpha\triangle ABC = \frac{1}{2}\, bc \sin A = \frac{1}{2}\, ac \sin B = \frac{1}{2}\, ab \sin C.$$

Dividing these three expressions for the area by $\dfrac{1}{2}$ and by abc gives

$$\frac{\sin A}{a} = \frac{\sin B}{b} = \frac{\sin C}{c}.$$

The cosine ratio appears in the following generalization of the Pythagorean Theorem relating the three sides of a triangle to one of its angles.

Theorem 55. The Law of Cosines

If the sides opposite $\angle A$, $\angle B$, and $\angle C$ of $\triangle ABC$ have lengths a, b, and c, then $c^2 = a^2 + b^2 - 2ab \cos C$.

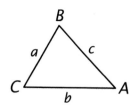

Given: $\triangle ABC$.

Prove: $c^2 = a^2 + b^2 - 2ab \cos C$.

Proof

Draw altitude BD and use the Pythagorean Theorem. In right $\triangle CBD$, $BD^2 + x^2 = a^2$; so $BD^2 = a^2 - x^2$. In right $\triangle ABD$, $BD^2 + (b - x)^2 = c^2$; so $BD^2 = c^2 - (b - x)^2$.

Substituting for BD^2, we have

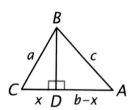

$$c^2 - (b - x)^2 = a^2 - x^2$$
$$c^2 - (b^2 - 2bx + x^2) = a^2 - x^2$$
$$c^2 - b^2 + 2bx - x^2 = a^2 - x^2$$
$$c^2 = a^2 + b^2 - 2bx.$$

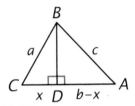

In right $\triangle$CBD, $\cos C = \dfrac{x}{a}$; so $x = a \cos C$. Substituting for x, we have

$$c^2 = a^2 + b^2 - 2b(a \cos C)$$
$$c^2 = a^2 + b^2 - 2ab \cos C.$$

The following examples show how these theorems can be used to solve the "basketball" triangle. More examples are included in the exercises.

Example 1:

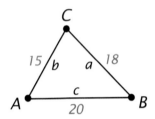

Given that $a = 18$, $b = 15$, and $c = 20$, find $\angle C$.

Solution:
By the Law of Cosines, $c^2 = a^2 + b^2 - 2ab \cos C$.
Substituting gives

$$20^2 = 18^2 + 15^2 - 2(18)(15)\cos C$$
$$400 = 324 + 225 - 540 \cos C$$
$$540 \cos C = 324 + 225 - 400 = 149$$
$$\cos C = \frac{149}{540}$$
$$\angle C \approx 74°.$$

Example 2:
For the same triangle, find $\angle A$ and $\angle B$.

Solution:

By the Law of Sines, $\dfrac{\sin A}{a} = \dfrac{\sin C}{c}$. Substituting gives

$$\frac{\sin A}{18} = \frac{\sin 74°}{20}$$
$$\sin A = \frac{18 \sin 74°}{20} \approx 0.865$$
$$\angle A \approx 60°.$$

Because $\angle A \approx 60°$ and $\angle C \approx 74°$, $\angle B = 180° - \angle A - \angle B \approx 46°$.

Exercises

Set I

Greek Equations. The following figure and equation appear in a Greek trigonometry book.

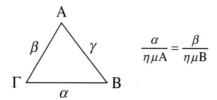

$$\frac{\alpha}{\eta\mu A} = \frac{\beta}{\eta\mu B}$$

1. What do you think $\eta\mu$ means?

2. What relation do the side and angle in each ratio have to each other?

3. What other ratio is equal to the two ratios in this equation?

4. What theorem do the figure and these ratios illustrate?

These equations also appear in the book.

$$\alpha^2 = \beta^2 + \gamma^2 - 2\beta\gamma\,\sigma\upsilon\nu A$$
$$\beta^2 = \alpha^2 + \gamma^2 - 2\alpha\gamma\,\sigma\upsilon\nu B$$

5. What do you think $\sigma\upsilon\nu$ means?

The first equation tells how to find side α if you know β, γ, and $\angle A$.

6. What relation does $\angle A$ have to side α?

7. What relation do sides β and γ have to $\angle A$?

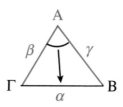

The second equation tells how to find side β if you know α, γ, and $\angle B$.

8. What relation does $\angle B$ have to side β?

9. What relation do sides α and γ have to $\angle B$?

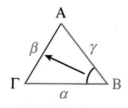

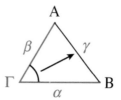

10. Write the equation that tells how to find γ if you know α, β, and $\angle\Gamma$.

11. What theorem do these equations illustrate?

Law of Sines. Use the Law of Sines to solve for x in each of the following figures. Express each length to the nearest tenth and each angle to the nearest degree.

Example:

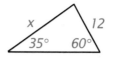

Solution:

$$\frac{x}{\sin 60°} = \frac{12}{\sin 35°}$$

$$x = \frac{12 \sin 60°}{\sin 35°} \approx 18.1$$

12.

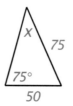

13.

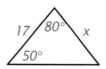

14.

Law of Cosines. Use the Law of Cosines to solve for *x* in each of the following figures. Express each length to the nearest tenth and each angle to the nearest degree.

Example:

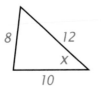

Solution:

$$8^2 = 12^2 + 10^2 - 2(12)(10)\cos x$$
$$64 = 144 + 100 - 240 \cos x$$
$$240 \cos x = 180$$
$$\cos x = \frac{180}{240} = 0.75$$
$$x \approx 41°.$$

15.

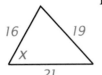

16.

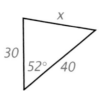

17.

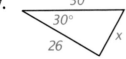

Sines of Supplementary Angles. In △ABC, AB = AD = *x*, and AC = *y*.

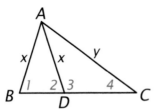

On the assumption that the Law of Sines applies to *all* triangles, regardless of their shape, copy and complete the following proportions.

18. In △ABC, $\dfrac{\sin \angle 1}{y} = \dfrac{\sin \angle 4}{?}$.

19. In △ADC, $\dfrac{\sin \angle 4}{x} = \dfrac{\sin \angle 3}{?}$.

20. What do your answers to exercises 18 and 19 imply about sin ∠1 and sin ∠3? Explain.

Given that ∠1 = 72°, find

21. ∠3.

22. sin ∠1.

23. sin ∠3.

24. What do your answers to exercises 22 and 23 suggest about the sines of supplementary angles?

Set II

Triangulation. In a book on how India was mapped, triangulation is explained:

Triangulation means simply "triangle-ing", or conceiving three mutually visible reference points, usually on prominent hills or buildings, as the corners of a triangle. Knowing the exact distance between two of these points, and then measuring at each the angles made by their connecting sight-line with those to the third point, the distance and position of the third point can be established by trigonometry.*

Some of the triangles used in mapping India are shown in the figure below. The

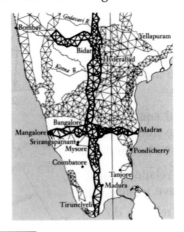

The Great Arc, by John Keay (HarperCollins, 2000).

exercises that follow show how the process worked.

Suppose in the figure below that the base line AB = 24.0 miles, ∠A = 73°, and ∠1 = 51°.

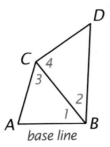

base line

25. Find ∠3.

26. Use the Law of Sines to find CB to the nearest 0.1 mile.

Given that ∠2 = 42° and ∠4 = 85°, find

27. ∠D.

28. DB to the nearest 0.1 mile.

29. CD to the nearest 0.1 mile.

30. Check your answer to exercise 29 by using the Law of Cosines to find CD.

Distance to the Moon. In the figure below (not to scale), A and B represent the positions of two observatories on Earth and M represents a mountain peak on the moon.*

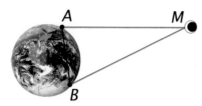

Given that AB = 5,820 miles, ∠A = 89.4°, and ∠B = 89.2°, find

31. ∠M.

32. AM to the nearest thousand miles.

33. BM to the nearest thousand miles.

_____

Pictorial Astronomy, by Dinsmore Alter, Clarence H. Cleminshaw, and John G. Phillips (Crowell, 1974).

The Case of the Equilateral Triangle. Verify that the Law of Cosines works for an equilateral triangle by doing the following exercises.

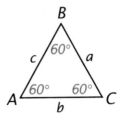

34. Write the equation for a^2 in terms of b, c, and cos A.

35. Substitute a for b and c and solve the equation for cos A.

36. Draw and label a 30°-60° right triangle to show that your answer is correct.

The Case of the Right Triangle. The Laws of Sines and Cosines can be shown to be true for *all* triangles, not just triangles that are acute.

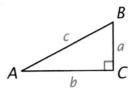

37. Starting with sin A, write the equation for the Law of Sines for the right triangle above.

38. According to your calculator, to what number is sin 90° equal?

39. Substitute this number into your answer to exercise 37.

40. Why does it follow from your answer

that $\sin A = \dfrac{a}{c}$ and $\sin B = \dfrac{b}{c}$?

41. What does the Law of Sines become for right triangles?

42. Write the equation for c^2 in terms of a, b, and cos C for the right triangle above.

43. According to your calculator, to what number is cos 90° equal?

44. Use this fact to simplify your answer to exercise 42.

45. What does the Law of Cosines become for right triangles?

The Case of the "Flattened" Triangle. The figure below shows a strange situation.

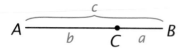

Sides CA and CB of △ABC have "opened out" so that ∠C = 180°. As a result, $c = a + b$.

46. Write the Law of Cosines equation for c^2 in terms of a, b, and cos C for this "flattened triangle."

47. According to your calculator, to what number is cos 180° equal?

48. Use this fact to simplify your answer to exercise 46.

49. Because $c = a + b$ in the figure, does your simplified answer make sense? Explain.

Euclid's Law of Cosines.

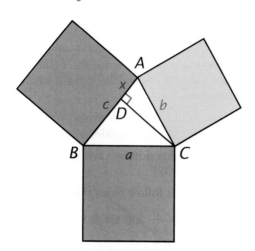

The theorems in this lesson are stated in the form of algebraic equations, something Euclid did not have when he wrote the *Elements.* Compare his statement of the Law of Cosines:

In an acute triangle, the square on the side opposite each angle is less than the sum of the squares on the sides including

that angle by twice the rectangle contained by one of the sides of the angle and the line segment cut off within it by the perpendicular towards the angle.*

with our algebraic version of it:

$$a^2 = b^2 + c^2 - 2bc \cos A.$$

The rectangle to which Euclid referred is illustrated in the figure below.

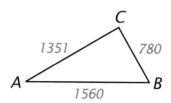

50. Show that its area is $bc \cos A$.

Set III

A Possible Case of Mistaken Identity.

1. Find ∠A.

2. Find ∠B.

3. What kind of triangle is △ABC? Explain.

_____

*Book II, Proposition 13.

Do you recognize the subject of the lesson illustrated on this Russian stamp of 1961?

CHAPTER 11 **Summary and Review**

Basic Ideas

Angle of inclination   461
Cosine   455
Pythagorean triple   437
Sine   455
Slope   461–462
Tangent   449

Theorems

49. The altitude to the hypotenuse of a right triangle forms two triangles similar to it and to each other.   429

Corollary 1. The altitude to the hypotenuse of a right triangle is the geometric mean between the segments into which it divides the hypotenuse.   429

Corollary 2. Each leg of a right triangle is the geometric mean between the hypotenuse and its projection on the hypotenuse. 429

The Pythagorean Theorem. In a right triangle, the square of the hypotenuse is equal to the sum of the squares of the legs.   435

50. *The Isosceles Right Triangle Theorem.* In an isosceles right triangle, the hypotenuse is $\sqrt{2}$ times the length of a leg.   442

Corollary. Each diagonal of a square is $\sqrt{2}$ times the length of one side.   442

51. *The 30°-60° Right Triangle Theorem.* In a 30°-60° right triangle, the hypotenuse is twice the shorter leg and the longer leg is $\sqrt{3}$ times the shorter leg.   442

Corollary. An altitude of an equilateral triangle having side s is $\dfrac{\sqrt{3}}{2}s$ and its area is $\dfrac{\sqrt{3}}{4}s^2$.   443

52. Two nonvertical lines are parallel iff their slopes are equal.   463

53. Two nonvertical lines are perpendicular iff the product of their slopes is -1.   463

54. *The Law of Sines.* If the sides opposite $\angle$A, $\angle$B, and $\angle$C of $\triangle$ABC have lengths a, b, and c, then $\dfrac{\sin A}{a} = \dfrac{\sin B}{b} = \dfrac{\sin C}{c}$.   469

55. *The Law of Cosines.* If the sides opposite $\angle$A, $\angle$B, and $\angle$C of $\triangle$ABC have lengths a, b, and c, then $c^2 = a^2 + b^2 - 2ab \cos C$. 469

Exercises

Set I

Greek Cross. An old puzzle consists of four pieces that can be arranged to form either a "Greek cross" or a square.

Find the slopes of the following segments in the "Greek cross" arrangement of the pieces shown below.

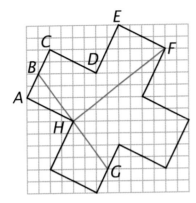

1. AC.
2. CD.
3. DE.
4. HF.
5. BG.

How are the lines in each of the following pairs related?

6. AC and CD.
7. AC and DE.
8. HF and BG.

What must be true about the slopes of two nonvertical lines if the lines are

9. parallel?
10. perpendicular?

Doubled Square. Baudhayana, who lived in India about 800 B.C., wrote: "The rope that is stretched across the diagonal of a square produces an area double the size of the original square."

In the figure below, *d* is both the length of a diagonal of the smaller square and the length of a side of the larger square.

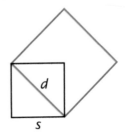

Show that Baudhayana was correct by doing each of the following exercises.

11. Express *d* in terms of *s*.
12. Express the area of the smaller square in terms of *s*.
13. Express the area of the larger square in terms of *d*.
14. Express the area of the larger square in terms of *s*.

Escalator Design. Escalators are designed so that they rise at an angle of 30° with the horizontal.

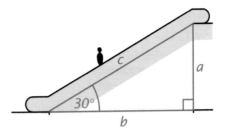

If the distance between floors, *a*, is 14 feet, find

15. the distance marked *c*.
16. the horizontal distance marked *b*.

If the length of the escalator is 40 feet, find

17. the distance between floors, *a*.
18. the horizontal distance.

Subway escalators have been built in which the horizontal distance is as long as 338 feet.

19. Find the vertical distance, *a*, traveled on such an escalator.

20. Find the length, *c*, of such an escalator.

Basketball Angles. A basketball is normally shot from at least 7.5 feet above the floor. Almost all direct shots in basketball are made at a horizontal distance, D, from 10 to 25 feet from the basket.*

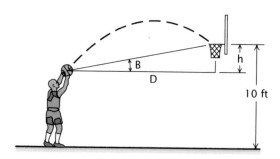

Find the angle of incline, B, if the ball is shot from a point 7.5 feet above the floor at a horizontal distance of

21. 25 feet.

22. 10 feet.

Equal Parts. In the figure below, CD is the altitude to the hypotenuse of right △ABC and AC = DB.†

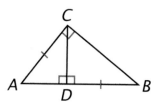

23. How many similar triangles does the figure contain?

Sport Science: Physical Laws and Optimum Performance, by Peter J. Brancazio (Simon & Schuster, 1984).
†From an idea by Mike Bolduan, Catlin Gabel School, Portland, Oregon.

24. State the theorem that is the basis for your answer.

25. How many pairs of equal angles do △ACD and △CBD have?

26. How many pairs of equal sides do they have?

27. How many pairs of equal parts do they have?

28. Are the two triangles congruent? Explain why or why not.

Pentagon. The pentagon has long been a popular choice for the shape of a fortress. An old method for laying out a pentagon on the ground was to stretch a rope into the shape of a right triangle.‡

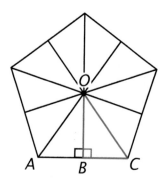

29. If all ten right triangles surrounding point O are congruent, what is the measure of ∠BOC?

30. If the perimeter of the pentagon is supposed to be 1,000 feet, how long is BC?

31. Use the tangent ratio in △OBC to find OB to the nearest 0.1 foot.

32. Use the sine ratio in △OBC to find OC to the nearest 0.1 foot.

33. Use the Pythagorean Theorem to see if your results for OB and OC seem reasonable.

34. What length of rope is needed to lay out △OBC on the ground?

------

‡*The Invention of Infinity: Mathematics and Art in the Renaissance,* by J. V. Field (Oxford University Press, 1997).

Three Ratios. In the figure below, △ABC is equilateral, ABDE is a square, and CF ⊥ AB.

Find each of the following ratios to two decimal places.

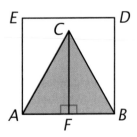

35. $\dfrac{CF}{EA}$.

36. $\dfrac{\rho \triangle ABC}{\rho ABDE}$.

37. $\dfrac{\alpha \triangle ABC}{\alpha ABDE}$.

Set II

Isosceles Right Triangles. The figure below shows a square divided into seven isosceles right triangles, no two of which are congruent.*

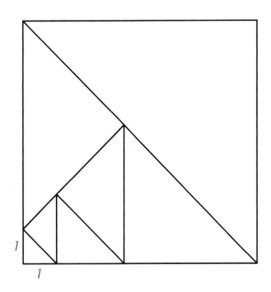

---

*Ivan Skvarca, *Journal of Recreational Mathematics*, 1989.

38. Trace the figure and mark it as needed to find each of the following measurements.

Given that each leg of the smallest triangle is 1 unit long, find the length of

39. each leg of the other six triangles.

40. the sides of the square.

41. Check your answers by finding the areas of the seven triangles and seeing if they add up to the area of the square.

Two Birds. This problem is from the *Liber Abaci* (Book of the Abacus), written in 1202 by the Italian mathematician Fibonacci.

Two birds start flying from the tops of two towers 50 feet apart; one tower is 30 feet high and the other is 40 feet high. Starting at the same time and flying at the same rate, they reach a fountain between the bases of the towers at the same moment.

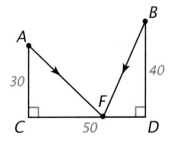

42. Copy the figure above and mark it as needed to answer the questions that follow.

43. From the description, which two lengths in the figure are equal?

44. Let CF = *x* and express FD in terms of *x*.

45. Write and solve an equation in terms of *x*.

46. How far is the fountain from each tower?

47. Approximately how far did each bird fly?

Road Systems. Jacob Steiner, a nineteenth-century German mathematician, invented this problem.

Four villages are located at the corners of a square with sides of one mile. What is the shortest system of roads that can be built to connect them?*

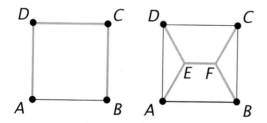

The figures above show two possible solutions. In the second figure, EF ∥ AB, the angles surrounding points E and F are equal, and AE = DE = CF = FB.

48. How many miles of road are needed in the first solution?

49. Copy the second figure and extend line EF to intersect the sides of the square as shown in the figure below. Mark the figure as needed to find how many miles of road are needed in the second solution.

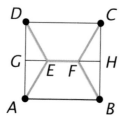

50. Which solution is better?

Sun and Moon. Aristarchus, a Greek astronomer who lived at about the time of Euclid, figured out a way to compare the distances of the sun and the moon from Earth.†

Introduction to Geometry, by H. S. M. Coxeter (Wiley, 1969).
†*Constructing the Universe,* by David Layzer (Scientific American Library, 1984).

The figure below (not to scale) shows the moon precisely at its first quarter so that ∠M = 90°. The centers of the moon and sun are M and S, and O represents the observer on Earth.

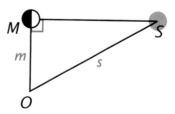

Aristarchus estimated the measure of ∠O to be 87°.

51. Show why it follows that $\dfrac{m}{s} = \dfrac{1}{19}$ (approximately).

52. Show why this equality gives $s = 19m$ (that is, that the sun is 19 times as far away as the moon).

The correct measure of ∠O is closer to 89.85°.

53. About how many times as far as the moon is the sun from Earth?

Eye Chart. The letter E at the top of the familiar eye chart is $3\dfrac{3}{4}$ inches tall.

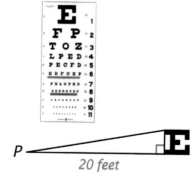

20 feet

54. Show that the visual angle formed by this letter at a distance of 20 feet is about 54 minutes.

Someone with 20-20 vision can distinguish letters that form a visual angle of 4.8 minutes.

55. Approximately how tall are these letters?

UFO Altitude. Two observers at A and B see a UFO hovering at point C. Its angles of elevation are $\angle A = 60°$ and $\angle B = 45°$, and AB = 820 feet.

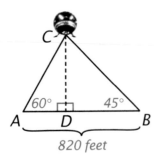

820 feet

Find the altitude of the UFO by doing each of the following exercises.

56. Find $\angle ACB$.

57. Find AC.

58. Use right $\triangle ACD$ to find CD.

Check your answer by doing the following exercises.

59. Find BC.

60. Use right $\triangle BCD$ to find CD.

Outdoor Lighting. The figure and table below show how trees should be pruned to prevent interference with light.*

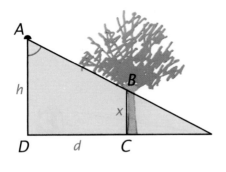

$\angle A$	x
70°	$h - 0.36d$
75°	$h - 0.27d$
80°	$h - 0.18d$

Barrier-Free Design, Department of Housing and Urban Development, Washington, DC, 1975.

61. Copy the figure. Draw a line through B parallel to DC. Let E be the point in which the line intersects AD.

62. Write an equation expressing tan $\angle ABE$ in terms of h, x, and d.

63. Solve the equation for x in terms of h, d, and tan $\angle ABE$.

64. Where did the three expressions for x in the table come from?

Number Mystery. This Babylonian clay tablet dated between 1900 B.C. and 1600 B.C. contains some interesting pairs of numbers. Some of them are listed below.[†]

45	75
65	97
319	481
541	769
799	1249
1679	2929

65. See if you can figure out what is interesting about them by using a calculator.

66. One pair of numbers has a mistake in it. Can you tell which pair is?

[†]*The History of Mathematics: An Introduction,* by David M. Burton (Allyn & Bacon, 1985).

Graphing Linear Equations

The graph of every equation that can be written in the form

$$Ax + By = C$$

is a *line* if both A and B are not zero. For this reason, such equations are called *linear equations in two variables*.

Point-Slope Form

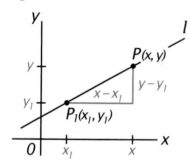

If a point $P_1(x_1, y_1)$ lies on a line with slope m and any other point $P(x, y)$ is chosen on the line, then it follows from the definition of slope that

$$m = \frac{\text{rise}}{\text{run}} = \frac{y - y_1}{x - x_1}$$

and so

$$y - y_1 = m(x - x_1).$$

This is called the *point-slope* form of the equation of a line; x_1 and y_1 are the coordinates of a point on the line and m is the slope of the line.

Slope-Intercept Form

If the line intersects the y-axis in the point $P_1(0, b)$, then the *point-slope* form,

$$y - y_1 = m(x - x_1),$$

becomes

$$y - b = m(x - 0)$$
$$y = mx + b.$$

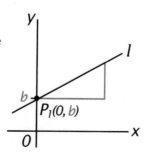

This form of the equation of a line is called the *slope-intercept* form; m is the slope of the line and b is its y-intercept.

Example 1: Write an equation for the line that contains the point (4, 1) and has a slope of 2; draw its graph.

Solution: From the point-slope form, $y - y_1 = m(x - x_1)$, we can write

$$y - 1 = 2(x - 4).$$

We can plot the point (4, 1) and use the fact that the slope is 2 to plot a second point and draw the line.

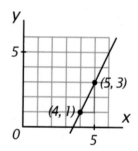

Example 2: Write an equation of the line of example 1 in the form $Ax + By = C$ in which $A > 0$.

Solution: Starting with

$$y - 1 = 2(x - 4),$$

it follows that

$$y - 1 = 2x - 8.$$

Writing the x and y terms on the left side and the constants on the right, we have

$$-2x + y = -8 + 1$$
$$-2x + y = -7$$

Multiplying both sides by -1 so that $A > 0$, we get

$$2x - y = 7.$$

Example 3: Draw a graph of the line whose *y*-intercept is 5 and whose slope is $-\dfrac{2}{3}$. Write an equation for the line.

Solution:

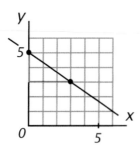

From the slope–intercept form, $y = mx + b$, we can write

$$y = -\frac{2}{3}x + 5.$$

Exercises

A line has the equation $3x + 4y = 24$.

1. Transform the equation into the form $y = mx + b$.

2. What are its slope and *y*-intercept?

3. Sketch its graph.

A line through the point $(-5, 1)$ has a slope of $\dfrac{1}{2}$.

4. Sketch its graph.

5. Write its equation in point–slope form.

6. Transform the equation into slope–intercept form.

7. What is its *y*-intercept?

Two lines have equations
$$y = 2x - 1 \quad \text{and} \quad y = 2x + 3.$$

8. Sketch them on a single pair of axes.

9. How can you tell from their equations that the two lines are parallel?

10. Write an equation for the line midway between them.

Two lines have equations
$$x + y = 5 \quad \text{and} \quad 5x - 5y = 15.$$

11. Write their equations in slope–intercept form.

12. Sketch them on a single pair of axes.

13. What are their slopes?

14. How can you tell from their slopes that the two lines are perpendicular?

A line has the equation $y - 4 = -\dfrac{1}{3}(x + 6)$.

15. What is its slope?

16. What is the *x*-coordinate of the point on the line whose *y*-coordinate is 4?

17. Sketch a graph of the line.

18. Transform its equation into slope–intercept form.

19. What are its *x*- and *y*-intercepts?

20. Write an equation for the line in the form $ax + by = c$ in which $a = 1$.

A line contains the points $A(0, -2)$ and $B(1, 3)$.

21. Sketch a graph of the line.

22. What is its slope?

23. Use the coordinates of point B to write an equation of the line in point–slope form.

24. Transform the equation into slope–intercept form.

25. Write an equation for the line in the form $ax + by = c$ in which $a > 0$.

A line has the equation $4x - 3y = 0$.

26. Transform its equation into slope–intercept form.

27. What are its slope and *y*-intercept?

28. Sketch a graph of the line.

29. What is its *x*-intercept?

30. Let A be the point on the line whose *x*-coordinate is -3 and B be the point on the line whose *y*-coordinate is 4. What is the distance between A and B?

Chapter 12

Circles

THE SCIENCE OF ILLUSIONS

JACQUES NINIO

This figure contains a hidden message. What is it?

In this chapter, we explore the properties of the circle, the most symmetric of all two-dimensional geometric figures. It is because of this symmetry that wheels, coins, and many other common objects are circular in shape. We will look at the properties of circles and their relation to lines and angles. These properties will eventually enable us to use regular polygons to develop the formulas for the circumference and area of a circle.

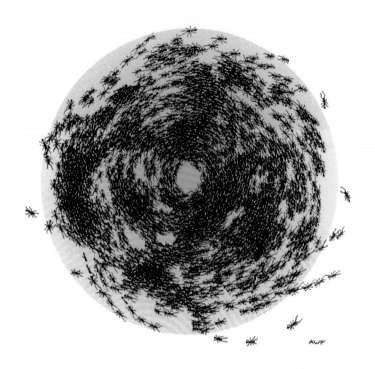

Circles, Radii, and Chords

Army ants are blind and find their way by following the scent trails left by other ants. When a group of these ants is prevented from traveling along its usual path, the ants sometimes begin milling about in circles. The ants shown in the drawing above walked for more than 30 hours, stopping only when all of them were dead.*

In this lesson, we review a few familiar terms about circles and introduce some new ones.

Definition
A *circle* is the set of all points in a plane that are at a given distance from a given point in the plane.

The given point is called the *center* of the circle and the given distance is called its *radius.*

The ants in the picture seem to be walking in *concentric* circles.

Definition
Circles are *concentric* iff they lie in the same plane and have the same center.

———————

*T. C. Schneirla, *Army Ants,* edited by H. R. Topoff (W. H. Freeman and Company, 1971.)

A circle is usually named for its center, and so the figure at the right illustrates circle O. It also illustrates a *radius* of the circle, line segment OP. Dictionaries list at least two different definitions of the word "radius": as a *distance* (that is, a *number*) or as a *line segment.* Mathematicians use both meanings, and the context will show which one is meant.

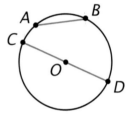

Definitions

A *radius* of a circle is a line segment that connects the center of the circle to any point on it. *The* radius of a circle is the length of one of these line segments.

A useful fact that follows directly from the definitions of "circle" and "radius" is:

Corollary to the Definition of a Circle

All radii of a circle are equal.

The figure at the right illustrates two other important terms related to circles: AB is called a *chord* of circle O, and CD is called a *diameter.* Like "radius," "diameter" has a double meaning.

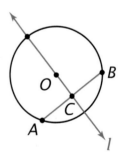

Definitions

A *chord* of a circle is a line segment that connects two points of the circle.
A *diameter* of a circle is a chord that contains the center. *The* diameter of a circle is the length of one of these chords.

The figure at the right illustrates a line that intersects a chord in a circle. It appears to show that line *l*
1. contains the center of the circle.
2. is perpendicular to chord AB.
3. bisects chord AB.

Given that any two of these statements are true, then it is easy to prove that all three are true. The proofs are considered in the exercises.

Theorem 56

If a line through the center of a circle is perpendicular to a chord, it also bisects the chord.

Theorem 57

If a line through the center of a circle bisects a chord that is not a diameter, it is also perpendicular to the chord.

Theorem 58

The perpendicular bisector of a chord of a circle contains the center of the circle.

Exercises

Set I

Roman Arch. The ancient Romans built stone arches like the one shown below in constructing their bridges.*

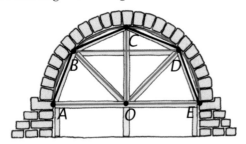

In the figure, the curve shown in red is half of a circle with its center at O; also,
AB = BC = CD = DE.

1. What are OA, OB, OC, OD, and OE called with respect to the circle?

2. What are BD and AE called?

3. What else is AE called?

4. What kind of triangles are triangles △AOB, △BOC, △COD, and △DOE? Explain.

5. What else can you conclude about these four triangles? Explain.

Old Figure. The figure below is from a book on trigonometry published in 1533.

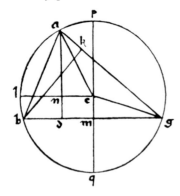

How many of each of the following line segments do you see in the figure?

6. Radii.

7. Diameters.

8. Chords.

9. How many points named with letters are on the circle?

Butterfly Spots. The wings of this butterfly are decorated with circular spots.

10. What word describes the circles in each spot?

11. What does the word mean?

12. What advantage do you think these spots might provide the butterfly?

Chord Problem. The following problem appeared in a book published in 1901:

Describe a circle, and then draw through a point within the circle the longest and the shortest chords that can be drawn.†

13. Use your straightedge and compass to do the problem. (The word "describe" meant "draw.")

14. What relation do the two chords have to each other?

15. How do the lengths of the longest and shortest chords depend on the location of the point?

---

* *Why Buildings Fall Down,* by Matthys Levy and Mario Salvadori (Norton, 1992).

† *First Steps in Geometry,* by G. A. Wentworth and G. A. Hill (Ginn, 1901).

Theorem 56. Complete the following proof of Theorem 56 by giving the reasons.

If a line through the center of a circle is perpendicular to a chord, it also bisects the chord.

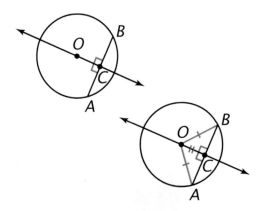

Given: OC ⊥ AB in circle O.
Prove: OC bisects AB.

Proof
16. Because OC ⊥ AB, ∠OCA and ∠OCB are right angles. Why?
17. Draw OA and OB. Why?
18. OA = OB. Why?
19. OC = OC. Why?
20. △ACO ≅ △BCO. Why?
21. AC = BC. Why?
22. OC bisects AB. Why?

Theorem 57. Complete the following proof of Theorem 57 by giving the reasons.

If a line through the center of a circle bisects a chord that is not a diameter, it is also perpendicular to the chord.

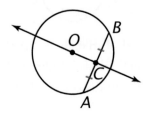

Given: OC bisects AB in circle O.
Prove: OC ⊥ AB.

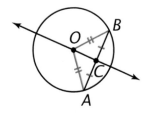

Proof
23. Because OC bisects AB, CA = CB. Why?
24. Draw OA and OB. Why?
25. OA = OB. Why?
26. Because O and C are equidistant from A and B, OC ⊥ AB. Why?

Theorem 58. Complete the following indirect proof of Theorem 58 by giving the reasons.

The perpendicular bisector of a chord of a circle contains the center of the circle.

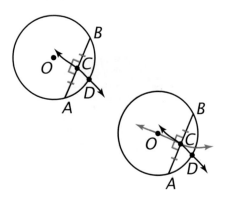

Given: CD is the perpendicular bisector of AB in circle O.
Prove: CD contains O.

Proof
Suppose CD does *not* contain O. Draw OC.
27. OC ⊥ AB. Why?

This means that through point C there are two lines perpendicular to AB.
28. What fact does this contradict?

This contradiction tells us that the assumption that CD does not contain O is false.
29. What conclusion follows?

Set II

SAT Problem. The figure below appeared in a problem on an SAT test.

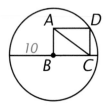

B is the center of the circle with radius 10 and ABCD is a rectangle.

30. What is the length of diagonal AC?

31. Explain your reasoning.

CBS Eye. The CBS eye is constructed from circles. Although the positions of the centers of the two complete circles are "obvious," the positions of the centers of the two partial circles are not.

32. Carefully trace the figure below showing part of the eye.

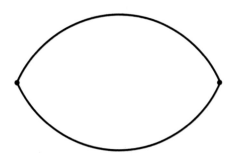

One of the theorems of this lesson can be used to find the centers of the two circles used to form the eye.

33. What does the theorem say?

32. (*continued*) Use your straightedge and compass to find the centers of the two circles by construction.

Red-Spot Puzzle. A puzzle called "Cover the Red Spot" consisted of a spot 65 mm in diameter printed on the cover of an envelope that contained four steel disks, each 46 mm in diameter. The directions said to "Hold the disks about four inches above the big spot on the envelope and try to drop the disks, one at a time on the spot, to cover the entire spot."*

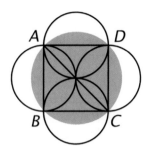

The diagram below shows the solution, in which diameters of the four disks are sides of the square ABCD and the diameter of the spot is one of its diagonals.

34. What kind of triangle is △ABC?

35. Given that AC = 65 mm, find AB.

36. How difficult do you think this puzzle is to solve? Explain.

---

* The Book of Ingenious and Diabolical Puzzles, by Jerry Slocum and Jack Botermans (Times Books, 1994).

Speed of Light. How the speed of light was first calculated is shown by the figure below. Point S represents the sun, and the two circles represent the orbits of Earth and Jupiter.

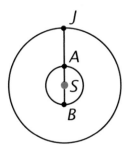

The distance from Earth to the sun is 93,000,000 miles. Light from Jupiter takes about 16 minutes, 40 seconds longer to reach Earth when Earth is at B than when it is at A.

Use this information to find each of the following measures.

37. The diameter of Earth's orbit around the sun.

38. The time that it takes light to travel across Earth's orbit in seconds.

39. The speed of light in miles per second.

Roundness. The roundness of a grain of sand is defined in terms of radius.*

Sand, by Raymond Siever (Scientific American Library, 1988).

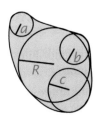

In the figure above of a cross section of a grain of sand, R is the radius of the largest circle and a, b, and c are the radii of the smaller circles. The roundness of the grain is

$$\frac{a + b + c}{3R}.$$

40. Find the roundness if $a = 2$, $b = 3$, $c = 5$, and $R = 9$.

41. Find the roundness if all four of these measurements are doubled.

42. Does your second answer seem to contradict the first one? Explain.

Three Circles. The figure below shows three circles, each with a radius of 1 unit, that intersect in a common point.[†]

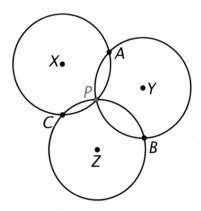

43. Use your compass to make a large copy of the figure. Draw PX, PY, and PZ.

44. What can you conclude about the lengths of these three line segments?

[†] *Knotted Doughnuts and Other Mathematical Entertainments,* by Martin Gardner (W. H. Freeman and Company, 1986).

43. (*continued*) Draw XA, XC, YA, YB, ZC, and ZB.

45. What kind of quadrilaterals have you drawn? Explain.

43. (*continued*) The three quadrilaterals look like three faces of a cube. Through A, B, and C, draw three line segments to complete the "cube." (Each segment should be parallel to some of the segments that you have already drawn.) Label the point in which the three line segments intersect O.

46. What can you conclude about the lengths of OA, OB, and OC? Explain.

47. A fourth circle with a radius of 1 unit could be added to the figure so that it contains points A, B, and C. Explain.

Steam Engine. The poster below from 1800 advertises an early steam engine. One end of a rod is attached to the midpoint of a spoke of a wheel. The other end of the rod moves up and down, causing the wheel to rotate.*

TREVITHICKS,
PORTABLE STEAM ENGINE.

Catch me who can.

Mechanical Power Subduing
Animal Speed.

Inventing the Modern World: Technology Since 1750, by Robert Bud, Simon Niziol, Timothy Boon, and Andrew Nahum (Dorling Kindersley, 2000).

In the figure below, line segments AB, CD, and EF represent three positions of the rod so that AB = CD = EF.

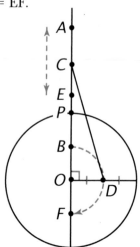

48. Make a large copy of the figure and mark it as needed to find each of the following measurements.

If the radius of the wheel is 28 inches and PE = 8 inches, find

49. EF, the length of the rod.

50. CD.

51. CO.

52. CE.

53. AC.

Set III

Island Puzzle. A small island is in the center of a deep circular lake, 300 yards in diameter. There are two trees at A and B. Someone who cannot swim has a rope a few yards longer than 300 yards. How can the rope be used as a way to get to the island?†

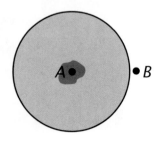

† *Wheels, Life, and Other Mathematical Amusements*, by Martin Gardner (W. H. Freeman and Company, 1983).

Tangents

A champion hammer thrower can throw a 16-pound hammer farther than a quarterback can throw a football! To be able to do so, the thrower swings the hammer around in a circle several times before releasing it.

The hammer is attached to one end of a steel wire and spun around a circle whose center is the other end of the wire. When the thrower lets go, the hammer leaves this circular path and flies along a path that appears to be a straight line. This line intersects the circle in exactly one point, the point that is the position of the hammer when the wire is released. Such a line is called a *tangent* to the circle.

Definition
A *tangent* to a circle is a line in the plane of the circle that intersects the circle in exactly one point.

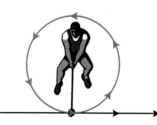

The hammer thrower knows that, when the hammer is released, it flies in a direction perpendicular to the thrower's arm. This means that it must be released when the wire is at 90° to the intended direction of throw.*

The athlete is applying a basic fact of geometry: that a tangent to a circle is perpendicular to the radius drawn to the point at which the tangent intersects the circle. This fact can be proved indirectly.

The Science of the Summer Games, by Vincent Mallette (Charles River Media, 1996).

Theorem 59

If a line is tangent to a circle, it is perpendicular to the radius drawn to the point of contact.

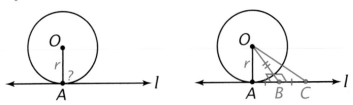

Given: l is tangent to circle O at point A.
Prove: $l \perp$ OA.

Proof
  Suppose that l is *not* perpendicular to OA (that is, OA is not perpendicular to l). Through point O, construct OB $\perp l$. Choose point C on l so that BC = BA. Draw OC.
  $\triangle$OBA $\cong$ $\triangle$OBC (SAS); so OC = OA = r. This means that C must be a point on the circle because a circle is the set of all points in the plane at a distance of the radius from the center.
  So l intersects the circle in *two* points: A and C. This contradicts the fact that l is tangent to the circle (a tangent to a circle intersects it in exactly one point). So our assumption that l is not perpendicular to OA is false, and so $l \perp$ OA.

  The converse of this theorem also is true. Here a direct proof is easier.

Theorem 60

If a line is perpendicular to a radius at its outer endpoint, it is tangent to the circle.

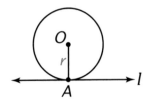 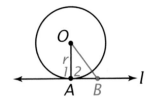

Given: Circle O with $l \perp$ OA.
Prove: l is tangent to circle O.

Proof
  Let B be any other point on l and draw OB. Because $l \perp$ OA, $\angle 1$ and $\angle 2$ are right angles, and so $\angle 1 = \angle 2$. $\angle 1$ is an exterior angle of $\triangle$OAB, and so $\angle 1 > \angle$OBA. Substituting $\angle 2$ for $\angle 1$ gives $\angle 2 > \angle$OBA. If two angles of a triangle are unequal, the sides opposite them are unequal in the same order; so, in $\triangle$OAB, OB > OA = r. Therefore, B lies outside circle O from which it follows that l intersects circle O only at point A. So l is tangent to circle O.

Exercises

Set I

Band Saw. The blade of a two-wheel band saw is driven by two identical wheels, one above the other.

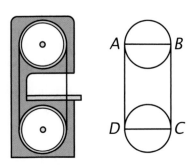

In the figures above, the blade is tangent to each wheel at the endpoints of a diameter.*

1. Why is AD ⊥ AB, BC ⊥ AB, AD ⊥ DC, and BC ⊥ DC?

2. Why is AD ∥ BC and AB ∥ DC?

3. Why is AD = BC?

Concentric Circles. In the figure below, O is the center of both circles, and radius OB bisects chord AC.

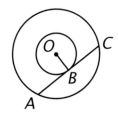

4. What else can you conclude about OB and AC?

5. What theorem is used in your answer?

6. What else can you conclude about line AC?

7. What theorem is used in your answer?

---

*The Complete Manual of Wood Working, by Albert Jackson, David Day, and Simon Jennings (Knopf, 1996).

Grid Exercise. In the figure below, lines *l* and *m* are tangent to circle C at A and B.

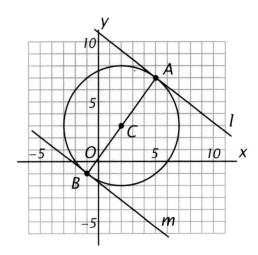

Find each of the following numbers.

8. The length of the radius of the circle.

9. The slope of diameter AB.

10. The slope of line *l.*

11. The slope of line *m.*

12. What relation do lines *l* and *m* have to AB?

13. What relation do lines *l* and *m* have to each other?

14. How are the slopes of *l, m,* and AB related?

Double Meaning.
In the figure at the right, OB is both a radius of circle O and a leg of right △OAB. Also, OB = 1.

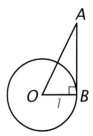

15. What relation does AB have to circle O?

16. What theorem is used in your answer?

17. What is the definition of the tangent *ratio?*

18. What is the tangent of ∠O?

Railroad Curve. Tangents are used to lay out railroad tracks so that they change direction smoothly.

In the figure below, lines *l* and *m* represent the original and final directions of a track.

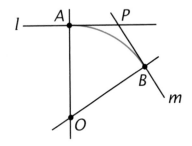

19. The following construction shows the method used to smooth the corner at P.

  (1) Draw lines *l* and *m* and let P be the point at which they intersect.

  (2) Use your compass to mark two points A and B on these lines so that PA = PB.

  (3) Construct a line perpendicular to *l* at A and a line perpendicular to *m* at B. Label their intersection O.

  (4) Draw OP.

20. What can you conclude about △APO and △BPO? Explain.

21. Why is OA = OB?

19. (*continued*) Use your compass to draw the arc of the circle whose center is O that connects points A and B.

22. Why are lines *l* and *m* tangent to this curve?

23. Will the train be jolted at A and B?

Tangents to Two Circles. The lines in the figure below are tangent to both circles.

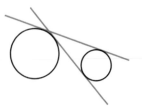

24. Copy the figure and draw two more lines that also are tangent to both circles.

The two circles in the figure below have one point in common.

25. Copy the figure and draw the lines that are tangent to both circles.

Draw a figure to illustrate two circles for which the number of lines that can be drawn tangent to both circles is

26. two.

27. one.

28. Is it possible to have two circles for which no lines can be drawn tangent to both? Explain.

Set II

Construction Problem. The figure below appears in Euclid's *Elements.**

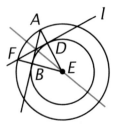

―――――――――
*Book III, Proposition 17. The red line has been added.

29. Use your straightedge and compass to construct it by doing the following.

(1) Draw a circle with a radius of 1 inch and label its center E.

(2) Choose a point about $\frac{1}{2}$ inch outside the circle and label the point A.

(3) Draw AE, and let D be the point in which AE intersects the circle.

(4) Draw a circle with radius EA and center E.

(5) Through D construct line $l \perp$ AE, and let F be one of the points in which l intersects the larger circle.

(6) Draw EF, and let B be the point in which EF intersects the smaller circle.

(7) Draw AB.

30. Why is line l tangent to the smaller circle?

31. Why is $\triangle$FDE $\cong$ $\triangle$ABE?

32. Why is $\angle$ABE a right angle?

33. What can you conclude about line AB?

Euclid's figure has reflection symmetry with respect to the red line.

34. What is the reflection of the tangent l through this line?

Tomahawk. The figure below shows a "tomahawk" angle trisector being used to trisect $\angle$XYZ.*

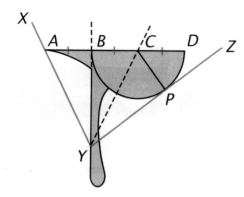

_____

The Trisection Problem, by Robert C. Yates (Franklin Press, 1942).

The tomahawk is designed so that AB = BC = CD, BY $\perp$ AD, and C is the center of a circle with radius BC. It is placed on $\angle$XYZ as shown, with YZ tangent to the circle at P.

35. Why is $\triangle$ABY $\cong$ $\triangle$CBY?

36. Why is CP $\perp$ YZ?

37. Why is $\triangle$CBY $\cong$ $\triangle$CPY?

38. Why does it follow that YB and YC trisect $\angle$XYZ?

Gothic Window. The figure below shows a design for placing a circular window in a Gothic arch.

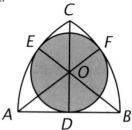

The base of the arch, AB, is tangent to the window at D. The two curved sides of the arch are parts of circles centered at A and B and with radii equal to AB.

39. Draw a line segment 8 cm long, label it AB and its midpoint D. Use your compass to draw the two curved sides of the arch and label its top C. Draw CD.

40. Why is CD $\perp$ AB? (Hint: What points are equidistant from A and B?)

41. Find the lengths of AD and AF in your figure.

42. Given that the radius of the circle in the arch is r cm, express the length of AO in terms of r.

43. Write an equation relating the lengths of the sides of $\triangle$AOD in terms of r and solve it for r.

44. What sort of right triangle is $\triangle$AOD?

39. (*continued*) Use what you know about $\triangle$AOD to find point O and draw the circular window.

45. How tall is the arch?

Tangent Puzzle. The following problem appeared in the 1800 edition of the *Ladies Diary*, a book published annually in London for more than a hundred years.*

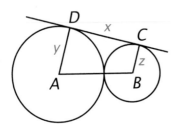

DC is tangent to the touching circles with radii y and z centered at A and B, respectively. Prove that $x^2 = 4yz$

One way to do so is to draw BE ∥ DC as shown below.

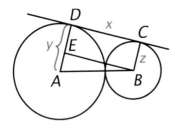

46. What relation does segment DC have to segments AD and BC? Explain.

47. What relation do segments AD and BC have to each other? Explain.

48. What kind of quadrilateral is BCDE?

49. What kind of triangle is △ABE?

50. Why is $AB^2 = AE^2 + EB^2$?

51. Express AB, AE, and EB in terms of x, y, and z.

52. Substitute your answers into the equation in exercise 50 to get an equation in terms of x, y, and z.

53. Simplify the equation to finish the proof.

Set III

Trip to the Moon. On a trip from the earth to the moon, where would the earth and the moon appear to be the same size?†

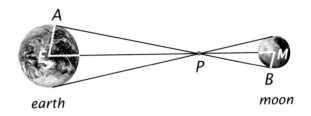

earth   moon

In the figure above (not to scale), they would appear to be the same size at P. Point P lies on the line joining the centers of the earth and the moon and on the two lines shown here tangent to both the earth and the moon. The radius of the earth is 3,960 miles, and the radius of the moon is 1,080 miles. Find EP, given that the distance EM is 234,000 miles. Show your reasoning.

I HATE TO TELL YOU THIS, BUT YOU GOT POCK MARKS ON YOUR SPACE HELMET.

POCK MARKS ON MY WHAT ?

Used by permission of Johnny Hart and Creators Syndicate, Inc.

Geometry Civilized: History, Culture, and Technique, by J. L. Heilbron (Clarendon Press, 1998).

†*Science Fiction Puzzle Tales,* by Martin Gardner (Clarkson N. Potter, Inc., 1981).

LESSON 3

Central Angles and Arcs

A rainbow is produced when sunlight hits a bank of raindrops in either a cloud or falling rain. The drops act as tiny prisms, the apparent color of each drop being determined by the angle at which it is viewed.

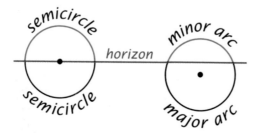

The rainbow is a set of circular arcs with a common center at a point opposite the sun. If the sun is on the horizon, exactly half of each of these circles, called a *semicircle*, can be seen. If the sun is above the horizon, the center of the rainbow is below the horizon. As a result, the visible part of the rainbow is less than a semicircle. It is a *minor arc*. The part of the rainbow below the horizon is more than a semicircle; it is a *major arc*.

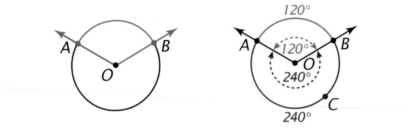

To indicate how much of the rainbow can be seen, it is convenient to relate its arc to an angle at its center. In the figure at the left above, the minor arc AB (written $\overset{\frown}{AB}$ or $\overset{\frown}{BA}$) is bounded by points A and B on the sides of ∠AOB. Because its vertex is at the center of the circle, ∠AOB is called a *central angle* of the circle.

Definition

A *central angle* of a circle is an angle whose vertex is the center of the circle.

Every pair of points on a circle determines two arcs. A minor arc is usually named by just these two points, called its endpoints. A major arc or a semicircle is named with three letters, the middle letter naming a third point on the arc. In the figure at the right above, for example, the symbol $\overset{\frown}{AB}$ refers to the minor arc and the symbol $\overset{\frown}{ACB}$ refers to the major arc.

As you know, the measurement of angles is based on dividing a circle into 360 degrees. It is natural to base the measurement of arcs on the same idea. For example, if ∠AOB = 120°, then we say that the degree measure of $\overset{\frown}{AB}$, represented by the symbol $m\overset{\frown}{AB}$, is 120°.

In our earlier treatment of angles, we limited their measures to no more than 180°. In working with circles, it is convenient to consider angles whose measures are more than 180°. The sides of central ∠AOB divide circle O into two arcs: a minor arc of 120° and a major arc of 240°. Corresponding to the minor arc, $\overset{\frown}{AB}$, is ∠AOB, whose measure is 120°. Corresponding to the major arc, $\overset{\frown}{ACB}$, is "another angle" having the same sides as ∠AOB but whose measure is 240°. To distinguish between these two angles, we call the larger one a *reflex angle*.

Definition

A *reflex angle* is an angle whose measure is more than 180°.

Keeping in mind that to every *major* arc there corresponds a central *reflex* angle, we can define the degree measure of any arc.

Definition

The *degree measure* of an arc is the measure of its central angle.

In the figure at the right, points A, B, and C determine three minor arcs whose measures are

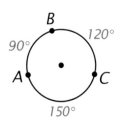

$$m\overset{\frown}{AB} = 90°, \ m\overset{\frown}{BC} = 120°, \text{ and } m\overset{\frown}{CA} = 150°.$$

The three points also determine three major arcs whose measures are

$$m\overset{\frown}{ABC} = m\overset{\frown}{AB} + m\overset{\frown}{BC} = 90° + 120° = 210°,$$
$$m\overset{\frown}{BCA} = m\overset{\frown}{BC} + m\overset{\frown}{CA} = 120° + 150° = 270°, \text{ and}$$
$$m\overset{\frown}{CAB} = m\overset{\frown}{CA} + m\overset{\frown}{AB} = 150° + 90° = 240°.$$

Arc measures can always be added in this way, a fact that follows from their definition and the Protractor Postulate. Although it is possible to prove this fact, we will make it a postulate.

Postulate 10. The Arc Addition Postulate
If C is on $\overset{\frown}{AB}$, then $m\overset{\frown}{AC} + m\overset{\frown}{CB} = m\overset{\frown}{ACB}.$

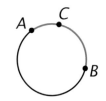

For simplicity, we will refer to arcs that have equal measures as "equal arcs." We can prove, by using congruent triangles, that two chords of a circle are equal iff they have equal arcs.

Theorem 61
In a circle, equal chords have equal arcs.

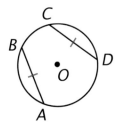 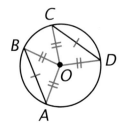

Given: In circle O, AB = CD.
Prove: $m\overset{\frown}{AB} = m\overset{\frown}{CD}$.

Proof
In circle O, AB = CD. Draw OA, OB, OC, and OD. OA = OC and OB = OD (all radii of a circle are equal); so △AOB ≅ △COD (SSS). From this congruence, we know that ∠AOB = ∠COD and, because $m\overset{\frown}{AB} = ∠AOB$ and $m\overset{\frown}{CD} = ∠COD$ (the degree measure of an arc is the measure of its central angle), $m\overset{\frown}{AB} = m\overset{\frown}{CD}$ by substitution.

The proof of Theorem 62, the converse of Theorem 61, is almost the same and is considered in the exercises.

Theorem 62
In a circle, equal arcs have equal chords.

PEANUTS reprinted by permission of United Features Syndicate, Inc.

Exercises

Set I

Routes to Japan. In planning to sail west from Portugal to the Indies (Japan), Columbus based his calculations on the figure below.*

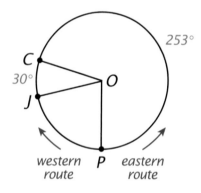

western   P   eastern
route   route

Points C, J, and P represent China, Japan, and Portugal. Marco Polo claimed that the eastern overland route from Portugal to China, the major arc going from P to C, had a measure of 253°. Polo thought Japan was 30° beyond China, and so $m\overarc{CJ} = 30°$.

1. What are ∠POJ and ∠JOC called with respect to circle O?

2. Name the minor arc that corresponds to ∠POJ.

3. Name the major arc that corresponds to reflex ∠POJ.

Geometry Civilized: History, Culture, and Technique, by J. L. Heilbron (Clarendon Press, 1998).

4. What is the measure of ∠JOC?

5. What is $m\overarc{PCJ}$?

6. What is $m\overarc{PJ}$?

7. What is the measure of ∠POJ?

Theorem 62. Complete the following proof of Theorem 62 by giving the reasons.

In a circle, equal arcs have equal chords.

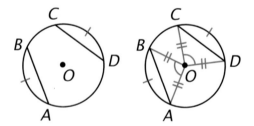

Given: In circle O, $m\overarc{AB} = m\overarc{CD}$.
Prove: AB = CD.

Proof

8. Draw OA, OB, OC, and OD. Why can we draw these lines?

9. OA = OC, and OB = OD. Why?

10. $m\overarc{AB} = ∠AOB$, and $m\overarc{CD} = ∠COD$. Why?

11. Because $m\overarc{AB} = m\overarc{CD}$, ∠AOB = ∠COD. Why?

12. △AOB ≅ △COD. Why?

13. AB = CD. Why?

Jupiter's Asteroids. As Jupiter travels in its orbit about the sun, two sets of asteroids travel with it.* In the figure below, the sun is at S, Jupiter is at J, and the two sets of asteroids are at A and B.

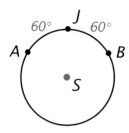

14. Draw the figure and add to it radii SA, SJ, and SB and chords AJ and JB.

15. Why is $m\widehat{AJ} = \angle ASJ$ and $m\widehat{JB} = \angle JSB$?

16. Why is $m\widehat{AJ} + m\widehat{JB} = m\widehat{AJB}$?

17. Why are $\triangle ASJ$ and $\triangle BSJ$ congruent?

18. What kind of triangles are they?

Arc Illusion. Here is an interesting optical illusion.[†]

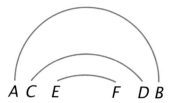

19. What kind of arc does $\widehat{AB}$ appear to be?

20. What kind of arcs are $\widehat{CD}$ and $\widehat{EF}$?

21. Which arc do you think comes from the largest circle?

Cover the parts of the figure to the left of E and to the right of F.

22. What seems to be true?

———————

Constructing the Universe, by David Layzer (Scientific American Library, 1984).

[†]*Can You Believe Your Eyes?* by J. R. Block and Harold E. Yuker (Brunner/Mazel, 1992).

Chords and Arcs. In the figure below, $\triangle ABC$ is a 30°-60° right triangle whose sides are chords of circle O.

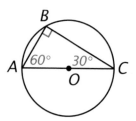

23. Why is $m\widehat{AB} + m\widehat{BC} = m\widehat{ABC}$?

24. Is AB + BC = AC? Explain.

25. Copy the figure and draw OB. Also, label its length r.

26. Find $m\widehat{AB}$, $m\widehat{BC}$, and $m\widehat{ABC}$.

27. Express AB, BC, and AC in terms of r.

28. AC = 2AB. How are $m\widehat{ABC}$ and $m\widehat{AB}$ related?

29. $m\widehat{BC} = 2m\widehat{AB}$. How are BC and AB related?

Set II

The Square That Isn't. Saint Peter's Square in Rome is actually oval in shape rather than square.[‡]

30. Use your straightedge and compass to construct the oval as follows.

———————

[‡]*Geometry Civilized: History, Culture, and Technique,* by J. L. Heilbron (Clarendon Press, 1998).

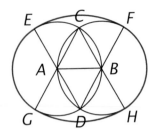

(1) Draw AB about 1 inch long and draw circles A and B with radius AB. Let C and D be the points in which the circles intersect.

(2) Draw diameters CG, CH, DE, and DF.

(3) With D as center, draw $\overset{\frown}{EF}$ and, with C as center, draw $\overset{\frown}{GH}$.

31. What can you conclude about △ABC and △ABD?

32. What kind of quadrilateral is ACBD?

30. (*continued*) Extend diameter ED beyond E and construct a line through E perpendicular to ED. Label the line *l*.

33. What can you conclude about line *l* and circle A? Explain.

34. Line *l* has the same relation to $\overset{\frown}{EF}$. Why?

35. Find the measures of the four arcs that form the oval: $\overset{\frown}{GE}$, $\overset{\frown}{EF}$, $\overset{\frown}{FH}$, and $\overset{\frown}{HG}$.

36. What is their sum?

Rainbow Distance. Olympiodorus, a sixth-century Greek scholar, used the figure below in an attempt to calculate an observer's distance to a rainbow.*

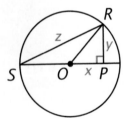

The observer is at O, the sun is at S, and the top of the rainbow is at R; RP ⊥ SP.

_____
The Rainbow: From Myth to Mathematics, by Carl B. Boyer (Princeton University Press, 1987).

37. Letting the radius of circle O be 1, write an equation relating the lengths of the sides of △ORP.

38. Write an equation relating the lengths of the sides of △SRP.

39. Use your equations to show that

$$x = \frac{z^2 - 2}{2}.$$

Night Sky. In the photograph below of the night sky, the stars appear as arcs of concentric circles rather than as points of light.

40. Why?

41. What can you conclude about the measures of the arcs?

42. Approximately how long do you think it took to take this photograph? Explain.

Original Proofs. Write proofs for the following exercises.

43.

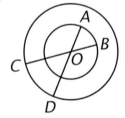

Given: Vertical angles ∠AOB and ∠COD are central angles of both circles.
Prove: $m\overset{\frown}{AB} = m\overset{\frown}{CD}$.

44.

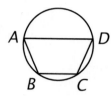

Given: The vertices of trapezoid ABCD
(AD ∥ BC) lie on a circle, and
$m\widehat{AB} = m\widehat{CD}$.
Prove: ∠B = ∠C.

45.

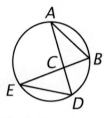

Given: Points A, B, D, and E lie on
a circle, and AB = DE.
Prove: AD = BE.

46.

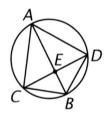

Given: Points A, B, C, and D lie on
a circle, $m\widehat{AC} = m\widehat{AD}$, and
$m\widehat{CB} = m\widehat{BD}$.
Prove: AB contains the center of the
circle.

47.

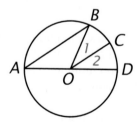

Given: AD is a diameter of circle O,
and AB ∥ OC.
Prove: $m\widehat{BC} = m\widehat{CD}$.

Set III

Obtuse Ollie drew the figure below with his
straightedge and compass.

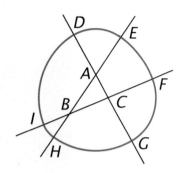

First, he drew the three lines that form △ABC.
Then, starting at A, he drew $\widehat{DE}$ with center A,
$\widehat{EF}$ with center B, $\widehat{FG}$ with center C, $\widehat{GH}$ with
center A, $\widehat{HI}$ with center B, and $\widehat{ID}$ with center
C.

  He thought that the sum of the measures
of the six arcs must be 360° because the curve
ends where it began. Acute Alice thought this
unlikely, because the curve is not a circle.

  Which one of them is correct? Explain.

LESSON 4

Inscribed Angles

The first demonstration of motion pictures in a theater took place on April 23, 1896, in New York City. At the time, the inventor, Thomas Edison, thought that ten movie theaters would be enough for the entire United States!*

If you have ever watched a movie from the first row of a theater, you know that it can be hard to see everything on the screen at once. The reason is that the angle that the side edges of the screen make with your eyes is very large. At the back of the theater, this angle is much smaller. You might conclude from this fact that, the farther you are from the screen, the smaller your viewing angle will be. But such is not the case.

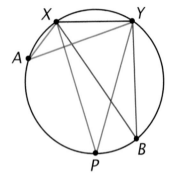

In the figure at the left, XY represents the screen and point P represents the center seat of the back row, directly under the projection window. For someone seated at P, the screen angle to which we have been referring is ∠P. Where else in the theater is the screen angle the same size?

The other locations having the same screen angle are on the circle that contains X, Y, and P. Every angle whose vertex is on the arc $\overset{\frown}{XPY}$

---

*Edison: The Man Who Invented the Future, by Ronald W. Clark (Putnam, 1977).

of this circle and whose sides pass through points X and Y is equal to the angle at P. You can check whether the angles at A and B equal the angle at P by measuring all three of them with a protractor.

Such angles are called *inscribed angles* and, to prove that they are equal, we will show that their measure is half that of the common arc, $\widehat{XY}$, that they intercept.

Definition

An *inscribed angle* is an angle whose vertex is on a circle, with each of the angle's sides intersecting the circle in another point.

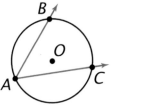 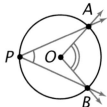

In the figure at the left above, $\angle A$ is an inscribed angle of circle O. Here, $\angle A$ *intercepts* $\widehat{BC}$ and is *inscribed* in $\widehat{BAC}$. Note that these two arcs make up the entire circle. Every inscribed angle in a circle divides the circle into two arcs, one of which the angle intercepts and the other in which it is inscribed.

The figure at the right above shows a central angle, $\angle O$, and an inscribed angle, $\angle P$, that intercept the same arc, $\widehat{AB}$. By definition, we know that $\angle O = m\widehat{AB}$. You can see that $\angle P$ is smaller than $\angle O$; so $\angle P < m\widehat{AB}$. We can prove that

$$\angle P = \frac{1}{2}m\widehat{AB}.$$

In our diagram, the center of the circle lies *inside* the inscribed angle. It could also lie *on* the angle or *outside* it as the figures at the right show. In all three cases, the result is the same: $\angle P = \frac{1}{2}m\widehat{AB}$.

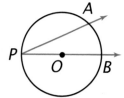

Theorem 63
An inscribed angle is equal in measure to half its intercepted arc.

This theorem has a couple of useful corollaries. The first of them justifies the claim that the screen angles at every point on the circle are equal. Look again at the drawing on the facing page to see why.

Corollary 1 to Theorem 63
Inscribed angles that intercept the same arc are equal.

$$\angle P = \frac{1}{2}m\widehat{AB}$$

Corollary 2 to Theorem 63
An angle inscribed in a semicircle is a right angle.

Exercises

Set I

Skeet Range. The figure below shows a skeet range.

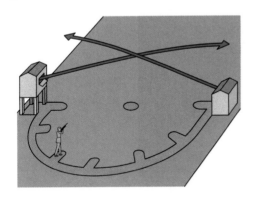

In the overhead view of it below, the shooting stations are located at seven equally spaced points, A through G, on circle O, and at point H centered on chord AG.*

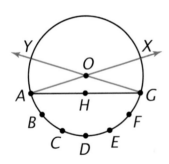

1. Given that ∠A = 16.5°, find ∠G.

2. Find ∠AOG.

3. Given that the six arcs between points A through G have equal measures, find the measure of each arc.

The clay pigeons are released in the directions AX and GY.

4. Find $m\widehat{GX}$ and $m\widehat{AY}$.

5. Find $m\widehat{YX}$.

---

*Rules of the Game, by the Diagram Group (St. Martin's Press, 1990).

Theorem 63. Complete the following proof of Theorem 63 by giving the reasons.

An inscribed angle is equal in measure to half its intercepted arc.

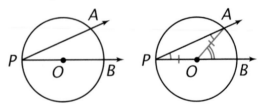

Given: ∠P is inscribed in circle O.

Prove: $\angle P = \frac{1}{2} m\widehat{AB}$.

Proof

Case 1. *The center of the circle lies on a side of the angle.*

6. Draw OA. Why?

7. OP = OA. Why?

8. ∠PAO = ∠P. Why?

9. ∠P + ∠PAO = ∠AOB. Why?

10. ∠P + ∠P = ∠AOB; so 2∠P = ∠AOB. Why?

11. $\angle P = \frac{1}{2} \angle AOB$. Why?

12. $m\widehat{AB} = \angle AOB$. Why?

13. $\angle P = \frac{1}{2} m\widehat{AB}$. Why?

Case 2. *The center of the circle lies inside the angle.*

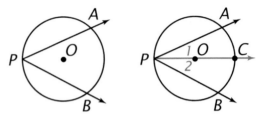

14. Draw PO intersecting the circle at C. Why?

15. ∠APB = ∠1 + ∠2. Why?

16. Because $\angle 1 = \frac{1}{2} m\widehat{AC}$ and $\angle 2 = \frac{1}{2} m\widehat{CB}$

(proved in case 1), $\angle APB = \frac{1}{2}m\widehat{AC} +$ $\frac{1}{2}m\widehat{CB} = \frac{1}{2}(m\widehat{AC} + m\widehat{CB})$. Why?

17. $m\widehat{AC} + m\widehat{CB} = m\widehat{AB}$. Why?

18. $\angle APB = \frac{1}{2}m\widehat{AB}$. Why?

There is one more case, which can be proved in a similar way.

19. What do you think it is?

Complete the following proofs of the corollaries to Theorem 63 by giving the reasons.

Corollary 1. Inscribed angles that intercept the same arc are equal.

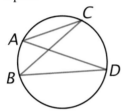

Given: $\angle A$ and $\angle B$ are inscribed angles that intercept $\widehat{CD}$.
Prove: $\angle A = \angle B$.

Proof

20. Because $\angle A$ and $\angle B$ are inscribed angles, $\angle A = \frac{1}{2}m\widehat{CD}$ and $\angle B = \frac{1}{2}m\widehat{CD}$. Why?

21. $\angle A = \angle B$. Why?

Corollary 2. An angle inscribed in a semicircle is a right angle.

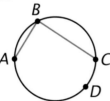

Given: $\angle B$ is inscribed in semicircle ABC.
Prove: $\angle B$ is a right angle.

Proof
Because $\angle B$ is inscribed in the semicircle ABC, the arc that it intercepts, $\widehat{ADC}$, is also a semicircle.

22. $m\widehat{ADC} = 180°$. Why?

23. $\angle B = \frac{1}{2}m\widehat{ADC}$. Why?

24. $\angle B = \frac{1}{2}(180°) = 90°$. Why?

25. $\angle B$ is a right angle. Why?

Inscribed Triangle. In the figure below, the vertices of $\triangle ABC$ lie on circle O.

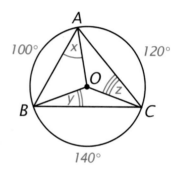

26. Copy the figure and mark it as needed to do the following exercises.

With respect to the circle, what are the three angles

27. whose vertex is O called?

28. of $\triangle ABC$ called?

29. Find the measures of $\angle AOB$, $\angle BOC$, and $\angle COA$.

30. Use your answers to find x, y, and z.

31. Use x, y, and z to find the measures of $\angle ABC$, $\angle BCA$, and $\angle CAB$.

32. Check your answers by using the measures of the three arcs to find the measures of $\angle ABC$, $\angle BCA$, and $\angle CAB$.

Set II

Forty Angles. In the figure below from a book on the number π, a circle has been divided into 40 equal arcs.* Each inscribed angle intercepts an arc equal in measure to 14 of these arcs.

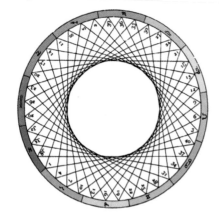

33. What is the measure of one of these arcs?

34. What is the measure of each inscribed angle?

Tangents, Chords, and Intercepted Arcs. In the figure below, line AT is tangent to circle O, and AB is a diameter. $\angle CAT$ intercepts $\overset{\frown}{CA}$.

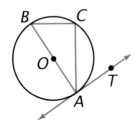

35. What can you conclude about $\angle BAT$? Explain.

36. What can you conclude about $\angle CAT$ and $\angle CAB$?

37. What can you conclude about $\angle C$? Explain.

38. What can you conclude about $\angle B$ and $\angle CAB$? Explain.

A History of Pi, by Petr Beckmann (Golem Press, 1971).

39. What can you conclude about $\angle CAT$ and $\angle B$? Explain.

40. Why is $\angle B = \frac{1}{2} m\overset{\frown}{CA}$?

41. Why is $\angle CAT = \frac{1}{2} m\overset{\frown}{CA}$?

42. What do exercises 35 through 41 prove about the relation of the measure of an angle formed by a tangent and a chord to the measure of its intercepted arc?

Similar Inscribed Triangles. In the figure below, $\triangle ABC \sim \triangle DEF$.

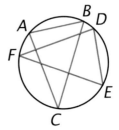

Given that $\angle C = n°$, find each of the following measures in terms of n.

43. $\angle F$.

44. $m\overset{\frown}{AB}$.

45. $m\overset{\frown}{DE}$.

46. What can you conclude about AB and DE? Explain.

47. What does your conclusion reveal about $\triangle ABC$ and $\triangle DEF$? Explain.

Square-Root Construction. The figure below shows a method, known since the time of Euclid, for constructing the square root of a number.†

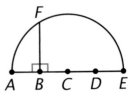

†*The History of Mathematics: An Introduction,* by David M. Burton (Allyn & Bacon, 1985).

48. Draw the figure as follows:

(1) Use your ruler to draw AE 4 inches long and mark points B, C, and D on it so that AB = BC = CD = DE = 1 inch.

(2) Draw the arc with center at C and radius CA.

(3) At point B, construct a line perpendicular to AE, and let F be the point in which the line intersects the arc.

(4) Draw AF and FE.

49. What can you conclude about ∠AFE? Explain

50. What relation does BF have to △AFE?

51. Write a proportion relating AB, BF, and BE.

52. Use the proportion and the lengths of AB and BE to find the exact length of BF.

53. Use your calculator to find the approximate length of BF to the nearest hundredth.

54. Measure BF with your ruler. Does the result seem to agree with your answer to exercise 53?

Intersecting Triangles and Circles. In the figure below, circles A and B intersect at C and D. Point C lies on △DEF and △DGH.

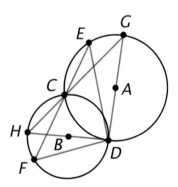

55. Copy the figure by first drawing circles A and B and then drawing △DEF and △DGH.

56. What can you conclude about △DEF and △DGH? Explain.

It is possible to tell which triangle is larger without doing any measuring or tracing.

57. Which triangle is larger? Explain.

55. (*continued*) Draw AB.

58. How is AB related to GH? Explain.

Set III

Finding the Center. A carpenter had carefully cut out four circular wooden disks to use as wheels for a toy. His next task was to find the center of each disk so that he could drill a hole for the axle. The only tools that he had on hand were a set square and a pencil.*

How could he use these tools to find the center of each wheel? Illustrate your answer with a drawing.

A Mathematical Jamboree, by Brian Bolt (Cambridge University Press, 1995).

LESSON 5

Secant Angles

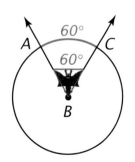

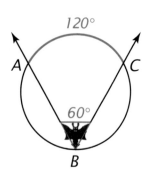

In this circular woodcut by Escher, pictures of angels and devils are fitted together like pieces in a jigsaw puzzle. But, unlike those of a jigsaw puzzle, the parts become progressively smaller and more numerous as they approach the edge. By this device, the artist has managed to convey an impression of the infinite within a finite region.

The intricate and orderly design of the picture shows that Escher was strongly influenced by ideas from geometry. For example, if the wing tips of the large devils and angels that meet in the center are connected to the center and to each other by line segments, six equilateral triangles are formed.

One of these triangles is shown in the first figure at the left. Because the triangle is equilateral, the angle at the center has a measure of 60°. If we extend the angle's sides so that they intersect the circle, the intercepted arc also must have a measure of 60°.

If the vertex of this angle were on the circle rather than at its center, as shown in the second figure, it would be an inscribed angle and would intercept a larger arc having a measure of 120°.

Figure 1   Figure 2   Figure 3   Figure 4

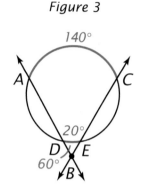

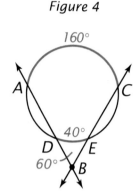

We know the relation between the measures of central and inscribed angles and the arcs that they intercept. What about other angles, such as those shown above?

In figures 1 and 2, the vertex of the angle is inside the circle. Although the size of the arc intercepted by the angle differs in each picture, the *sum of the measures of that arc and the arc intercepted by its vertical angle does not change.* A comparable result holds for figures 3 and 4, where the vertex of the angle is outside the circle. Here, *the difference of the measures of the two intercepted arcs does not change.*

The lines that form the angles in these figures are called *secants.*

Definition

A *secant* is a line that intersects a circle in two points.

The angles labeled ∠ABC in the figures are called *secant angles.*

Definition

A *secant angle* is an angle whose sides are contained in two secants of a circle so that each side intersects the circle in at least one point other than the angle's vertex.

The four figures above suggest the following theorems.

Theorem 64

A secant angle whose vertex is inside a circle is equal in measure to half the sum of the arcs intercepted by it and its vertical angle.

Theorem 65

A secant angle whose vertex is outside a circle is equal in measure to half the difference of its larger and smaller intercepted arcs.

Exercises

Set I

Complete the following proof of Theorem 64 by giving the reasons.

Theorem 64. A secant angle whose vertex is inside a circle is equal in measure to half the sum of the arcs intercepted by it and its vertical angle.

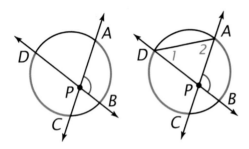

Given: Secant ∠APB with P inside the circle.

Prove: $\angle APB = \frac{1}{2}(m\widehat{AB} + m\widehat{CD})$.

Proof

1. Draw DA. Why?
2. $\angle APB = \angle 1 + \angle 2$. Why?
3. $\angle 1 = \frac{1}{2}m\widehat{AB}$ and $\angle 2 = \frac{1}{2}m\widehat{CD}$. Why?
4. $\angle APB = \frac{1}{2}m\widehat{AB} + \frac{1}{2}m\widehat{CD} = \frac{1}{2}(m\widehat{AB} + m\widehat{CD})$. Why?

In the figure below, chords AB and CD cut the circle into four arcs whose measures are given in terms of x.

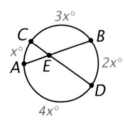

5. Find x.
6. Find the measures of the four arcs.
7. Find the measures of the angles formed by the chords.

Complete the following proof of Theorem 65 by giving the reasons.

Theorem 65. A secant angle whose vertex is outside a circle is equal in measure to half the difference of its larger and smaller intercepted arcs.

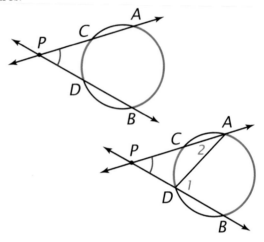

Given: Secant ∠APB with P outside the circle.

Prove: $\angle APB = \frac{1}{2}(m\widehat{AB} - m\widehat{CD})$.

Proof

8. Draw DA. Why?
9. $\angle 1 = \angle APB + \angle 2$. Why?
10. $\angle APB = \angle 1 - \angle 2$. Why?
11. $\angle 1 = \frac{1}{2}m\widehat{AB}$ and $\angle 2 = \frac{1}{2}m\widehat{CD}$. Why?
12. $\angle APB = \frac{1}{2}m\widehat{AB} - \frac{1}{2}m\widehat{CD} = \frac{1}{2}(m\widehat{AB} - m\widehat{CD})$. Why?

In the figure below, the sides of △ABC cut the circle into four arcs, three of whose measures are given.

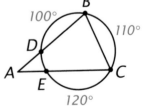

13. Find $m\widehat{DE}$.
14. Find ∠A.
15. Find ∠B.
16. Find ∠C.

Danger Angle. A "danger angle" is used by navigators to avoid a hazardous region near a coast.*

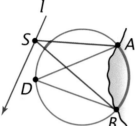

In the figure above, line l represents the path of a ship and points A and B represent two lighthouses on the coast. The hazardous region is inside the circle.

17. What is the danger angle, $\angle D$, called with respect to the circle?

18. Given that $m\widehat{AB} = 110°$, find $\angle D$.

19. What is $\angle S$ called with respect to the circle?

20. What can you conclude about the measure of $\angle S$ when the ship is at S?

21. What could you conclude about the measure of $\angle S$ if S were inside the danger circle?

Perpendicular Chords. In the figure below, $AB \perp CD$.

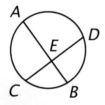

What can you conclude about

22. $\angle AED$?

23. $m\widehat{AD} + m\widehat{CB}$?

24. $m\widehat{AC} + m\widehat{DB}$?

Given that $m\widehat{AD} = 110°$ and $m\widehat{DB} = 80°$, find

25. $m\widehat{CB}$.

26. $m\widehat{AC}$.

Dutton's Navigation and Piloting, by Elbert S. Maloney (Naval Institute Press, 1985).

Star Problem 1. In the figure below, the star divides the circle into equal arcs.

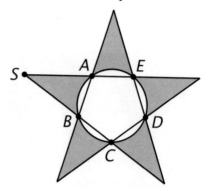

Find each of the following measures.

27. $m\widehat{AB}$.

28. $m\widehat{CDE}$.

29. $\angle S$.

30. $m\widehat{CDA}$.

31. $\angle ABC$.

32. What is the sum of the five angles at the points of the star?

Star Problem 2. In the figure below, the points of the star divide the circle into equal arcs.

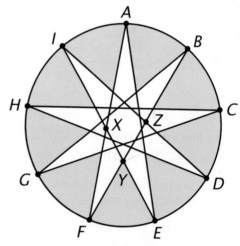

Find each of the following measures.

33. $m\widehat{EF}$.

34. $\angle A$.

35. $\angle AXI$.

36. $\angle FYE$.

37. $\angle BZD$.

38. What is the sum of the nine angles at the points of the star?

Set II

Angle of View. The angle of view of a camera lens is about 50°.*

The figure below shows an overhead view of the photograph setup. The camera is at C so that a group of people standing between A and B just fits in its angle of view.

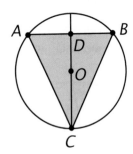

39. Given that ∠ACB = 50°, find $m\widehat{AB}$.

40. Given that AD = DB, why is CD ⊥ AB?

41. Why is △ACD ≅ △BCD?

Suppose the people standing between A and B form a row 16 feet long, making AB = 16.

42. Find CD to the nearest foot.

43. To where else could the photographer move so that the row of people just fits into the camera's angle of view?

44. What effect would moving the camera toward AB along CD have on the photograph?

*The Camera (Time-Life Books, 1970).

The Seasons. The Greek astronomer Hipparchus used the figure below to explain the lengths of the four seasons.†

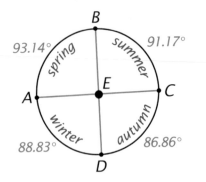

He thought that, during a year, the sun traveled in a circle at a steady speed around the earth.

45. Given that chords AC and BD intersect at E, find the measures of the four angles at E corresponding to the four seasons.

46. Did Hipparchus place the earth, E, at the center of the circle? Explain.

47. According to the figure, which season lasts the longest?

48. A year is 365.25 days; according to Hipparchus, how many days did summer last?

Place Kicker. The figure below (not to scale) shows an overhead view of a football field with a place kicker at P and goal posts at A and B.

49. Copy the circle and lines inside it and mark your figure as needed to do each of the following exercises.

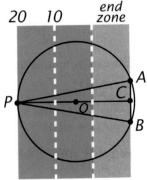

†*The Cambridge Illustrated History of Astronomy,* Michael Hoskin, ed. (Cambridge University Press, 1997).

50. Given that O is the center of the circle and PC ⊥ AB, what can you conclude about point C? Explain.

Given that the kicker is on the 20-yard line (which makes PC = 90 feet) and that AB (the distance between the goal posts) is 18.5 feet, find each of the following measures to the nearest degree.

51. ∠APC.

52. ∠APB.

53. m⌢AB.

54. For what other positions of the kicker is the angle between the goal posts the same?

55. What would happen to the angle if the kicker were to move from P to a place outside the circle?

Angles Problem. The figure below consists of six line segments and a circle divided into 18 equal arcs.

56. What is the measure of each small arc?

57. Use your protractor and ruler to make a large copy of the figure. Find and mark the measures of as many angles in your figure as you can.

58. Name the triangles in the figure that are isosceles.

59. Name two triangles that are similar.

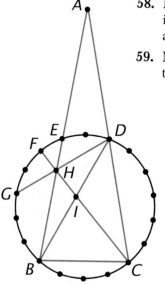

Used by permission of Johnny Hart and Creators Syndicate, Inc.

The King of Id has commissioned a statue of himself for the village square. Unfortunately, what the royal sculptor has turned out so far doesn't seem to be what the king has in mind.

The figure below shows three positions of the king as he walks toward the original statue. The measure of the angle formed by the king's lines of sight to the top and bottom of the statue depends on where the king is standing. Can you describe what happens to it as the king walks from a great distance away to the base of the statue?

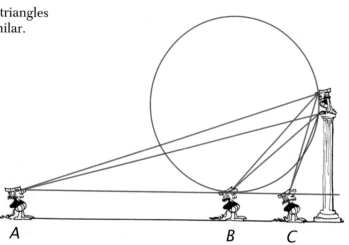

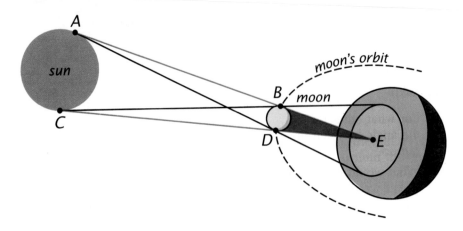

Tangent Segments and Intersecting Chords

A total eclipse of the sun is a spectacular sight. The first recorded description of a solar eclipse was on October 22, 2137 B.C. It was seen in China, and the people ran through the streets beating drums and shooting fireworks to try to scare away the dragon that was swallowing the sun.*

Such an eclipse occurs when the moon passes between the earth and the sun in such a way that its shadow touches the earth. This shadow is a cone. Because of the relative sizes of the moon and sun and their relative distances from the earth, the tip of the cone often misses the earth. But when it touches the earth, a total eclipse can be seen by those in the area of contact.

At the same time, a partial eclipse of the sun can be seen from a much larger region, shaded blue in the diagram. Within this region, the disk of the sun is only partly covered by the moon.

The lines of the shadows in the figure are tangent to the circles that represent the sun and moon. Two of them, AB and CD, meet in point E. The segments EA and EC are called *tangent segments* from point E to the circle of the sun; segments EB and ED are tangent segments from point E to the circle of the moon.

Sun and Earth, by Herbert Friedman (Scientific American Library, 1986).

Definition

If a line is tangent to a circle, then any segment of the line having the point of tangency as one of its endpoints is a *tangent segment* to the circle.

It is easy to prove that the two tangent segments from an external point to a circle are always equal, no matter where the point and circle may be.

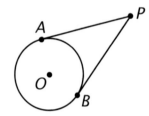

Theorem 66. The Tangent Segments Theorem

The tangent segments to a circle from an external point are equal.

> *Given:* Circle O with tangent segments PA and PB.
> *Prove:* PA = PB.

Proof

Draw PO, OA, and OB. Because PA and PB are tangent segments to circle O, PA ⊥ OA and PB ⊥ OB (if a line is tangent to a circle, it is perpendicular to the radius drawn to the point of contact). Therefore, ∠PAO and ∠PBO are right angles; so △PAO and △PBO are right triangles. Because OA = OB (all radii of a circle are equal) and PO = PO, △PAO ≅ △PBO (HL). Therefore, PA = PB.

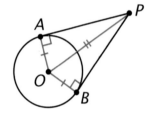

The Tangent Segments Theorem is not surprising. Another theorem about two segments related to a circle is quite surprising. This theorem is about two chords that intersect inside a circle.

Theorem 67. The Intersecting Chords Theorem

If two chords intersect in a circle, the product of the lengths of the segments of one chord is equal to the product of the lengths of the segments of the other chord.

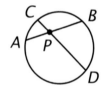

In regard to the figure at the right in which chords AB and CD intersect at P, this theorem says that AP · PB = CP · PD. The proof is easier than you might guess and is included in the exercises.

Exercises

Set I

Korean Proof. At the right is the proof of one of the theorems of this lesson as it appears in a Korean geometry book.

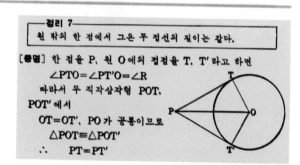

정리 7
원 밖의 한 점에서 그은 두 접선의 길이는 같다.

[증명] 한 점을 P, 원 O에의 접점을 T, T′ 라고 하면
  ∠PTO=∠PT′O=∠R
따라서 두 직각삼각형 POT,
POT′ 에서
  OT=OT′, PO 가 공통이므로
  △POT≡△POT′
∴   PT=PT′

1. What do you think the statement that ∠PTO = ∠PT′O = ∠R means?

2. Why is OT = OT′?

3. Why is △POT ≅ △POT′?

4. Why is PT = PT′?

5. State the theorem that has been proved as a complete sentence.

Complete the following proof of Theorem 67 by giving the reasons.

Theorem 67. If two chords intersect in a circle, the product of the lengths of the segments of one chord is equal to the product of the lengths of the segments of the other chord.

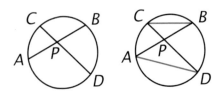

Given: Chords AB and CD intersect at point P in the circle.
Prove: PA · PB = PC · PD.

Proof

6. Draw CB and AD. Why?

7. ∠A = ∠C and ∠D = ∠B. Why?

8. △APD ~ △CPB. Why?

9. $\dfrac{PA}{PC} = \dfrac{PD}{PB}$. Why?

10. PA · PB = PC · PD. Why?

Lunar Eclipse. The figure below (not to scale) represents an eclipse of the moon. Segments AP and CP are tangent to the circles of the sun and the earth.

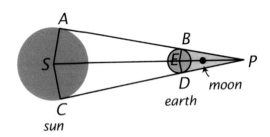

11. Why is SA ∥ EB and SC ∥ ED?

12. Why is AP = CP and BP = DP?

13. Why is △SAP ≅ △SCP?

14. Why does PS bisect ∠APC?

15. Why is △SAP ~ △EBP?

Intersecting Chords. In the figure below, chords AB, CD, EF, and GH intersect in point P.

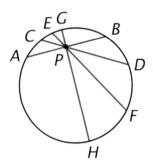

As the chords get longer, what happens to

16. the sum of the lengths of the two segments into which P divides them?

17. the product of the lengths of the two segments into which P divides them?

Tangent Construction. A method for constructing the tangents to a given circle from a given external point is illustrated by the figures below.

18. Draw a circle with center at O and choose an external point P as shown above.

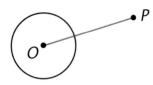

(1) Draw OP.

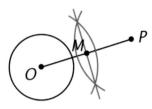

(2) Bisect OP and label its midpoint M.

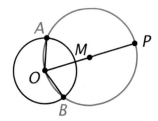

(3) Draw a circle with M as center and MO as radius. Let A and B be the two points in which this circle intersects circle O.

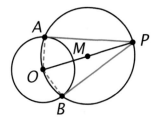

(4) Draw PA and PB.

Explain how the construction works by answering each of the following questions.

19. What kind of angles are ∠OAP and ∠OBP? Explain.

20. What relation does PA have to OA and PB have to OB?

21. Why are PA and PB tangent to circle O?

Tangent Triangle. The sides of △ABC are tangent to circle O at D, E, and F; AC = 9, CB = 12, and AB = 15.

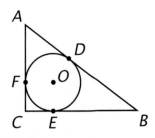

22. Copy the figure and mark it as needed to do each of the following exercises.

23. What can you conclude about △ABC? Explain.

22. (*continued*) Draw OF and OE.

24. What can you conclude about CFOE?

22. (*continued*) Given OF = OE = *r*, express the other lengths in the figure in terms of *r*.

25. Write an equation and solve it for *r*.

Tangent Quadrilateral. In the figure below, the sides of quadrilatereal ABCD are tangent to the circle at points E, F, G, and H; AE = *w*, EB = *x*, DG = *y*, and GC = *z*

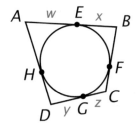

26. Copy the figure and label the lengths of the other four tangent segments.

27. What do you notice about the opposite sides of ABCD? Explain.

Set II

Grid Exercise 1. On graph paper, draw a pair of axes extending 10 units in each direction from the origin.

28. Use your compass to draw a circle with its center at (0, 0) and radius 5.

29. Use the distance formula to show that, if P(*x*, *y*) is on this circle, then $x^2 + y^2 = 25$.

28. (*continued*) Label the following points on the circle: A(0, 5) and B(4, −3).

30. Show that the coordinates of points A and B are solutions to the equation $x^2 + y^2 = 25$.

28. (*continued*) Plot point P(10, 5) and draw PA, PB, and OB.

31. How do you know that PA is tangent to circle O?

32. Use the slopes of PB and OB to show that PB also is tangent to the circle.

33. Find the lengths of PA and PB.

28. (*continued*) Label the following points on the circle: C(−4, 3) and D(−3, −4).

34. From what point can tangent segments be drawn to touch the circle at C and D?

Ridiculous Question. The following problem was once posed as a "ridiculous question" in *Scientific American* magazine.*

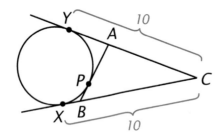

Tangent segments CX and CY have been drawn from point C to the circle. Each has a length of 10 units. Point P has been randomly chosen on the circle and AB then drawn tangent to the circle at P.

35. What is the perimeter of △ABC?

36. Explain your reasoning.

37. Why do you suppose the problem of finding the perimeter of △ABC was called "ridiculous"?

Grid Exercise 2. On graph paper, draw a pair of axes extending 15 units to the right and 15 units up from the origin.

38. Use your compass to draw a circle with its center at (9, 8) and radius 5.

39. Use the distance formula to show that, if P(x, y) is on this circle, then $(x − 9)^2 + (y − 8)^2 = 25$.

38. (*continued*) Label the following points on the circle: A(9, 13), B(14, 8), C(13, 11), and D(6, 4).

Mathematical Magic Show, by Martin Gardner (Knopf, 1977).

40. Show that the coordinates of these points are solutions to the equation $(x − 9)^2 + (y − 8)^2 = 25$.

38. (*continued*) Draw AB and CD and let P be the point in which they intersect.

41. The coordinates of P are integers. What are they?

42. Find the exact lengths of PA, PB, PC, and PD.

43. Find PA · PB and PC · PD.

Chord Division. In the figure below, diameter AB of circle O is perpendicular to chord CD; CP = x, OP = d, and OB = r.

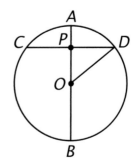

44. Copy the figure and mark it as needed to do each of the following exercises.

45. Why is PD = x?

Name a line segment in the figure whose length is

46. r + d.

47. r − d.

48. Use the Intersecting Chords Theorem to show that $x^2 = r^2 − d^2$.

44. (*continued*) Draw another chord through P and label its endpoints E and F.

49. Show that EP · PF = $r^2 − d^2$.

The result of exercise 49 shows how the product of the lengths of the segments into which a point divides a chord, EP · PF, is determined by r and d.

50. What do r and d represent with respect to the circle and the chord?

Suppose a circle has a radius of 5.

51. Where would you draw a chord, EF, and where would you choose a point P on it so that EP · PF is as large as possible?

52. To what number would EP · PF be equal?

Earth's Shadow. The following problem is based on the drawing for exercises 11 through 15.

53. Given that the radii of the sun and the earth are 432,000 miles and 3,960 miles, respectively, and that the distance between their centers is 93,000,000 miles, find EP, the length of the earth's shadow.

Set III

The Brick Moon. The first known proposal for a space station above the earth appeared in a story titled "The Brick Moon" published in 1869.*

According to the story, the "Brick Moon" should be in an orbit 4,000 miles high.

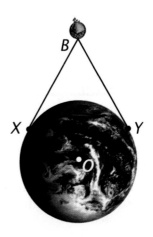

Copy the figure above in which circle O represents the earth, point B represents the Brick Moon, and X and Y represent the farthest points on the earth from which the Brick Moon can be seen. Use 4,000 miles as the radius of the earth and find the distance from the Brick Moon to these two points.

Space Travel: A History, by Wernher von Braun and Frederick I. Ordway, III (Harper & Row, 1985).

CHAPTER 12 Summary and Review

Basic Ideas

Courtesy of Elmer Atkins; © 1963 Saturday Review, Inc.

Postulate

10. *The Arc Addition Postulate.* If C is on $\overset{\frown}{AB}$, then $m\overset{\frown}{AC} + m\overset{\frown}{CB} = m\overset{\frown}{ACB}$.   499

Theorems

Corollary to the definition of a circle. All radii of a circle are equal.   485

56. If a line through the center of a circle is perpendicular to a chord, it also bisects the chord.   485

57. If a line through the center of a circle bisects a chord that is not a diameter, it is also perpendicular to the chord.   485

58. The perpendicular bisector of a chord of a circle contains the center of the circle.   485

59. If a line is tangent to a circle, it is perpendicular to the radius drawn to the point of contact.   492

60. If a line is perpendicular to a radius at its outer endpoint, it is tangent to the circle.   492

61. In a circle, equal chords have equal arcs.   499

62. In a circle, equal arcs have equal chords.   499

63. An inscribed angle is equal in measure to half its intercepted arc.   505

Corollary 1. Inscribed angles that intercept the same arc are equal.   505

Corollary 2. An angle inscribed in a semicircle is a right angle.   505

64. A secant angle whose vertex is inside a circle is equal in measure to half the sum of the arcs intercepted by it and its vertical angle.   511

65. A secant angle whose vertex is outside a circle is equal in measure to half the difference of its larger and smaller intercepted arcs.   511

66. *The Tangent Segments Theorem.* The tangent segments to a circle from an external point are equal.   517

67. *The Intersecting Chords Theorem.* If two chords intersect in a circle, the product of the lengths of the segments of one chord is equal to the product of the lengths of the segments of the other chord.   517

Exercises

Set I

Panoramic Camera. The photograph above of Paris was taken in 1846 with a camera whose lens could turn through an angle of 150°.

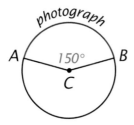

The figure above shows an overhead view with the camera at C. The scene photographed lies within the purple arc of ∠C.

1. What are AC and CB called with respect to circle C?

2. What is ∠C called?

3. What kind of arc is the arc of the photograph?

4. What is $m\widehat{AB}$?

Chords and Radius. An exercise in an old geometry book says to "draw a circle and then draw a chord equal to the radius. Also draw a chord equal to twice the radius."*

*First Steps in Geometry, by G. A. Wentworth and G. A. Hill (Ginn, 1901).

5. Use your straightedge and compass to make the drawing described.

6. What is a chord equal to twice the radius called?

7. What is the measure of the minor arc associated with the chord equal to the radius?

8. What is the measure of one of the arcs associated with the chord equal to twice the radius?

Finding Lengths and Angles. Solve for x in each of the following figures. The points labeled O are the centers of the circles.

9.

10.

11.

12.

13.

14.

15.

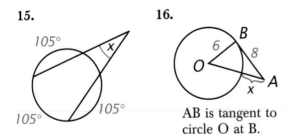

16.

AB is tangent to circle O at B.

Two Equilateral Triangles. In the figure below, △ABC and △ADE are equilateral and A is the center of both circles. AB = 4 and BD = 2.

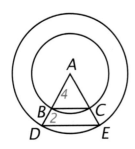

Find the following measures.

17. BC.

18. $m\widehat{BC}$.

19. DE.

20. $m\widehat{DE}$.

21. How do BC and DE compare in length?

22. How do $\widehat{BC}$ and $\widehat{DE}$ compare in measure?

Not Quite Right. In the figure below, sides AB and AD of quadrilateral ABCD are tangent to circle C.

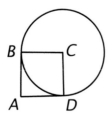

What can you conclude about

23. ∠B and ∠D? Why?

24. ∠A and ∠C? Why?

25. AB and AD? Why?

26. BC and CD? Why?

Three Ratios. In the figure below, circles have been drawn with two sides of equilateral △ABC as their diameters.

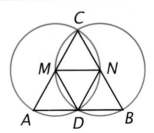

27. What relation do the four small triangles have to △ABC?

Comparing one of these triangles with △ABC, find the ratio of their

28. corresponding angles.

29. corresponding sides.

30. perimeters.

31. areas.

Set II

Tangent Circles. In the figure below, circles O and P intersect at A. Also, AC and AD are chords of circle P.

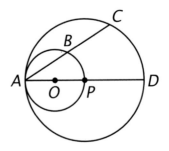

32. Copy the figure and draw PB.

33. What is the measure of ∠ABP? Explain.

34. What does the measure of ∠ABP tell us about PB and AC?

35. What can you conclude about AB and BC? Explain.

32. (*continued*) Draw OB and PC.

36. What kind of triangles are △AOB and △APC?

37. What else can you conclude about them? Explain.

38. What can you conclude about OB and PC? Explain.

Arch Problem. The arches in the dome of Santa Maria del Fiore in Florence, Italy, are based on the geometric figure below.*

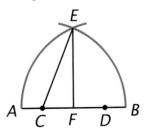

39. Draw the figure as follows:

(1) Use your ruler to draw AB 5 cm long. Mark points C and D on AB so that AC = 1 cm and DB = 1 cm.

(2) With C as center and CB as radius, draw an arc as shown. With D as center and AD as radius, draw a second arc. Let E be the point in which the arcs intersect.

(3) From E, construct EF ⊥ AB. Also draw CE.

Calculate the following lengths. Mark each length on your figure as you find it.

40. CE.

41. CF.

42. EF.

43. Find $\dfrac{EF}{AB}$, the ratio of the arch's rise to its span.

44. Find $m\widehat{AE}$, the measure of one of the two arcs of the arch.

Prehistoric Ring. The inhabitants of prehistoric England constructed rings of standing stones in different geometric shapes.[†]

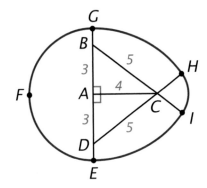

One egg-shaped ring consisting of four arcs is shown in the figure above. Use the following information and the fact that △BAC and △DAC are 3-4-5 right triangles to find the measure of each of the following arcs to the nearest degree.

45. $\widehat{EFG}$, whose center is A.

46. $\widehat{GH}$, whose center is D.

47. $\widehat{HI}$, whose center is C.

48. $\widehat{IE}$, whose center is B.

49. How do the degree measures of the two parts of the ring on either side of GE seem to compare?

50. Explain, by using △BCD and ∠HCI, why $m\widehat{GH} + m\widehat{HI} + m\widehat{IE} = 180°$.

---

*Why Buildings Fall Down, by Matthys Levy and Mario Salvadori (Norton, 1992).

†Geometry and Algebra in Ancient Civilizations, by B. L. van der Waerden (Springer, 1983).

Circular Saw. The figure below shows the blade of a circular saw cutting into a board. The radius OD of the blade is perpendicular to the board.

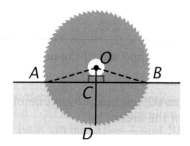

51. What can you conclude about point C?

If the diameter of the blade is 10 inches and the cutting depth, CD, is 3.75 inches,

52. find the length of the cut from A to B.

53. find the measure of ∠AOD.

54. find $m\overarc{ADB}$.

Golden Ratio. In the figure below, circles A, B, and C have radii equal to 1 and are tangent to a diameter of circle O.*

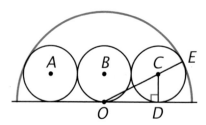

Find the exact length of

55. OD.

56. OC.

57. OE.

58. Find the exact ratio of the radius of circle O to the diameter of circle C.

59. Find the value of this ratio to six decimal places.

60. Find the exact ratio of the diameter of circle C to the radius of circle O.

—————————

*The Loom of God: Mathematical Tapestries at the Edge of Time, by Clifford A. Pickover (Plenum, 1997).

61. Find the value of this ratio to six decimal places.

62. What do you notice?

Pond Problem. The following problem is from a book published in London in 1754.†

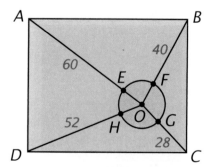

The figure above is an overhead view of a rectangular garden that contains a round pond. AO, BO, CO, and DO connect the corners of the garden to the center of the pond. Given that AE = 60 yards, BF = 40 yards, CG = 28 yards, and DH = 52 yards, the problem is to find the radius of the pond.

The figure below suggests a way to solve the problem. In it, OI, OJ, OK, and OL have been drawn so that they are perpendicular to the sides of the rectangle.

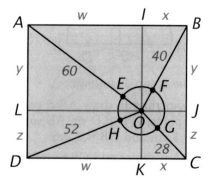

63. Can you figure out a way to find the radius of the pond?

—————————

†"The Ladies Diary," in Geometry Civilized: History, Culture, and Technique, by J. L. Heilbron (Clarendon Press, 1998).

Solving Systems of Equations

To solve a system of two equations in two variables means to find every ordered pair of numbers that can simultaneously replace the variables in both equations to make them true. If the equations are linear, this solution corresponds to finding the coordinates of the point in which two lines intersect. (If the two lines are parallel, they have no point in common and so the system has no solutions.)

Solving by Substitution

For some systems of equations, it is convenient to first solve one of the equations for one variable in terms of the other. The expression that results can then be substituted into the other equation. These steps, together with the rest of the method, are illustrated by the following examples.

Example 1: Solve the system

$$2x + y = 11$$
$$y = x + 5$$

Solution: The second equation is already solved for y in terms of x. Because y and $x + 5$ are the same number, we can substitute $x + 5$ for y in the first equation:

$$2x + (x + 5) = 11$$

Solving for x, we have

$$3x + 5 = 11$$
$$3x = 6$$
$$x = 2$$

Substituting this value for x in the second equation gives

$$y = 2 + 5$$
$$y = 7$$

The solution to the system is $(2, 7)$.

A graph of the two lines of this system and their point of intersection is shown below.

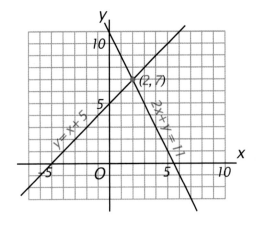

Example 2: Solve the system

$$x - y = 11$$
$$3x + 2y = 8$$

Solution: In this case, we might begin by solving the first equation for x and substituting the result in the second equation.

$$x = y + 11$$
$$3(y + 11) + 2y = 8$$
$$3y + 33 + 2y = 8$$
$$5y + 33 = 8$$
$$5y = -25$$
$$y = -5$$

We have already shown that $x = y + 11$, and so $x = -5 + 11 = 6$. The solution to the system is $(6, -5)$.

Solving by Linear Combination

Another way to solve a system of equations is to combine the equations to form an equation that contains only one of the variables. The solution to this equation can then be substituted into either of the original equations to find the other variable.

Example 3: Solve the system

$$4x + 3y = 34$$
$$x - 3y = 1$$

Solution: We can eliminate y by adding the two equations:

$$4x + 3y = 34$$
$$\underline{x - 3y = 1}$$
$$5x = 35$$

Dividing both sides of the resulting equation by 5, we get

$$x = 7.$$

Substituting 7 for x in the first equation, we get

$$4(7) + 3y = 34$$
$$28 + 3y = 34$$

$$3y = 6$$
$$y = 2.$$

The solution is (7, 2).

Example 4: Solve the system

$$3x + 7y = 25$$
$$5x + 4y = 11$$

Solution: We can eliminate x by multiplying the first equation by 5, multiplying the second equation by -3, and then adding the resulting equations:

$$5(3x + 7y) = 5(25) \rightarrow 15x + 35y = 125$$
$$-3(5x + 4y) = -3(11) \rightarrow \underline{-15x - 12y = -33}$$
$$23y = 92$$
$$y = 4$$

$$3x + 7(4) = 25$$
$$3x + 28 = 25$$
$$3x = -3$$
$$x = -1.$$

The solution is $(-1, 4)$.

Exercises

Solve the following systems of equations.

1. $x = y$
   $2x = y + 8$

2. $y = 2x$
   $4x - y = 14$

3. $y = x - 2$
   $3(x + 1) = 4y$

4. $y = x - 7$
   $y = 5x - 19$

5. $x = y + 1$
   $2x = 3y + 3$

6. $y = 3x - 1$
   $x + 2y = 33$

7. $x + 11 = 5y$
   $x = 2(3y - 8)$

8. $x + y = 14$
   $y = 3x$

9. $x = 5y$
   $2x - 7y = 27$

10. $y = x + 3$
    $x + 4y = 2$

11. $2x + y = -40$
    $8y - 3 = x$

12. $9x = y + 5$
    $4y - 3x = -20$

13. $x + y = 35$
    $x - y = 67$

14. $5x - 7y = 92$
    $5x + y = 4$

15. $3x - 5y = 51$
    $x + 5y = 23$

16. $8x - 7y = 62$
    $4x - 7y = 66$

17. $x + y = 7$
    $3x + 2y = 25$

18. $4x + 3y = 31$
    $2x - 9y = 5$

19. $2x + 5y = 29$
    $4x - y = 25$

20. $5x + 4y = 53$
    $x - 2y = 5$

21. $8x - 3y = 32$
    $7x + 9y = 28$

22. $6x + 6y = 24$
    $10x - y = -15$

23. $5x - 7y = 54$
    $2x - 3y = 22$

24. $7x - 5y = 40$
    $3x - 2y = 16$

Chapter 13

The Concurrence Theorems

One meaning of the word "concurrence" is "agreement in opinion," as illustrated by the person(s?) and shadow(s?) shaking hands in the figure above. In geometry, the word "concurrence" has a somewhat related meaning: the meeting of lines in a common point. A somewhat amazing fact is that, no matter what the shape of a triangle may be, several sets of lines related to the triangle are always concurrent. In this chapter, we will see why and will look at some other relations between points and lines that are quite surprising.

© 2003 Harold R. Jacobs

Triangles and Circles

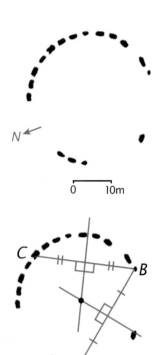

0   10m

One of the earth's ancient mysteries is Stonehenge, a monument of huge stones on the Salisbury Plain in England. Its construction is thought to have started in about 3000 B.C. when surveyors attached one end of a long rope to a post and the other end to a pointed stake. Using this primitive compass, they drew an enormous circle in the ground. In a period of more than a thousand years, more than 160 stone blocks weighing as much as 50 tons were moved into place–how and why no one knows.*

The first figure at the left shows the positions of the stones that still stand in the main circle. The second figure shows how any three of them can be used to find the circle's center. Drawing AB, BC, and AC produces a triangle whose sides are chords of the circle. The perpendicular bisectors of the chords of a circle contain its center; so the center of Stonehenge is at the point in which these lines intersect.

Because the vertices of △ABC lie on a circle, the triangle is said to be *cyclic.*

Definition
A polygon is *cyclic* iff there exists a circle that contains all of its vertices.

_____

Stonehenge Complete, by Christopher Chippindale (Cornell University Press, 1983).

It is easy to prove that *every* triangle, no matter what its shape, is cyclic.

Theorem 68

Every triangle is cyclic.

Given: △ABC.
Prove: △ABC is cyclic.

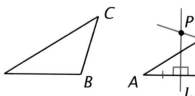

Proof

Let l_1 and l_2 be the perpendicular bisectors of AB and BC and let P be the point at which they intersect. Draw PA, PB, and PC.

△AMP ≅ △BMP and △BNP ≅ △CNP (SAS); so PA = PB and PB = PC. Because PA = PB = PC, the circle of radius PA contains A, B, and C. So △ABC is cyclic.

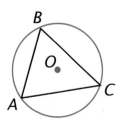

In the figure at the right, △ABC is *inscribed* in circle O, and circle O is *circumscribed* about △ABC. Circle O is called the *circumcircle* of △ABC, and point O is called the *circumcenter* of △ABC.

Definitions

A polygon is *inscribed in a circle* iff each vertex of the polygon lies on the circle.
The circle is *circumscribed about the polygon*.

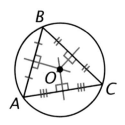

In our proof that every triangle is cyclic, we showed that the perpendicular bisectors of two of its sides intersect at the center of its circumcircle. All the sides of △ABC in the figure at the right are chords of circle O. We know from Theorem 58 that the perpendicular bisectors of the chords of a circle contain the center of the circle. Because lines that contain the same point are concurrent, this result establishes the following corollary.

Corollary to Theorem 68

The perpendicular bisectors of the sides of a triangle are concurrent.

Theorem 68 and its corollary suggest that we need only to construct the perpendicular bisectors of any two sides of a triangle to find the triangle's circumcenter.

Construction 9

To circumscribe a circle about a triangle.

Exercises

Set I

Hot Tub. The figure below shows a design for a hot tub as seen from overhead.*

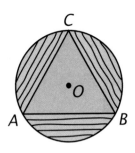

1. What are the sides of △ABC called with respect to the circle?

2. What are the angles of △ABC called with respect to the circle?

3. What word describes a polygon for which there is a circle that contains all of its vertices?

4. What is circle O called with respect to △ABC?

5. What relation does △ABC have to circle O?

6. What relation do points A, B, and C have to point O?

Circumcircles. The figures below suggest something about the circumcircles of different types of triangles.

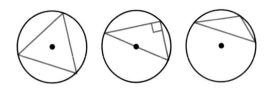

7. What kind of arcs do the angles of an acute triangle intercept?

---

*Indoor Sports Spaces, by Robin Crane and Malcolm Dixon (Van Nostrand Reinhold, 1991).

8. What kind of arc does the right angle of a right triangle intercept?

9. What kind of arc does the obtuse angle of an obtuse triangle intercept?

For what kind of triangle is the circumcenter

10. inside it?

11. *on* it?

12. outside it?

13. What is the hypotenuse of a right triangle called with respect to its circumcircle?

14. What point is the circumcenter of a right triangle?

RGB Color. The primary colors of light (red, green, blue) are mixed in varying proportions to produce the colors on a television screen or computer monitor.

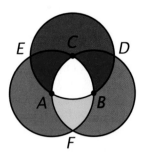

The figure above illustrates the basic combinations of these colors.

15. Construct the figure by doing the following steps.

    (1) Construct an equilateral triangle with sides 1 inch long, and label its vertices A, B, and C.

    (2) Draw three circles with their centers at A, B, and C and radius 1 inch.

    (3) Label the points D, E, and F in which the circles intersect.

15. (*continued*) Draw AD, BE, and CF.

16. What do you notice about these three lines?

17. Why is it true?

18. In the figure below, three circles having different radii intersect in six points.

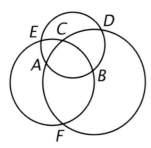

(1) Use your compass to draw a figure like it. Label the six intersection points as indicated.

(2) Draw △ABC.

(3) Draw AD, BE, and CF.

19. Are these three lines the perpendicular bisectors of the sides of △ABC?

20. Do they seem to be concurrent?

18. (*continued*) Label the point P in which AD, BE, and CF seem to intersect.

21. Given that they do intersect in P, explain why AP · PD = BP · PE = CP · PF.

Four Lines and Four Circles. In the figure below, four lines intersect in six points.

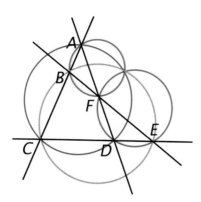

22. Name the triangles that they form.

23. How are the circles in the figure related to these triangles?

24. How many points are needed to determine a circle?

25. Although there is nothing special about the four lines, there *is* something unusual about the four circles. What is it?

Equilateral Triangle. In the figure below, △ABC is equilateral, it is inscribed in circle O, and AE, BF, and CD are its altitudes.

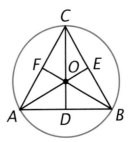

26. It follows that AE, BF, and CD are also the perpendicular bisectors of the sides of △ABC. Why?

27. Into what kind of right triangles do AE, BF, and CD divide △ABC?

28. How does the length of OA compare with the length of OD? Explain.

29. How does the radius of circle O compare in length with one of the altitudes of △ABC?

Nearest School. In the figure below, A, B, and C represent the locations of three high schools. Students are assigned to the school closest to where they live.

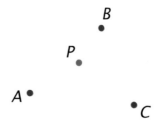

30. If a high-school student lives at P, to which school does he or she go?

Make a large drawing similar to this figure on your paper.

31. Use your straightedge and compass to construct a line separating all points closer to A from those closer to B. Draw a second line separating all points closer to B from those closer to C. Draw a third line separating all points closer to C from those closer to A. Darken the parts of the lines that are the edges of the three regions in which students going to the three schools live.

32. What is the point called that is equidistant from A, B, and C?

Set II

Folding Experiment. The figure below shows a triangle with sides of lengths 10, 11, and 12.

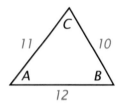

33. Use your straightedge and compass to construct it by using lengths of 10 cm, 11 cm, and 12 cm for the sides. Label the three vertices of the triangle A, B, and C *inside* the triangle as shown in the figure.

   (1) Construct the three perpendicular bisectors of the sides of the triangle.

   (2) Cut the triangle out. Fold it so that vertex A falls on vertex B. Open the triangle out flat and fold it again so that vertex B falls on vertex C. Open the triangle out flat and fold it again so that vertex C falls on vertex A.

34. What do you notice about the three folds?

33. (*continued*) Label the point P in which the folds intersect. Tape the triangle on your paper.

35. How is point P related to the vertices of the triangle?

36. Use your ruler to find the radius of the triangle's circumcircle.

37. Use your ruler and compass to draw a triangle having sides of lengths 9 cm, 12 cm, and 15 cm. Cut the triangle out and fold each pair of vertices together as described in exercise 33. Tape the triangle on your paper.

38. What kind of triangle is it? Explain.

39. What do you notice about the three folds?

40. Use your ruler to find the radius of the triangle's circumcircle.

Inscribed Triangles. In the figure below, △ABC and △ADE are inscribed in circle O and DE ⊥ AC.

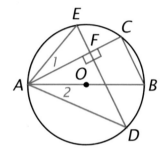

41. Copy the figure and draw BD.

42. ∠E = ∠ABD. Why?

43. What can you conclude about ∠ADB? Explain.

44. ∠AFE = ∠ADB. Why?

45. What can you conclude about ∠1 and ∠2? Explain.

Babylonian Problem. In 1936, some Babylonian tablets dating from 1900 B.C. to 1650 B.C. were discovered in Iran. On one of these tablets appears the following problem:

   Find the radius of the circumcircle of a triangle whose sides are 50, 50, and 60.*

46. Use your straightedge and compass to construct a triangle ABC whose sides are 50 mm, 50 mm, and 60 mm, with the 60 mm side as a horizontal base, AB.

———————

*An Introduction to the History of Mathematics, Howard Eves (Saunders, 1990).

Construct its circumcircle; draw a radius and label it *r*.

47. Use your ruler to measure the radius in millimeters.

48. Let O be the circumcenter of △ABC. Use your drawing and what you know about it to find the *exact* answer to the Babylonian problem.

Diameters and Sines. Circle O is the circumcircle of △ABC and BD is a diameter.

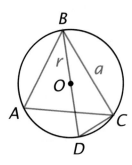

49. What can you conclude about △BCD? Explain.

50. Why is ∠A = ∠D?

51. Express sin D in terms of *a* and *r*.

Because ∠A = ∠D, sin A = sin D. By the Law of Sines, $\dfrac{a}{\sin A} = \dfrac{b}{\sin B} = \dfrac{c}{\sin C}$.

52. Express $\dfrac{a}{\sin A}$ in terms of *r*.

53. What does this result reveal about the ratio of the length of any side of a triangle to the sine of the opposite angle?

Set III

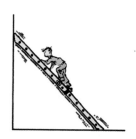

The Slipping Ladder. Obtuse Ollie put a tall ladder against a wall so that it made equal angles with the wall and floor. When his feet were halfway up the ladder, the top end started slipping and slid all the way down the wall. Ollie was too startled to do anything but hold on.

1. Draw two perpendicular line segments to represent the wall and the floor. Make an accurate drawing of the path of Ollie's feet as the ladder slid down the wall by using one of the shorter edges of a file card to represent the ladder as shown below.

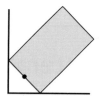

2. What kind of a path do you think Ollie's feet traveled?

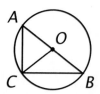

3. Use the fact that the midpoint of the hypotenuse of a right triangle is its circumcenter to explain why the path has the shape that it does. •

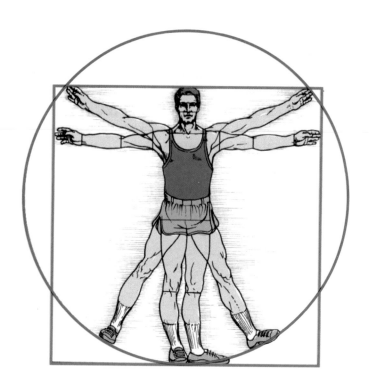

LESSON 2

Cyclic Quadrilaterals

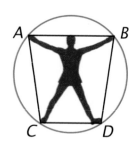

Leonardo da Vinci used geometry to study the human figure. The illustration above is based on a drawing from one of da Vinci's notebooks. In one position, the man's fingers, feet, and head touch the square. In the other position, his fingers and feet touch the circle. If *you* stood with your arms outstretched and your feet apart, would *your* hands and feet also touch a circle?

The answer to this question depends on whether the quadrilateral whose vertices correspond to the positions of your hands and feet is cyclic. Unlike triangles, not every quadrilateral is cyclic. Whether a convex quadrilateral has vertices that lie on a circle is determined by its angles. In stating the following theorem, we use our assumption that polygons are convex, unless told otherwise.

Theorem 69

A quadrilateral is cyclic iff a pair of its opposite angles are supplementary.

First, we will prove that, if a quadrilateral is cyclic, its opposite angles are supplementary.

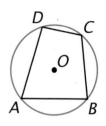

> *Given:* Quadrilateral ABCD is cyclic.
> *Prove:* ∠A and ∠C are supplementary and ∠B and ∠D are supplementary.

Proof

Because quadrilateral ABCD is cyclic, let circle O contain its vertices (if a polygon is cyclic, there exists a circle that contains all of its vertices).

In the circle, $\angle A = \frac{1}{2} m\widehat{DCB}$ and $\angle C = \frac{1}{2} m\widehat{BAD}$ (an inscribed angle is equal in measure to half its intercepted arc). Because

$\angle A + \angle C = \frac{1}{2} m\widehat{DCB} + \frac{1}{2} m\widehat{BAD}$ (addition), $\angle A + \angle C = $

$\frac{1}{2}(m\widehat{DCB} + m\widehat{BAD}) = \frac{1}{2}(360°) = 180°$ (a circle has a degree measure

of 360°). Therefore, ∠A and ∠C are supplementary. Because the sum of the angles of a quadrilateral is 360°, ∠A + ∠B + ∠C + ∠D = 360°. We know that ∠A + ∠C = 180° and so, by subtraction, ∠B + ∠D = 180°; so ∠B and ∠D also are supplementary.

Now we will prove the converse: if a pair of opposite angles of a quadrilateral are supplementary, then the quadrilateral is cyclic.

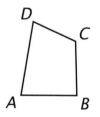

> *Given:* ∠B and ∠D are supplementary.
> *Prove:* Quadrilateral ABCD is cyclic.

Proof

Draw a circle through points A, B, and C (points A, B, and C determine a triangle and every triangle is cyclic). Point D lies either *outside* this circle, *inside* it, or *on* it.

Suppose that D lies outside the circle. Let the second point in which AD intersects the circle be called E. Draw EC. Then ABCE is cyclic.

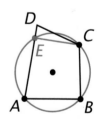

Now, ∠B and ∠AEC are supplementary (if a quadrilateral is cyclic, its opposite angles are supplementary), and ∠B and ∠D are supplementary (given); so ∠AEC = ∠D (supplements of the same angle are equal). But this equality contradicts the fact that ∠AEC > ∠D (an exterior angle of a triangle is greater than either remote interior angle), and so our original assumption must be false. In other words, D cannot lie outside the circle.

A similar argument can be used to establish that D cannot lie inside the circle. Therefore D must lie on the circle, and so quadrilateral ABCD is cyclic.

Exercises

Set I

Quilt Quadrilaterals. Four shapes frequently used in quilt patterns are shown below.

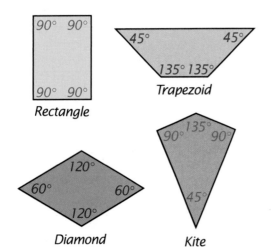

Rectangle

Trapezoid

Diamond

Kite

1. How is it possible to tell whether each of these figures is cyclic without drawing any circles?

2. Which of these figures are not cyclic?

Cyclic and Noncyclic. The figures below suggest another difference between cyclic and noncyclic quadrilaterals.

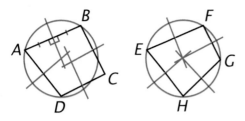

3. How do you suppose the lines intersecting AB, BC, CD, and DA were constructed?

4. For a quadrilateral to be cyclic, what must be true about these four lines?

5. What relation does the center of the circumscribed circle of a cyclic quadrilateral have to the vertices?

Euclid's Proof. Euclid's proof that the opposite angles of a cyclic quadrilateral are supplementary is based on the figure below.

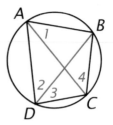

Give the reason for each of the following statements in his proof.

6. Draw AC and BD.

7. $\angle 1 + \angle ABC + \angle 4 = 180°$.

8. $\angle 1 = \angle 3$ and $\angle 2 = \angle 4$.

9. $\angle ADC = \angle 2 + \angle 3$.

10. $\angle ADC = \angle 4 + \angle 1$.

11. $\angle ADC + \angle ABC = \angle 4 + \angle 1 + \angle ABC$.

12. $\angle ADC + \angle ABC = 180°$.

A Different Proof. Another proof that the opposite angles of a cyclic quadrilateral are supplementary is based on the figure below.

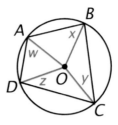

13. Copy the figure, including the four radii and w, x, y, and z, which are the measures of the four angles indicated.

14. What can you conclude about the four triangles in the figure? Explain.

13. (*continued*) Label the other four angles whose measures are w, x, y, and z.

15. To what number is $2w + 2x + 2y + 2z$ equal? Explain.

16. To what number is $w + x + y + z$ equal?

17. How does this result prove that the opposite angles of a cyclic quadrilateral are supplementary?

Isosceles Trapezoid. ABCD is an isosceles trapezoid with bases AB and DC.

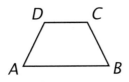

18. What can you conclude about AB and DC? Why?

19. What can you conclude about ∠A and ∠D? Why?

20. What can you conclude about ∠A and ∠B? Why?

21. What can you conclude about ∠B and ∠D?

22. What does this conclusion indicate about ABCD? Why?

23. What do exercises 18 through 22 prove about isosceles trapezoids?

Equilateral Triangles on the Sides. In the figure below, equilateral triangles have been constructed on the sides of △ABC.

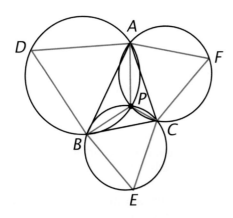

24. What do you notice about the circumcircles of these three triangles?

25. What kind of quadrilaterals are APBD, APCF, and BPCE?

26. What can you conclude about the three angles at P? Explain.

27. Use your straightedge and compass to do each of the following steps.

(1) Construct a triangle having a different shape.

(2) Construct equilateral triangles on its sides.

(3) Construct their three circumcircles.

28. Do the conclusions that you drew in exercises 24 through 26 seem to be true about your drawing?

Set II

Cyclic or Not. For each of the following figures, tell whether you think quadrilateral ABCD is cyclic or not. In each case, explain your reasoning.

29.

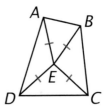

In the figure above, E is a point inside quadrilateral ABCD such that AE = BE = CE = DE.

30. In the figure at the right, AB ⊥ AD, DC ⊥ AD, and ∠B is obtuse.

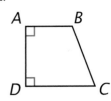

31.

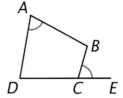

In the figure above, ∠BCE is an exterior angle of quadrilateral ABCD and ∠BCE = ∠A.

Brahmagupta's Theorem. Brahmagupta, an Indian mathematician who lived in the seventh century, discovered several theorems about cyclic quadrilaterals. One of them is about a cyclic quadrilateral whose diagonals are perpendicular to each other.

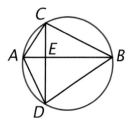

32. Make a drawing similar to the one above by doing each of the following steps.

   (1) Draw a large circle and construct two perpendicular chords of unequal lengths in it. Label them AB and CD and their point of intersection E.

   (2) Connect the four points on the circle to form the cyclic quadrilateral ACBD.

   (3) Through point E, construct a line perpendicular to side BD and extend the line to intersect side AC. Label the points of intersection X and Y as shown in the figure below.

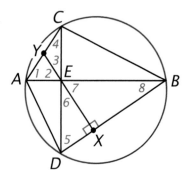

33. ∠2 = ∠7 and ∠3 = ∠6. Why?

34. ∠7 = ∠5 and ∠6 = ∠8. Why?

35. ∠5 = ∠1 and ∠8 = ∠4. Why?

36. ∠2 = ∠1 and ∠3 = ∠4. Why?

37. What do the equations in exercise 36 reveal about the relation of point Y to segment AC? Explain.

The same reasoning can be used to show that lines drawn through E perpendicular to the other sides of ACBD are related to the opposite sides in the same way.

38. Use this reasoning to copy and complete the following statement of Brahmagupta's Theorem:

   If a cyclic quadrilateral has perpendicular diagonals, then any line through their point of intersection that is perpendicular to a side of the quadrilateral . . .

Area Formula.
You may remember that the ancient Egyptians used a formula for the area of a quadrilateral that didn't always work.*
   Brahmagupta found a formula for the area of a *cyclic* quadrilateral that does always work. The formula is

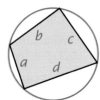

$A = \sqrt{(s-a)(s-b)(s-c)(s-d)}$ in which a, b, c, and d are the lengths of the sides of the quadrilateral and s is half its perimeter.

39. Show that this formula works for a rectangle, where $c = a$ and $d = b$.

40. Use it to find the area of the cyclic quadrilateral at the right, which Brahmagupta used as an example.

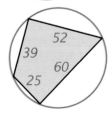

41. The figure below shows another quadrilateral whose sides have the same lengths: 25, 39, 52, and 60.
   Do you think it has the same area as the quadrilateral in exercise 40? Explain why or why not.

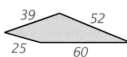

_____

*Chapter 1, Lesson 5, pp. 30–31.

Ptolemy's Theorem. Claudius Ptolemy, an astronomer and mathematician who lived in Alexandria, proved the following theorem in about 150 A.D.:

> The sum of the products of the opposite sides of a cyclic quadrilateral is equal to the product of its diagonals.

In the figure below, this theorem means that $AB \cdot DC + AD \cdot BC = AC \cdot BD$.

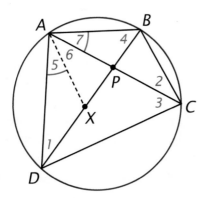

Give the reason for each of the statements in the following proof of Ptolemy's Theorem.

42. Draw AX so that $\angle 5 = \angle 7$.

43. $\angle 1 = \angle 2$.

44. $\triangle DAX \sim \triangle CAB$.

45. $\dfrac{DX}{CB} = \dfrac{AD}{AC}$.

46. $DX = \dfrac{CB \cdot AD}{AC}$.

47. $\angle 5 + \angle 6 = \angle 7 + \angle 6$.

48. $\angle DAC = \angle XAB$.

49. $\angle 3 = \angle 4$.

50. $\triangle DAC \sim \triangle XAB$.

51. $\dfrac{XB}{DC} = \dfrac{AB}{AC}$.

52. $XB = \dfrac{DC \cdot AB}{AC}$.

53. $DX + XB = \dfrac{CB \cdot AD}{AC} + \dfrac{DC \cdot AB}{AC}$.

54. $DB = \dfrac{CB \cdot AD + DC \cdot AB}{AC}$.

55. $AB \cdot DC + AD \cdot BC = AC \cdot BD$.

Two Applications. When Ptolemy's Theorem is applied to a rectangle, the theorem turns into something else.

56. Apply it to the figure at the right to show how it does so.

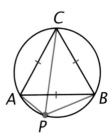

In the second figure at the right, equilateral $\triangle ABC$ is inscribed in the circle and P is any point on $\overset{\frown}{AB}$.

57. Use Ptolemy's Theorem to show that $PA + PB = PC$.

Set III

Overlapping Cards Puzzle. The figure below shows two overlapping rectangular cards.*

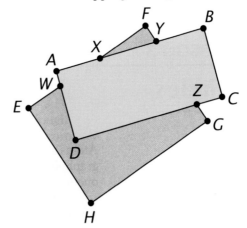

1. A circle can be drawn through points A, B, C, and D or through points E, F, G, and H. Why?

2. Find another set of four points in the figure through which a circle can be drawn. Which points did you find? Why are they cyclic? (Copy the figure and mark it to illustrate your answer.)

---

*Adapted from a puzzle by Stephen Barr in his *2nd Miscellany of Puzzles, Mathematical and Otherwise* (Macmillan, 1969).

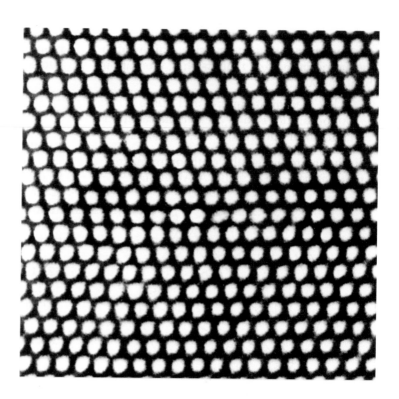

LESSON 3

Incircles

Atoms are so small that it is hard to imagine that they could be photographed. An atom of gold, for example, has a radius of only about one-hundred millionth of a centimeter.

In 1979, Hatsujiro Hashimoto and his research team at Osaka University in Japan used a powerful electron microscope to produce the photograph above. It shows a piece of gold film so highly magnified that the individual atoms can be seen as yellow dots.

The pattern of the atoms is illustrated in the diagram at the left. In this diagram, each atom is represented by a circle. Each circle is *inscribed* in a rhombus.

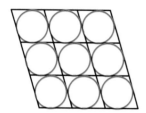

Definitions
A circle is *inscribed in a polygon* iff each side of the polygon is tangent to the circle.
The polygon is *circumscribed about the circle.*

The circle is called the *incircle* of the polygon, and its center is called the *incenter* of the polygon.

In Lesson 1 of this chapter, we showed that the center of the circumcircle of a triangle is the point in which the perpendicular bisectors of any two of its sides intersect. From this fact, it followed that all three of these bisectors must be concurrent. In this lesson, we will show that the center of the incircle of a triangle is the point in which the bisectors of any two of its *angles* intersect. From this fact, it follows that all three angle bisectors must be concurrent.

Theorem 70

Every triangle has an incircle.

Given: △ABC.
Prove: △ABC has
  an incircle.

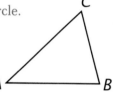
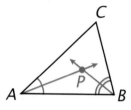
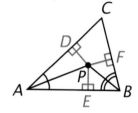

Proof

Let two rays bisect ∠A and ∠B and let P be the point in which they intersect. Through P, draw PD ⊥ AC, PE ⊥ AB, and PF ⊥ BC.

△APD ≅ △APE and △BPE ≅ △BPF (AAS); so PD = PE and PE = PF. Because PD = PE = PF, a circle can be drawn with P as center and PD as radius that contains all three points, D, E, and F. Because AC ⊥ PD, AB ⊥ PE, and BC ⊥ PF, the sides of the triangle are tangent to circle P (if a line is perpendicular to a radius at its outer endpoint, it is tangent to the circle.) Therefore, circle P is an incircle of △ABC.

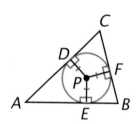

In our proof that △ABC has an incircle, we showed that the bisectors of two of its angles, ∠A and ∠B, intersect at the center of the circle. What about the bisector of the third angle, ∠C?

Draw ray CP. Because △CPD ≅ △CPF (HL), ∠DCP = ∠FCP. So CP bisects ∠ACB. Because all three angle bisectors pass through point P, they are concurrent. We state this result as the following corollary.

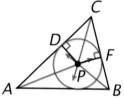

Corollary to Theorem 70

The angle bisectors of a triangle are concurrent.

Theorem 70 and its corollary suggest that, to find the incenter of a triangle, we can bisect two of its angles. To find the radius of the incircle, we can then construct a perpendicular from the triangle's incenter to one of the triangle's sides.

Construction 10

To inscribe a circle in a triangle.

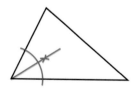
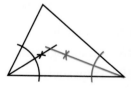
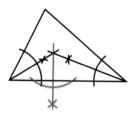
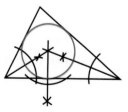

Exercises

Set I

Video Class. The picture on the video monitor illustrates a special property of the angles of a triangle.

1. What is this property?
2. What is the name of the point in which the angle bisectors intersect?

Circumcircle and Incircle. The figures below compare the construction of the circumcircle and incircle of a triangle.

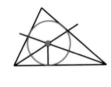

3. How many lines are needed in the construction of the circumcircle?
4. How are these lines related to the triangle?
5. From what is the center of the circumcircle equidistant?
6. How many lines are needed in the construction of the incircle?
7. What lines are drawn to find the *center* of the incircle?
8. What is drawn to find the *radius* of the incircle?

9. From what is the center of the incircle equidistant?

Circumscribed Quadrilateral. Each side of quadrilateral ABCD is tangent to circle O.

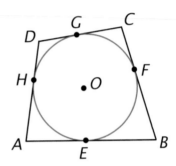

10. What is circle O called with respect to ABCD?
11. What is point O called with respect to ABCD?
12. Copy the figure and draw OE, OF, OG, and OH.
13. What relation do these segments have to the sides of ABCD? Explain.
12. (*continued*) Draw AO, BO, CO, and DO.
14. What relation do these lines have to the angles of ABCD? Explain.
15. If a circle can be inscribed in a quadrilateral, what must be true about the lines that bisect its angles?
12. (*continued*) Use tick marks to mark the tangent segments in the figure that are equal.
16. If a circle can be inscribed in a quadrilateral, what must be true about the sums of the lengths of the quadrilateral's opposite sides?

Use these conclusions to tell under what conditions it is possible for the following quadrilaterals to have incircles.

17. Rectangles.
18. Parallelograms.
19. Trapezoids.

Equilateral Triangle. The incircle and circumcircle of an equilateral triangle are concentric.

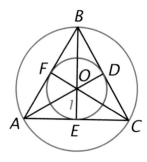

20. What does *concentric* mean?

What relation do lines AD, BE, and CF have to

21. the sides of △ABC?

22. its angles?

23. What kinds of triangles do you see in the figure?

Given that the radius of the incircle is 1, what is

24. the radius of the circumcircle?

25. the circumference of each circle?

26. the area of each circle?

Construction Problem. The sides of the triangle below are 8, 9, and 10 units.

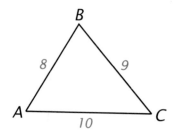

27. Use your ruler and compass to construct an enlargement of it, using sides of lengths 8 cm, 9 cm, and 10 cm, in the center of a sheet of paper. Label its vertices A, B, and C.

(1) Circumscribe a circle around △ABC.

(2) Inscribe a circle in △ABC.

(3) Choose any point on the larger circle and label the point D. Use your ruler to draw two lines from D that appear to be tangent to the smaller circle. Label the two points in which these lines intersect the larger circle points E and F. Draw EF.

28. What seems to be true?

29. Does △DEF appear to be congruent to △ABC?

30. On the basis of your results, does it appear possible for two different triangles to have the same incircle and circumcircle?

Set II

Ship Location. The figure below from a book on navigation shows a method for finding the location of a ship by bisecting three angles.*

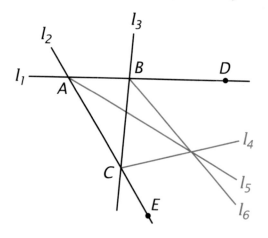

Three position lines, l_1, l_2, and l_3, form △ABC.

31. Which of the three bisector lines, l_4, l_5, or l_6, bisects an angle of △ABC?

32. What are the other two bisected angles, ∠DBC and ∠BCE, called with respect to the triangle?

33. What relation do the three bisector lines appear to have to one another?

Dutton's Navigation and Piloting, by Elbert S. Maloney (Naval Institute Press, 1985).

34. Copy the part of the figure, shown below, in which the point in which l_4 and l_6 intersect has been labeled P. From P, draw PF ⊥ AD, PG ⊥ BC, and PH ⊥ AE.

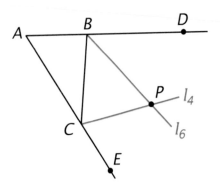

35. What can you conclude about the four right triangles that are formed? Explain.

36. What can you conclude about PF, PG, and PH? Explain.

34. (*continued*) Draw AP.

37. What can you conclude about △FAP and △HAP? Explain.

38. What does your conclusion prove about AP and ∠DAE?

39. What do exercises 34 through 38 prove about the three bisector lines?

Incircle Problem 1. ABCD is a square and circle O is its incircle.

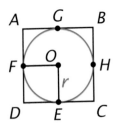

40. What can you conclude about FDEO?

Given that OE = *r*, express each of the following in terms of *r*.

41. AB.

42. The circumference of circle O.

43. The perimeter of ABCD.

44. The area of circle O.

45. The area of ABCD.

Find the exact value of each of the following ratios.

46. The ratio of the circumference of circle O to the perimeter of ABCD.

47. The ratio of the area of circle O to the area of ABCD.

Incircle Problem 2. △ABC is a 3-4-5 right triangle and circle O is its incircle.

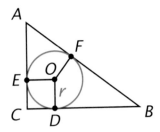

48. What can you conclude about ECDO?

Given that OD = *r*, express each of the following lengths in terms of *r*.

49. AE.

50. DB.

51. AB.

52. Use your answer to exercise 51 to solve for *r*.

Find the exact value of each of the following numbers.

53. The circumference of circle O.

54. The perimeter of △ABC.

55. The area of circle O.

56. The area of △ABC.

57. The ratio of the circumference of circle O to the perimeter of △ABC.

58. The ratio of the area of circle O to the area of △ABC.

Incircle Problem 3. Quadrilateral ABCD is circumscribed about circle O with radius *r*.

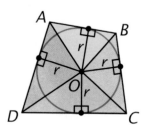

59. $\alpha\triangle AOB = \dfrac{1}{2}AB \cdot r$, $\alpha\triangle BOC = \dfrac{1}{2}BC \cdot r$,

$\alpha\triangle COD = \dfrac{1}{2}CD \cdot r$, and

$\alpha\triangle DOA = \dfrac{1}{2}DA \cdot r$. Why?

60. Use the fact that $\alpha ABCD = \alpha\triangle AOB + \alpha\triangle BOC + \alpha\triangle COD + \alpha\triangle DOA$ to write an expression for $\alpha ABCD$ in terms of *r* and its perimeter, *p*.

Write an expression for each of the following ratios in terms of *r* and *p*.

61. The ratio of the circumference of circle O to the perimeter of ABCD.

62. The ratio of the area of circle O to the area of ABCD.

Trisector Challenge. In the figure below, the rays from B and C trisect two of the angles of △ABC.

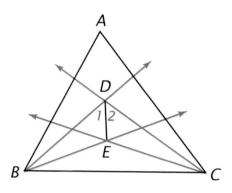

63. $\angle 1 = \angle 2$. Why?

Set III

Excircles. In the figure below, circle O is inscribed in △ABC, and circles X, Y, and Z are tangent to the lines that contain its sides. The lines that contain the sides of △XYZ bisect the exterior angles of △ABC.

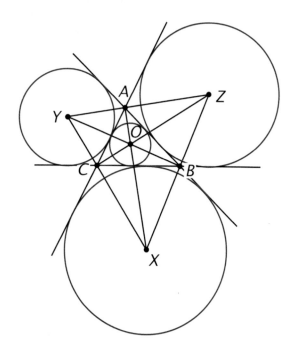

1. What relation do XA, YB, and ZC appear to have to △XYZ?

2. Using the part of the figure shown below, explain why your guess is true.

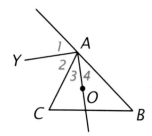

LESSON 4

The Centroid of a Triangle

Tortoises walk very slowly. To keep its shell from scraping the ground, a tortoise generally moves just one of its feet at a time. Having the other three feet on the ground helps, because three noncollinear points determine a plane. For the tortoise to keep its balance, however, its center of gravity must always fall inside the triangle determined by these three points.*

The center of gravity of the tortoise is the point in which it is "perfectly balanced." In the pictures above, this point is obviously not the balancing point of the triangles determined by the tortoise's feet.

Where is the center of gravity of a triangle? By this question we mean, at what point should a triangular board having uniform thickness and density be supported so that it will balance?

If we try to find this point by trial and error with a large board in the shape of a scalene triangle, we find that this point is not the circumcenter, the point in which the perpendicular bisectors of the sides are concurrent. Neither is it the incenter, the point in which the angle bisectors are concurrent. Instead, it is determined by the *medians* of the triangle.

Exploring Biomechanics: Animals in Motion, by R. McNeill Alexander (Scientific American Library, 1992).

Definition

A *median* of a triangle is a line segment that joins a vertex to the midpoint of the opposite side.

The fact that the balancing point of a triangle is determined by its medians suggests that they are concurrent, a fact whose proof is included in the exercises.

Theorem 71

The medians of a triangle are concurrent.

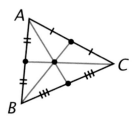

It was Archimedes who showed that the point in which its medians are concurrent is the center of gravity of a triangular board of uniform thickness and density.* Mathematicians refer to it as the *centroid* of the triangle.

Definition

The *centroid* of a triangle is the point in which its medians are concurrent.

At this point, it will probably come as no surprise to you that there are other sets of lines related to a triangle that also are concurrent. One of these sets contains its altitudes.

Theorem 72

The lines containing the altitudes of a triangle are concurrent.

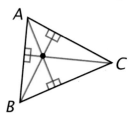

Definition

The *orthocenter* of a triangle is the point in which the lines containing its altitudes are concurrent.

The proof of Theorem 72 also is included in the exercises.

Archimedes: What Did He Do Besides Cry Eureka? by Sherman Stein (Mathematical Association of America, 1999), Chapter 3.

Exercises

Set I

"Ortho" Words. The Greek word *orthos* means "right." Can you think of a word that begins with *ortho* that refers to

1. someone who makes teeth right?

2. a right belief?

3. shoes to make your feet right?

4. To what does the "ortho" in orthocenter refer?

Theorem 71. Complete the following proof of Theorem 71 by giving the reasons.

The medians of a triangle are concurrent.

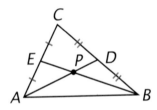

Given: AD and BE are medians of △ABC.
Prove: AD and BE are concurrent with the third median of △ABC.

Proof

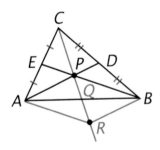

5. Draw line CP. Why?

6. Choose point R on line CP so that CP = PR. Why?

7. Draw AR and RB. Why?

8. EPB ∥ AR and APD ∥ RB. Why?

9. APBR is a parallelogram. Why?

10. Q is the midpoint of AB. Why?

11. CQ is the third median of △ABC. Why?

12. AD and BE are concurrent with CQ. Why?

Theorem 72. Complete the following proof of Theorem 72 by giving the reasons.

The lines containing the altitudes of a triangle are concurrent.

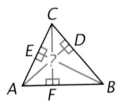

Given: AD, BE, and CF are the altitudes of △ABC.
Prove: AD, BE, and CF are concurrent.

Proof

13. AD ⊥ BC, BE ⊥ AC, and CF ⊥ AB. Why?

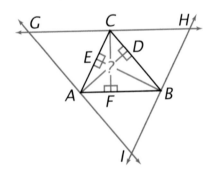

14. Through A, draw GI ∥ BC; through B, draw IH ∥ AC; and through C, draw GH ∥ AB. Why?

15. GCBA and CHBA are parallelograms. Why?

16. GC = AB and CH = AB. Why?

17. GC = CH. Why?

18. CF ⊥ GH. Why?

So CF is the perpendicular bisector of side GH of △GHI. In the same way, AD can be shown to be the perpendicular bisector of GI, and BE can be shown to be the perpendicular bisector of HI.

19. AD, BE, and CF are concurrent. Why?

Median Construction.
The sides of the triangle at the right are 8, 9, and 10 units.

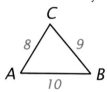

20. Use your ruler and compass to construct an enlargement of it, using sides of lengths 8 cm, 9 cm, and 10 cm. Label its vertices A, B, and C.

(1) Construct the medians from A and B to the opposite sides. Label them AD and BE and let F be the point in which they intersect.

(2) Bisect AF and FB and label their midpoints G and H.

(3) Draw EDHG.

21. What relation do ED and GH have to AB? Explain.

22. What can you conclude about EDHG? Explain.

23. What can you conclude about GD and EH? Explain.

24. AG = GF = FD and BH = HF = FE. Why?

25. Find $\dfrac{AF}{FD}$ and $\dfrac{BF}{FE}$.

Points D and E are points of bisection of CB and CA.

26. What are points G and F with respect to AD, and what are points F and H with respect to BE?

Altitude Construction. One of the altitudes of △ABC has been constructed in the figure below.

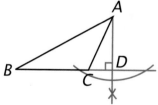

27. Use your straightedge and compass to copy △ABC and construct the altitude AD as shown.

28. What is it about △ABC that causes the altitude to fall outside it?

27. (*continued*) Construct the other two altitudes of △ABC and label them BE and CF.

29. Are the three line segments that are the altitudes of △ABC concurrent? Explain.

30. Are the three lines that contain the altitudes of △ABC concurrent? Explain.

31. Which of the following points can lie outside a triangle: its incenter, its orthocenter, its centroid, its circumcenter?

Set II

Other Triangles, Other Orthocenters. The figure below illustrates an interesting observation made by Lazare Carnot, who was both a political leader and a mathematician at the time of the French Revolution.

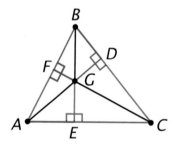

In the figure, G is the orthocenter of △ABC.

32. Which three line segments are the altitudes of △AGC?

33. Where is the orthocenter of △AGC?

34. Which three line segments are the altitudes of △AGB?

35. Where is the orthocenter of △AGB?

36. Which three line segments are the altitudes of △BGC?

37. Where is the orthocenter of △BGC?

Medians as Bisectors. The figure below suggests that a median of a triangle bisects more than just the side of the triangle to which it is drawn.

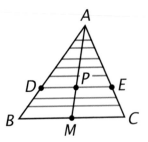

38. What relation do the green line segments appear to have to BC?

39. What relation does AM appear to have to these line segments?

40. Given that DE ‖ BC, what can you conclude about △ADP and △ABM and about △APE and △AMC? Explain.

41. Why is $\dfrac{DP}{BM} = \dfrac{AP}{AM}$ and $\dfrac{PE}{MC} = \dfrac{AP}{AM}$?

42. Why is $\dfrac{DP}{BM} = \dfrac{PE}{MC}$?

43. Given that AM is a median of △ABC, what can you conclude about BM and MC?

44. Why is $\dfrac{DP}{MC} = \dfrac{PE}{MC}$?

45. Why is DP = PE?

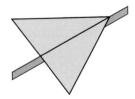

46. What do exercises 38 through 45 suggest would happen if △ABC were cut from a sheet of cardboard and placed with median AM along the edge of a ruler as shown above?

Doing Without a Compass. The figure below appeared in *The Old Farmer's Almanac* with the following question: Can you construct, using just an unmarked straightedge, a line through P perpendicular to *l*?*

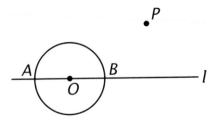

47. Use your straightedge and compass to draw the figure. Then use your straightedge to draw the following lines.

 (1) Draw line PA and let C be the point in which PA intersects the circle. Draw line PB and let D be the point in which PB intersects the circle.

 (2) Draw lines AD and CB and let E be the point in which they intersect each other.

 (3) Draw PE. Let F be the point in which PE intersects line *l.*

48. What can you conclude about ∠ACB and ∠ADB? Explain.

49. What relation do PD and EC have to △APE?

50. What is point B with respect to △APE?

51. What can you conclude about AF with respect to △APE? Explain.

52. What fact follows about PE and line *l*?

53. Follow the directions for exercise 47 in regard to the figure below.

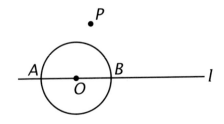

---

*Problem by Don Scholten, *The Old Farmer's Almanac,* 1988.

54. Look again at exercises 48 through 52. Which of the conclusions in these exercises are still true?

Engineering Challenge. The figure below is from a book for engineering students.*

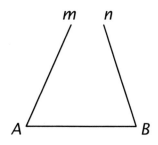

The problem is to construct a line perpendicular to AB that would pass through the point in which lines *m* and *n* intersect. The catch is to do so without extending lines *m* and *n*.

55. Copy the figure and use your straightedge and compass to construct such a line.

56. Explain how your method works.

Set III

Balancing Point. You know that, if a triangle is cut out of a piece of cardboard, it can be balanced on its centroid, the point in which the medians of the triangle are concurrent.

If the board were in the shape of a quadrilateral instead, where would its balancing point be? The following geometric construction for finding this point was not discovered until the nineteenth century.

The first step in finding the balancing point is to trisect the sides of the quadrilateral. Trace the figure at the bottom of this page, in which the sides have been trisected.

Now, draw EF, GH, IJ, and KL and extend them until they meet in four points outside the figure. Label these points M, N, O, and P.

1. What seems to be true about MNOP?

The balancing point of the original quadrilateral ABCD is the same as the balancing point of MNOP.

2. Where do you suppose it is?

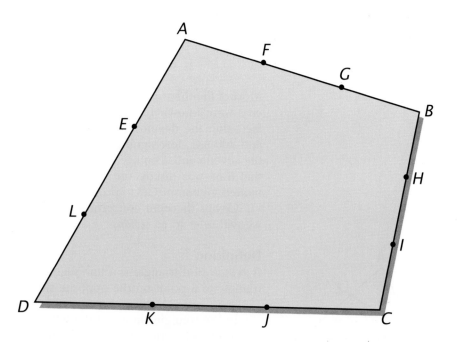

Graphics, by Alexander S. Levens (Wiley, 1962).

LESSON 5

Ceva's Theorem

Most of the theorems that we have encountered in our study of geometry were known to Euclid, who included them in the *Elements*. In fact, after the development of geometry in Greece between 600 B.C. and 200 B.C., few significant additions to the subject were made until the seventeenth century. One of the new theorems that appeared at that time was discovered by an Italian mathematician and engineer named Giovanni Ceva (pronounced "chay va").

Ceva's theorem concerns sets of line segments in a triangle that we will refer to as *cevians*.

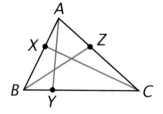

Definition
A *cevian* of a triangle is a line segment that joins a vertex of the triangle to a point on the opposite side.

In the triangle shown at the left, three cevians have been drawn, one from each vertex. They are AY, BZ, and CX. The cevians divide the sides of the triangle into six segments: AX, XB, BY, YC, CZ, and ZA.

In the figure at the right, the three cevians are concurrent at point P. Ceva's theorem states that they are concurrent if and only if

$$\frac{AX}{XB} \cdot \frac{BY}{YC} \cdot \frac{CZ}{ZA} = 1.$$

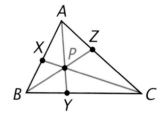

Several different ways to prove this theorem have been discovered. The appearance of the ratios in the equation suggests that one way might be to use similar triangles. Although no similar triangles are ordinarily formed by three concurrent cevians, some simple additions to the figure produce pairs of similar triangles that make such a proof possible.

Theorem 73. Ceva's Theorem
Three cevians, AY, BZ, and CX, of △ABC are concurrent iff

$$\frac{AX}{XB} \cdot \frac{BY}{YC} \cdot \frac{CZ}{ZA} = 1.$$

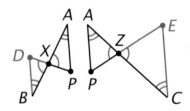

Proof that, if the three cevians are concurrent, then

$$\frac{AX}{XB} \cdot \frac{BY}{YC} \cdot \frac{CZ}{ZA} = 1.$$

Through B and C, draw lines parallel to AY. Let the points in which they intersect CX and BZ be called D and E, respectively.

Because of equal vertical angles and equal alternate interior angles, △AXP ~ △BXD and △CZE ~ △AZP. Therefore,

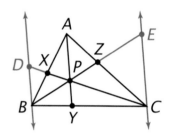

$$\frac{AX}{BX} = \frac{AP}{BD} \quad \text{and} \quad \frac{CZ}{AZ} = \frac{CE}{AP}.$$

Because of the common angle and equal corresponding angles, △BYP ~ △BCE and △BCD ~ △YCP. Therefore,

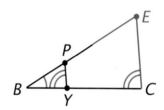

$$\frac{BY}{BC} = \frac{YP}{CE} \quad \text{and} \quad \frac{BC}{YC} = \frac{BD}{YP}.$$

We can now build the conclusion of Ceva's Theorem by multiplying the left and right sides of these equations.

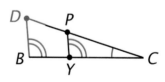

$$\frac{AX}{BX} \cdot \frac{BY}{BC} \cdot \frac{BC}{YC} \cdot \frac{CZ}{AZ} = \frac{AP}{BD} \cdot \frac{YP}{CE} \cdot \frac{BD}{YP} \cdot \frac{CE}{AP}.$$

Simplifying, we have

$$\frac{AX}{BX} \cdot \frac{BY}{\cancel{BC}} \cdot \frac{\cancel{BC}}{YC} \cdot \frac{CZ}{AZ} = \frac{\cancel{AP}}{\cancel{BD}} \cdot \frac{\cancel{YP}}{\cancel{CE}} \cdot \frac{\cancel{BD}}{\cancel{YP}} \cdot \frac{\cancel{CE}}{\cancel{AP}},$$

and so, by algebra and by using BX = XB and AZ = ZA, we have

$$\frac{AX}{XB} \cdot \frac{BY}{YC} \cdot \frac{CZ}{ZA} = 1.$$

Proof of the converse.

If $\dfrac{AX}{XB} \cdot \dfrac{BY}{YC} \cdot \dfrac{CZ}{ZA} = 1$, then the three cevians AY, BZ, and CX of $\triangle ABC$ are concurrent.

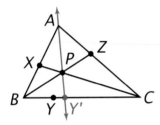

Let CX and BZ intersect in point P. Draw AP, and let the point in which it intersects BC be called Y'.

Now, from the first part, we know that

$$\frac{AX}{XB} \cdot \frac{BY'}{Y'C} \cdot \frac{CZ}{ZA} = 1$$

and, by hypothesis, we have

$$\frac{AX}{XB} \cdot \frac{BY}{YC} \cdot \frac{CZ}{ZA} = 1.$$

We will now show that these imply that Y' and Y are the same point. From the two equations above, we know that

$$\frac{AX}{XB} \cdot \frac{BY'}{Y'C} \cdot \frac{CZ}{ZA} = \frac{AX}{XB} \cdot \frac{BY}{YC} \cdot \frac{CZ}{ZA}.$$

Dividing, we get

$$\frac{BY'}{Y'C} = \frac{BY}{YC}.$$

Adding 1 to each side of this equation, we get

$$\frac{BY'}{Y'C} + 1 = \frac{BY}{YC} + 1 \quad \text{or}$$

$$\frac{BY' + Y'C}{Y'C} = \frac{BY + YC}{YC}.$$

Because BY' + Y'C = BC and BY + YC = BC,

$$\frac{BC}{Y'C} = \frac{BC}{YC}.$$

Multiplying means and extremes, we get

$$BC \cdot YC = BC \cdot Y'C.$$

Dividing by BC gives

$$YC = Y'C.$$

Because CY = CY', Y and Y' are the same point. This conclusion follows from the Ruler Postulate, which says that the points on a line can be numbered so that, to every real number, there corresponds exactly one point. Because Y and Y' are the same point, AY and AY' are the same line. Therefore, AY, BZ, and CX all contain point P and are concurrent.

Exercises

Set I

Which Is Which? The figure below illustrates four special types of line segments related to a triangle.

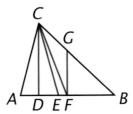

Which line segment appears to

1. be a median of the triangle?

2. lie on the perpendicular bisector of a side?

3. be an altitude of the triangle?

4. lie on an angle bisector of the triangle?

5. Are all four of these line segments cevians? Explain.

Using Ceva's Theorem. Given that the cevians in each of the following triangles are concurrent, solve for *x*.

Example:

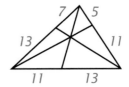

Solution: $\dfrac{2}{16} \cdot \dfrac{x}{6} \cdot \dfrac{x}{3} = 1$; so

$\dfrac{2x^2}{288} = 1$, $2x^2 = 288$,

$x^2 = 144$, and $x = 12$.

6.

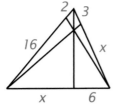

7.

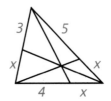

Appearances can be deceiving. Use Ceva's Theorem to determine whether the cevians in the following accurately drawn figures are concurrent.

8.

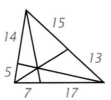

9.

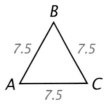

Equilateral Triangle. △ABC is an equilateral triangle with sides 7.5 units long.

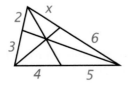

10. Construct the figure by doing the following steps.

   (1) Construct an enlargement of △ABC by using sides of length 7.5 cm.

   (2) Mark the point on AB that is 5 cm from A and label the point X. Draw CX.

   (3) Mark the point on BC that is 5 cm from B and label the point Y. Draw AY.

   (4) Draw the cevian from B that is concurrent with AY and CX. Label its other endpoint Z.

Find each of the following ratios.

11. $\dfrac{AX}{XB}$.

12. $\dfrac{BY}{YC}$.

Without doing any measuring, what would you expect

13. $\dfrac{CZ}{ZA}$ to be? Explain.

14. the length of AZ to be? Explain.

10. (*continued*) Measure AZ to check the accuracy of your figure and your reasoning.

Ratio Relations. Medians AY, BZ, and CX are concurrent at P, the centroid of △ABC.

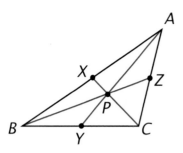

The centroid of a triangle is a point of trisection of each of its medians. What can you conclude about

15. $\dfrac{AP}{PY} \cdot \dfrac{BP}{PZ} \cdot \dfrac{CP}{PX}$?

16. $\dfrac{PX}{CX} + \dfrac{PY}{AY} + \dfrac{PZ}{BZ}$?

17. $\dfrac{CX}{PX} + \dfrac{AY}{PY} + \dfrac{BZ}{PZ}$?

18. $\dfrac{AP}{AY} + \dfrac{BP}{BZ} + \dfrac{CP}{CX}$?

19. $\dfrac{AX}{XB} \cdot \dfrac{BY}{YC} \cdot \dfrac{CZ}{ZA}$?

20. $\dfrac{AB}{AX} + \dfrac{BC}{BY} + \dfrac{CA}{CZ}$?

Right Triangle. △ABC is a right triangle with BC = 8 and CA = 6. CY = CZ = 2.

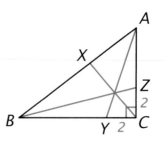

21. Find $\dfrac{BY}{YC}$.

22. Find $\dfrac{CZ}{ZA}$.

23. Use Ceva's Theorem to find $\dfrac{AX}{XB}$.

24. Find AX and XB.

Ollie's Equations. In applying Ceva's Theorem to the figure below, Acute Alice wrote $\dfrac{a}{b} \cdot \dfrac{c}{d} \cdot \dfrac{e}{f} = 1$ and Obtuse Ollie wrote $\dfrac{b}{c} \cdot \dfrac{d}{e} \cdot \dfrac{f}{a} = 1$.

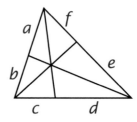

Alice told Ollie that his equation must be wrong because he should have started with *a*.

25. Do you agree? Explain.

Ollie then changed his equation to $\dfrac{a}{f} \cdot \dfrac{e}{d} \cdot \dfrac{c}{b} = 1$.

26. Is his new equation correct? Explain.

27. What conclusions do exercises 25 and 26 suggest?

Set II

The Theorem of Menelaus. Menelaus, a Greek mathematician who lived in Alexandria in about 100 A.D., made the following discovery long before Ceva was born.

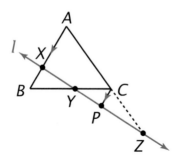

Line *l* intersects two sides of △ABC at X and Y and the line containing the third side at Z. Line CP has been drawn parallel to AB.

28. Because of CP, the figure contains two pairs of similar triangles. Which are they?

29. Why is $\dfrac{AX}{CP} = \dfrac{AZ}{CZ}$ and $\dfrac{BY}{YC} = \dfrac{XB}{CP}$?

30. Why is AX · CZ = CP · AZ and BY · CP = YC · XB?

31. Why is
    AX · CZ · BY · CP = CP · AZ · YC · XB
    and AX · CZ · BY = ZA · YC · XB?

32. Why is $\dfrac{AX}{XB} \cdot \dfrac{BY}{YC} \cdot \dfrac{CZ}{ZA} = 1$?

33. To what does this result seem closely related?

Concurrent or Not? In the figure below, AY is a median of △ABC, XZ ∥ BC, and BZ and CX are cevians.

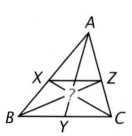

34. Why is $\dfrac{AX}{XB} = \dfrac{ZA}{CZ}$?

35. What can you conclude about
    $\dfrac{AX}{XB} \cdot \dfrac{BY}{YC} \cdot \dfrac{CZ}{ZA}$? Explain.

36. What does this result prove?

What Kind of Triangle? In the figure below, AY, an altitude of △ABC, is concurrent with BZ and CX at point P. △DYE has been drawn so that DE ∥ BC.

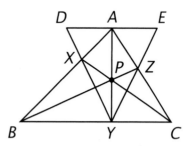

37. Use your ruler to draw a larger copy of this figure.

38. What kind of triangle does △DYE appear to be?

39. Why is △AXD ~ △BXY and △CZY ~ △AZE?

40. Why is $\dfrac{AX}{BX} = \dfrac{AD}{BY}$ and $\dfrac{CZ}{AZ} = \dfrac{CY}{AE}$?

41. What do you know about
    $\dfrac{AX}{BX} \cdot \dfrac{BY}{CY} \cdot \dfrac{CZ}{AZ}$?

42. What can you conclude about
    $\dfrac{AD}{BY} \cdot \dfrac{BY}{CY} \cdot \dfrac{CY}{AE}$? Explain.

43. What can you conclude about $\dfrac{AD}{AE}$?
    Explain.

44. Why is AD = AE?

45. Why is AY ⊥ DE?

46. What can you conclude about △DYA and △EYA? Explain.

47. What does this relation between △DYA and △EYA prove about △DYE? Explain.

The Gergonne Point. Joseph Gergonne, a French mathematician of the nineteenth century, discovered something about the incircle of a triangle.

48. Draw a large scalene triangle and labeled its vertices A, B, and C.

   (1) Use your straightedge and compass to inscribe a circle in the triangle. Label the points of tangency D, E, and F so that D is on BC, E is on AC, and F is on AB.

   (2) Draw AD, BE, and CF.

49. What do you notice?

50. Why is it true?

51. What point do you think was named after Gergonne?

Another Look at Altitudes.
In the figure at the right, AY, BZ, and CX are perpendicular to the sides of △ABC.
   Write a similarity correspondence between each of the following triangles and another triangle in the figure.

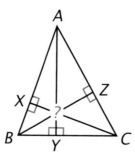

52. △AXC.

53. △BYA.

54. △CZB.

Use your correspondences to copy and complete the following proportions.

55. $\dfrac{AX}{AZ} = \dfrac{XC}{?}$.

56. $\dfrac{BY}{BX} = \dfrac{YA}{?}$.

57. $\dfrac{CZ}{CY} = \dfrac{ZB}{?}$.

58. Show how it follows from these equations and Ceva's Theorem that AY, BZ, and CX are concurrent.

59. What theorem do your answers to exercises 52 through 58 prove?

Set III

Area Puzzle. Rather than being concurrent, the three cevians in △ABC intersect to form a smaller triangle, △GHI.

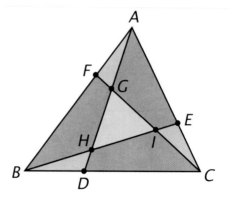

Given that D, E, and F are points of trisection of the sides of △ABC, it can be proved that the blue regions have equal areas and the purple regions have equal areas; it can also be proved that, if the area of a blue region is x, the area of a purple region is $5x$.
   Find the areas of the following triangles in terms of x.

1. △ABD.   2. △ADC.   3. △GHI.

4. What fraction of the area of △ABC is the area of △GHI?

5. How does the figure below suggest a different way to arrive at the same conclusion?

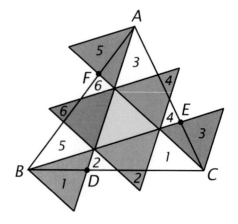

Napoleon's Discovery and Other Surprises

The popular picture above, published in England many years ago, is of the ghost of Napoleon visiting his grave on the remote island where he died. Its success was due in part to the fact that some people could not immediately find Napoleon in the figure.

Napoleon enjoyed mathematics and even taught geometry for a time at a university. He may have been the first person to discover something about triangles now known as Napoleon's Theorem.

In the figure shown at the right, equilateral triangles have been drawn on the sides of an equilateral triangle. If the centers of these three triangles are connected, the result is another equilateral triangle. Because of the symmetry of the figure, the fact that this triangle also is equilateral seems natural and Euclid would have seen immediately that it was true.

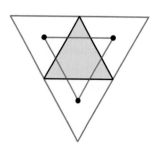

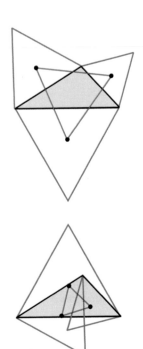

Suppose, instead, that equilateral triangles are drawn on the sides of a triangle having no special shape. If the centers of the three added triangles are connected, you might expect that the result is no longer anything special or, at most, that it might be a triangle similar to the original triangle. Amazingly, this is not the case. As the figure at the left suggests, the new triangle is again equilateral!

Now imagine that the three equilateral triangles on the sides of the triangle point inward instead of outward. The centers of the three added triangles still determine an equilateral triangle! Regardless of its shape, *every* triangle has two such equilateral triangles associated with it, known as the "outer and inner Napoleon triangles."

Much like the hidden image of Napoleon in the picture at the beginning of this lesson, many remarkable results in geometry remained hidden for many centuries after Euclid's time, not because they are hard to see but because no one had ever thought to look for them.

Eric Temple Bell, a historian of mathematics, wrote:

> Geometry is a richer treasure house of more interesting and half-forgotten things . . . than any other division of mathematics.*

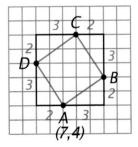

In the exercises that follow, you will see some more examples of results in geometry that are unexpected and, at times, surprising.

Exercises

Set I

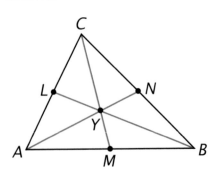

(7, 4)

Tilted Square. The figure above shows a "tilted square" on a coordinate grid.

1. Which sides have a slope of $\frac{2}{3}$?

2. What is the slope of the other two sides?

3. Why is the product of the slopes of two consecutive sides −1?

4. How long is each side of the tilted square?

5. If A has coordinates (7, 4), what are the coordinates of B, C, and D?

Euler's Discovery. Leonard Euler made an interesting discovery about the orthocenter, centroid, and circumcenter of a triangle. It is illustrated in the following series of exercises.

On graph paper, draw a pair of axes extending 20 units to the right and 15 units up from the origin.

The Centroid.

6. Plot the following points and connect them to form △ABC: A(0, 0), B(18, 0), C(6, 12). Find the midpoints of AB and AC and label them M and L as shown.

The Development of Mathematics (McGraw-Hill, 1940).

7. What are the coordinates of points M and L?

8. Draw CM and BL. Let Y be the point in which they intersect. What are the coordinates of point Y?

9. Draw AY and extend it to intersect CB at N. What are the coordinates of point N?

10. How are the coordinates of N related to the coordinates of B and C?

11. Use the distance formula to find CN and NB.

12. What is point Y called with respect to △ABC?

13. What are AN, BL, and CM called?

The Circumcenter.

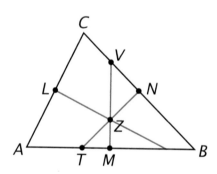

14. Through M on the same figure, draw a line perpendicular to AB and extend the line to intersect CB at point V. What are the coordinates of V?

15. Through N, construct a line perpendicular to CB and extend the line to intersect AB at point T. What are the coordinates of T?

16. Find the slopes of NT and CB.

17. Are these slopes related in the way that you would expect? Explain.

18. Let Z be the point in which VM and NT intersect. What are the coordinates of Z?

19. What is point Z called with respect to △ABC?

20. Draw ZL. Find the slopes of AC and ZL.

21. What do their slopes indicate about AC and ZL?

22. What are lines VM, NT, and ZL called with respect to △ABC?

The Orthocenter.

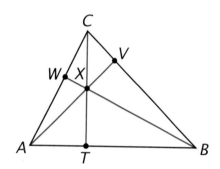

23. On the same figure, draw CT. What relation does CT have to AB?

24. Through A, construct a line perpendicular to CB. Where does this line intersect CB?

25. Find the slope of AV.

26. Does AV have the slope that you would expect? Explain.

27. Let X be the point in which CT and AV intersect. What are the coordinates of X?

28. What is point X called with respect to △ABC?

29. Draw line BX and extend it to intersect AC at W. What are CT, AV, and BW called with respect to △ABC?

Euler's Conclusions.

30. What relation do points X, Y, and Z appear to have?

31. Find the slopes of XY and YZ.

32. How do XY and YZ compare in length? Explain.

33. Which point in the figure is equidistant from A, B, and C?

34. Find each of the three distances to see if you are correct.

Triangles on Four Sides. In the figure below, ABCD is a square and the four triangles are equilateral.

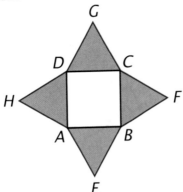

35. Make an accurate enlargement of the figure on graph paper by doing each of the following steps.

   (1) Draw square ABCD so that each side is 6 units long.

   (2) Use your straightedge and compass to construct the four equilateral triangles on its sides.

36. What is the perimeter of the octagonal star, GCFBEAHD?

37. What is the measure of ∠CBE?

38. What is the measure of ∠HAE?

35. (*continued*) Draw HC and DE.

39. What relation do these lines appear to have?

35. (*continued*) Draw HE and CE.

40. What do you notice about △HDC, △CBE, and △EAH? Explain.

41. What does what you noticed about these three triangles prove about △HCE?

42. What do your conclusions prove about HC and DE?

Squares on Three Sides. On graph paper, draw a pair of axes extending 20 units to the right and 20 units up from the origin.

43. Plot the following points and connect them to form △ABC: A(5, 8), B(13, 8), C(7, 12).

44. Find the slope of each side of △ABC.

45. Is △ABC a right triangle? Explain.

43. (*continued*) Draw squares on the sides of △ABC and label them as shown in the figure below. If you have drawn the squares accurately, the coordinates of F should be (1, 10) and those of H should be (11, 18).

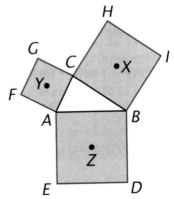

46. Find the coordinates of G and I.

43. (*continued*) Find the centers of the squares and label them as shown in the figure.

47. Find the coordinates of X, Y, and Z.

43. (*continued*) Draw AX, BY, and CZ.

48. What relation do these lines appear to have?

43. (*continued*) Draw △XYZ.

49. How do AX, BY, and CZ appear to be related to the sides of △XYZ?

50. Show whether this relation is really true.

51. How do AX, BY, and CZ compare in length with the sides of △XYZ?

Squares on Four Sides. On graph paper, draw a pair of axes extending 15 units to the right and 15 units up from the origin.

52. Plot the following points and connect them to form quadrilateral ABCD: A(4, 6), B(10, 6), C(11, 9), D(5, 9).

53. Find the length of each side of ABCD.

54. What kind of quadrilateral is ABCD?

55. How do you know?

52. (*continued*) Draw squares on the sides of ABCD. Find the centers of the squares and label them as shown in the figure below.

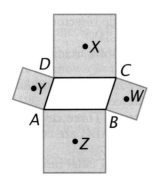

56. Find the coordinates of W, X, Y, and Z.

52. (*continued*) Draw XZ and WY.

57. Find the slopes of XZ and WY.

58. What do their slopes prove about XZ and WY?

59. How do XZ and WY compare in length?

52. (*continued*) Draw quadrilateral WXYZ.

60. What kind of quadrilateral is it?

Napoleon Triangles. In the figure below illustrating Napoleon's discovery, equilateral triangles △ACE, △ABF, and △BCD have been drawn outward on the sides of △ABC, a triangle having no special shape.

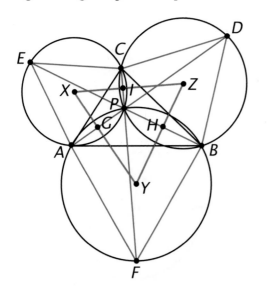

It can be proved that the line segments AD, BE, and CF are equal and concurrent and that they form 60° angles with each other.

61. It follows that the three quadrilaterals APCE, APBF, and BPCD must be cyclic. Why?

As a result, the circumcircles X, Y, and Z of the three equilateral triangles intersect at point P.

62. If △XYZ is drawn, it follows that the three segments concurrent at P must be perpendicular to the triangle's sides. Why? (Hint: Notice that X is equidistant from A and P.)

63. Quadrilaterals PGXI, PGYH, and PHZI can now be used to explain why △XYZ is equilateral. How?

Set III

Alternating Triangles. The figures below suggest a theorem about quadrilaterals.

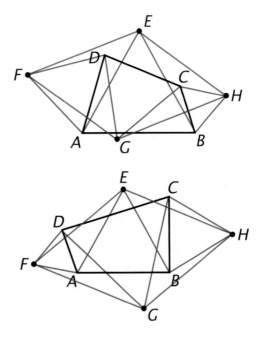

1. What do you think it is?

2. Make a drawing with a concave quadrilateral to see if your theorem seems to apply to it.

CHAPTER 13 Summary and Review

Basic Ideas

Centroid   549
Cevian   554
Circumcircle and circumcenter   531
Circumscribed polygon   542
Cyclic polygon   530
Incircle and incenter   542
Inscribed polygon   531
Median   549
Orthocenter   549

Theorems

68. Every triangle is cyclic.   531
Corollary. The perpendicular bisectors of the
    sides of a triangle are concurrent.   531
69. A quadrilateral is cyclic iff a pair of its
    opposite angles are supplementary.   536

70. Every triangle has an incircle.   543
Corollary. The angle bisectors of a triangle are
    concurrent.   543
71. The medians of a triangle are concurrent.
    549
72. The lines containing the altitudes of a
    triangle are concurrent.   549
73. *Ceva's Theorem.* Three cevians, AY, BZ,
    and CX, of △ABC are concurrent iff
    $$\frac{AX}{XB} \cdot \frac{BY}{YC} \cdot \frac{CZ}{ZA} = 1. \quad 555$$

Constructions

9. To circumscribe a circle about a triangle.
   531
10. To inscribe a circle in a triangle.   543

Exercises

Set I

Cyclic Triangle. The figure below shows that
△ABC is cyclic.

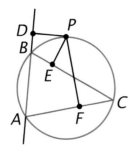

1. What does saying that a polygon is cyclic
   mean?

2. What word describes the way in which
   △ABC is related to the circle?

3. What relation do PD, PE, and PF appear
   to have to the lines containing the sides
   of the triangle?

Although there is nothing special about △ABC
or point P, there *is* something special about the
way in which D, E, and F are related.

4. What do you think it is?

Circumcircle and Incircle. The circles in the
figure below are circumscribed about and
inscribed in △ABC; AB is a diameter of
circle O.

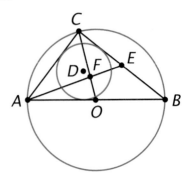

5. Use your straightedge and compass to construct the figure by doing the following steps.

(1) Draw a circle with a radius of about 2 inches and label its center O.

(2) Draw the diameter AB.

(3) Choose a point C on the circle in about the position shown in the figure and draw CA and CB.

(4) Draw radius OC.

(5) Inscribe a circle in △ABC and label its center D.

(6) Bisect CB and label its midpoint E.

(7) Draw AE and let F be the point in which AE and CO intersect.

6. What kind of triangle is △ABC? Explain.

7. Name one of its medians.

8. Name one of its altitudes.

9. Name a pair of points that determine one of its angle bisectors.

Which point in the figure is its

10. incenter?

11. circumcenter?

12. centroid?

13. orthocenter?

Three Trapezoids. For each of the following trapezoids, the measures of two angles are given.

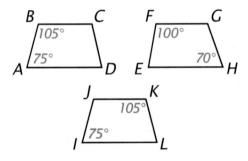

Which trapezoid(s)

14. must be cyclic?

15. cannot be cyclic?

16. Explain.

Double Identity. In the figure below, GE, HF, and ID are the perpendicular bisectors of the sides of △ABC.

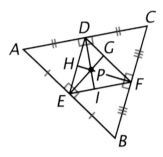

17. What is point P called with respect to △ABC?

18. What are DE, EF, and DF called with respect to △ABC?

19. What relation do the sides of △DEF have to the sides of △ABC?

20. What are GE, HF, and ID called with respect to △DEF?

21. What is point P called with respect to △DEF?

22. Which points in the figure are equidistant from point P?

Ceva's Theorem. The sides of the triangle below are 5, 6, and 7 units.

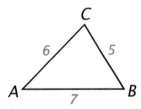

23. Use your ruler and compass to construct an enlargement of it by using sides of lengths 5 cm, 6 cm, and 7 cm. Mark point X on CA so that CX = 2 cm, point Y on AB so that AY = 4 cm, and point Z on BC so that BZ = 3 cm.

Find each of the following numbers.

24. AX, YB, and ZC.

25. $\dfrac{CX}{XA}$, $\dfrac{AY}{YB}$, and $\dfrac{BZ}{ZC}$.

26. $\dfrac{CX}{XA} \cdot \dfrac{AY}{YB} \cdot \dfrac{BZ}{ZC}$.

27. What does the answer to exercise 26 indicate?

23. (*continued*) Add the appropriate line segments to your figure to see if your answer to exercise 27 is true.

Five Circles. The figure below illustrates a surprising geometric fact.

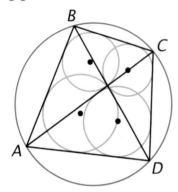

28. What kind of quadrilateral is ABCD?

29. What relation does the largest circle in the figure have to this quadrilateral?

Each of the smaller circles is tangent to three lines in the figure.

30. How are these circles related to some of the triangles in the figure?

31. What is surprising about their centers?

Centroid. Architects know that one of the properties that affects how efficiently a structural shape supports a building load is its centroid.*

32. Use your straightedge and compass to construct right △ABC having legs of $2\frac{1}{4}$ inches and 3 inches as shown in the figure at the top of the next column. Draw cevians AD and BE to find its centroid. Label the centroid P.

*Architectural Exam Review, Vol. 1, Structural Topics, by David Kent Ballast (Professional Publications, 1992).

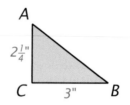

Use your ruler to measure the distance from P to

33. AC.

34. CB.

35. How do these distances compare with the lengths of CB and AC?

Set II

Soap-Film Geometry. The figure below shows a frame made of two parallel glass plates connected by four identical pins that are perpendicular to both plates.

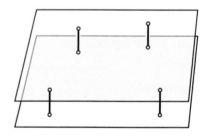

The next figure shows what happens if the frame is dipped into a soap solution and then withdrawn. Five walls of soap film are formed between the pins.†

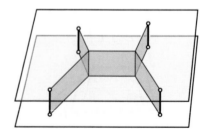

† *The Parsimonious Universe: Shape and Form in the Natural World,* by Stefan Hildebrandt and Anthony Tromba (Copernicus, 1996).

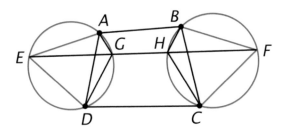

In the figure above, points A, B, C, and D mark the positions of the four pins. Equilateral triangles △ADE and △BCF and their circumcircles have been constructed on opposite sides of ABCD, and line EF has been drawn to intersect the circles at G and H.

36. What can you conclude about ∠AED + ∠AGD? Why?

37. What can you conclude about the measure of ∠AGD? Why?

38. What can you conclude about ∠EGD and ∠EAD? Why?

What can you conclude about the measures of the following angles? Explain how you found each answer.

39. ∠EGD.   **43.** ∠FHC.

40. ∠DGH.   **44.** ∠GHC.

41. ∠AGH.   **45.** ∠BHG.

42. ∠BHC.

The line segments meeting at G and H correspond to the positions of the five walls of soap film.

46. What do these results suggest about the angles formed where the walls meet?

Irrelevant Information. In the figure below, point D is the incenter of △ABC.

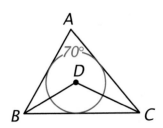

47. If ∠A = 70° and ∠ABC = 60°, find ∠D.

48. If ∠A = 70° and ∠ABC = 40°, find ∠D.

49. If ∠A = 70° and the measure of ∠ABC is not known, find ∠D.

Medians Theorem. Ceva's Theorem can be used to prove that the medians of a triangle are concurrent.

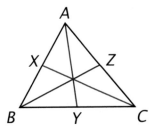

50. Use the figure above in which AY, BZ, and CX are the medians of △ABC to explain how.

Irregular Billiard Table. In the figure below, the diagonals of quadrilateral ABCD intersect at point P.

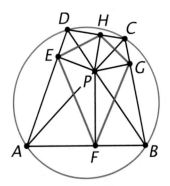

51. What kind of quadrilateral is ABCD?

What relation do PE, PF, PG, and PH appear to have to

52. ABCD?

53. EFGH?

54. Given that both of these relations are true and that a billiard table was built in the shape of ABCD, where do you think a ball at E would go if it were hit in the direction EF?

Perimeter Problem. △ABC is a right triangle with legs of lengths a and b. The radius of its incircle is r and the radius of its circumcircle is R.

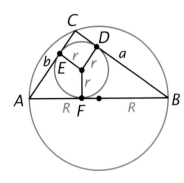

Name the line segments in the figure whose length is

55. $a - r$.

56. $b - r$.

57. $(a - r) + (b - r)$.

58. $2R$.

59. Use your answers to exercises 57 and 58 to show that the perimeter of △ABC is $2r + 4R$.

Squares on the Sides. On graph paper, draw a pair of axes extending 20 units to the right and 20 units up from the origin.

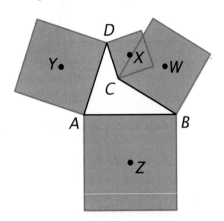

60. Plot the following points and connect them to form quadrilateral ABCD:
A(6, 8), B(14, 8), C(9, 11), D(8, 14).

61. What kind of quadrilateral is ABCD?

60. (*continued*) Draw squares on the sides of ABCD. Find the centers of the squares and label them as shown in the figure.

62. Find the coordinates of W, X, Y, and Z.

60. (*continued*) Draw XZ and WY.

63. What relations do XZ and WY have?

Area Problem. In the figure below, O is the circumcenter of △ABC, and AD is one of its altitudes.

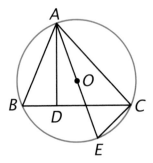

64. Which triangle in the figure is similar to △ABD?

65. Explain how you know.

66. Why does it follow that
AB · AC = AD · AE?

67. If the radius of circle O is r, why does it follow that the area of △ABC is equal to the product of the lengths of its three sides divided by $4r$? (Hint: Start with $\dfrac{AB \cdot AC \cdot BC}{4r}$.)

Chapter 14

Regular Polygons and the Circle

A polygon is regular if it is both equilateral and equiangular. As the number of sides of such a polygon increases, it looks more and more like a circle. This observation enabled the Greek mathematician Archimedes to make accurate estimates of the circumference and area of a circle. In this chapter, you will see how the trigonometric ratios and the idea of a limit can be used to achieve the same result.

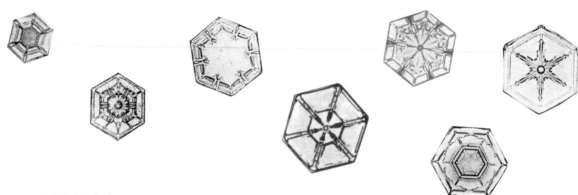

Regular Polygons

Snowflakes are a beautiful example of geometry in nature. Wilson Bentley, a farmer-meteorologist in Vermont, spent many winters taking photographs of thousands of them through a microscope; some of his pictures are shown above.*

Although it has been said that no two snowflakes are alike, those illustrated here have several basic properties in common. All are six-sided and hence hexagonal in shape. Furthermore, each is convex and has equal sides and equal angles; such polygons are called *regular*.

Definition

A *regular polygon* is a convex polygon that is both equilateral and equiangular.

Used by permission of Johnny Hart and Creators Syndicate, Inc.

Snow Crystals, by W. A. Bentley and W. J. Humphreys (McGraw-Hill, 1931).

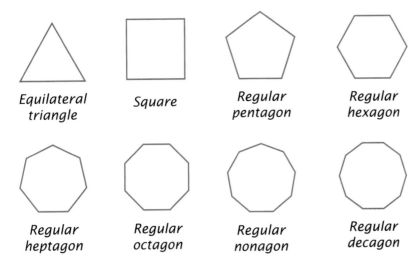

| Equilateral triangle | Square | Regular pentagon | Regular hexagon |

| Regular heptagon | Regular octagon | Regular nonagon | Regular decagon |

Figures representing regular polygons having from three through ten sides are shown above. Notice that, as the number of sides of a regular polygon increases, it looks more and more like a circle–a consequence of the fact that every regular polygon is cyclic.

Theorem 74

Every regular polygon is cyclic.

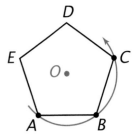

> *Given:* ABCDE is a regular polygon.
> *Prove:* ABCDE is cyclic.

To illustrate our proof, we will use a regular pentagon. The proof, however, applies to all regular polygons because it does not depend on the number of sides of the pentagon.

The idea is to draw a circle through three consecutive vertices of the polygon and then prove, by means of congruent triangles, that the next vertex also lies on this circle. From this fact, it follows that the rest of the vertices lie on this circle.

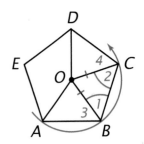

Proof

Draw the circle that contains points A, B, and C and let its center be called O. Draw OA, OB, OC, and OD.

We know that OB = OC (all radii of a circle are equal), and so ∠1 = ∠2 (if two sides of a triangle are equal, the angles opposite them are equal). Because ∠ABC = ∠BCD (a regular polygon is equiangular), ∠3 = ∠4 (subtraction). Also, AB = CD (a regular polygon is equilateral), and so △OBA ≅ △OCD (SAS). Therefore, OD = OA. Because OA is the radius of the circle, it follows that OD also is a radius. Hence, D lies on circle O, because a circle is the set of all points in a plane at a distance of one radius from its center.

To prove that E also lies on circle O, OE can be drawn and △ODE proved congruent to △OCB in the same way.

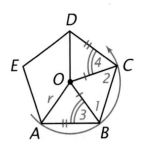

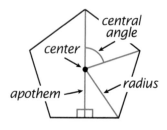

Recall that a polygon whose vertices lie on a circle is *inscribed* in the circle and that the circle is *circumscribed* about the polygon. Because every regular polygon is cyclic, some of the words that we have been using with circles are also used with regular polygons. The *center* of a regular polygon is the center of its circumscribed circle. The word *radius*, as for circles, can refer either to a line segment or to a distance: a line segment that connects the center of a regular polygon to a vertex or the distance between the center and that vertex. A *central angle* of a regular polygon is an angle formed by radii drawn to two consecutive vertices.

A new word, used only in geometry, is *apothem*.

Definition

An *apothem* of a regular polygon is a perpendicular line segment from its center to one of its sides.

Exercises

Set I

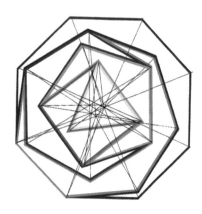

Geometry in Art. Swiss artist and designer Max Bill created a series of pictures titled *Fifteen Variations on a Single Theme.* Two of them are shown above.

The left-hand figure contains a series of regular polygons.

1. Name the regular polygons that you see.

2. In what way is each successive polygon related to the preceding one?

3. What do the thin lines represent?

The right-hand figure is related to the left-hand one.

4. What do you think the right-hand figure illustrates?

Geometry in Nature. Triangles appear naturally in this cross section of the mineral tourmaline.

5. If a triangle is equilateral, can you conclude that it is regular? Explain.

6. Can you conclude that it is cyclic?

7. If a triangle is cyclic, can you conclude that it is regular? Explain.

Squares appear naturally as the faces of crystals of iron pyrite, also known as "fool's gold."

Can you conclude that a quadrilateral is cyclic if it is

8. equilateral?

9. equiangular?

10. regular?

11. If a quadrilateral is cyclic, can you conclude that it is regular? Illustrate your answer with a drawing.

Cell Pattern. When a liquid is heated from below, a pattern of cells, made visible here by metal flakes suspended in the fluid, develops spontaneously.*

12. What shape do these cells appear to have?

The figure below suggests a simple way to construct this polygon.

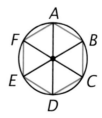

The points divide the circle into six equal arcs.

13. What is the measure of each arc in degrees?

14. What kind of triangles surround the center of the circle?

15. How do the sides of the hexagon compare in length with the radius of the circle?

16. Use this fact to construct a regular hexagon by inscribing it in a circle.

17. How does the perimeter of the hexagon compare with the diameter of the circle?

---

*The Self-Made Tapestry: Pattern Formation in Nature, by Philip Ball (Oxford University Press, 1999).

Regular Dodecagon. Some of the diagonals of the regular dodecagon below are the sides of other regular polygons.

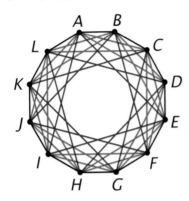

For example, the red diagonals form two regular hexagons. Notice that $2 \times 6 = 12$.

18. What do the green diagonals form?

19. What do the blue diagonals form?

20. How are the numbers of sides of these polygons related to the number of sides of the dodecagon?

What regular polygons could be formed if diagonals were drawn in this way in a regular

21. 15-gon?

22. 16-gon?

23. 17-gon?

Polygonal Knot. The figure below shows a regular polygon produced when a strip of paper is tied in a certain type of knot and pressed flat.*

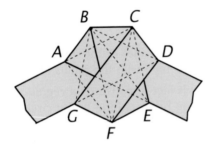

24. Which regular polygon is it?

Mathematical Models, by H. Martyn Cundy and A. P. Rollett (Oxford University Press, 1961).

Does the polygon have any

25. parallel sides?

26. parallel diagonals?

In general, what regular polygons do you think have

27. parallel sides?

28. parallel diagonals?

Set II

Mason's Pentagon. A method used by masons in the Middle Ages to draw a pentagon is illustrated by the figure below.†

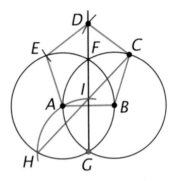

29. Use your straightedge and compass to construct it by doing each of the following steps.

(1) Draw a line segment AB about 4 cm long and two circles with centers at A and B and with radius AB.

(2) Let F and G be the points in which the circles intersect, and draw line FG.

(3) With G as center, draw an arc through A that intersects circle A at H and line FG at I.

(4) Draw line HI, extending it to intersect circle B at C.

(5) With C as center and radius AB, draw an arc intersecting line FG at D.

(6) With D as center and the same radius, draw an arc intersecting circle A at E.

---

† *Geometry Civilized: History, Culture, and Technique,* by J. L. Heilbron (Clarendon Press, 1998).

(7) Draw ABCDE.

30. Is ABCDE equilateral? Explain.

ABCDE *is not regular.*

31. Explain why it cannot be regular.

29. *(continued)* Draw AF and FB.

32. Is △ABF regular? Explain.

Folding an Octagon. The figure below shows how a square sheet of paper can be folded to form an octagon.*

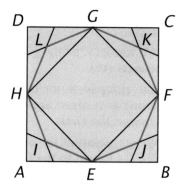

Points E, F, G, and H are the midpoints of the sides of ABCD.

33. What kind of triangles are △AEH, △BEF, △CFG, and △DGH?

34. Why are they congruent?

The lines in these triangles bisect their acute angles.

35. Why is EF = FG = GH = HE?

36. What kind of triangles are △EHI, △EFJ, △FGK, and △GHL?

37. Why are they congruent?

38. What can you conclude about the sides of the octagon EJFKGLHI?

Find the measures of the following angles.

39. ∠AEI.

*Geometric Exercises in Paper Folding, by T. Sundara Row (Open Court, 1905).

40. ∠EIH.

41. ∠IEJ.

42. What can you conclude about the angles of octagon EJFKGLHI?

43. What do exercises 38 and 42 prove about octagon EJFKGLHI?

Hexagonal Fastener. Fasteners have been made with heads in the shape of regular hexagons for hundreds of years. They were even used to hold armor together in the fifteenth century.†

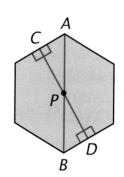

The regular hexagon in the figure above represents one of these fastener heads; AB and CD intersect at its center, P.

44. What are PA and PB called with respect to the hexagon?

45. What are PC and PD called?

46. Why is △APC ≅ △BPD? Explain.

47. What type of right triangles are they?

If PA = 0.25 inch, find

48. AC and PC.

49. AB and CD.

50. Which length, AB or CD, would be used to give the size of the wrench needed to turn the head? Explain.

†Sizes: The Illustrated Encyclopedia, by John Lord (Harper Perennial, 1995).

Inscribed Pentagon. In the figure below, regular pentagon ABCDE is inscribed in the circle, and diagonals AC and BD intersect at F.

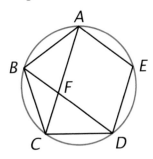

51. Copy the figure and mark it as needed to answer each of the following questions.

52. Why can you conclude that the five arcs into which the pentagon divides the circle are equal?

What is the measure of

53. each arc?

54. ∠ABD?

55. ∠AFB?

56. ∠BAC?

57. ∠BCA?

58. How many triangles are in the figure?

59. All the triangles have something in common. What is it?

60. What can you conclude about AEDF? Explain.

61. What can you conclude about AEDB and AEDC?

Set III

A Close Construction. No one has ever found a way to construct a regular heptagon by using just a straightedge and compass, and no one ever will!

The following construction, however, is close enough that, if you do it accurately, you won't be able to tell the difference.

1. Use your straightedge and compass to construct the figure at top of the next column by doing each of the following steps.

(1) Draw circle O with a radius of about 2 inches.

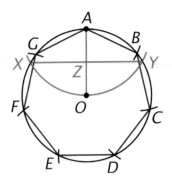

(2) Choose a point A on it and draw AO.

(3) With A as center, draw an arc with radius AO that intersects the circle in points X and Y.

(4) Draw XY and let Z be the point in which XY intersects AO.

(5) Adjust the compass to the distance ZY and, starting at A, draw arcs having this radius around the circle.

(6) Label the endpoints of the arcs B through G as shown in the figure.

(7) Draw ABCDEFG.

2. To check the method used, draw AX, XO, AY, and YO. What kind of triangles are △AXO and △AYO?

3. What relation does AO have to XY?

4. What special kind of triangle is △OZY?

Letting OY = *r*, find each of the following lengths in terms of *r*.

5. OZ.

6. ZY.

7. AB.

8. Let M be the midpoint of AB and draw OM. Find AM in terms of *r*.

9. Use your calculator to find the measure of ∠AOM in right △AMO to as many decimal places as you can.

To as many decimal places as you can, find

10. ∠AOB.

11. 7∠AOB.

12. What does the answer to exercise 11 reveal about ABCDEFG? Explain.

The Perimeter of a Regular Polygon

One of the most famous temples of ancient Greece was the Tholos at Delphi. Circular in shape, it had 20 outer columns set at the vertices of a regular polygon called an icosagon. The temple was built in about 370 B.C., and only three of its columns still stand.*

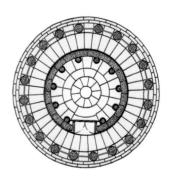

The ground plan of the temple is shown in the figure at the right. A regular icosagon with vertices at the centers of the bases of the 20 columns is shown in red. Because the icosagon has so many sides, it looks a lot like a circle, suggesting that we could approximate the measurements of a circle by using measurements of a regular polygon having a large number of sides. For example, the circumference of a circle should be close to the perimeter of a regular icosagon having the same radius as that of the circle.

The perimeter of a regular polygon can be found by multiplying the length of a side by the number of sides. Doing so gives us the equation

$$p = ns,$$

where p is the perimeter of the polygon, n is the number of sides, and s is the length of one side. This formula cannot be applied to a circle, however, because a circle doesn't have any sides.

*Euclid: The Creation of Mathematics, by Benno Artmann (Springer, 1999).

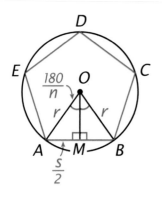

There is another way to express the perimeter of a regular polygon that can be extended to measuring a circle. This method is based on the length of the polygon's radius. In the figure at the left, a regular pentagon with sides of length s has been inscribed in a circle with radius r.

Radii OA and OB of the circle have been drawn, as well as apothem OM. Since OM $\perp$ AB, $\triangle$AOM $\cong$ $\triangle$BOM (HL). From equal corresponding parts of congruent triangles, we can conclude that OM bisects central $\angle$AOB as well as chord AB. It follows that AM $= \dfrac{s}{2}$ and, because a central angle of a regular n-gon has a measure of $\dfrac{360}{n}$, that

$$\angle \text{AOM} = \frac{1}{2}\left(\frac{360}{n}\right) = \frac{180}{n}.$$

To see how r and s are related, we can apply the sine ratio to right $\triangle$AOM:

$$\sin\frac{180}{n} = \frac{\frac{s}{2}}{r}.$$

Multiplying both sides of this equation by r gives

$$r\sin\frac{180}{n} = \frac{s}{2}$$

and by 2 gives

$$s = 2r\sin\frac{180}{n}.$$

Because $p = ns$, it follows by substitution that

$$p = n\left(2r\sin\frac{180}{n}\right) = 2\left(n\sin\frac{180}{n}\right)r.$$

To understand this expression better, we notice that the product $n\sin\dfrac{180}{n}$ depends only on n. This is the part of the formula determined by the number of sides of our regular polygon. We represent it by the single letter N, and so $N = n\sin\dfrac{180}{n}$. We substitute N in the equation above to get

$$p = 2Nr.$$

This formula shows that the perimeter of a regular polygon is proportional to its radius. The formula does not depend on the fact that we used a polygon with five sides to derive it, and so we can state it as a general theorem.

Theorem 75

The perimeter of a regular polygon having n sides is $2Nr$, in which

$N = n \sin\dfrac{180}{n}$ and r is its radius.

Knowing that the radius of the regular icosagon in the ground plan of the Tholos temple at Delphi is 24 feet, we can now find its

perimeter. Because it has 20 sides, $N = 20 \sin\dfrac{180}{20} = 20 \sin 9°$. There-

fore,

$$p = 2(20 \sin 9°)(24) \approx 150.$$

The perimeter of the temple is approximately 150 feet.

Exercises

Set I

Perimeter Equations. The expression for the perimeter of a regular polygon introduced in this lesson has two parts:

$$p = 2Nr \quad \text{and} \quad N = n \sin\dfrac{180}{n}.$$

1. What does r represent?

2. What does n represent?

3. What is the smallest number that n can be for a polygon?

Use your calculator to find the value of N to four decimal places

4. if $n = 10$.

5. if $n = 100$.

6. if $n = 1,000$.

7. if $n = 10,000$.

As n increases, what happens to

8. the value of N?

9. the shape of the regular polygon?

Angles and Radii. ABCDEFG is a regular polygon with center P.

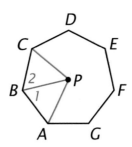

10. What are PA, PB, and PC called with respect to the polygon?

What can you conclude about

11. $\triangle ABP$ and $\triangle CBP$? Why?

12. $\angle 1$ and $\angle 2$? Why?

13. Do your answers to exercises 11 and 12 depend on the fact that the polygon has seven sides?

14. How is the radius PB related to $\angle ABC$?

Italian City. During the Renaissance, new cities were sometimes planned in the shape of regular polygons.

The figure above shows the design of the walled city of Palma Nuova in Italy. The core of the city is shown in color.

15. How many sides does the regular polygon have that surrounds the core of the city?

Express the value of *N* for this polygon

16. by using a trigonometric ratio.

17. to the nearest thousandth.

18. Given that the radius of the city is 1,100 feet, find the perimeter of its core to the nearest foot.

Hydrogen Fluoride. Hydrogen fluoride gas, used to etch glass, has been found to contain rings of atoms having the following shapes.*

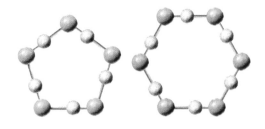

The hydrogen atoms are shown in white and the fluorine atoms in yellow.

---

*The Architecture of Molecules, by Linus Pauling and Roger Hayward (W. H. Freeman and Company, 1964).

19. What is the name of each shape?

20. How do the sides of the two shapes appear to compare in length?

21. How do the radii of the two shapes appear to compare in length?

What is the measure of the angle at each corner of

22. the first ring?

23. the second ring?

Given that the distance between two consecutive corners in each ring is 2.5 angstroms, find the perimeter of

24. the first ring.

25. the second ring.

Find the value of *N* for

26. the first ring.

27. the second ring.

28. Use your answers to exercises 24 and 26 to find the radius of the first ring.

29. Use your answers to exercises 25 and 27 to find the radius of the second ring.

Dollar Coin. In 1979, the United States Mint issued a dollar coin with an unusual design. Each side showed a regular polygon having 11 sides inscribed in a circle.

The radius of the circle was 12 mm. Find each of the following lengths to the nearest millimeter.

30. The circumference of the circle.

31. The perimeter of the polygon.

32. The length of one side of the polygon.

Set II

Phone Cells. Cell-phone networks consist of hexagonal cells, each having a base station at its center.*

33. Given that the radius of each cell is *r*, use Theorem 75 to find the perimeter of each cell in terms of *r*.

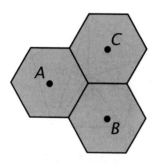

34. Copy the figure above and draw the radii of each cell.

35. What kind of triangles do you get? Use them to get the answer to exercise 33 in a different way.

36. Draw △ABC. What kind of triangle is it?

37. Find the distance between two neighboring base stations in the cell-phone network in terms of *r*.

38. Use your answer to exercise 37 to express the perimeter of △ABC in terms of *r*.

39. Use Theorem 75 and your calculator to find the perimeter of △ABC in terms of *r*.

Scientific American: How Things Work Today, edited by Michael Wright and M. N. Patel (Crown, 2000).

40. Do your answers to exercises 38 and 39 agree with each other? Explain.

Ten Pentagons. In the figure below, 10 regular pentagons form a ring around a regular decagon. Point X is the center on one of the pentagons.

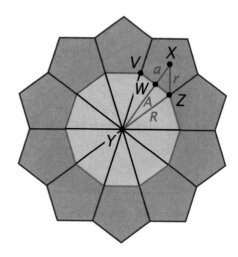

41. What is the ratio of the perimeter of the decagon to the perimeter of one of the pentagons?

42. Find ∠X.

43. Find ∠XYZ.

44. In △XYZ, why is $\dfrac{\sin \angle X}{R} = \dfrac{\sin \angle XYZ}{r}$?

45. Use your answers to exercises 42 through 44 to find the ratio $\dfrac{R}{r}$.

46. Why is XY ⊥ VZ?

47. Why is $\tan \angle X = \dfrac{WZ}{a}$, and why is $\tan \angle XYZ = \dfrac{WZ}{A}$?

48. Use your answers to exercises 42, 43, and 47 to find the ratio $\dfrac{A}{a}$.

Euclid's Discovery. Euclid discovered a surprising connection between the three figures below.

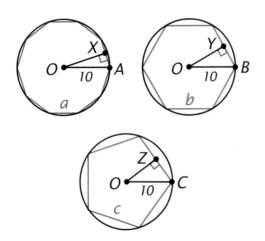

a

b

c

To find out what the connection is, do each of the following exercises.

Find the measure of $\angle O$ in the

49. decagon.

50. hexagon.

51. pentagon.

Use the sine ratio to find each of the following lengths to as many decimal places as you can.

52. AX.

53. BY.

54. CZ.

Find each of the following numbers to as many decimal places as you can.

55. a^2.

56. b^2.

57. c^2.

58. What do you think Euclid discovered?

Set III

Golden-Heather. The petals of this flower are arranged like the radii of a regular pentagon.

Suppose that each petal is 1 unit long.

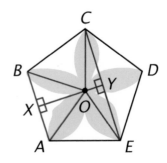

1. Show that the distance between the tips of two consecutive petals, such as AB, is $2 \sin 36°$.

2. Show that the distance between the tips of two nonconsecutive petals, such as CE, is $2 \sin 72°$.

Strange as it might seem,

$$\frac{2 \sin 72°}{2 \sin 36°} = 2 \sin 54°.$$

3. Use your calculator to see if this equality seems reasonable.

Even more strangely,

$$2 \sin 54° = 1 + \frac{1}{2 \sin 54°}.$$

4. What famous number is $2 \sin 54°$?

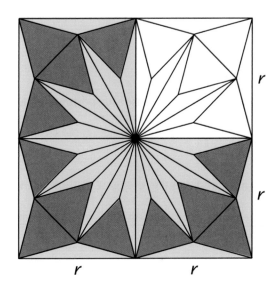
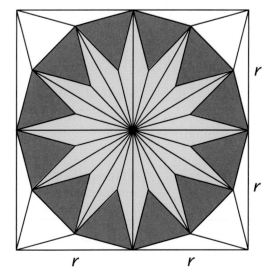

The Area of a Regular Polygon

In 1898, a Hungarian mathematician named József Kürschák made an interesting discovery illustrated by the figures above. The figures show a regular dodecagon inside a square. The square is divided into four smaller squares and the entire figure is divided into two sets of congruent triangles: equilateral triangles and 15°-15°-150° isosceles triangles.

Because the entire figure contains four squares, each with side r, its area is $4r^2$. The triangles filling three of these squares, then, have a total area of $3r^2$. They can be rearranged as shown in the second figure to fill the regular dodecagon, showing that the area of a regular dodecagon whose radius is r is $3r^2$.

This result is remarkable in that it is so simple. In general, to find the area of a regular polygon from its radius is much more complicated. In figuring out how to do it, we will again reason in terms of a regular pentagon, but our argument and conclusion, like those for the perimeter of a regular polygon, are valid for a regular polygon having any number of sides.

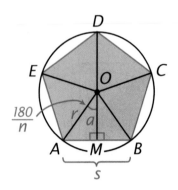

The radii of a regular polygon divide it into n congruent triangles. (In this pentagon, there are five of these triangles.) The area of one of these triangles, such as $\triangle AOB$, is $\frac{1}{2}sa$ because apothem OM is the altitude to base AB. Thus, the total area of the n triangles is $n\left(\frac{1}{2}sa\right)$, and so

$$A = \frac{1}{2}nsa$$

where A is the area of the entire figure. Because the perimeter of a regular polygon having n sides is ns, we can also write

$$A = \frac{1}{2}pa. \tag{1}$$

This equation expresses the area of a regular polygon in terms of its apothem and perimeter.

As we did for the perimeter of a regular polygon, we can restate this formula in terms of the number of sides of the polygon and its radius. By Theorem 75,

$$p = 2Nr = 2n \sin\frac{180}{n} r. \tag{2}$$

Applying the cosine ratio to $\triangle AOM$, we get

$$\cos\frac{180}{n} = \frac{a}{r}.$$

Multiplying both sides of this equation by r gives

$$a = r \cos\frac{180}{n}. \tag{3}$$

Substituting the expressions for p and a from equations 2 and 3 into equation 1, we get

$$A = \frac{1}{2}\left(2n \sin\frac{180}{n} r\right)\left(r \cos\frac{180}{n}\right)$$
$$= \left(n \sin\frac{180}{n} \cos\frac{180}{n}\right)r^2.$$

Again, we can simplify the appearance of this equation by noticing that the product $n \sin\frac{180}{n} \cos\frac{180}{n}$ depends only on n, the number of sides of our regular polygon. We represent it by the single letter M, and so $M = n \sin\frac{180}{n} \cos\frac{180}{n}$. We substitute M into the equation above to get

$$A = Mr^2.$$

This formula shows that the area of a regular polygon is proportional to the *square* of its radius. Our argument can be applied to any regular polygon; so we can state it as a general theorem.

Theorem 76

The area of a regular polygon having n sides is Mr^2, in which $M = n \sin\dfrac{180}{n} \cos\dfrac{180}{n}$ and r is its radius.

To check this result, we return to the area of the regular dodecagon pictured at the beginning of this lesson. A calculator gives us the product of the sine and cosine.

$$\begin{aligned}
A = Mr^2 &= \left(n \sin\frac{180}{n} \cos\frac{180}{n} \right)r^2 \\
&= \left(12 \sin\frac{180}{12} \cos\frac{180}{12} \right)r^2 \\
&= 12(\sin 15° \cos 15°)r^2 \\
&= 12(0.25)r^2 \\
&= 3r^2.
\end{aligned}$$

The area of the regular dodecagon is $3r^2$.

Exercises

Set I

Area Equations. The expression for the area of a regular polygon introduced in this lesson has two parts:

$$A = Mr^2 \quad \text{and} \quad M = n \sin\frac{180}{n} \cos\frac{180}{n}.$$

1. What does r represent?

2. What does n represent?

Use your calculator to find the value of M

3. if $n = 1$.

4. if $n = 2$.

5. if $n = 3$, to two decimal places.

6. if $n = 180$, to two decimal places.

7. For a regular polygon, what is the smallest number than n can equal?

Inscribed Polygon. In the figure above, a regular nonagon is inscribed in a circle with radius r.

Tell what each of the following expressions represents in the figure.

Example: $\left(9 \sin\dfrac{180°}{9} \cos\dfrac{180°}{9} \right)r^2$ or $(9 \sin 20° \cos 20°)r^2$.

Answer: The area of the nonagon.

8. πr^2.

9. $2\left(9 \sin\dfrac{180°}{9} \right)r$ or $(18 \sin 20°)r$.

10. $(2 \sin 20°)r$.

11. $2\pi r$.

The Area of a Square. The word "radius" is usually used in referring to a circle.

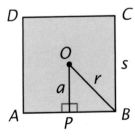

12. What does the word "radius" mean in referring to a square?

Write an expression for the area of square ABCD in terms of the length of

13. its side, s.

14. its apothem, a.

15. What kind of triangle is $\triangle OPB$?

Write an equation relating

16. r to a.

17. r^2 to a^2.

18. Use your answers to exercises 14 and 17 to write an expression for $\alpha ABCD$ in terms of r.

19. Use the formula for the area of a regular polygon to write an expression for $\alpha ABCD$ in terms of r.

Close But Not Quite. One of the figures below is a circle and the other is a regular 60-gon.

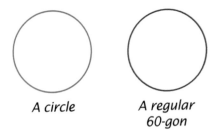

A circle   A regular 60-gon

Suppose that they each have a radius of 100 units.

20. What is the "perimeter" of a circle usually called?

21. Use the formula $c = 2\pi r$ to find the "perimeter" of the circle to the nearest unit.

22. Find the perimeter of the 60-gon to the nearest unit.

23. Which figure actually has the greater perimeter?

24. Find the ratio of the "perimeter" of the circle found in exercise 21 to twice its radius.

25. Find the ratio of the perimeter of the 60-gon found in exercise 22 to twice its radius.

26. Which figure has the greater area?

27. Use the formula $a = \pi r^2$ to find the area of the circle to the nearest square unit.

28. Find the area of the 60-gon to the nearest square unit.

Set II

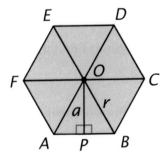

Honeycomb Geometry. Bees build the cells of honeycombs in the shape of regular hexagons.
 The radii of regular hexagon ABCDEF divide the hexagon into six triangles.

29. What kind of triangles are they?

30. What is OP called with respect to the hexagon?

31. Into what kind of triangles does OP divide △AOB?

Write an expression for

32. PB in terms of *r*.

33. *a* in terms of *r*.

34. α△AOB in terms of *r*.

35. αABCDEF in terms of *r*.

36. Use the formula for the area of a regular polygon to write an expression for αABCDEF in terms of *r*.

Use △BOP to show that

37. $\sin 30° = \dfrac{1}{2}$.   **38.** $\cos 30° = \dfrac{\sqrt{3}}{2}$.

39. Substitute the results of exercises 37 and 38 into your expression for exercise 36 and simplify.

40. Does your result turn out to be what you would expect? Explain.

Kürschák Triangles. The figure below is one of the four identical parts of the Kürschák figure shown at the beginning of this lesson. ABCD is a square, and the purple triangles are equilateral.

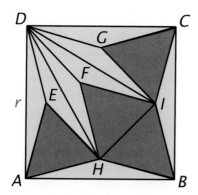

41. Which two triangles must be congruent? Explain.

The purple triangles are congruent and the yellow triangles are congruent.

42. What else can you conclude about the yellow triangles?

What can you conclude about

43. the measures of their acute angles?

44. the measures of their obtuse angles?

45. the measures of ∠AHI and ∠HIC?

Given that the length of each side of ABCD is *r*, find each of the following lengths in terms of *r*.

46. DH and DI.

47. AH, HI, and IC.

48. DE, DF, and DG.

Find each of the following areas in terms of *r*.

49. αBAHIC.

50. αDAHIC.

51. α△DAH.

Rats!

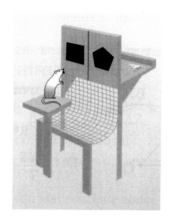

Even rats take geometry lessons! In this experiment, a rat learned to distinguish between two regular polygons marking two doors. If the rat jumps toward the "correct" polygon, the door swings open and the rat is rewarded by landing near some food on the other side. The other door is latched so that, if the rat jumps toward it, it bumps its nose and falls in the net.*

---

*The Animal Mind, by James L. Gould and Carol Grant Gould (Scientific American Library, 1994).

Suppose the two polygons have the same area.

52. How do you think the radii of the two polygons compare?

53. How do you think their perimeters compare?

Suppose the area of each polygon is 100 square centimeters. Find each of the following lengths to one decimal place.

54. The radius of the square.

55. The radius of the pentagon.

56. Find the perimeter of the square without using the formula for the perimeter of a regular polygon.

57. Use the formula for the perimeter of a regular polygon to find the perimeter of the pentagon to the nearest integer.

58. Did you guess the answers to exercises 52 and 53 correctly?

Hebrew Exercise. The problem below is from a geometry book in Hebrew.

39) מצא את שטחו של המתומן
המשוכלל ABCDEFGH החסום
במעגל שמחוגו R.

.2√2 R² :תשובה

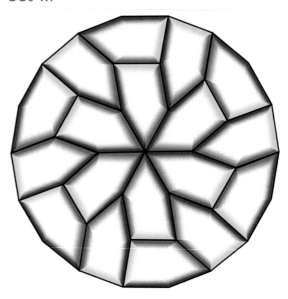

Set III

Congruent Pentagons. The figure above is based on a discovery by Marjorie Rice of San Diego, California. It consists of congruent pentagons, one of which has been enlarged below.

59. What do you think the problem is?

60. Show whether your guess seems to be correct.

61. If your guess seems to be correct, use △AOH to prove it. (Hint: Draw △AOH on your paper and find its exact area by drawing the altitude from A to HO.)

1. From the arrangement, what can you conclude about the pentagons?

2. What kind of shape is the boundary of the figure? Explain.

3. Given that each line segment in it is 1 unit long, find the radius of the figure to two decimal places.

Find the area of

4. the entire figure.

5. one of the pentagons.

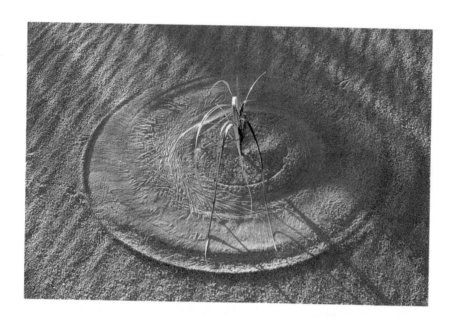

From Polygons to Pi

The circle in the photograph above, taken at the Great Sable Dunes in Michigan, was drawn by blades of grass blown by the wind! Imagine trying to measure the distance around it with a ruler. If the ruler were equal in length to the radius, r, of the circle, the figure at the right suggests that the result would actually be the perimeter, $6r$, of the inscribed hexagon.

The six arcs of the circle are obviously longer than these chords. If we bisect each arc and draw the resulting chords to get a regular dodecagon, it follows from the Triangle Inequality Theorem that its perimeter must be greater than $6r$. For example, in $\triangle AMB$ shown in the second figure at the right, $AM + MB > AB$.

The Greek mathematician Archimedes, who lived in about 250 B.C., saw how he could find the circumference of a circle by using inscribed and circumscribed polygons. Beginning with a regular hexagon, Archimedes successively doubled the number of sides to get regular polygons of 12, 24, 48, and 96 sides. The more sides he used, the better his approximation to the circumference became.

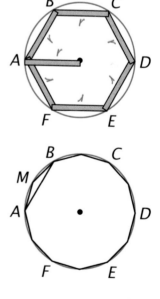

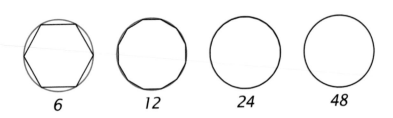

6   12   24   48

As the figures above reveal, the polygons become rounder and rounder until they are hard to distinguish from the circles in which they are inscribed. About 500 years after Archimedes, a Chinese mathematician named Liu Hui continued the doubling by using polygons with 192, 384, 768, 1536, and 3072 sides in his calculations.

From the triangle inequality argument, it is evident that the perimeters of the polygons keep getting larger. The polygons, however, are inscribed in the circles; so there is a *limit* to how large the perimeters can get. Intuitively, this limit is the "length," or *circumference,* of the circle.

Neither Archimedes nor Liu Hui had the convenience of a calculator with which to do their computations. With your calculator, you can easily check some of the values of N given to eight digits in the table at the left.

From the table, it appears that N is getting closer and closer to a specific number. The number, its *limit,* is π. As a result, the perimeters of the polygons are getting closer and closer to the number $2\pi r$. This finding suggests that the circumference of a circle should be defined as follows:

n	$p = 2Nr$
6	$2(3.0000000)r$
12	$2(3.1058285)r$
24	$2(3.1326286)r$
48	$2(3.1393502)r$
96	$2(3.1410319)r$
192	$2(3.1414524)r$
384	$2(3.1415576)r$
768	$2(3.1415838)r$
1536	$2(3.1415904)r$
3072	$2(3.1415921)r$
circle	$2\pi r$

Definition

The *circumference* of a circle is the limit of the perimeters of the inscribed regular polygons.

This definition in turn suggests the following theorem, which we state without formal proof.

Theorem 77

If the radius of a circle is r, its circumference is $2\pi r$.

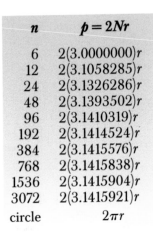

Because the diameter of a circle is twice its radius, it follows from the equations $c = 2\pi r$ and $d = 2r$ that $c = \pi d$.

Corollary to Theorem 77

If the diameter of a circle is d, its circumference is πd.

Dividing both sides of the equation $c = \pi d$ by d gives

$$\frac{c}{d} = \pi.$$

This result is the basis for the dictionary definition of π as "the ratio of the circumference of a circle to its diameter."

The number π is irrational; so its decimal form neither ends nor repeats. Its value is now known to more than 200 billion decimal places! Every scientific calculator has a key for it. Rounded to eight digits, sufficient for almost any calculation, π is

$$3.1415927.$$

Exercises

Set I

Circumference. The formula $c = 2\pi r$ relates the circumference of a circle to its radius.

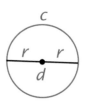

1. Explain why it follows that $c = \pi d$.

What is the ratio of the circumference of a circle to its

2. diameter? 3. radius?

Hat Sizes. To find your hat size, you need to know the size of your head.

This chart shows two examples.

Head size	Hat size
22	7
22¾	7¼

4. Find the ratio of each head size to the corresponding hat size.

The numbers in the chart are based on inches. What measurement of the hat do you think is given by

5. your head size?

6. your hat size?

The Moon's Orbit. The orbit of the moon around Earth is close to being circular, with an average radius of 238,857 miles.

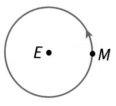

7. Find the distance traveled by the moon in one orbit around Earth.

The moon's average speed in orbiting Earth is 2,287 miles per hour.
Find the time that it takes the moon to travel once around Earth

8. in hours.

9. in days.

Semicircles. In the figure below, three semicircles are centered at A, B, and C.

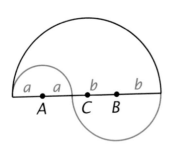

Express the following lengths in terms of *a* and *b*.

10. The length of semicircle A.

11. The length of semicircle B.

12. The length of semicircle C.

13. What can you conclude from these answers?

14. Does the conclusion depend on the relative sizes of *a* and *b*?

Steamboat Geometry. In designing his steamboat, Robert Fulton planned for it to travel 8 miles per hour.*

What speed is 8 miles per hour in

15. feet per hour? (1 mile = 5,280 feet)

16. feet per minute?

The paddle wheels were 14 feet in diameter.

17. What was their exact circumference?

Fulton figured out the number of revolutions that the wheels would have to make per minute for the paddles, moving along their rims, to travel 8 miles per hour.

18. Use your answers to exercises 16 and 17 to find the number that Fulton got.

Babylonian Problem. The following problem appears on a Babylonian clay tablet from about 1600 B.C.†

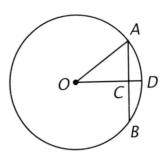

The circumference of circle O was given to be 60 units, OD ⊥ AB, and CD = 2.

19. Copy the figure and mark it as needed to answer the following questions.

From the numbers used in the problem, it appears that the writer thought that $\pi = 3$. If π were equal to 3,

20. what would be the radius of the circle?

21. what would be the length of OC?

22. what would be the length of AC?

23. What is it about △OAC that suggests that the person who wrote the problem meant OA to be 10?

24. What relation must AC have to AB? Explain.

25. The problem was to find the length of the chord AB. What is it?

---

*The Innovators: The Engineering Pioneers Who Made America Modern, by David P. Billington (Wiley, 1996).

†The History of Mathematics: An Introduction, by David M. Burton (Allyn & Bacon, 1985).

Viète's Calculation. In the sixteenth century, French mathematician Francois Viète used a regular polygon having 393,216 sides to calculate the value of π.

26. Letting $n = 393,216$, use your calculator to find $N = n \sin\dfrac{180}{n}$.

27. If it were carried out precisely, would Viète's calculation give the *exact* value of π? Explain why or why not.

Perimeters and Diameters. Here we compare the ratios of perimeters to diameters for various figures. Use the figures below as a guide to seeing how these ratios depend on shape.

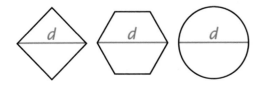

28. Find the exact ratio of the perimeter of a square to the length of one of its diagonals, its diameter.

29. Find the value of this ratio to two decimal places.

30. Find the ratio of the perimeter of a regular hexagon to the length of one of its longest diagonals, its diameter.

31. Find the exact ratio of the circumference of a circle to the length of one of its longest chords, its diameter.

32. Find the value of this ratio to two decimal places.

33. What would you guess the approximate ratio of the perimeter of a regular 100-gon to the length of one of its longest diagonals to be?

34. Check your answer by using the formula for the perimeter of a regular polygon.

Set II

Going in Circles. Whether awake or asleep, you are always traveling in circles. In 1 day (24 hours), Earth rotates once on its axis.

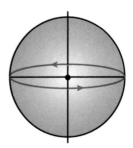

35. Given that Earth's radius is 3,960 miles, find the approximate length of the equator.

36. How far does someone living on the equator travel about Earth's axis in 1 hour?

37. Owing to Earth's rotation, how fast is that person traveling in miles per hour?

In 1 year, Earth travels once around the sun.

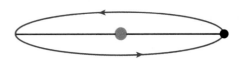

38. Given that the radius of Earth's orbit is about 93,000,000 miles, find its approximate circumference.

39. How far does Earth travel in 1 day?

40. How far does it travel in 1 hour?

41. Owing to Earth's motion around the sun, how fast are you traveling in miles per hour?

42. How fast are you traveling in miles per second?

Two Squares. In the figures below, circles O and P have the same radius, *r*.

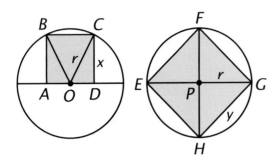

ABCD is a square with side AD lying on a diameter of circle O. EFGH is a square inscribed in circle P.

43. Why is △ABO ≅ △DCO? Explain.

44. Express OD in terms of *x*.

45. Express r^2 in terms of x^2.

46. Express r^2 in terms of y^2.

47. Express x^2 in terms of y^2.

48. How does the area of ABCD compare with the area of EFGH?

SAT Problem. This problem appeared on an SAT exam.

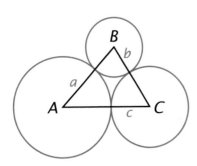

The circles with centers A, B, and C have three points of contact as shown.

Letting *a*, *b*, and *c* be the respective radii of the three circles, find

49. the perimeter of △ABC.

50. the sum of the circumferences of the three circles.

51. the ratio of the perimeter of △ABC to the sum of the circumferences of the three circles.

Videotape. A VHS videotape playing at SP speed moves through the recorder at the rate of 1.375 inches per second.*

52. Given that the tape plays for 2 hours, how many feet long is it?

When the take-up reel is empty, it has a radius of 0.5 inch.

53. What length of tape does it take up in its first revolution?

When the take-up reel is full, it has a radius of 1.5 inches.

54. What length of tape does it take up in its last revolution?

55. What length of tape do you think it takes up during an average revolution?

56. On the basis of your answer to exercise 55, about how many times does the take-up reel turn in 2 hours?

---

*Scientific American: How Things Work Today, edited by Michael Wright and M. N. Patel (Crown, 2000).

Kochansky's Construction. Here is a remarkable construction discovered by Adam Kochansky, a Jesuit priest, in 1685.

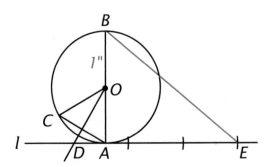

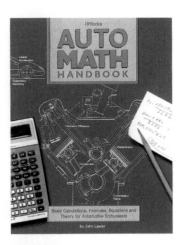

57. Construct the figure above by doing each of the following steps.

   (1) Draw circle O with radius 1 inch, and draw diameter AB.

   (2) Construct line *l* ⊥ AB at A.

   (3) With A as center and AO as radius, draw an arc intersecting the circle at C. Draw △COA.

   (4) Bisect ∠COA and let D be the point in which it intersects *l*.

   (5) Starting at D, mark off three arcs with radius AO along line *l*.

   (6) Let E be the endpoint of the third arc as shown, and draw BE.

What kind of triangle is

58. △OCA?

59. △ODA?

Find each of the following lengths to as many decimal places as you can.

60. DA.

61. AE.

62. BE.

63. What is interesting about the length of BE?

Tire Change. The introduction to a book for automotive enthusiasts begins with these words:

If you're seriously interested in auto-mobiles and how they perform, sooner or later you'll have to deal with mathematics. Virtually all aspects of motor sports, from bore and stroke, through power and torque, to time and speed, involve math-ematical calculations.*

One of the many practical problems considered in the book follows:

Someone with a four-wheel-drive truck with 28.9-inch-diameter tires replaces them with 33-inch tires to increase the ground clearance. If the truck's speedometer was accurate with the original tires, how fast would the truck actually be going on the new tires when the speedometer reads 70 mph?

Can you show, by using your knowledge of the circumference of a circle, how to solve the problem?

———————

Auto Math Handbook, by John Lawlor (HP Books, 1991).

LESSON 5

The Area of a Circle

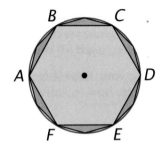

The German city of Cologne was originally a colony of the Roman Empire. Located on the Rhine River, the city took the shape of half a circle in 1180 when a semicircular wall was built to protect it. On the medieval map of the city shown above, it is called "Colonia Agrippina," the name that it was given in 50 A.D.

Why was the wall built with a semicircular shape? The reason is that, for walls of a given length built against a boundary such as this river, a circular wall encloses the greatest *area.*

We have learned that, to measure the circumference of a circle, Archimedes and others following him thought of it as the limit of the perimeters of the inscribed regular polygons. Each time the arcs of the circle are bisected and chords are drawn to produce the next polygon, the new polygon looks more like the circle. The areas enclosed by the successive polygons increase because of the new triangles that result. There is a limit, however, to how large these areas can get. The area of the circle is defined to be this limit.

Definition
The *area* of a circle is the limit of the areas of the inscribed regular polygons.

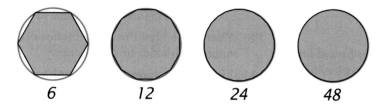

n	$a = Mr^2$
6	$(2.5980762)r^2$
12	$(3.0000000)r^2$
24	$(3.1058285)r^2$
48	$(3.1326286)r^2$
96	$(3.1393502)r^2$
192	$(3.1410319)r^2$
• 384	$(3.1414524)r^2$
768	$(3.1415576)r^2$
1536	$(3.1415838)r^2$
3072	$(3.1415904)r^2$
circle	πr^2

The table at the right shows what happens to the area of a regular polygon as n, the number of sides, is successively doubled. The first eight digits of M are given, and it is apparent that, like N, M is getting closer and closer to a specific number and that number is π. Hence, the areas of the polygons are getting closer and closer to the number πr^2.

This finding suggests the following theorem, which we state without formal proof.

Theorem 78

If the radius of a circle is r, its area is πr^2.

The walled city of Cologne had a radius of 0.9 mile. Because the city occupied roughly half a circle, its area was about $\frac{1}{2}\pi r^2 = \frac{1}{2}\pi(0.9)^2 \approx 1.3$ square miles.

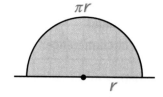

Suppose that, instead of having the shape of half a circle, Cologne had the shape of half a square. With the use of the figures shown at the right, it is easy to show that, if the protecting walls were the same length, the area of the half-square would be less than that of the half-circle.

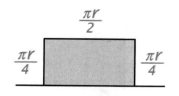

If the radius of the semicircular wall is r, its length is $\frac{1}{2}(2\pi r) = \pi r$ and the area of the city is $\frac{1}{2}(\pi r^2) = \frac{\pi r^2}{2}$. If a wall of the same length surrounded half a square, its dimensions would be $\frac{\pi r}{2}$ and $\frac{\pi r}{4}$. The area of the city would be $\frac{\pi r}{2} \cdot \frac{\pi r}{4} = \frac{\pi^2 r^2}{8}$.

Using a calculator to compare these areas, we get

$$\frac{\pi r^2}{2} \approx 1.57r^2 \quad \text{and} \quad \frac{\pi^2 r^2}{8} \approx 1.23r^2.$$

This comparison shows that the semicircular wall encloses a greater area than does the "semisquare" wall. Perhaps surprisingly, this result is obtained for *every* shape other than a semicircle that you might think of. No matter what other shape the citizens of Cologne might have chosen for their wall, mathematicians have since proved that the semicircle is the best.

Exercises

Set I

Hurricanes. A hurricane is a circle of wind and clouds that spins like a top. At its center is the "eye of the storm," a circular region of relative calm.

A typical hurricane has a radius of about 150 miles.* What is its approximate

1. diameter?

2. circumference?

3. area?

The area of the eye can be as much as 700 square miles. What is its approximate

4. radius?

5. circumference?

Square and Circular Inches. Although a square inch is a familiar unit of area, few people other than electricians have heard of a circular inch.

 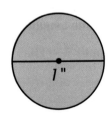

One square   One circular
inch   inch

6. What is meant by one square inch?

7. Judging from the figure above, what is meant by one circular inch?

8. Which unit of area is larger?

9. If two squares have sides of *x* inches and 1 inch, what is the ratio of their areas?

10. What is the area in square inches of a square with sides of 10 inches?

11. If two circles have diameters of *x* inches and 1 inch, what is the ratio of their areas?

12. What is the area of a circle in circular inches with a diameter of 10 inches?

Ripples.

A problem in a calculus book states:

A stone is dropped into a lake, creating a circular ripple that travels outward at a speed of 60 centimeters per second. Express the area of this circle as a function of time *t* (in seconds).[†]

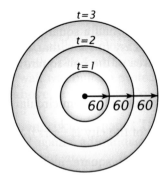

13. Find the radius of the ripple at the end of 1 second.

14. Find its area (in terms of π) at the end of 1 second.

15. Find the radius of the ripple at the end of *t* seconds.

16. Find its area (in terms of π) at the end of *t* seconds.

---

*Waves, Wind and Weather, by Nathaniel Bowditch (David McKay Company, 1977).

†*Calculus*, by James Stewart (Brooks/Cole, 1995).

Equal Areas. In his book *Measurement of a Circle*, Archimedes compared the areas of the circle and right triangle shown below.

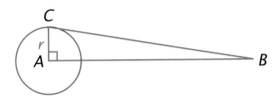

17. If the areas are equal, what would AB equal? Explain.

Central-Pivot Irrigation. In central-pivot irrigation, a sprinkler pipe rotates about one end to water a circular area.

18. In which of the two arrangements shown below do you think the watered area would be greater?

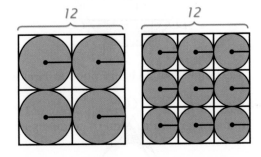

Express in terms of π the area watered in

19. the left-hand arrangement.

20. the right-hand arrangement.

21. How do the watered areas actually compare?

Pi Square. The side of the square in the figure below is equal to the radius of the circle.

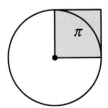

Given that the area of the square is π, find

22. the exact length of each of its sides.

23. the area of the circle.

24. the ratio of the area of the circle to the area of the square.

Circle on a Grid. The figure below shows a circle drawn on a square grid. The number, P, of corner points of the grid on or inside the circle, shown in red, is 113.*

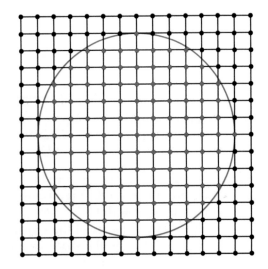

25. Given that the sides of the small squares on the grid are 1 unit, what is the radius, r, of the circle?

26. Find the value of $\dfrac{P}{r^2}$.

_____

Geometry and the Imagination, by David Hilbert and Stephan Cohn-Vossen (Chelsea, 1952).

If the circle were larger, with $r = 20$, the number of corner points on or inside it would be 1,257.

27. Find the value of $\dfrac{P}{r^2}$.

If the circle were even larger, with $r = 300$, the number of corner points on or inside it would be 282,697.

28. Find the value of $\dfrac{P}{r^2}$.

29. What do these results suggest about the limit of the ratio $\dfrac{P}{r^2}$ as r increases?

30. Approximately how many corner points do you think would be on or inside a circle with $r = 100$?

Set II

Area Problems. Write an expression in terms of x^2 for the area of the shaded region in each of the following figures.

Example:

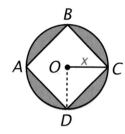

Square ABCD is inscribed in circle O.

Solution: The area of the circle is πx^2 because its radius is x. $\triangle OCD$ is an isosceles right triangle with $OC = x$; so $CD = x\sqrt{2}$. The area of the square is $(x\sqrt{2})^2 = 2x^2$. So the shaded area is $\pi x^2 - 2x^2 = (\pi - 2)x^2$.

31.

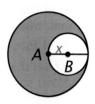

The centers of the circles are A and B.

32.

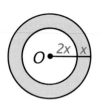

The two circles are concentric with center O.

33.

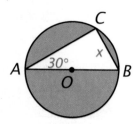

Circle O is inscribed in square ABCD.

34.

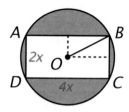

Right $\triangle ABC$ is inscribed in circle O.

35.

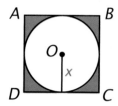

Rectangle ABCD is inscribed in circle O.

36.

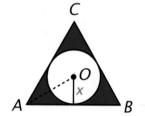

Circle O is inscribed in equilateral $\triangle ABC$.

Cable Disaster. The following story is true.*

A rigger in a steel mill noticed that a cable on a crane was damaged. Its diameter was 1 inch but the only cable available had a diameter of ½ inch. The foreman told the rigger to replace the 1-inch cable with two ½-inch cables. After this had been done, the new cables snapped, 10 tons of steel fell 25 feet, and several workers were almost killed.

37. Make a scale drawing to show the 1-inch cable and the two ½-inch cables.

The foreman's reasoning was wrong.

38. What do you think should have been done instead? Explain your thinking.

Slicing a Circle. The figure below is from a book by the seventeenth-century Japanese mathematician Sawaguchi Kazuyuki.[†]

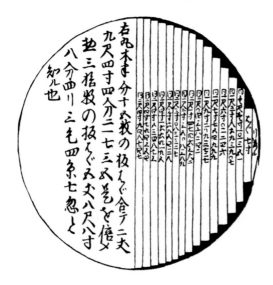

39. On graph paper, draw a pair of axes extending 10 units to the right and 10 units up from the origin.

A History of the Circle: Mathematical Reasoning and the Physical Universe, by Ernest Zebrowski, Jr. (Rutgers University Press, 1999).
[†]*A History of Japanese Mathematics*, by David Eugene Smith and Yushio Mikami (Open Court, 1914).

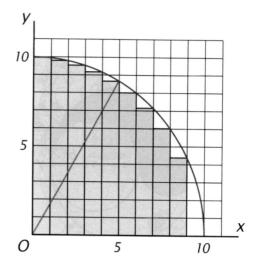

(1) Use your compass to draw a quarter of a circle with its center at O and a radius of 10 units as shown in the figure above.

(2) Use your ruler to draw rectangular strips 1 unit wide inside the quarter circle as shown.

40. Explain why the exact area of the fifth strip is $\sqrt{75}$.

41. Find the exact areas of the other eight strips.

42. Use your calculator to find the sum of the areas of the nine strips to one decimal place.

43. On the basis of this answer, estimate the area of a circle with radius 10 to the nearest integer.

44. How would you expect your answer to compare with the actual area of the circle? Explain.

If the same method were used, but with strips half as wide, the sum of the areas of the 19 strips would be 75.7 to one decimal place.

45. Why would you expect this answer to lead to a better estimate of the area of the circle than the preceding one?

46. How could this method be continued to get better and better estimates of the area of the circle?

Tangent Circles. In the figure below, the centers of the three circles are on XY. The radii of the two smaller circles are *a* and *b*.

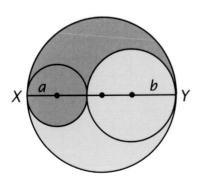

47. What is the radius of the large circle?

Write an expression in terms of *a* and *b* for

48. the blue area.

49. the yellow area.

50. Write an expression for the ratio of the blue area to the yellow area and simplify it.

51. If *a* = *b*, does your ratio make sense? Explain.

52. Write an expression for the ratio of the border of the blue area to the border of the yellow area.

Set III

Lull's Claim. A famous thirteenth-century poet and mystic named Ramon Lull claimed that the circle and middle square in the figure below have the same perimeter and area.

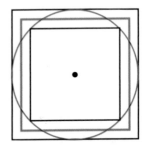

It is possible to decide whether Lull's claim is correct without even considering the geometry of the figure.

Suppose the radius of the circle is *r* and the side of the middle square is *s*. Write an equation stating that the circle and the middle square have

1. the same perimeter.

2. the same area.

3. What happens when you solve your system of two equations for π?

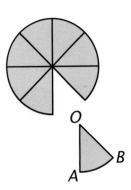

Used by permission of Tom Henderson.

Sectors and Arcs

When a pizza is cut into slices, they usually have the shape of *sectors*. A *sector* of a circle is a region bounded by an arc of the circle and the two radii to the endpoints of the arc.

If a circle is divided into sectors with equal arcs, the sectors are congruent to one another and have equal areas. With the use of this fact, it is easy to find the area of each one. For example, if a pizza with a radius of 12 inches is cut into eight equal pieces, the area of each piece is

$$\frac{1}{8}\pi(12)^2 = 18\pi \approx 57 \text{ square inches.}$$

Because the border of the pizza (the 360° arc of a circle) also is divided into eight congruent pieces, each sector has an arc (and central angle) with a measure of

$$\frac{1}{8}360° = 45°.$$

The lengths of these eight equal arcs add up to give the circumference of the circle; so each arc has length

$$\frac{1}{8}2\pi(12) = 3\pi \approx 9 \text{ inches.}$$

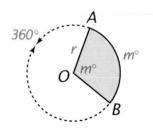

360°

These examples illustrate the general pattern. Suppose that the central angle (and hence arc) of a sector has a measure of $m°$ and that the radius of the sector is r. Because the arc of every circle has a measure of 360°, the *area* of the sector must be $\dfrac{m}{360}$ times the area of the circle, or $\dfrac{m}{360}\pi r^2$. The *length* of its arc is $\dfrac{m}{360}$ times the circumference of the circle, or $\dfrac{m}{360}2\pi r$.

The idea is simple:

If a sector is a certain fraction of a circle, then its area is the same fraction of the circle's area. If an arc is a certain fraction of a circle, then its length is the same fraction of the circle's circumference.

In sports events such as the shot put and the discus and hammer throws, the region into which the object is thrown is in the shape of a sector. In the Olympics, the angle of the sector in each of these events has a measure of 40°. For the shot put, the radius is usually about 30 meters. To find the area of the shot-put sector, we can reason as above:

$$\frac{40}{360}\pi 30^2 = 100\pi \approx 314.$$

The shot put is thrown into a region having an area of about 314 square meters.

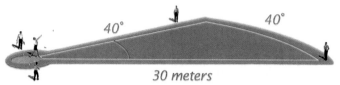

40°   40°

30 meters

Exercises

Set I

Orange Slices. The photograph at the left shows oranges sliced in half to reveal eight equal parts.

1. What is the shape of each part?

2. What is the degree measure of its arc?

Given that the radius of the orange is r, what is

3. the length of each arc?

4. the area of each part?

Sonar Beams. A dolphin projects a beam of sound in front of it to find food and avoid obstacles.*

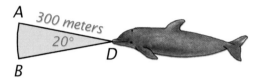

What does each of the following expressions represent?

5. $\dfrac{20}{360}2\pi 300.$

6. $\dfrac{20}{360}\pi 300^2.$

Find

7. the length of $\overset{\frown}{AB}$ to the nearest meter.

8. the area of sector DAB to the nearest hundred square meters.

Latitude. Latitude measures how many degrees north or south you are of the equator.

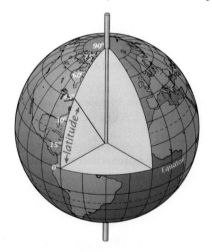

The figure above shows that the North Pole is 90° from the equator.

9. Given that the radius of the earth is 3,960 miles, how many miles is it from the equator to the North Pole?

Animal Navigation, by Talbot H. Waterman (Scientific American Library, 1989).

10. How far north do you travel when you increase your latitude by 1°?

The latitude of the Hawaiian Islands is 20°N.

11. How far are they from the equator?

Driveway Design. The figure below shows the design of a "Y turn" residential driveway.†

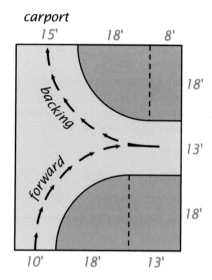

Use the dimensions given to find the following areas, each to the nearest square foot.

12. The total area of the figure.

13. The lawn area (shown in green).

14. The paved area (shown in yellow).

Two Sectors. In the figure at the right, $m\overset{\frown}{AB} = 90°$ and $m\overset{\frown}{OB} = 180°$.
  Express each of the following areas in terms of r.

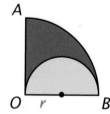

15. The yellow area.

16. The area of the entire figure.

17. How does the yellow area compare with the blue area?

---

†*Landscape Development,* Field Technical Office, U. S. Department of the Interior.

Reuleaux Triangle. The Reuleaux triangle, named after a nineteenth-century engineer, is interesting in that its width in every direction is the same. It has been used in the design of a rotary drill that can drill square holes!

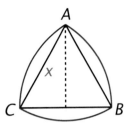

A Reuleaux triangle is constructed by drawing three arcs on the sides of an equilateral triangle. Each arc is centered on one of the triangle's vertices.

18. Find $m\overset{\frown}{AB}$.

19. Find the length of $\overset{\frown}{AB}$.

20. Find the perimeter of $\triangle ABC$.

21. Find the perimeter of the Reuleaux triangle.

22. Find the diameter of a circle whose circumference is equal to the perimeter of the Reuleaux triangle.

Sound Delay. Most sounds that you hear reach one of your ears before the other. Suppose your head is round and has a diameter of 7 inches.*

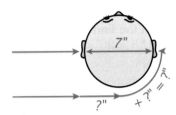

When a sound from the left reaches your left ear, it still has to go past your head to reach your right ear. Your brain can detect the resulting time delay.

———————
*Human Information Processing: An Introduction to Psychology, by Peter H. Lindsay and Donald A. Norman (Harcourt Brace Jovanovich, 1977).

23. How many extra inches does the sound have to go?

Sound travels about 1,100 feet per second in air.

24. How many *inches* does it travel in a second?

25. How much extra time does it take to reach the right ear?

The Radian. A unit of angle measure used in advanced mathematics is the *radian*. As you might guess from its name, it has something to do with the radius of a circle. A radian is defined as the measure of a central angle that intercepts an arc equal in length to the radius of the circle.

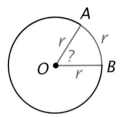

26. What is the length of a circle in terms of its radius?

27. What is the measure of a circle in terms of degrees?

28. What fraction of the length of the circle is the length of $\overset{\frown}{AB}$?

29. Find $m\overset{\frown}{AB}$.

30. What is the approximate measure of 1 radian in degrees?

Set II

Windshield Wipers. The figure below shows the region covered by a windshield wiper of a car.

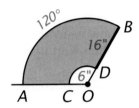

Use the measurements in the figure to find the following numbers.

31. The distance traveled by the tip of the wiper in going from A and B, to the nearest inch.

32. The area wiped by the wiper, to the nearest square inch.

33. A car has two windshield wipers. Is it possible, from the information given in the figure, to find the total area wiped by both wipers? Explain.

Land Area. Lucius Columella, a Roman farmer who lived in the first century, wrote a book on agriculture in which he showed how to calculate areas of land.

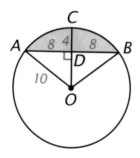

In one example, Columella claimed that the area of the orange region in the figure above was more than 44 square units.*

34. Use your calculator and the sine ratio in △ADO to find ∠AOC.

35. Find ∠AOB.

36. Find m$\widehat{AB}$.

37. Find the area of the sector bounded by OA, OB, and $\widehat{AB}$.

38. Find the area of △ABO.

39. Find the area of the orange region.

40. Was Columella correct?

Mathematics and Measurement, by O. A. W. Dilke (University of California Press, 1987).

Running Track. The figure below represents the measure line (shown in green) of the first lane of a 400-meter running track.

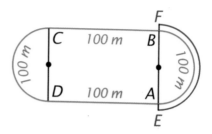

41. Find AB to the nearest 0.01 meter.

EF represents part of the measure line of the second lane. Because each lane is 1.2 meters wide, AE = BF = 1.2 m.

42. Find EF to the nearest 0.01 meter.

43. Find the length of $\widehat{EF}$ to the nearest 0.01 meter.

44. How many laps around the track does someone make in running a 10,000-meter race?

45. In this number of laps, how much farther would someone who stayed in the second lane run than someone who stayed in the first lane?

A runner's right leg travels farther than the left leg on each curve because the race is run counterclockwise.

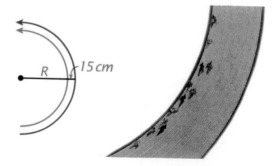

46. If the difference in the radii of the two paths is 15 cm (0.15 m), how much farther does the runner's right leg travel during the race?

Four Crescents. In the figure below, circle O is circumscribed about square ABCD and semicircles have been drawn with the sides of the square as their diameters. M is the midpoint of AB.

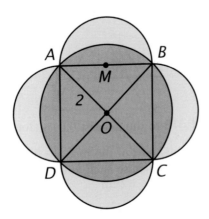

Given that OA = 2, find

47. AB.

48. AM.

Find the exact area of each of the following parts of the figure.

49.

50.

51.

52.

53.

54.

55.

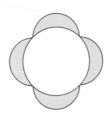

56. What do your answers to exercises 50 and 55 prove?

Drop-Leaf Table.

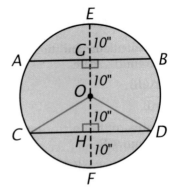

The figure below shows the design of a drop-leaf table. The two leaves are hinged along chords AB and CD of circle O; diameter EF is perpendicular to both chords.

Use the measurements given to find each of the following numbers.

57. The radius of the table.

58. The area of the table to two decimal places.

59. ∠COH.

60. ∠COD.

61. The area of the sector bounded by OC, OD, and $\overset{\frown}{CD}$.

62. CD to two decimal places.

63. The area of △COD.

64. The area of one of the leaves of the table to the nearest square inch.

65. The area of the top of the table when the two leaves are down to the nearest square inch.

Salt Cellar. The Greek mathematician Archimedes proved that the yellow region in the figure below, which he called a "salt cellar," has the same area as the red circle.

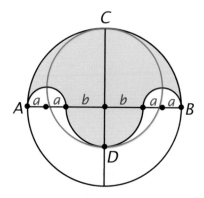

The boundary of the "salt cellar" consists of four semicircles drawn on AB. CD is a diameter of the red circle.

Express each of the following numbers in terms of *a* and *b*.

66. The radius of the longest semicircle.

67. The diameter of the red circle.

68. The radius of the red circle.

69. The area of the red circle.

70. Show that the area of the "salt cellar" is equal to the area of the red circle.

Set III

Pizza Puzzle. Acute Alice and Obtuse Ollie decided to share a pizza. Ollie cut it into four pieces with two perpendicular cuts, but he didn't cut the pizza through the center. He told Alice that he would eat the two pieces shown in orange and she could have the rest.

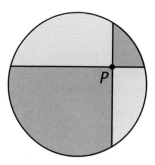

Not being sure that she liked this idea, Alice cut the pizza two more times by bisecting the four angles at P. She told Ollie that he could now take his pick between the four orange pieces or the four yellow ones.

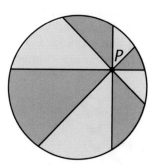

Do you think either way is fair? Make some drawings in which P is in different places to see what you discover.

Basic Ideas

Theorems

75. The perimeter of a regular polygon having n sides is $2Nr$, in which

$$N = n \sin\frac{180}{n} \text{ and } r \text{ is its radius.}$$ 581

76. The area of a regular polygon having n sides is Mr^2, in which

$$M = n \sin\frac{180}{n} \cos\frac{180}{n} \text{ and } r \text{ is its radius.}$$

587

77. If the radius of a circle is r, its circumference is $2\pi r$.   592

Corollary. If the diameter of a circle is d, its circumference is πd.   592

78. If the radius of a circle is r, its area is πr^2.   599

Exercises

Set I

Molecule. A cholesterol molecule contains 74 atoms. The left-hand figure below shows a model of this molecule, and the right-hand figure shows its line formula, a picture of the way in which its atoms are connected.*

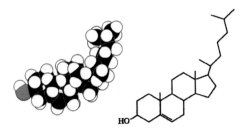

1. What regular polygons do you see in the line formula?

2. What must be true for a polygon to be regular?

Molecules, by P. W. Atkins (Scientific American Library, 1987).

3. What happens to the shape of a regular polygon as its number of sides increases?

A Regular 15-gon. In the *Elements*, Euclid showed how to inscribe a regular polygon with 15 sides in a circle. He started by constructing equilateral △ABC and regular pentagon ADEFG.

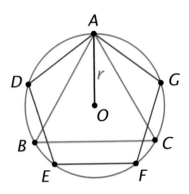

Find each of the following arc measures.

4. $m\overset{\frown}{AB}$. **6.** $m\overset{\frown}{DB}$.

5. $m\overset{\frown}{AD}$. **7.** $m\overset{\frown}{BE}$.

8. Which points on the circle could be connected to form sides of the regular 15-gon? Explain.

Use your calculator to find, to two decimal places, the following numbers for a regular 15-gon.

9. $N = n \sin \dfrac{180}{n}$.

10. $M = n \sin \dfrac{180}{n} \cos \dfrac{180}{n}$.

11. What number is the limit of N and M as n increases?

Suppose a regular 15-gon is inscribed in a circle with radius r. Write an expression in terms of r and to two decimal places for

12. the perimeter of the polygon.

13. the area of the polygon.

14. the length of each of its sides.

Penny Farthing Bicycle. Before the invention of the chain drive, all bicycles used direct drive. One turn of the pedals resulted in one turn of the front wheel.*

Mathematics Meets Technology, by Brian Bolt (Cambridge University Press, 1991).

The typical radius of the front wheel on a "penny farthing" bicycle is 2 feet.

15. How many turns of the pedals would be needed to get the bicycle to travel 1 mile (5,280 feet)?

Given that the radius of the back wheel is 0.6 foot, find

16. its circumference.

17. the number of turns that it would make in traveling 1 mile.

SAT Questions. The following questions have appeared on SAT tests. Give your answers in terms of π.

18. What is the circumference of a circle with radius π?

19. What is the diameter of a circle with circumference 1?

20. What is the area of a circle whose circumference is 4π?

Semicircles on the Sides. About a century after Pythagoras's time, a mathematician named Hippocrates claimed that, if semicircles are drawn on the sides of a right triangle, the sum of the areas of the semicircles on the legs is equal to the area of the semicircle on the hypotenuse.

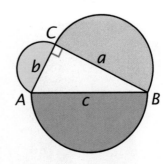

21. Find the areas of the three semicircular regions in the figure above.

22. Is what Hippocrates claimed true? Explain why or why not.

Area Comparisons. In the figure below, $m\widehat{AB} = 90°$, $m\widehat{OB} = 180°$, and OC bisects ∠AOB.

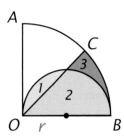

Express each of the following sums in terms of *r.*

23. The sum of the yellow and orange areas.

24. The sum of the orange and red areas.

25. How does the yellow area compare with the red area? Explain.

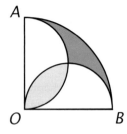

26. What can you conclude about the figure above?

Gothic Arch. The Gothic arch was a popular shape in medieval architecture.

27. Use your straightedge and compass to construct a Gothic arch by doing each of the following steps.

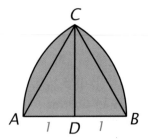

(1) Draw segment AB 2 inches long.

(2) With A and B as centers and AB as radius, draw the two arcs intersecting at C.

(3) Draw △ABC.

(4) Construct CD ⊥ AB.

Find the areas of each of the following regions, both in terms of π and roots and numerically to three decimal places.

28. △ABC.

29. The sector bounded by radii AC and AB and $\widehat{CB}$.

30. The region bounded by segment CB and $\widehat{CB}$.

31. The entire arch.

Set II

Cup Problem. In the drawing of a cup below, EF divides rectangle ABCD into square ABFE and rectangle EFCD; AB = 1.

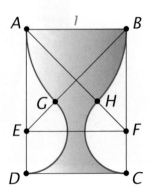

The cup is formed from four arcs: $\widehat{AG}$ with center B, $\widehat{GD}$ with center E, $\widehat{BH}$ with center A, and $\widehat{HC}$ with center F.

32. How do these arcs appear to compare in length?

33. Find $m\overset{\frown}{AG}$.

34. Find the length of $\overset{\frown}{AG}$ to two decimal places.

35. Find the exact length of EG.

36. Find $m\overset{\frown}{GD}$.

37. Find the length of $\overset{\frown}{GD}$ to two decimal places.

38. Were you right in your answer to exercise 32 about how $\overset{\frown}{AG}$ and $\overset{\frown}{GD}$ compare in length?

Time Zones. The earth is divided into 24 time zones, one for each hour of the day.

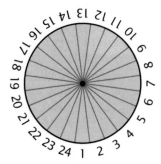

39. Given that the radius of the earth is 3,960 miles, what is the width along the equator of each time zone?

The average latitude of the contiguous United States is 40°N.

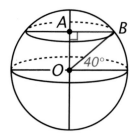

40. Use △ABO to find the radius, AB, of the circle of latitude 40°.

41. Find the circumference of this circle.

42. What is the width along this circle of each time zone?

The contiguous United States spreads across four time zones.

43. What is the approximate width of the contiguous United States?

From Dodecagon to Square. The figures below show how a regular dodecagon can be cut into six pieces that can be rearranged to form a square.*

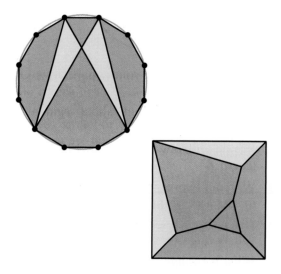

In the first figure, the dodecagon is inscribed in a circle.

44. What kind of triangle is the blue piece? Explain how you know.

Given that the area of the dodecagon is 6 square units, find each of the following numbers.

45. Its radius, from the area formula.

46. The radius of the square.

47. The perimeter of the dodecagon to two decimal places.

48. The perimeter of the square to two decimal places.

49. What happens to the perimeter of the figure when the pieces are rearranged to form the square?

---

*Geometric Dissections, by Harry Lindgren (Van Nostrand, 1964).

Chord and Ring. The two circles in the figure below are concentric, and chord AB of the larger circle is tangent to the smaller circle at point C.

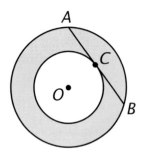

50. Draw the figure on your paper. Draw OC and label its length *r*.

51. What can you conclude about segments OC and AB?

50. *(continued)* Draw OA and label its length *R*.

52. Write an expression in terms of *R* and *r* for the area of the yellow ring.

53. Given that AB = 2, find the area of the yellow ring.

54. What is strange about this problem?

Half a Heart. The heart-shaped curve below consists of two equal semicircles that meet another semicircle on AB. CD is any line through O, the center of the large semicircle.

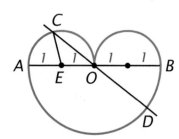

55. Write an expression for the length of the border of the "heart" in terms of π.

Given that $\angle AOD = x°$, write an expression in terms of *x* for

56. $\angle AOC$.

57. $\angle OCE$.

58. $\angle AEC$.

59. the length of $\overparen{AC}$.

60. the length of $\overparen{AD}$.

61. the length of $\overparen{CAD}$.

62. What can you conclude about line CD? Explain.

Biting Region. Obtuse Ollie tied his pet bulldog with a rope 15 feet long to one corner of a shed 12 feet long and 10 feet wide.

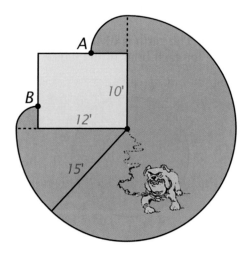

The green region shows where the dog can go.

63. If the dog continually pulls at the rope, how far can it run in going from A to B?

64. Find the area within biting distance of the dog.

Chapter 15

Geometric Solids

So far, our study of geometry has been mostly limited to two-dimensional figures such as polygons and circles. In this chapter, we consider some familiar three-dimensional figures, the sets of geometric solids known as prisms, pyramids, cylinders, cones, and spheres. You will become familiar with how to recognize and draw these figures and will learn from where the formulas for their surface areas and volumes come. The chapter ends with the topics of similar solids and the regular polyhedra.

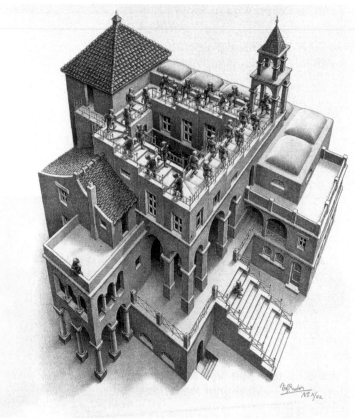

LESSON 1

Lines and Planes in Space

In creating a picture, an artist depicts our three-dimensional world on a two-dimensional surface. A technique called perspective is used to represent space on a single plane. Some artists, including Maurits Escher, play tricks with perspective. An example is the staircase on the roof of the building in the picture above by Escher titled *Ascending and Descending.* The trick is that the people walking in one direction are *always* ascending, whereas those walking in the other direction are *always* descending!

Escher's picture depends on special line and plane relations in space and on the way that we see them. In this lesson, we will look at some of these relations.

At the beginning of our study of geometry, we made two assumptions about points, lines, and planes:

Postulate 1. Two points determine a line.

Postulate 2. Three noncollinear points determine a plane.

618   Chapter 15: Geometric Solids

To this list, we now add two more assumptions.

Postulate 11

If two points lie in a plane, the line that contains them lies in the plane.

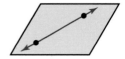

This postulate expresses the fact that, if you mark two points on a flat sheet of paper and draw a straight line through them, the line also is on the paper.

Postulate 12

If two planes intersect, they intersect in a line.

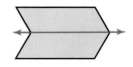

This postulate expresses the fact that, if you fold a sheet of paper into two parts (two planes), the planes meet along the crease in the paper (a line).

Escher's picture is filled with lines and planes that are parallel or perpendicular. In *plane* geometry, two lines either intersect or are parallel. In the geometry of three-dimensional space, there is a third possibility. Two lines can be *skew*.

In the detail from Escher's picture at the right, the line labeled *l* contains the peak of the roof, and line *m* contains one of its lower edges. These lines neither intersect nor are parallel; they are skew.

skew lines

Definition

Two lines are *skew* iff they are not parallel and do not intersect.

For two planes in space, or a line and a plane, the word "parallel" simply means "nonintersecting." Like any two parallel lines, two parallel planes are separated by a constant perpendicular distance.

Definitions

Two planes, or *a line and a plane, are parallel* iff they do not intersect.

In the detail of Escher's picture at the right, plane *R* is parallel to the plane of the ground, *P*; line *n* also is parallel to plane *P*.

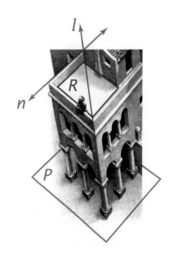

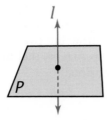

In the same picture, line *l* is *perpendicular* to plane *P*. It is tempting to say that a line is perpendicular to a plane if they form right angles, but where are the right angles in the figure above?

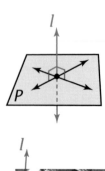

The figure at the left shows that right angles exist when we look at *lines* in the plane that pass through the point of intersection. We can base our definition on this fact.

Definition
A *line and a plane are perpendicular* iff they intersect and the line is perpendicular to every line in the plane that passes through the point of intersection.

Finally, the detail at the left from Escher's picture illustrates two *planes that are perpendicular*. If there is a line, such as *l*, in plane *R* that is perpendicular to plane *P*, then plane *R* is perpendicular to plane *P*.

Definition
Two planes are perpendicular iff one plane contains a line that is perpendicular to the other plane.

In the geometry of space, a line and a plane (or two planes) that are neither parallel nor perpendicular are said to be *oblique*.

Exercises

Set I

Visual Planes. Each of the figures below gives the impression of a plane in space.*

1. Which figure seems to illustrate a vertical plane?

2. Which part of this plane appears to be closest?

Intelligence: The Eye, the Brain, and the Computer, by Martin A. Fischler and Oscar Firschein (Addison-Wesley, 1987).

3. In interpreting the figure in this way, what shape are you assuming the quadrilaterals to be?

4. What type of plane does the other figure seem to illustrate?

5. Which part of it appears to be closest?

6. In interpreting the figure in this way, what shape are you assuming the curves to be?

Pole People. The figure below is from a book on perspective published in Paris in 1642. The artist drew the two people holding the poles to help suggest that the scene is three-dimensional.

7. What relation does the line of the pole at D appear to have to the ground?

8. What kind of plane, horizontal or vertical, seems to contain both of the dotted lines through E and F?

9. What do the dotted lines seem to indicate about EF and the two vertical segments at the upper left of EF?

10. What might be assumed about those dotted lines if EF and the two vertical segments at the upper left of it were not included in the figure?

Posts and Walls. The figures below are from a chapter on form and space in a book on architecture.*

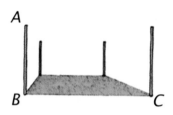

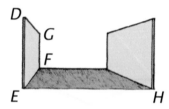

11. Can you conclude that the post labeled AB in the upper figure is perpendicular to the "floor" if it is perpendicular to line BC? Use the definition of a line perpendicular to a plane to explain why or why not.

12. Can you conclude that the plane of the wall labeled DEFG in the lower figure is perpendicular to the "floor" if it is perpendicular to line EH? Use the definition of perpendicular planes to explain why or why not.

Architecture: Form, Space, and Order, by Francis D. K. Ching (Wiley, 1996).

3-D Shading. The figure below was created by psychologist Ted Adelson.†

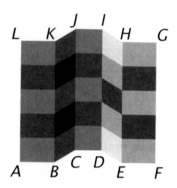

Each of its 25 regions is bounded by a quadrilateral. What kind of quadrilateral do they seem to be if the figure is viewed

13. as flat?

14. as three-dimensional?

If you view the figure as three-dimensional,

15. which part appears as if it might lie in the same plane as ABKL?

16. which part appears as if it might lie in a plane parallel to the plane of ABKL?

17. which two parts might lie in perpendicular planes?

18. there is something strange about the position of CDIJ with respect to the rest of the figure. Can you tell what it is?

Compare the grays in the two rectangles in the figure above, which correspond to the rectangles labeled 1 and 2 in the figure below.

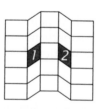

19. Which one looks darker?

20. *Is* it actually darker?

---

†*Visual Intelligence: How We Create What We See*, by Donald D. Hoffman (Norton, 1998).

Polarized Light. The figure below shows the electric and magnetic fields in a wave of polarized light.*

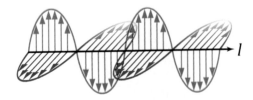

The two fields lie in different planes.

21. What relation do the two planes have to line *l*?

22. What relation do the two planes appear to have to each other?

23. By definition, what must hold for this relation to be true?

Kilroy in Space. The figure below represents three planes in space.†

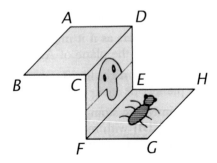

24. If plane ABCD is parallel to plane EFGH, what relation does line CD have to line FE?

25. If plane ABCD is parallel to plane EFGH and line CF is perpendicular to plane ABCD, what relation does CF have to plane EFGH?

*Lasers: Harnessing the Atom's Light, by James P. Harbison and Robert E. Nahory (Scientific American Library, 1998).
†"Illusions of the Third Dimension," by Martin Gardner, *Psychology Today* (August 1983), reprinted in *Gardner's Whys and Wherefores* (University of Chicago Press, 1989).

26. If planes ABCD and EFGH are perpendicular to line DE, what relation do the planes have to each other?

Use your answers to exercises 24 through 26 to copy and complete the following statements.

27. If a plane intersects two parallel planes, it intersects them in . . . ?

28. If a line is perpendicular to one of two parallel planes, it . . . ?

29. Two planes perpendicular to the same line are . . . ?

30. Can Kilroy (the character looking over the wall) see the bug?

Set II

Triangles in Perspective. In the figure below, △ABC and △A′B′C′ are said to be "in perspective" because the lines through their corresponding vertices are concurrent in point P.

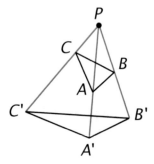

The pairs of lines containing their corresponding sides intersect in points X, Y, and Z.

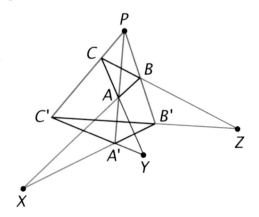

31. What seems to be true about points X, Y, and Z?

If you think of the figure as being three-dimensional, then points A, B, and C determine a plane.

32. Why?

It follows that the three lines containing these points also lie in the plane determined by the points.

33. Why?

34. What relation do points X, Y, and Z have to this plane?

If the figure is three-dimensional, then △ABC and △A′B′C′ appear to lie in different planes.

35. What relation do points X, Y, and Z have to the plane determined by points A′, B′, and C′?

36. If two planes in space intersect, in what do they intersect?

37. What can you conclude about points X, Y, and Z?

Impossible Slice. This figure was designed by Japanese graphic artist Mitsumasa Anno.*

It appears to show a cube from which a piece has been cut off to produce a flat circular face.

38. If this description were true, what fact about intersecting planes would it contradict?

---

*The Unique World of Mitsumasa Anno, translated by Samuel Crowell Morse (Philomel Books, 1980).

39. What fact about noncollinear points such as A, B, and C does the figure contradict? Explain.

Uneven Bars. The uneven bars in women's gymnastics are parallel to the floor—that is, horizontal.

40. If two lines in space are horizontal, does it follow that they are parallel? Explain.

41. If two lines are parallel, does it follow that they lie in the same plane? Explain.

The bars lie in parallel vertical planes that are 43 cm apart. The figure below is a view from one end.

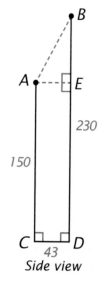

Side view

Given that the lower bar is 150 cm above the floor and the upper bar is 230 cm above the floor, find

42. AB, the clearance between the bars.

43. ∠BAE, the inclination of the plane of the parallel bars to the horizontal.

Pyramid. In this figure of a pyramid, EF is perpendicular to the plane of its base, AC and BD intersect at F, and FA = FB = FC = FD.

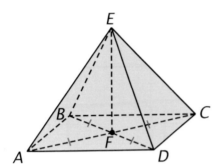

44. EF ⊥ AC and EF ⊥ BD. Why?
45. △EFA ≅ △EFB ≅ △EFC ≅ △EFD. Why?
46. EA = EB = EC = ED. Why?
47. ABCD is a parallelogram. Why?
48. AB = DC and AD = BC. Why?
49. △EAB ≅ △EDC and △EAD ≅ △EBC. Why?
50. △FAB ≅ △FDC and △FAD ≅ △FBC. Why?

Lopsided Box. Although Obtuse Ollie built this open-topped box from five flat pieces of wood, it ended up being lopsided.

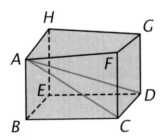

He did manage to make AB perpendicular to the bottom (BCDE) and CD perpendicular to the front (ABCF).

51. Which faces of the box must be perpendicular to each other?
52. Name the angles in the box that are definitely right angles.
53. Is it possible to tell how AC and AD compare in length? Explain.

Cube and Hypercube. The photograph below shows a "hypercube" kite, designed by José Yturralde.*

The following figure shows one way to unfold and flatten out a three-dimensional cube into a two-dimensional pattern of polygons called a "net."

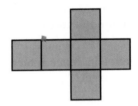

54. How many square faces does a cube have?
55. In how many lines do the edges of the faces of the unfolded cube lie?

The figure below shows one way to unfold a four-dimensional hypercube in three dimensions.

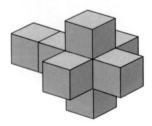

56. How many cube faces does a hypercube have?
57. In how many planes do the square faces of the cube faces of the unfolded hypercube lie?

Beyond the Third Dimension: Geometry, Computer Graphics, and Higher Dimensions, by Thomas F. Banchoff (Scientific American Library, 1990).

Set III

This picture by Escher, titled *Belvedere*, illustrates another impossible building. What do you see in the picture that appears to be impossible?

Impossible figures created by Oscar Reutersvärd
on stamps issued in Sweden in 1982.

Solid Geometry as a Deductive System

Years ago, students spent a full year learning plane geometry before taking a course in solid geometry. In the following lessons of this chapter, we will study in an informal way some of the basic topics included in that second course. Instead of continuing to define every term precisely as we did in the preceding lesson, we will take for granted the meanings of words in some of the definitions throughout the rest of this chapter. Furthermore, we will not attempt to prove every theorem but will merely use informal arguments to make the theorems seem reasonable. This approach will enable us to explore a wider variety of topics than would otherwise be possible.

As with the algebra reviewed earlier, you are already familiar with many ideas from solid geometry. Several examples beyond those of Lesson 1 are given on this page and the next.

Determining a Plane

One of the first assumptions in our logical development of geometry was

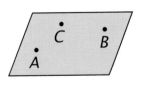

Postulate 2. Three noncollinear points determine a plane.

It is possible to prove that other configurations also determine a plane by means of this postulate and the two assumptions of the preceding lesson:

Postulate 11. If two points lie in a plane, the line that contains them lies in the plane.

Postulate 12. If two planes intersect, they intersect in a line.

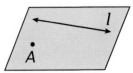 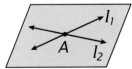 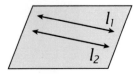

Theorem. A line and a point not on the line determine a plane.

Theorem. Two intersecting lines determine a plane.

Theorem. Two parallel lines determine a plane.

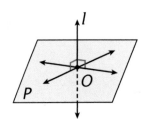

In our definition of a line and a plane that are perpendicular, we said that they intersect and that the line is perpendicular to *every line* in the plane that passes through the point of intersection. From this definition, the following theorem can be proved.

Theorem. A line and a plane are perpendicular if they intersect and the line is perpendicular to *two lines* in the plane that pass through the point of intersection.

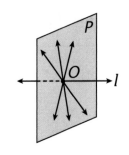

More examples of statements that can be proved in solid geometry are stated below and illustrated at the right.

Theorem. If three lines are perpendicular to a line at the same point, the three lines are coplanar.

Theorem. Planes perpendicular to the same line are parallel to one another.

Theorem. Lines perpendicular to the same plane are parallel to one another.

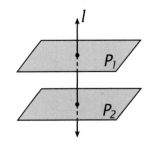

Theorem. A plane perpendicular to one of two parallel lines is perpendicular to both of them.

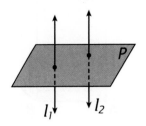

Many other ideas of plane geometry also extend to space. Here are three examples. In *space*, two points each equidistant from the end-points of a line segment determine a *plane* that is the perpendicular bisector of the line segment. Reflection in a *plane* can be defined in a way similar to our definition of reflection in a *line*. Our two-dimensional coordinate system with *two* axes perpendicular to each other in a *plane* can be extended to a three-dimensional coordinate system with *three* axes perpendicular to one another in *space*.

It is possible to develop all of solid geometry as a deductive system in the way with which you are now very familiar. Euclid was one of the first to do so. The final three books of the *Elements* contain proofs of 75 theorems in the geometry of three dimensions.

Rectangular Solids

Near the beginning of the film *2001: A Space Odyssey*, a mysterious monolith appears, and then from behind it rises a glowing sun directly below the crescent of the moon. Later, another monolith is discovered buried beneath the surface of the moon. The monoliths are tall black slabs, and their appearance creates an eerie effect due in part to their shape. Their shape, a *rectangular solid* with straight sharp edges meeting at right angles, in contrast with the natural surroundings of the monoliths, suggests that they were created by a higher intelligence.

A rectangular solid is a special type of *polyhedron.*

Definition
A *polyhedron* is a solid bounded by parts of intersecting planes.

The intersecting planes form polygonal regions that are the *faces* of the polyhedron. Their sides are the *edges* of the polyhedron, and their vertices are its *vertices*. Generally, our polyhedra will be convex.

Definition
A *rectangular solid* is a polyhedron that has six rectangular faces.

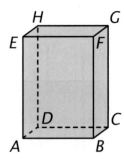

In the figure at the left, all six faces of a rectangular solid are shown. Its intersecting faces lie in perpendicular planes, and its opposite faces lie in parallel planes. Two vertices of the solid that are not vertices of the same face are *opposite vertices*. For example, in the figure, one pair of opposite vertices is A and G and another pair is C and E.

A line segment that connects two opposite vertices of a rectangular solid is a *diagonal* of the solid. Every rectangular solid has four diagonals, and it is easy to prove that they have equal lengths. (These diagonals are sometimes called the interior diagonals of the solid to distinguish them from the diagonals of its faces.)

The lengths of the three edges of a rectangular solid that meet at one of its vertices are the *dimensions* of the solid and are usually called its *length*, *width*, and *height*.

The dimensions of the solid shown at the right are l, w, and h. The length of one of the diagonals, x, of the solid, can be expressed in terms of the solid's dimensions by using the Pythagorean Theorem.

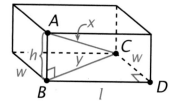

If BC is drawn, then $\triangle ABC$ and $\triangle BCD$ are right triangles (AB is perpendicular to the plane of the base of the solid, and so it must be perpendicular to BC). In right $\triangle ABC$,

$$x^2 = y^2 + h^2$$

and, in right $\triangle BCD$,

$$y^2 = l^2 + w^2.$$

Substituting, we get

$$x^2 = l^2 + w^2 + h^2$$

and, taking square roots, we get

$$x = \sqrt{l^2 + w^2 + h^2}.$$

Theorem 79

The length of a diagonal of a rectangular solid with dimensions l, w, and h is $\sqrt{l^2 + w^2 + h^2}$.

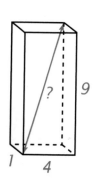

The monoliths in the film *2001* had dimensions 1 unit by 4 units by 9 units. To find the length of one of their interior diagonals, we can use Theorem 79 to write

$$\sqrt{1^2 + 4^2 + 9^2} = \sqrt{1 + 16 + 81} = \sqrt{98} = \sqrt{49 \cdot 2} = 7\sqrt{2}.$$

The length is exactly $7\sqrt{2}$ units, or approximately 9.9 units.

If all three dimensions of a rectangular solid are equal, it is a *cube*. If we let e represent the length of one edge of a cube, it follows that the length of one of its diagonals is

$$\sqrt{e^2 + e^2 + e^2} = \sqrt{3e^2} = e\sqrt{3}.$$

Corollary to Theorem 79

The length of a diagonal of a cube with edges of length e is $e\sqrt{3}$.

Exercises

Set I

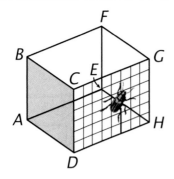

Inside or Outside? The box in the figure above is a rectangular solid.*

1. How many faces does a rectangular solid have?

2. How many vertices does it have?

3. How many edges does it have?

4. Which vertex is opposite D?

5. Which edges are parallel to AB?

6. Which edges are perpendicular to AB?

7. Which edges are skew to AB?

8. Is the beetle inside or outside the box?

Deck of Cards. A deck of playing cards is a fairly good model of a rectangular solid.†

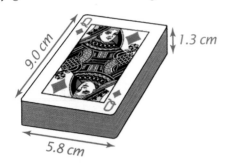

9. What change in the shape of the cards would make the model better?

Mathematical Circus, by Martin Gardner (Knopf, 1979).
†*Wonders of Numbers: Adventures in Mathematics, Mind and Meaning,* by Clifford A. Pickover (Oxford University Press, 2001).

10. Given the dimensions of the deck shown in the figure and the fact that it contains 52 cards, find the thickness of each card.

11. What is the area of the front face of each card?

12. What is the area of one of the long edges of each card?

13. What is the area of one of the short edges of each card?

Integer Lengths. Seven lengths are associated with a rectangular solid: the lengths of its edges, the lengths of its face diagonals, and the length of its interior diagonals.

No one knows whether all seven of these numbers can be integers, but the solid (not drawn to scale) shown here comes close.

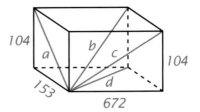

Use the lengths given to find each of the following lengths.

14. *a.*

15. *b.*

16. *c.*

17. *d.*

SAT Problem. The following problem appeared on an SAT test.

A cubic box with edge of length *x* inches is tied with a string 106 inches long. The string crosses itself at right angles on the top and bottom of the box. If the bow required 10 inches of string, what is the maximum number of inches *x* could be?

18. Write an equation based on this information.

19. Solve the equation for *x.*

Slicing a Cube. The photograph below shows a transparent cube half filled with liquid. The top surface of the liquid illustrates a *cross section* of the cube, the intersection of the cube with a plane.*

20. What shape does the cross section appear to be?

In the cube at the right, M and N are the midpoints of AE and EF.

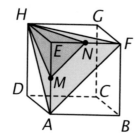

21. What can you conclude about △HEM and △HEN?

22. What kind of triangle is △HMN?

23. What can you conclude about △HDA and △FBA?

24. What kind of triangle is △HAF?

In the cube at the right, O and P are the midpoints of EH and HG.

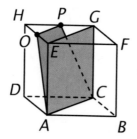

25. What can you conclude about ∠EAC?

Beyond the Third Dimension, by Thomas F. Banchoff (Scientific American Library, 1990).

26. What kind of quadrilateral is ACGE? Are AE and EG equal?

27. What can you conclude about OP and EG?

28. What kind of quadrilateral is ACPO?

Set II

An Inside Job. Obtuse Ollie gave Acute Alice the brick shown below and said to her, "I'll bet you can't find the length of one of its inside diagonals with this ruler."

Ollie's challenge

After thinking it over, Alice figured out a way to do it.[†]

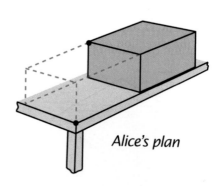

Alice's plan

29. What did Alice do?

The brick was 18 cm long and 9 cm wide, and Alice got 21 cm for the length of the diagonal.

30. How thick was the brick?

31. Which is thicker: the brick or Ollie's head?

[†]*Mathematical Cavalcade,* by Brian Bolt (Cambridge University Press, 1992).

Diagonals. Three diagonals have been drawn from vertex A of this cube: two on its faces and one inside the cube.

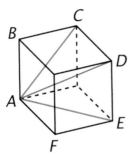

Find the measures of the following angles.

32. ∠BAC.

33. ∠CAE.

34. ∠ACD.

35. ∠CAD.

36. ∠DAF.

37. Is ∠CAD + ∠DAE = ∠CAE? Explain why or why not.

Hole Through a Cube. In the figure below, a square hole, ABCD, has been cut through a cube along the direction of a diagonal of the cube.*

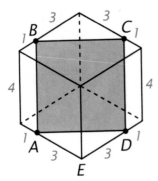

The edges of the cube are each 4 centimeters long, and the corners of the square hole are each 1 centimeter from a corner of the cube.

38. Find the area of one of the faces of the cube.

Mathematical Carnival, by Martin Gardner (Knopf, 1975).

39. Find the exact length of a side of the square hole.

40. Find the area of square ABCD.

41. Find the length of each side of the square hole to two decimal places.

Imagine two cubes, one 4 centimeters on a side and the other 4.1 centimeters on a side.

42. Is it possible to cut a hole through the smaller cube that the larger cube could pass through? Explain.

Bond Angles. Methane, a component of natural gas, is a molecule consisting of four hydrogen atoms bonded to a carbon atom. (In the ball-and-stick model shown here, a bond is represented by a stick.) The hydrogen atoms are arranged as if they were at four corners (A, B, C, and D) of a cube with the carbon atom at its center (O). Chemists have measured the molecule's bond angles and found that they are each 109.5°.[†]

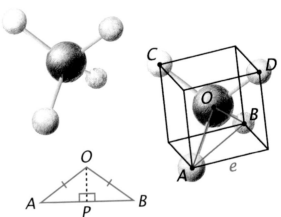

Find each of the following lengths in terms of e, the length of the edge of the cube.

43. AB.

44. AO.

45. AP.

46. Find ∠AOP to two decimal places.

47. Find ∠AOB to one decimal place.

[†] *The Architecture of Molecules,* by Linus Pauling and Roger Hayward (W. H. Freeman and Company, 1964).

Soma Puzzles. A popular puzzle is the Soma cube, created by Piet Hein in 1936. It consists of the seven pieces shown below.*

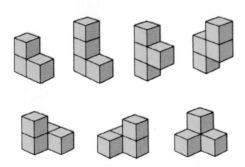

The pieces consist of small cubes glued together along their faces.

48. How many of these small cubes are there in all?

Each of the following structures was made from a set of the seven pieces, but each has at least one hidden hole. How many holes does each structure have? Explain each of your answers.

49.   **50.**

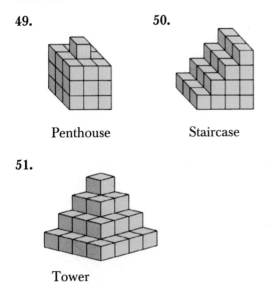

Penthouse   Staircase

51.

Tower

This wall appears to consist of nine geometrically similar columns of cubes, but it cannot be built from the seven Soma pieces.

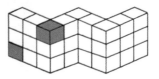

52. How many "corner cubes" such as the two shown in red does it seem to contain?

53. How many of these corner cubes can be made from the seven Soma pieces? (Look at each one to answer this question.)

54. Why can't the wall be built from the seven Soma pieces?

Set III

Flattened Cube. The surface of a cube can be cut and flattened out in eleven different ways to form a net of the cube. Below, on the left, is a flattened cube with letters on all six faces. On the right is a cube cut and flattened in a different way, with the letter on one of its faces shown.

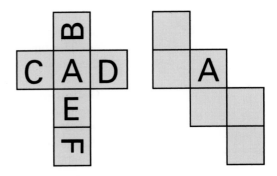

Copy the second figure. Can you fill in the remaining five faces so that, when the nets for both cubes are folded back together, they will be identical?[†]

Knotted Doughnuts and Other Mathematical Entertainments, by Martin Gardner (W. H. Freeman and Company, 1986).

[†]*Are You as Smart as You Think?* by Terry Stickels (Thomas Dunne Books, 2000).

LESSON 3

Prisms

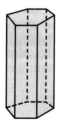

There is a strange rock formation in the Sierra Nevada mountains of California called the Devil's Post Pile. It consists of a set of tall columns of rock, some of which are 60 feet high. The tops of most of these columns are pentagonal and hexagonal in shape. Those that have fallen over reveal that the columns themselves have the shape of polyhedra called *prisms*.

Every prism has two congruent faces, its *bases*, which lie in parallel planes. The line segments that connect the corresponding vertices of these faces are parallel to each other.

The figures below illustrate the general idea, which is stated in the following definition.

Definition

Suppose that A and B are two parallel planes, R is a polygonal region in one plane, and *l* is a line that intersects both planes but not R. The solid made up of all segments parallel to line *l* that connect a point of region R to a point of the other plane is a *prism*.

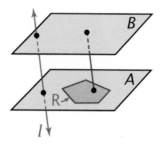
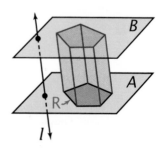

The *bases* of the prism, then, lie in these parallel planes. The rest of the faces of the prism, its *lateral faces*, are parallelograms. The edges in which the lateral faces intersect one another are its *lateral edges*.

Prisms are classified according to two properties: (1) the relation of their lateral edges to the planes containing their bases and (2) the shape of their faces.

If the lateral edges of a prism are perpendicular to the planes of its bases, the prism is a *right prism* and its lateral faces are rectangles. The prism representing one of the columns of the Devil's Post Pile is a *right hexagonal* prism.

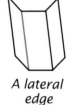

A lateral face   A lateral edge

If the lateral edges of a prism are oblique to the planes of its bases, the prism is an *oblique prism*. The prism shown between planes A and B in the figure on the facing page is an *oblique pentagonal* prism.

One way to make a model of the surface of a prism is to draw a pattern of its faces on a sheet of paper, cut it out, and fold it together. Such a pattern is called a *net* for the resulting polyhedron. The figure at the right is a net for the right hexagonal prism illustrated at the beginning of this lesson. Its six lateral faces are shown in yellow and its two bases in tan. The area of the yellow region is the *lateral area* of the prism; together, the areas of the yellow and tan regions make up the prism's *total area*.

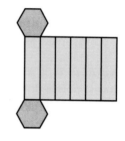

Definitions

The *lateral area* of a prism is the sum of the areas of its lateral faces. The *total area* of a prism is the sum of its lateral area and the areas of its bases.

Exercises

Set I

3-D Lettering. Obtuse Ollie printed Acute Alice's name in two-dimensional letters

and then added some lines to make the letters look three-dimensional:

1. Which letters are polygons in their two-dimensional versions?

2. What are the names of the polygons?

3. What geometric solid do these letters look like in their three-dimensional versions?

Prismane. In 1973, two chemists at Columbia University synthesized an organic compound that they named "prismane."* Its molecular structure is shown in the figure below.

4. Why is "prismane" an appropriate name for it?

5. How many bases does the structure have?

6. How many lateral faces?

———————————
*Thomas Katz and Nancy Acton.

The vertices of the figure represent carbon atoms and its edges represent the bonds between them.

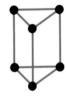

7. How many carbon atoms does a prismane molecule contain?

8. How many carbon–carbon bonds?

The bonds form rectangles and equilateral triangles.

9. What are the sizes of the angles that the bonds make with one another?

Polyhedral Nets. The figures below show patterns, polyhedral nets, that can be folded to form the first three prisms whose faces are all regular polygons.

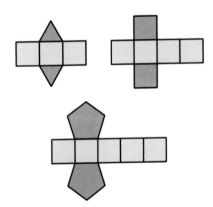

With respect to the prisms, what are the faces shown in

10. blue called?

11. yellow called?

If one of the bases of a prism is an *n*-gon, how many

12. lateral faces does the prism have?

13. faces does the prism have altogether?

14. If each edge of one of these prisms has length *e*, what does the expression ne^2 represent?

15. What is another name for the second prism?

Inside a Prism. You may be reading this while you are sitting inside a prism. Most rooms have the shape of rectangular solids and every rectangular solid is a prism.

16. If the floor and ceiling are considered to be the bases, what are the four walls?

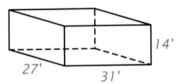

Use the dimensions shown in the figure above to find

17. the area of the floor.

18. the area of the four walls.

A Hexagonal Surprise. The figure below illustrates a remarkable connection between the vertices of a hexagon and the vertices of a prism.*

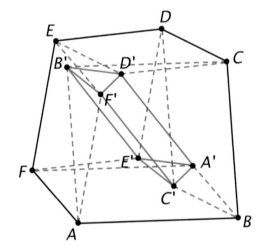

Points A and A′ are opposite vertices of ABA′F.

19. What special type of quadrilateral does ABA′F appear to be?

───────────

*The Penguin Dictionary of Curious and Interesting Geometry, by David Wells (Penguin, 1991).

Name the quadrilateral of which two opposite vertices are points

20. B and B'.
21. C and C'.
22. D and D'.
23. E and E'.
24. F and F'.

25. What type of quadrilateral does each of these quadrilaterals appear to be?

What appears to be true about

26. A'D', B'E', and C'F'?
27. △A'C'E' and △B'D'F'?

Although the figure is two-dimensional, the segments shown in green appear to be the edges of a polyhedron.

28. What special type of polyhedron does it appear to be? (Name it with two words.)

Set II

Long House. The figure below illustrates a "long house," a type of dwelling constructed by the Iroquois in North America in about 1600.*

The long house has the shape of a right prism. What kind of polygons are

29. the bases of the prism?
30. its lateral faces?
31. How many lateral edges does it have?

Architecture: Form, Space, and Order, by Francis D. K. Ching (Wiley, 1996).

Use the dimensions given in the figure below to find the following areas.

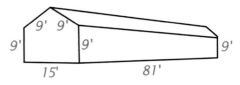

32. The area of the floor of the long house.
33. The area of the roof.

34. Find the approximate distance of the highest part of the roof above the ground. Draw a figure to illustrate your method.

Crystal Forms. The basic shapes from which all crystals are formed are prisms.[†]

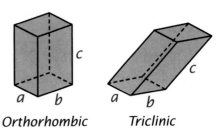

Orthorhombic   Triclinic

Two of them are shown above; both have edges of three different lengths.
    In an orthorhombic crystal, every pair of intersecting edges forms a right angle.

35. What can you conclude about the shapes of the faces of an orthorhombic crystal?

    In a triclinic crystal, there are no right angles.

36. What relation do the lateral edges of a triclinic crystal have to the planes of its bases?

37. What type of quadrilateral must the faces of these crystals be? Explain.

[†] *Crystals and Crystal Growing,* by Alan Holden and Phylis Singer (Anchor Books, 1960).

Feeding Trough. Troughs used in feeding animals often have the shape of a prism.

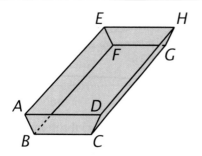

The prism shown above is a right prism in which ABCD and EFGH are isosceles trapezoids (AB = CD and EF = GH).

38. Are the bases of this prism congruent? Explain why or why not.

39. Can you conclude anything about AB and GH? Explain.

40. Can you conclude anything about AE and CG? Explain.

41. What can you conclude about ABFE and DCGH?

Magic Box. The figure below shows the design of a box used in magic tricks.

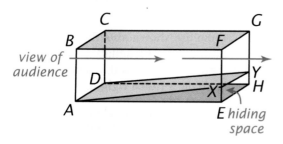

view of audience

E hiding space

The ends ABCD and XFGY are open so that an audience looking through the box thinks it is empty. According to a book on magic:

The modern mind is so attuned to the geometry of boxes and perspective effects that it perceives the sloping false bottom as the flat bottom of the box.*

Abracadabra! Secret Methods Magicians and Others Use to Deceive Their Audience, by Nathaniel Schiffman (Prometheus Books, 1997).

The shape of the box is such that ABCD and EFGH are the bases of a right rectangular prism and plane AXYD intersects EFGH so that EX = HY.

42. What kind of polygon is EXYH?

43. Why is △AXE ≅ △DYH?

44. How do AX and AE compare in length?

45. How do AXYD and AEHD compare in area?

46. What kind of polyhedron has the shape of the hiding space?

47. Which polygons are its bases?

48. What kind of polyhedron has the shape of the empty space (the region through which the audience sees)?

49. Which of its faces lie in parallel planes?

Euler's Discovery.

In 1752, Swiss mathematician Leonhard Euler discovered something about prisms that has been associated with his name ever since.

Suppose that the bases of a prism are n-gons. Write an expression in terms of n for

50. its number of vertices, V.

51. its number of faces, F.

52. its number of edges, E.

The Random House Dictionary of the English Language defines the "Euler characteristic" as "the number of vertices plus the number of faces minus the number of edges of a given polyhedron."

53. Use this definition and your expressions for exercises 50 through 52 to find the Euler characteristic for all prisms.

Set III

Topaz Angles. Scientists studying crystals in the eighteenth century made an interesting discovery that led them to conclude that crystals are made up of small "building blocks."*

If the outline of a topaz crystal such as the one in the photograph above, for example, is traced, the indicated angles are found to have measures of about 24.5° and 42.3°.

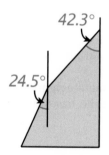

If we suppose that the crystal consists of a stack of small rectangular prisms, the two angles might be identified with ∠1 and ∠2 in the figure below.

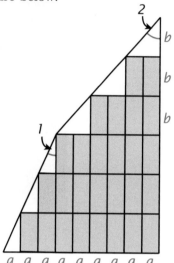

1. Given that two edges of these prisms have lengths *a* and *b* as shown, express tan ∠1 and tan ∠2 in terms of *a* and *b*.

2. What relation does tan ∠2 have to tan ∠1?

3. Letting ∠1 = 24.5°, use your calculator to find tan ∠1 to four decimal places.

4. Use your answers to exercises 2 and 3 to find tan ∠2 to four decimal places.

5. Use your calculator to find ∠2 to the nearest tenth of a degree.

6. Do your calculations fit with the measurements of the angles of topaz found by tracing?

Crystals and Light, by Elizabeth A. Wood (Van Nostrand, 1964).

LESSON 4

The Volume of a Prism

Cross sections of four popular candy bars are shown in the photographs above. How many of them can you identify?* Do you know which one is biggest?

Many candy bars are shaped somewhat like right prisms with their ends as the bases. The distance between the bases (the length of the bar) is the length of the prism's *altitude*.

Definition

An *altitude* of a prism is a line segment that connects the planes of its bases and that is perpendicular to both of them.

The question of which of the candy bars is "biggest" is about their *volumes*. The *volume* of an object is the amount of space that it occupies. You know that distances in one dimension are measured in *linear* units, whereas areas in two dimensions are measured in *square* units. Volumes in three dimensions are measured in *cubic* units. The figures at the left, for example, represent 1 centimeter, 1 square centimeter, and 1 cubic centimeter.

1 cm

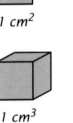

1 cm²

1 cm³

---

*From the Web site of the Science Museum of Minnesota.

Finding the volume of a rectangular solid such as the one shown at the right is easy. A layer of $3 \times 4 = 12$ cubes covers the 12 square units of its base. The altitude of the solid, 2, is the number of layers of cubes, and so there are $2 \times 12 = 24$ cubes in all. The volume of the solid is 24 cubic units.

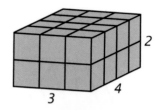

Similarly, if the dimensions of a rectangular solid are l, w, and h, then its volume is

$$V = lwh,$$

or, because $B = lw$, in which B is the area of one of the bases,

$$V = Bh.$$

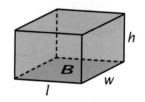

This equality is true whether or not the solid can be divided into a whole number of unit cubes as in our example.

A seventeenth-century Italian mathematician, Bonaventura Cavalieri, thought of an idea that allows us to apply this method to other geometric solids. It is based on *cross sections* such as those shown in the photographs of the candy bars.

Definition

A *cross section* of a geometric solid is the intersection of a plane and the solid.

Suppose that two candy bars have equal lengths and that we cut them into equal numbers of slices as if they were loaves of bread. Cavalieri thought that, if every pair of corresponding slices have equal areas, then the candy bars must have equal volumes. This claim is known as Cavalieri's Principle.

Postulate 13. Cavalieri's Principle

Consider two geometric solids and a plane. If every plane parallel to this plane that intersects one of the solids also intersects the other so that the resulting cross sections have equal areas, then the two solids have equal volumes.

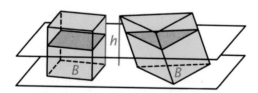

Cavalieri's Principle shows that the formula $V = Bh$ for rectangular solids also works for *any prism, right or oblique.* Suppose, for example, that both the rectangular prism and the triangular one shown above have bases with the same area, B, and that they have the same altitude, h. All cross sections of a prism formed by planes parallel to the bases are congruent to the bases, and so they have the same area as that of the bases. From this fact and from Cavalieri's Principle, it follows that these two prisms have equal volumes.

The following postulate expresses this fact.

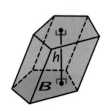

Postulate 14

The volume of any prism is the product of the area of its base and its altitude:

$$V = Bh.$$

The familiar formulas for the volumes of a rectangular solid and cube can be seen as corollaries to this postulate.

Corollary 1 to Postulate 14

The volume of a rectangular solid is the product of its length, width, and height:

$$V = lwh.$$

Corollary 2 to Postulate 14

The volume of a cube is the cube of its edge:

$$V = e^3.$$

Exercises

Set I

Squares and Cubes. The figure below shows why the expression x^2 is read as "x squared."

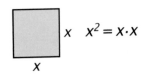

$x \quad x^2 = x \cdot x$

1. What does x^2 represent with respect to the square?

2. What is the expression x^3 read as?

3. Draw a figure to show why.

4. What does x^3 represent with respect to your figure?

From that fact that 1 yard = 3 feet, it follows that $(1 \text{ yard})^2 = (3 \text{ feet})^2$, or 1 square yard = 9 square feet.

5. It also follows that $(1 \text{ yard})^3 = (3 \text{ feet})^3$. How many cubic feet are in 1 cubic yard?

Because 1 foot = 12 inches, it follows that

$(1 \text{ foot})^2 = (12 \text{ inches})^2$, or 1 square foot = 144 square inches.

6. It also follows that $(1 \text{ foot})^3 = (12 \text{ inches})^3$. How many cubic inches are in 1 cubic foot?

7. How many inches are in 1 yard?

8. How many square inches are in 1 square yard?

9. How many cubic inches are in 1 cubic yard?

Largest Suitcase. The largest dimensions allowed by airlines for a carry-on suitcase are 22 inches by 14 inches by 9 inches.

10. Find the volume of a suitcase having these dimensions in cubic inches.

11. How many cubic inches are in 1 cubic foot?

12. Find the volume of the suitcase in cubic feet.

Noah's Ark. According to Genesis 6:15, Noah's ark was 300 cubits long, 50 cubits wide, and 30 cubits high. A cubit is the length of a forearm, conventionally taken as 18 inches long.

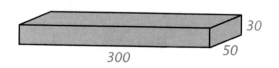

Find the approximate volume of the ark in

13. cubic cubits.

14. cubic feet.

15. Given that the capacity of a standard railroad box car is about 3,000 cubic feet, approximately how many box cars would have the same volume as the ark?

Weathering Rock. The figures below illustrate with cubes how the surface area of rock changes as it is broken up into smaller particles by cycles of weathering.*

If the length of each edge of a cube is 1 meter, what is

16. its volume in cubic meters?

17. its surface area in square meters?

_____

Environmental Geology, by Dorothy J. Merritts, Andrew de Wet, and Kirsten Menking (W. H. Freeman and Company, 1998).

Suppose that the cube is broken up into cubes each of whose edges is 0.5 meter long.

18. How many cubes are formed?

19. What is their total volume?

20. What is their total surface area?

Suppose these cubes in turn are broken up into cubes each of whose edges is 0.25 meter long.

21. How many cubes are formed?

22. What is their total volume?

23. What is their total surface area?

As rock breaks into smaller particles, what happens to its

24. volume?

25. surface area?

Keng-chih's Principle. In the fifth century, the Chinese mathematician Tsu Keng-chih wrote:

If volumes are constructed of piled up blocks and corresponding areas are equal, then the volumes cannot be unequal.

26. What postulate from this lesson do these words suggest?

The figure below shows two sets of piled-up blocks on a table.

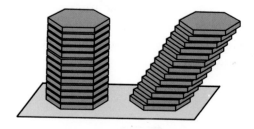

27. What kind of prism does each pile of blocks appear to form?

28. What does the figure suggest about two prisms whose bases have equal areas and whose altitudes are equal?

Lesson 4: The Volume of a Prism   **643**

Hole in the Ground. Obtuse Ollie asked Acute Alice, "How much dirt is there in a hole in the ground that is 123 feet long, 123 feet wide, and 123 feet deep?"

As he watched her type in the numbers on her calculator, Ollie told Alice that he didn't think she would get the right answer.

29. What answer do you think Alice got?

30. Why did Ollie think that her answer would be wrong?

Prism Volumes. Find the volumes of the following prisms.

31.

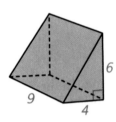

This is a right prism whose bases are right triangles.

32.

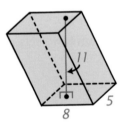

This is an oblique prism whose bases are rectangles.

33.

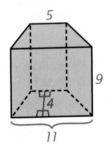

This is a right prism whose bases are trapezoids.

Candy Bars. The four candy bars pictured at the beginning of this lesson are identified here.

3 Musketeers   Snickers

Butterfinger   Milky Way

34. Assuming that the 3 Musketeers bar is a rectangular solid 3.0 cm wide, 2.1 cm thick, and 12.5 cm long, find its volume to the nearest cubic centimeter.

35. Assuming that the Snickers and Milky Way bars are rectangular solids 3.3 cm wide, 2.0 cm thick, and 10.0 cm long, find their volumes to the nearest cubic centimeter.

36. Assuming that the Butterfinger bar is a right prism 14.5 cm long with trapezoid bases with bases of 2.3 cm and 3.5 cm and with an altitude of 1.3 cm, find its volume to the nearest cubic centimeter.

37. Which candy bar is largest? Must it also weigh the most?

Set II

Ream of Paper. A ream of paper contains 500 sheets and is 2 inches thick. "Letter size" paper measures 8.5 inches by 11 inches.

Thinking of a single sheet of paper as a right rectangular prism having its two sides as its bases, find each of the following measures.

38. Its altitude.

39. Its volume.

40. Its *total* area.

Binomial Cube. The figure below shows a cube with edges of length $a + b$ that has been sliced into pieces by three planes parallel to its faces.

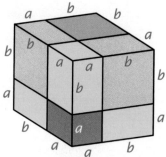

41. Write an expression for the volume of the cube in terms of a and b.

42. Into how many pieces is the cube cut?

43. How many of these pieces also are cubes?

Write an expression in terms of a and b for the volume of

44. one of the yellow pieces.

45. one of the orange pieces.

46. the cube as the sum of the volumes of its pieces.

Chinese Problem. In an ancient Chinese text, the *Chiu Chang Suan Shu,* methods are given for finding the volumes of various solids, including the one shown below.

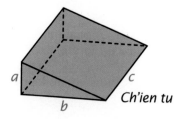

Ch'ien tu

The faces of a "ch'ien tu" are rectangles and right triangles.

47. What kind of geometric solid is it?

Write an expression in terms of a, b, and c for

48. its volume.

49. its total area.

SAT Problem. The figure below appeared in a problem on an SAT exam.

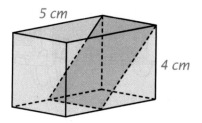

It shows an empty box with a flap lid that has an area of 15 square centimeters. One of the three unattached edges of the lid rests on the bottom of the box as shown and separates it into two compartments.

50. Draw the figure and mark it as needed to answer each of the following questions.

51. What is the third dimension of the box?

Given that the lid is flat, what is the volume of

52. the smaller, closed compartment?

53. the larger, open compartment?

Filling a Pool. The figure below shows a cross section of water in a rectangular swimming pool having the shape of a right prism. The pool is 40 feet long and 20 feet wide.

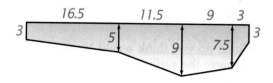

54. Find the area of the cross section in square feet.

55. Find the volume of the water in the pool in cubic feet.

56. How long would it take to fill the pool if it can be filled at the rate of 2 cubic feet per minute?

Advertising Claim. A television commercial for the Toyota Camry began:

How can it be that an automobile that's a mere nine inches larger on the outside gives you over two feet more room on the inside?*

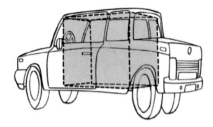

Suppose the passenger compartment of the car has the shape of a rectangular solid 6 feet long, 4 feet wide, and 3 feet high.

By how many cubic feet would its volume be increased if the passenger compartment were 9 inches

57. longer?

58. wider?

59. higher?

60. What is strange about the wording of the commercial?

Measuring a Toad. These figures show a toad and its shed skin.†

61. Which do you think would be easier to measure: the surface area of a toad or its volume?

62. How would you do it?

Set III

Molecule Experiment. One of Benjamin Franklin's many discoveries was that, if he dropped a teaspoon of oil onto the surface of a pond, it would spread out to cover half an acre but no more.

A teaspoon of oil has a volume of about 4 cubic centimeters and an acre is equal to about 4,000 square meters.

1. How thick was the layer of oil on the pond?

2. If the oil film was one molecule thick and we think of each molecule as a little cube, approximately how many molecules might be in a teaspoon of oil?

---

*200% of Nothing, by A. K. Dewdney (Wiley, 1993).
†Envisioning Information, by Edward R. Tufte (Graphics Press, 1990).

Used with permission of Ed Fisher

Pyramids

The Egyptians built more than 70 pyramids between 2700 B.C. and 2200 B.C. The word "pyramid" has become so identified with these structures that the first definition given of it in one dictionary is: "(In ancient Egypt) a quadrilateral masonry mass having steeply sloping sides meeting at an apex, used as a tomb."*

Although the Egyptians always chose the square for the shape of the bases of their pyramids, we use the word "pyramid" to refer to any geometric solid of which one face is in the shape of a polygon (its base) and the other faces are in the shape of triangles that meet at a point.

Definition

Suppose that A is a plane, R is a polygonal region in plane A, and P is a point not in plane A. The solid made up of all segments that connect P to a point of region R is a *pyramid.*

The face of the pyramid that lies in this plane is its *base.* The rest of its faces are the *lateral faces* and the edges in which they intersect each other are its *lateral edges.* The lateral edges meet at the *apex* of the pyramid.

The Random House Dictionary of the English Language.

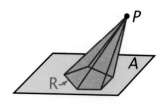

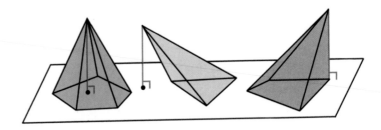

The height of a pyramid is measured by the length of its *altitude.*

Definition
The *altitude* of a pyramid is the perpendicular line segment connecting the apex to the plane of its base. It is also the length of this segment.

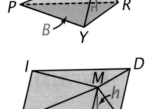

As the figures above show, the altitude of a pyramid can lie inside it, lie outside it, or even be one of its lateral edges.

The volume of a pyramid, like that of a prism, is determined by the area of its base and the length of its altitude. The figures at the left show a pyramid and a prism that has been drawn with the same base and altitude as those of the pyramid. This was done by constructing PI and RD so that they are both parallel to YM and equal to it in length. Points M, I, and D are connected to determine the upper base of the prism.

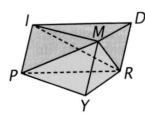 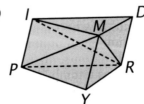 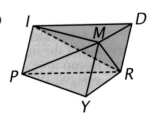

The prism thus formed can be cut into three pyramids, one of which is the original pyramid. Each pyramid is shown in one of the figures above. Cavalieri's Principle can be used to show that these pyramids have equal volumes. Hence the volume of each pyramid is one-third the volume of the prism, or $\frac{1}{3}Bh$. Because every pyramid can be viewed as being made up of triangular pyramids with their bases in a common plane and having a common apex, this result holds for all pyramids. These ideas can be used to establish the following theorem.

Theorem 80
The volume of any pyramid is one-third of the product of the area of its base and its altitude:

$$V = \frac{1}{3}Bh.$$

Exercises

Set I

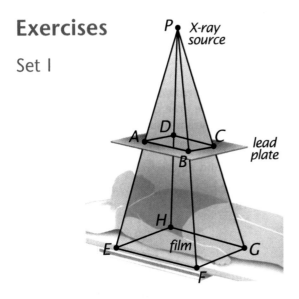

P • X-ray source

D

A • C

B

lead plate

H

E • film • G

F

X-Ray Beam. In radiography, an X-ray tube projects a beam of X-rays through the body and onto a film.*

1. What kind of geometric solid does the beam appear to form?

With respect to this solid, what is

2. point P, the X-ray source?
3. EFGH, the film?
4. ABCD, the opening in the lead plate?
5. △PEF?

Ferrocene. The figure below shows the arrangement of atoms in a ferrocene molecule.†

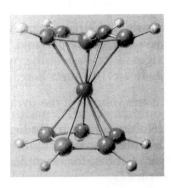

Scientific American: How Things Work Today, edited by Michael Wright and M. N. Patel (Crown, 2000).
†*The Architecture of Molecules*, by Linus Pauling and Roger Hayward (W. H. Freeman and Company, 1964).

The atom shown in red is iron, the ten large atoms above and below it are carbon, and the small atoms are hydrogen.

6. What shape do the bases of the pyramids have that appear in the molecule?
7. Where is the iron atom with respect to these pyramids?
8. What are the sticks that represent the bonds between the iron atom and the carbon atoms called with respect to these pyramids?
9. What kind of triangles do the sticks representing the bonds appear to form?

Pyramid Volumes. Find the volumes of the following pyramids.

10.

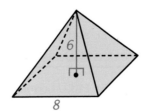

6

8

The base of this pyramid is a square.

11.

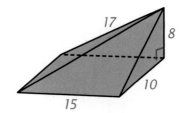

17   8

15   10

The base of this pyramid is a rectangle.

12.

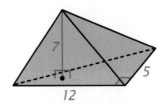

7

12   5

The base of this pyramid is a right triangle.

A Regular Pyramid. The base of the pyramid in the figure below is a regular polygon. Point O is the center of its base, and PO is its altitude.

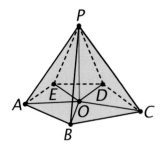

What can you conclude about

13. OA, OB, OC, OD, and OE?

14. ∠POA, ∠POB, ∠POC, ∠POD, and ∠POE?

15. △POA, △POB, △POC, △POD, and △POE?

16. PA, PB, PC, PD, and PE?

17. △PAB, △PBC, △PCD, △PDE, and △PEA?

Leonardo's Claim. In 1483, Leonardo da Vinci made the sketch below and wrote: "If a man is provided with . . . linen fabric with a length of 12 yards on each side and 12 yards high, he can jump from any great height whatsoever, without injury to his body."

18. What does his sketch show?

19. Use da Vinci's numbers to find the volume of air that would fill it.

20. Does the man seem to be the correct size with respect to the rest of the figure? Explain.

Triangle and Pyramid Compared. The formulas for the area of a triangle and the volume of a pyramid are similar but different.

21. What is the area, *A*, of a triangle having base *b* and altitude *h*?

22. What is the volume, *V*, of a pyramid having base of area *B*, and altitude *h*?

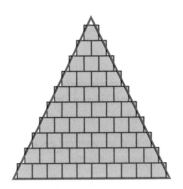

In the figure above, the base and altitude of the red triangle are each 10.5 units long.

23. What is its area?

An estimate of its area might be made by counting the squares shown in blue.

24. How many squares are there in all?

The red triangle in the figure can also be seen as a side view of a square pyramid.* In this case, the edges of the base of the pyramid and its altitude are 10.5 units long.

25. What is the volume of the pyramid?

An estimate of its volume might be made by counting the cubes shown in blue. (The bottom layer of cubes, for example, contains $10^2 = 100$ cubes.)

26. How many cubes are there in all?

---

*Based on an idea in *Geometrical Investigations*, by John Pottage (Addison-Wesley, 1983).

Set II

The Divided Cube. Nicholas Saunderson, blinded by smallpox when he was 12, later became a professor of mathematics at Cambridge University.*

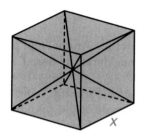

He thought of a way to get the formula for the volume of a pyramid by using the figure above. It shows a cube divided into six congruent pyramids whose apexes are at its center and whose bases are its faces.

Express the following measures in terms of the length, *x*, of the edges of the cube.

27. The volume of the cube.

28. *V*, the volume of one of the pyramids, based on your answer to exercise 27.

29. *B*, the area of the base of one of the pyramids.

30. *h*, the length of the altitude of one of the pyramids.

31. *Bh*.

Compare your answers to exercises 28 and 31.

32. What relation does *V*, the volume of one of the pyramids, have to *Bh*, the product of the area of its base and the length of its altitude?

Pyramid Numbers. The Greek historian Herodotus is said to have learned from the Egyptian priests that the square of the altitude of the Great Pyramid is equal to the area of one of its lateral faces.†

---

* The Penguin Book of Curious and Interesting Mathematics, by David Wells (Penguin, 1997).
† *Gnonom: From Pharoahs to Fractals,* by Midhet J. Gazalé (Princeton University Press, 1999).

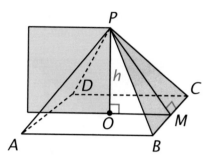

The base of the Great Pyramid, ABCD, is a square with sides of length 756 feet, its altitude PO has length 481 feet, and M is the midpoint of BC.

33. Find the square of the altitude to the nearest thousand square feet.

34. Find PM to the nearest foot.

35. Find the area of one of the lateral faces to the nearest thousand square feet.

36. Based on your answers to exercises 33 and 35, might the claim of the Egyptian priests be true?

37. Find the volume of the Great Pyramid to the nearest million cubic feet.

More on the Euler Characteristic. Suppose that the base of a pyramid is an *n*-gon.

Write an expression in terms of *n* for

38. its number of vertices, *V*.

39. its number of faces, *F*.

40. its number of edges, *E*.

The Euler characteristic is $V + F - E$.

41. What can you conclude from your expressions for exercises 38 through 40 about the Euler characteristic for pyramids?

Salt Funnel. The figure below shows a funnel used in Africa in producing salt.*

42. Make a model of the funnel by doing the following steps.

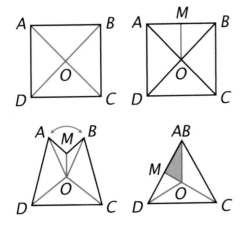

(1) Take a square piece of paper and fold it along both diagonals (see the upper left-hand figure above).

(2) Fold an apothem (see the upper right-hand figure).

(3) Bring △AOD and △BOC together as in the lower left-hand figure, with point M being up and point O being down.

(4) Tape or clip the "double triangle" together as shown in the lower right-hand figure.

_____

*_Geometry from Africa_, by Paulus Gerdes (Mathematical Association of America, 1999).

43. What shape is the funnel?

44. What is the shape of its top?

45. What is the shape of its other faces?

Given that each side of the square from which the funnel is folded has length *s*, what is the funnel's

46. lateral area?

47. volume? (Hint: Any face of the funnel can be considered its base.)

The Frustum of a Pyramid. A _frustum_ of a pyramid is the part of the pyramid included between its base and a plane parallel to its base. The figure below shows a square pyramid from which a smaller square pyramid has been cut off.

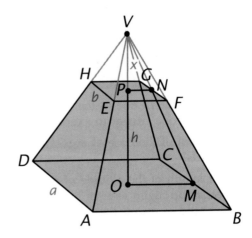

Each edge of the base of the large pyramid has length *a*, and its altitude, VO, has length $x + h$.

48. Write an expression for the volume of the large pyramid.

Each edge of the base of the small pyramid has length *b* and its altitude, VP, has length *x*.

49. Write an expression for its volume.

50. Write an expression for the volume of the frustum (the part shown in green.)

Given that OM and PN are apothems of ABCD and EFGH, it can be shown that △VOM ~ △VPN.

51. Write expressions for OM and PN in terms of a and b.

52. Why is $\dfrac{VO}{VP} = \dfrac{OM}{PN}$?

53. Rewrite this proportion in terms of x, h, a, and b.

54. Solve your equation for x in terms of h, a, and b.

55. Substitute for x in your answer to exercise 50 and show that the volume of the frustum is $\dfrac{1}{3}(a^2 + ab + b^2)h$.

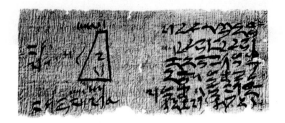

There is evidence that the Egyptians used this expression to find the volume of the frustum of a square pyramid as early as 1890 B.C.*

56. Find the volume of such a frustum for which $a = 12$, $b = 3$, and $h = 8$.

The ancient Babylonians used a different expression, $\dfrac{1}{2}(a^2 + b^2)h$, to find the volume of the frustum of a square pyramid.

57. Is this expression also correct? Explain.

Set III

How Many Faces? The following question appeared on a PSAT exam.

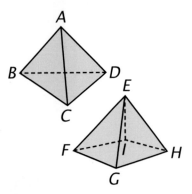

In pyramids ABCD and EFGHI shown above, all faces except base FGHI are equilateral triangles of equal size. If face ABC were placed on face EFG so that the vertices of the triangles coincide, how many exposed faces would the resulting solid have?

(A) Five.

(B) Six.

(C) Seven.

(D) Eight.

(E) Nine.

Daniel Lowen, when he took the test as a student at Cocoa Beach High School in Florida, showed that the "expected" answer to the question was wrong.

1. What do you think the "expected" answer was? Explain.

Make models of the two pyramids and put them together as described in the question.

2. What do you think the correct answer to the question is? Explain.

*Beyond the Third Dimension, by Thomas F. Banchoff (Scientific American Library, 1990).

LESSON 6

Cylinders and Cones

The picture above, part of a painting titled *Euclidean Walks* by René Magritte, contains several visual tricks. One of them concerns the roof of the tower and the street extending out to the horizon. They are almost identical in appearance, and yet the tower roof is a *cone*, a three-dimensional solid, whereas the street is a two-dimensional figure bounded by parallel lines.

A cone is like a pyramid. Its base, however, is bounded by a circle rather than a polygon. And, instead of having a set of flat triangular faces, it has a single curved surface called its *lateral surface*.

Just as the term *polygonal region* refers to the union of a polygon and its interior, the term *circular region* refers to the union of a circle and its interior. To define the term *cone*, we can simply replace the word "polygonal" in the definition of a pyramid with the word "circular."

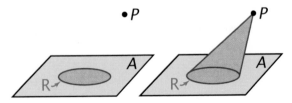

Definition
Suppose that A is a plane, R is a circular region in plane A, and P is a point not in plane A. The solid made up of all segments that connect P to a point of region R is a *cone*.

The words *base*, *apex*, and *altitude* are used in the same sense with respect to cones that they are with pyramids. The line segment connecting the apex of a cone to the center of its base is called its *axis*. A cone is either *right* or *oblique*, depending on whether its axis is perpendicular or oblique to its base.

Just as cones are the circular counterparts of *pyramids*, cylinders are the circular counterparts of *prisms*. Changing the word "polygonal" to "circular" turns the definition of a prism into that of a cylinder.

A right cone

An oblique cone

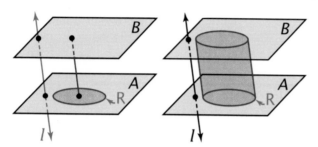

Definition

Suppose that A and B are two parallel planes, R is a circular region in one plane, and *l* is a line that intersects both planes but not R. The solid made up of all segments parallel to line *l* that connect a point of region R to a point of the other plane is a *cylinder*.

Every cylinder has three surfaces: two flat ones, which are its *bases*, and a curved one, which is its *lateral surface*. The word *altitude* is used in the same sense with respect to cylinders as it is with respect to prisms. The *axis* of a cylinder is the line segment connecting the centers of its bases. Cylinders, like cones, are classified as *right* or *oblique*, depending on the direction of their axes with respect to their bases.

Because a cylinder can be closely approximated by a prism and a cone can be approximated by a pyramid, the formulas for the volumes of prisms and pyramids can be used to find the volumes of cylinders and cones as well. They are restated as the following theorems without out proof.

A right cylinder

An oblique cylinder

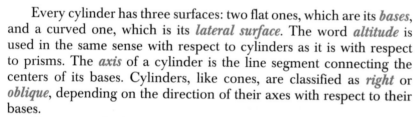

 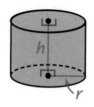

Theorem 81

The volume of a cylinder is the product of the area of its base and its altitude:

$$V = Bh = \pi r^2 h.$$

Theorem 82

The volume of a cone is one-third of the product of the area of its base and its altitude:

$$V = \frac{1}{3}Bh = \frac{1}{3}\pi r^2 h.$$

Exercises

Set I

Primitive Perspective. The "three-dimensional" figures below are shown in the style in which they were usually drawn in the fifteenth century.*

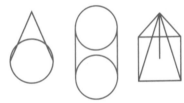

1. What geometric solids do you think they illustrate?

2. Redraw each figure in a more correct perspective.

Italian into English. Compare the following two statements from an Italian geometry book.

Il volume di un cilindro è dato dal prodotto dell'area di base per l'altezza.

Il volume di un cono è dato da un terzo del prodotto dell'area di base per l'altezza.

3. Which words appear to be the same in Italian and English?

---

*The Invention of Infinity: Mathematics and Art in the Renaissance, by J. V. Field (Oxford University Press, 1997).

What do you think the following words mean?

4. Cilindro.

5. Cono.

6. Prodotto.

7. Un terzo.

8. Altezza.

9. In which statement do you think one of the words could be correctly replaced by "piramide"?

Solids of Revolution. A cylinder can be thought of as a "solid of revolution" because it can be generated by revolving a rectangle about one of its sides.

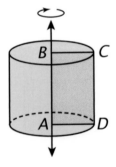

10. What is the side AB about which the rectangle revolves called with respect to the cylinder?

11. What is the length of AB called?

12. What is the curved surface generated by the opposite side CD called with respect to the cylinder?

13. What do sides AD and BC generate?

14. What relation does line AB have to the planes that contain the bases of the cylinder?

Suppose the rectangle is a 3-inch-by-5-inch file card and that it is revolved about a 5-inch side, as shown on page 656.

15. Find the volume of the cylinder generated in cubic inches. Leave your answer in terms of π.

Suppose the rectangle is revolved about one of its shorter sides, as shown below.

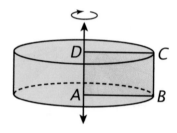

16. Does the cylinder generated have the same volume as that of the preceding one? Explain.

A cone also can be thought of as a "solid of revolution."

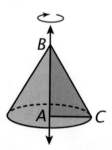

17. What figure can be revolved to generate it?

18. Would a cone be generated regardless of which side of the figure the figure is revolved about? Explain.

Hockey Puck. Although a sphere (the ball) is important in most sports, a cylinder (the puck) is important in ice hockey.

A hockey puck has a diameter of 3 inches and an altitude of 1 inch.

19. Find the area of ice covered by one of its bases to the nearest square inch.

20. Find its volume to the nearest cubic inch.

Cylindrical Tunnel. One of the tunnel-boring machines used to construct the Channel tunnel connecting France and England is shown in the photograph below. The machine can bore a cylindrical tunnel with a diameter of 9 meters, advancing by 75 meters per day.

21. Find the area to the nearest square meter of one of the bases of this section of tunnel.

22. Find the volume to the nearest hundred cubic meters of a day's worth of this machine's tunneling.

Sliced Solids. The figures below are overhead views of two geometric solids and corresponding cross sections produced by a set of planes parallel to their bases. Each plane is equidistant from the neighboring ones.

23. What kind of solids do they appear to be?

24. Sketch figures to show what side views of the two solids might look like.

25. What can you conclude about the two solids if every pair of corresponding cross sections have equal areas?

26. What is the basis for your conclusion?

Sausages in a Can. Vienna sausages are sold in cans that contain seven sausages.

The diameter of each sausage is 2 cm and the diameter of the can is 6 cm. The sausages are 5 cm long and the can is 6 cm high.
   Find the total volume in cubic centimeters of the seven sausages

27. as an exact number in terms of π.

28. to the nearest integer.

   Find the volume in cubic centimeters of the can

29. as an exact number in terms of π.

30. to the nearest integer.

31. What percentage of the volume of the can do the sausages fill?

Triangles or Cones. Compare the figures below.

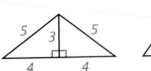

32. If they are seen as isosceles triangles, how do the triangles compare in area? Explain.

33. If they are seen as side views of right cones, how do the cones compare in volume? Explain.

Set II

Pipe Puzzle. The following question appears in a popular book of puzzles.*

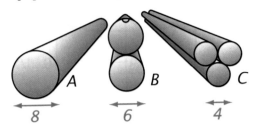

Which arrangement of lengths of pipes would hold the most water?

34. To answer this question, what would you assume about the pipes?

35. Which arrangement is the correct answer?

Cake Pans. The directions on a typical box of cake mix say to use either a round pan with a 9-inch diameter or a square pan with sides of 8 inches. Both pans are $1\frac{1}{2}$ inches deep.

The Mammoth Book of Brainstorming Puzzles, by David J. Bodycombe (Carroll & Graf, 1996).

36. Find the volume of each pan to the nearest cubic inch.

37. How would you expect the heights of the cakes produced in the two pans to compare? Explain.

Engine Displacement. Cylinders are basic parts of gasoline engines. According to an automobile handbook,

> The swept volume in cubic inches of an individual cylinder is found by multiplying pi/4 by the bore in inches squared by the stroke in inches.

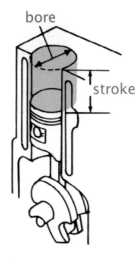

What dimension of the cylinder (shown in green) is

38. the bore?

39. the stroke?

40. Letting the radius of the cylinder be r and its altitude be h, show why the description above gives the correct expression for the "swept volume."

The "displacement" of an engine is the total swept volume of its cylinders.

41. Find the displacement to the nearest cubic inch of an eight-cylinder engine with a bore of 4.0 inches and a stroke of 3.5 inches.

Stage Lighting. Cones of light are used in stage lighting.*

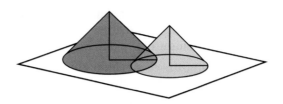

Suppose that one of these light cones is shaped so that the radius of its base is always equal to its altitude.

Write an expression for each of the following measures in terms of h, the distance of the light above the stage.

42. The area of the stage lighted by it.

43. The volume of space lighted by it.

Suppose the distance of the light above the stage is doubled to $2h$.

44. Exactly how does the area of the stage lighted by it increase?

45. Exactly how does the volume of space lighted by it increase?

Paper Towels. A popular brand of paper towels contains, according to the package, "80.6 square feet" of towels. Each towel measures 11 inches by 6 inches.

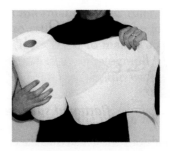

46. How many towels do you think are in the package?

————————
Beyond the Third Dimension, by Thomas F. Banchoff (Scientific American Library, 1990).

The towels are wrapped around a cardboard tube so that the package has the shape of a cylinder that is 11 inches long and has a diameter of 6 inches. The diameter of the cardboard tube is 1.75 inches.

Find the volumes of

47. the roll of towels, including the tube, to the nearest cubic inch.

48. the towels, not including the tube, to the nearest cubic inch.

49. one towel, to the nearest 0.1 cubic inch.

Cylinder and Cone Areas. The lateral area of a right cylinder or cone is the area of its curved surface.

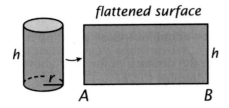

flattened surface

50. What does the curved surface of a right cylinder look like if the cylinder is slit down one side and flattened out?

51. Write an expression for AB in terms of *r*.

52. Write an expression for the lateral area of a right cylinder in terms of *r* and *h*.

53. What does the expression $2\pi r(r + h)$ represent for a right cylinder?

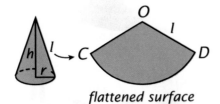

flattened surface

54. What does the curved surface of a right cone look like if the cone is flattened out?

55. Write an expression for the length of arc CD in terms of *r*.

56. What fraction of the area of circle O is the lateral area? Express your answer in terms of *r* and *l*.

57. Write an expression for the lateral area of a right cone in terms of *r* and *l*.

58. Write an expression for the lateral area in terms of *r* and *h*.

59. What does the expression $\pi r(r + l)$ represent for a right cone?

Coin Wrappers. Coin wrappers come in different sizes according to the dimensions of the coins that they are made to hold.

A wrapper for nickels, for example, is 34 mm wide when pressed flat.

60. Show that this size is appropriate for nickels, given that the diameter of a nickel is 21 mm.

61. How wide would you expect a wrapper for dimes to be, given that the diameter of a dime is 18 mm?

62. In general, approximately how wide should a wrapper for a set of coins be if the diameter of each coin is *x* mm?

Rolling Cones. A right circular cone rolls on a flat horizontal surface.*

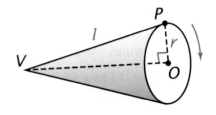

63. Describe what happens to the cone.

———————

Mathematics Meets Technology, by Brian Bolt (Cambridge University Press, 1991).

Suppose the cone returns to the same spot
after rotating twice about its axis.

64. What can you conclude about ∠PVO?
Explain.

Set III

Iron Ore. The photograph above is an
overhead view of a conical pile of iron ore
ready to be loaded into train cars.*

The cars are 10 feet wide and the "angle of
repose" of iron ore (∠R in the side view of the
pile below) is 34°.

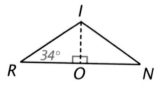

Taking Measures Across the American Landscape, by
James Corner and Alex S. MacLean (Yale University
Press, 1996).

Use this information, your ruler, and a
calculator to estimate each of the following
measures. (It is easiest to make your
measurements on the photograph in
millimeters. For example, the width of the
cars is 4 mm.)

1. The diameter of the pile in feet.
2. The height of the pile.
3. The area of ground covered by the pile.
4. The volume of ore in the pile.
5. The number of 4,400-cubic-foot gondola
   cars needed to haul the pile away.

LESSON 7

Spheres

In 360 B.C., the Greek philosopher Plato wrote:

> Wherefore he [the Creator] made the world in the form of a sphere, round as from a lathe, having its extremes in every direction equidistant from the center.*

On December 7, 1972, when on the Apollo 17 mission to the moon, American astronaut Harrison Schmitt confirmed Plato's words as he took the famous photograph of Earth shown above. The familiar shape of Africa is visible at the upper left, and snow-covered Antarctica can be seen at the bottom.

Plato's description of a sphere, written before Euclid was born, is the basis for our definition.

Definition

A *sphere* is the set of all points in space that are at a given distance from a given point.

---

*Timaeus, translated by Benjamin Jowett.

Notice that this definition is like that of a circle except that the words "in space" replace "in a plane." As a result, words such as *center*, *radius*, and *diameter* have the same meanings for spheres as they do for circles.

You know that two useful measures of a circle are its circumference and area, both of which can be determined from its radius: $c = 2\pi r$ and $a = \pi r^2$.

Two useful measures of a sphere are its *surface area* and *volume*. By the volume of a sphere, we mean the volume of the solid consisting of the sphere and its interior. You may already know the remarkable fact that the surface area and volume of a sphere, like the circumference and area of a circle, can be expressed in terms of its radius and pi.

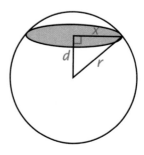

First, we can use Cavalieri's Principle to find the volume. The figure at the right shows a sphere of radius r sliced by a plane at a distance d from the sphere's center. The cross section of the sphere is a circle; we will let its radius be x.

By the Pythagorean Theorem,

$$x^2 + d^2 = r^2, \quad \text{so} \quad x^2 = r^2 - d^2.$$

Because the cross section is a circle, its area is πx^2. Substituting for x^2 gives

$$A_{\text{cross section}} = \pi(r^2 - d^2) = \pi r^2 - \pi d^2.$$

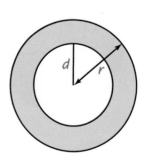

This result can be interpreted as the difference between the areas of two circles having radii r and d. In the figure at the right, this difference is the area of the yellow region between the two circles.

To apply Cavalieri's Principle to finding the volume of a sphere, we use a geometric solid that has this kind of cross section. It consists of a right cylinder from which two identical cones have been removed, as shown in the figure below. The cylinder has the same radius, r, and the same height, $2r$, as those of the sphere and is situated so that the two solids rest on the same plane. The two hollowed-out cones meet at the center of the cylinder and each shares one or the other of its bases.

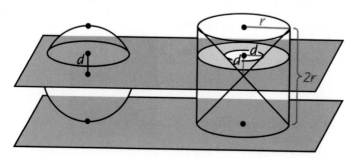

A cross section of this solid chosen at a distance d from the solid's center is bounded by two circles with radii r and d; so the area of the cross section is

$$\pi r^2 - \pi d^2.$$

This area is the same as that of the corresponding cross section of the sphere; so, from Cavalieri's Principle, it follows that the volumes of the two solids are the same.

It is easy to find the volume of the cylindrical solid. It is equal to

$$V_{\text{cylinder}} - V_{\text{two cones}} =$$

$$\pi r^2 (2r) - 2\left[\frac{1}{3}\pi r^2(r)\right] =$$

$$2\pi r^3 - \frac{2}{3}\pi r^3 = \frac{4}{3}\pi r^3.$$

It follows that this volume is also that of the sphere.

Theorem 83

The volume of a sphere is $\frac{4}{3}\pi$ times the cube of its radius:

$$V = \frac{4}{3}\pi r^3.$$

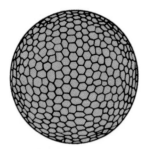

We can use this result and an intuitive argument to find a formula for the surface area of a sphere. First, we divide the sphere into a large number of small "pyramids." Imagine that the surface of the sphere is separated into a large number of tiny "polygons." They are not actually polygons, because there are no straight line segments on the surface of a sphere. However, the shorter the "line segments," the closer they come to forming polygons.

Imagine connecting the corners of all of these "polygons" to the center of the sphere so that they become the bases of a set of "pyramids" all with a common apex, the center of the sphere. All of the pyramids, then, have altitudes equal to the radius of the sphere.

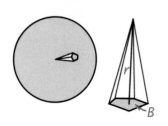

The volume of one of these pyramids is $\frac{1}{3}Br$, in which B is the area of the pyramid's base and r is the length of its altitude. The volume of the sphere is the sum of the volumes of all of the pyramids. If the areas of their bases are B_1, B_2, B_3, and so on, then their volumes are $\frac{1}{3}B_1 r$, $\frac{1}{3}B_2 r$, $\frac{1}{3}B_3 r$, and so on, and

$$V_{\text{sphere}} = \frac{1}{3}B_1 r + \frac{1}{3}B_2 r + \frac{1}{3}B_3 r + \cdots$$

$$= \frac{1}{3}r(B_1 + B_2 + B_3 + \cdots)$$

Now $A_{\text{sphere}} = B_1 + B_2 + B_3 + \cdots$, and so

$$V_{\text{sphere}} = \frac{1}{3}r(A_{\text{sphere}}).$$

Solving this equation for A_{sphere}, we get

$$A_{\text{sphere}} = \frac{3V_{\text{sphere}}}{r}.$$

But $V_{\text{sphere}} = \frac{4}{3}\pi r^3$, and so

$$A_{\text{sphere}} = \frac{3\left(\frac{4}{3}\pi r^3\right)}{r} = 4\pi r^2.$$

Our intuitive argument is only approximately correct. We have been thinking about polygons and pyramids in a situation in which such figures cannot really exist. It is possible, however, to obtain the same result by means of the calculus, without making any of the approximations that we have made.

Theorem 84

The surface area of a sphere is 4π times the square of its radius:
$$A = 4\pi r^2.$$

Exercises

Set I

Earth Shadow. In this painting by Mitsumasa Anno titled *The Shadow of the Earth,* the earth and its shadow have the same radius.

1. How does the length of the earth's equator compare with the circumference of the shadow?

2. How does the area of the earth compare with the area of the shadow?

Black Hole. For our sun to collapse to a "black hole," it would have to be compressed into a sphere with a radius of 1 kilometer.

3. What would its surface area be?

4. What would its volume be?

Suppose another spherical "black hole" has a surface area in square kilometers that is numerically equal to its volume in cubic kilometers.

5. What would its radius be?

6. What would its surface area and volume be?

Archimedes' Discoveries. Archimedes (287–212 B.C.) wrote a book titled *On the Sphere and Cylinder.*

One of his discoveries was about a cone, a hemisphere (half a sphere), and a cylinder that have the same radius and height.

Write an expression in terms of *x* for the volume of

7. the cone.

8. the hemisphere.

9. the cylinder.

10. In what ways are the volumes of these three solids related?

Flatland. Flatland, a science-fiction novel by Edwin A. Abbott, is a story about life in a two-dimensional world.

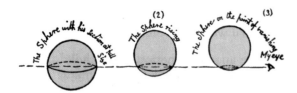

This illustration from the book is of a sphere visiting Flatland. All that Flatland's inhabitants can see is the intersection of the sphere with their plane.

The figure below can be used to explain why they see a circle. Points A and B represent any two points in which sphere O intersects plane P, and OM is perpendicular to plane P.

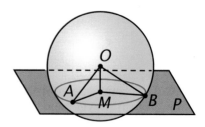

11. Why is OA = OB?

12. Why is OM ⊥ MA and OM ⊥ MB?

13. Why is △OMA ≅ △OMB?

14. Why is MA = MB?

15. What does this equality imply about the curve that is the intersection of sphere O and plane P? Explain.

Sound Wave. According to a book on sound, "when a point source . . . radiates into free space, the intensity of the sound . . . is given by

$$I = \frac{W}{4\pi r^2}$$

where *W* is the power of the source."*

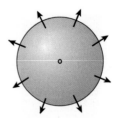

The sound wave being described is spherical in shape.

16. Where is the "point source" with respect to the sphere?

17. What does $4\pi r^2$ measure with respect to the sphere?

———————

*The Science of Sound, by Thomas D. Rossing (Addison-Wesley, 1990).

18. According to the formula, what happens to the intensity of the sound as the radius of the sphere increases?

Volume and Density. Scale drawings of a baseball and a golf ball are shown below.

diameter =
7.4 cm

diameter =
4.3 cm

Find the volume to the nearest cubic centimeter of

19. a baseball.

20. a golf ball.

The density of an object is its mass per unit volume. One cubic centimeter of water has a mass of 1 gram; so its density is $\dfrac{1 \text{ g}}{1 \text{ cm}^3} = 1$ gram per cubic centimeter.

21. Use the fact that a baseball has a mass of 145 g to find its density to the nearest 0.1 g/cm^3.

An object will float if its density is less than that of water; it will sink if its density is more.

22. Will a baseball float on water or sink?

As every golfer knows, a golf ball will sink in water.

23. What can you conclude about its mass?

Chocolate Packing. The photograph below shows 16 chocolates packed in a box.

Compare the side view of the box below with an identical box that contains 2 chocolates having twice the diameter of the chocolates in the original box.

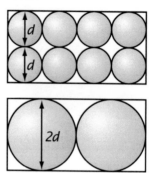

24. Which box do you think contains more chocolate?

25. Find the volume in terms of *d* of chocolate in each box to check your answer.

The chocolates are wrapped in paper.

26. Which box do you think would contain more wrapping paper?

27. Write appropriate expressions in terms of *d* to check your answer.

Set II

Half Sphere. This sculpture by Swiss artist Max Bill is titled *Half Sphere Around Two Axes.*

Write an expression for each of the following measures in terms of *r*, the radius of the half sphere.

28. Its volume.

29. The area of its curved surfaces.

30. The area of its flat surfaces.

31. Its total surface area.

Hollow Earth. A cult once believed that the earth is hollow and that we and the entire universe are inside it.

In the figure below, circle O represents the hollow earth. To every point P outside the earth, there corresponds a point P′ inside the earth such that PT is tangent to circle O and TP′ ⊥ OP.

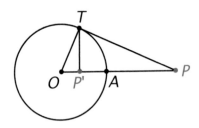

32. What can you conclude about △OTP? Explain.

33. It follows that $\dfrac{OP}{OT} = \dfrac{OT}{OP'}$. Why?

If the moon is at P, the "hollow earth" people thought that it was actually at P′. For the moon, OP ≈ 240,000 miles; the radius of the earth OT ≈ 3,960 miles.

34. Find OP′ to the nearest mile.

35. If we are at point A so that the moon is directly overhead, how far "above" us would the moon in the hollow earth be?

If the sun is at P, OP ≈ 93,000,000 miles.

36. Find OP′ for the sun to the nearest hundred feet. (1 mile = 5,280 feet.)

37. From these results, where do you think the hollow-earth people thought the stars were?

Melting Snowball. A problem in a calculus book begins:

> A spherical snowball is melting in such a way that its volume is decreasing at a rate of 1 cm³ per minute.*

Suppose that the diameter of the snowball before it begins to melt is 12 cm and that the snowball melts at a constant rate. Approximately how many hours would it take for the snowball

38. to melt completely?

39. to shrink to a diameter of 6 cm?

Find the surface area of the snowball to the nearest square centimeter

40. before it begins to melt.

41. when it has shrunk to a diameter of 6 cm.

As the snowball in the problem melts, its volume decreases at a constant rate.

42. Does its diameter decrease at a constant rate? Explain.

43. Does its surface area decrease at a constant rate? Explain.

Earth Under Water. If the earth were perfectly spherical in shape, the water in its oceans would cover its surface to a depth of 1.65 miles.

Using 3,960 miles as the radius of the earth under the water, estimate the volume of the water to the nearest million cubic miles by using the formula for

44. the volume of a sphere.

45. the surface area of a sphere.

———————

*Calculus, by James Stewart (Brooks/Cole, 1995).

Doughnuts. Most doughnuts have the shape of a geometric solid called a *torus.*

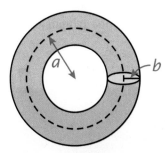

Two expressions for measuring a torus are:

(1) $2\pi^2 ab^2$
(2) $4\pi^2 ab$

One expression is for its surface area and the other is for its volume.

46. Explain how it is possible to tell from these expressions which is which.

47. Which expression would be more appropriate for finding the amount of frosting on a doughnut?

What would happen to the volume of a doughnut if

48. *a* were doubled but *b* stayed the same?

49. *b* were doubled but *a* stayed the same?

Spheres in Different Dimensions. Here are the formulas for the volumes of "spheres" in different dimensions.*

Dimensions	Volume	Dimensions	Volume
1	$2r$	5	$\frac{8}{15}\pi^2 r^5$
2	πr^2		
3	$\frac{4}{3}\pi r^3$	6	$\frac{1}{6}\pi^3 r^6$
4	$\frac{1}{2}\pi^2 r^4$	7	$\frac{16}{105}\pi^3 r^7$

50. Judging from this table, what is our name for a two-dimensional "sphere"?

_____

*Surfing Through Hyperspace: Understanding Higher Universes in Six Easy Lessons, by Clifford A. Pickover (Oxford University Press, 1999).

51. What is our name for its volume?

52. What does the volume of a one-dimensional "sphere" appear to measure?

53. Use the table and your calculator to find the volumes of spheres of radius 1 in each of these dimensions, each to the nearest hundredth.

54. What happens to the volume as the number of dimensions increases?

Set III

In the movie *Raiders of the Lost Ark*, Indiana Jones barely escapes from a huge spherical boulder rolling along a tunnel in an underground cave.[†]

Suppose the boulder, 30 feet in diameter, perfectly fits a square passageway as shown in the cross-sectional view at the right.

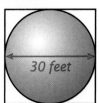

30 feet

1. If you couldn't get out of the tunnel and the boulder were rolling toward you, could you avoid being squashed by it? Explain.

2. Do you think your method would have worked for Indiana Jones?

_____

[†] *The Mammoth Book of Brainstorming Puzzles,* by David J. Bodycombe (Carroll & Graf, 1996).

Similar Solids

Although the *Titanic* was one of the largest ships of its time, the "Titanic" in the picture above is only 44 feet long! The ship in the picture is one of several models of the actual *Titanic* that were constructed for the 1997 movie.

The model is convincing because, like all accurate models, it is similar to the object that it represents. Two geometric solids are *similar* if they have the same shape. For two such solids to be similar, every pair of distances between pairs of corresponding points in the two solids must be proportional.

The actual *Titanic* was about 880 feet long. Comparing its length with 44 feet, the length of the model, we get

$$\frac{880}{44} = 20.$$

The actual ship was 20 times as long as the model. Because the ship and model are similar, the ship must also have been 20 times as wide as the model and 20 times as high.

All these measurements are of *lengths*. What about *areas* and *volumes?* Were the surface area and volume of the *Titanic* also 20 times those of the model? As you may suspect from what you know about similar polygons, the answer is *no.*

To see why, we will consider two similar solids that are polyhedra. If two polyhedra are similar, their corresponding faces are similar; so their corresponding dimensions are proportional. For example, the two rectangular solids shown here are similar if

$$\frac{l_1}{l_2} = \frac{w_1}{w_2} = \frac{h_1}{h_2}.$$

Letting these ratios equal r, we have

$$\frac{l_1}{l_2} = r, \quad \frac{w_1}{w_2} = r, \quad \text{and} \quad \frac{h_1}{h_2} = r,$$

and so

$$l_1 = rl_2, \quad w_1 = rw_2, \quad \text{and} \quad h_1 = rh_2.$$

What is the ratio of the *surface areas* of these solids? Their surface areas are

$$A_1 = 2(l_1w_1 + w_1h_1 + l_1h_1) \quad \text{and} \quad A_2 = 2(l_2w_2 + w_2h_2 + l_2h_2);$$

so

$$\frac{A_1}{A_2} = \frac{2(l_1w_1 + w_1h_1 + l_1h_1)}{2(l_2w_2 + w_2h_2 + l_2h_2)} = \frac{l_1w_1 + w_1h_1 + l_1h_1}{l_2w_2 + w_2h_2 + l_2h_2}.$$

Substituting for l_1, w_1, and h_1, we get

$$\frac{A_1}{A_2} = \frac{(rl_2)(rw_2) + (rw_2)(rh_2) + (rl_2)(rh_2)}{l_2w_2 + w_2h_2 + l_2h_2}$$

$$= \frac{r^2(l_2w_2 + w_2h_2 + l_2h_2)}{l_2w_2 + w_2h_2 + l_2h_2} = r^2. \quad \text{So} \quad \frac{A_1}{A_2} = r^2.$$

The ratio of the surface areas of two similar rectangular solids is equal to the *square* of the ratio of any pair of corresponding dimensions.

What is the ratio of the *volumes* of the same solids? Their volumes are

$$V_1 = l_1w_1h_1 \quad \text{and} \quad V_2 = l_2w_2h_2;$$

so

$$\frac{V_1}{V_2} = \frac{l_1w_1h_1}{l_2w_2h_2}.$$

Substituting for l_1, w_1, and h_1, we get

$$\frac{V_1}{V_2} = \frac{(rl_2)(rw_2)(rh_2)}{l_2w_2h_2} = \frac{r^3(l_2w_2h_2)}{l_2w_2h_2} = r^3. \quad \text{So} \quad \frac{V_1}{V_2} = r^3.$$

The ratio of the volumes of two similar rectangular solids is equal to the *cube* of the ratio of any pair of corresponding dimensions.

These relations can be proved true for *any* pair of solids that are similar, regardless of their shape. We state them as the following useful theorems.

Theorem 85

If the ratio of a pair of corresponding dimensions of two similar solids is r, then the ratio of their surface areas is r^2.

Theorem 86

If the ratio of a pair of corresponding dimensions of two similar solids is r, then the ratio of their volumes is r^3.

These theorems make it easy to compare the properties of two similar solids regardless of their shape. We can apply them, for example, to the actual *Titanic* and the model of it pictured at the beginning of this lesson. From the fact that the ratio of their corresponding dimensions is 20, we can conclude that the ratio of their surface areas is $20^2 = 400$ and the ratio of their volumes is $20^3 = 8,000$.

Although the *Titanic* is 20 times as long as the model, its surface area is 400 times as great and its volume is 8,000 times as great.

Exercises

Set I

Similar or Not? Two geometric solids are similar if they have the same shape.

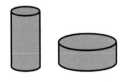

The cylinders above are not similar, because they have different shapes.

Tell whether or not you think the solids in each of the following exercises are always similar. If you think they are not similar, draw a figure to show why.

1. Two cones.

2. Two cubes.

3. Two triangular prisms.

4. Two spheres.

5. Two square pyramids.

Scaling Up. The Statue of Liberty is approximately 20 times life size. In designing it, the sculptor started with a model and scaled it up several times.*

The strength of the supports of a structure depends on its cross-sectional *area*; the weight of a structure depends on its *volume*.

———————
Poetry of the Universe, by Robert Osserman (Anchor Books, 1995).

If the scale of a structure is multiplied by 3, what happens to

6. the strength of its supports?

7. its weight?

If the scale of a structure is multiplied by 20, what happens to

8. the strength of its supports?

9. its weight?

If the scale of a structure is multiplied by *n*, what happens to

10. the strength of its supports?

11. its weight?

Giant Windmill. The windmill below, part of NASA's wind-energy program, has blades 125 feet long that weigh 2,500 pounds.*

NASA proposed to build a larger windmill with blades 400 feet long. If it were geometrically similar to the one in the photograph,

12. how many times longer would the larger blades have been?

13. how many times greater would their surface areas have been?

14. how many times greater would their volumes have been?

15. Approximately how much would one of the blades have weighed?

---

*The Science of Structures and Materials, by J. E. Gordon (Scientific American Library, 1988).

Gulliver in Lilliput. In *Gulliver's Travels* by Jonathan Swift, Gulliver's first voyage took him to Lilliput, a land of tiny people. The emperor of Lilliput decreed that Gulliver was to be given "a quantity of meat and drink sufficient for the support of 1,728 Lilliputians." The emperor's mathematicians had measured Gulliver and found that he was 12 times as tall as they were.

16. How did they calculate the number 1,728 from 12?

17. What did they assume about Gulliver's body with respect to their own bodies?

Later in the story, the emperor's tailors make Gulliver a suit of clothes.

18. If the suit was made from the same fabric as their own, how many times as much material did they need?

Earth and Mars. Mars is smaller than Earth. The radius of Earth is about 3,960 miles, whereas the radius of Mars is 2,100 miles.

19. How many times the radius of Mars is the radius of Earth?

20. How many times the surface area of Mars is the surface area of Earth?

21. How many times the volume of Mars is the volume of Earth?

Olive Sizes. Olives are graded according to their sizes. "Jumbo" olives are about 18 millimeters wide and 23 millimeters long and weigh about 5 grams.

*Side view of a
"giant" olive
shown at actual size*

22. Use your ruler to draw a side view of a jumbo olive.

23. Assuming that all olives are similar in shape, find the width of "supercolossal" olives that are 28 millimeters long.

24. Use your ruler to draw a side view of a supercolossal olive.

25. How many times the volume of a jumbo olive is the volume of a supercolossal olive?

26. How much would you expect a supercolossal olive to weigh?

Three Pyramids. The three pyramids at Giza are right pyramids with square bases. They are thought to have originally had the following dimensions in meters.

Pyramid	Base edge	Height
Cheops	236	147
Chephren	216	144
Mycerinus	109	66

27. Find the ratio of the height to the base edge for each pyramid to the nearest hundredth.

28. Which two pyramids were closest to having the same shape? Explain.

Set II

Doubling a Cube. According to Greek legend, King Minos was unhappy with a tomb that had been built for his son because it was too small. The tomb was in the shape of a cube, and Minos demanded that it be doubled in size.*

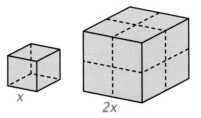

Suppose that each edge of the small tomb had length x and each edge of the new tomb had length $2x$.

Write an expression in terms of x for

29. the total surface area of the small tomb.

30. the total surface area of the new tomb.

31. the volume of the small tomb.

32. the volume of the new tomb.

The ratio of the corresponding dimensions of the tombs (comparing larger with smaller) is

$$\frac{2x}{x} = 2.$$

What is the ratio of

33. their surface areas?

34. their volumes?

What power of the ratio of their corresponding dimensions is the ratio of

35. their surface areas?

36. their volumes?

———————————
An Introduction to the History of Mathematics, by Howard Eves (Saunders, 1990).

Plato's Method. Plato is thought to have considered the figure below with respect to the cube-doubling problem.

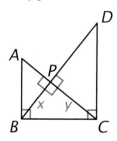

In it, AB ⊥ BC, BC ⊥ CD, and AC ⊥ BD.

37. Why is $\dfrac{PA}{PB} = \dfrac{PB}{PC}$ and $\dfrac{PB}{PC} = \dfrac{PC}{PD}$?

Suppose PA = 1, PB = x, PC = y, and PD = 2.

38. Use this information and the equations in exercise 37 to solve for x and y.

39. Find the volumes of four cubes having edges of lengths PA, PB, PC, and PD.

40. How does the volume of each successively larger cube compare with that of the preceding one?

Suppose that, in the same figure, PA = 1, PB = x, PC = y, and PD = 3.

41. Find x and y in this case.

42. Find the volumes of four cubes having edges of lengths PA, PB, PC, and PD in this case.

43. How does the volume of each successively larger cube compare with that of the preceding one in this case?

Rubber Bands. "Number 10" rubber bands are $1\frac{1}{4}$ inches long and $\frac{1}{16}$ inch wide, and "number 31" rubber bands are $2\frac{1}{2}$ inches long and $\frac{1}{8}$ inch wide.

44. Does it follow from these dimensions that they are geometrically similar? Explain.

45. If it is assumed that the bands are similar in shape, how many number 10 bands would you expect to weigh the same as one number 31 band?

There are 5,780 number 10 bands in a pound and 1,420 number 31 bands in a pound.

46. What conclusions seem to follow from this information?

Two Cups. The figures below show two cups, both partly filled with liquid. One is in the shape of a right cone, and the other is in the shape of a right cylinder.

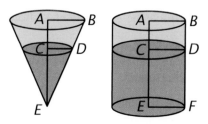

In the left-hand figure, △ABE and △CDE are right triangles.

47. Does it necessarily follow that △ABE ~ △CDE? Explain why or why not.

48. Does the liquid in this cup have a shape geometrically similar to the space enclosed by the cup itself? Explain.

In the right-hand figure, ABFE and CDFE are rectangles.

49. Does it necessarily follow that ABFE ~ CDFE? Explain why or why not.

50. Does the liquid in this cup have a shape geometrically similar to the space enclosed by the cup itself?

Height and Weight. A person's weight is approximately proportional to his or her volume. Suppose that someone is 6 feet tall and weighs 160 pounds.
  About how much would a person similar in shape weigh who is

51. 4 feet tall?

52. 5 feet tall?

53. 7 feet tall?

54. 8 feet tall?

Heated Ring. A piece of solid iron in the shape of a doughnut is expanded by heating.*

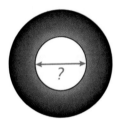

55. Do you think the diameter of its hole will get *larger* or *smaller*?

When the doughnut expands with heat, its shape stays the same.

56. What does this fact indicate about the diameter of its hole? Explain.

Teddy Bear Trouble. Obtuse Ollie's grandmother makes 20 identical teddy bears each month for a local toy shop. To do so, she uses 6 square meters of material for the fur, 5 kilograms of kapok for the stuffing, 4 meters of ribbon for bows around their necks, and 40 buttons for their eyes.

The owners of the toy shop asked her to make 20 bears twice as large; so she doubled the order for all her materials.†

Mathematical Carnival, by Martin Gardner (Knopf, 1975).
†This problem is by Brian Bolt and is from his book titled *Mathematical Cavalcade* (Cambridge University Press, 1992).

57. Do you think doubling the amount of materials makes sense? If not, what do you think she should have ordered?

58. Which material did Ollie's grandmother use up first?

59. How many large bears did she make?

60. Of which material(s) would she have had exactly enough to make 20 of the large bears?

Set III

Colossal Clam. Clams range in size from as little as a pinhead to more than 4 feet in length! If a clam 2.4 inches long weighs 1 ounce, how much would you expect a clam having the same shape and a length of 4 feet to weigh? Explain your reasoning.

Used by permission of Johnny Hart and Creators Syndicate, Inc.

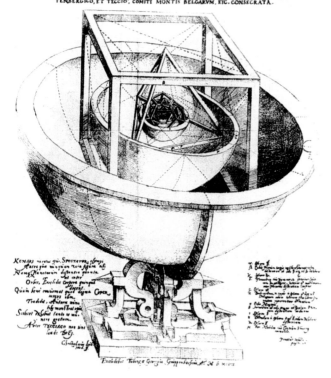

The Regular Polyhedra

Perhaps the most famous picture of geometric solids ever drawn is the above illustration from the book *Mysteries of the Cosmos* published in 1596. The book was written by the astronomer Johannes Kepler and the picture was titled "Model of the Orbits of the Planets." At the time, only six planets were known to exist, and Kepler thought he could explain their number and their distances from the sun by means of five geometric solids known as the *regular polyhedra.* He wrote:

> The orbit of the Earth is a circle: round the sphere to which this circle belongs, describe a *dodecahedron*; the sphere including this will give the orbit of Mars. Round Mars, describe a *tetrahedron*; the circle including this will be the orbit of Jupiter. Describe a *cube* round Jupiter's orbit; the circle including this will be the orbit of Saturn. Now inscribe in the Earth's orbit an *icosahedron*; the circle inscribed in it will be the orbit of Venus. Inscribe an *octahedron* in the orbit of Venus; the circle inscribed in it will be Mercury's orbit. This is the reason of the number of the planets.

The solids to which Kepler referred were the last figures to be included by Euclid in the *Elements*, so it is appropriate to consider them as we come to the end of our study of Euclidean geometry.

Definition
A *regular polyhedron* is a convex solid having faces that are congruent regular polygons and having an equal number of polygons that meet at each vertex.

Tetrahedron

Octahedron

Icosahedron

Cube

Dodecahedron

There are three regular polyhedra whose faces are *equilateral triangles*: the *tetrahedron*, with 4 faces, the *octahedron*, with 8 faces, and the *icosahedron*, with 20 faces.

The most familar regular polyhedron is the one whose faces are *squares*: the *cube*. Finally, there is one regular polyhedron whose faces are *regular pentagons*: the *dodecahedron*, which has 12 faces in all.

Long before Kepler attempted to use them in explaining the solar system and even before Euclid wrote about them, the regular polyhedra were studied by a group of Greek mathematicians under the leadership of Pythagoras. Plato gave instructions for making models of them and claimed that the atoms of the four elements of ancient science had the shape of regular polyhedra. Atoms of fire were thought to have the shape of tetrahedrons; atoms of earth, cubes; atoms of air, octahedrons, and atoms of water, icosahedrons. The universe itself was thought to be in the shape of a dodecahedron.

Although such ideas are no longer taken seriously, the regular polyhedra, also known as the *Platonic solids*, have proved to be important not only in mathematics but also in such fields as molecular chemistry, art, and architecture.

Exercises

Set I

Numbers and Names. Polygons are named according to their number of sides; polyhedra are named according to their number of faces.

What is the number for

1. an octagon or octahedron?

2. a dodecagon or dodecahedron?

What name do you think we commonly use for

3. a tetragon?

4. a regular hexahedron?

If you were to look them up in a dictionary,

you would find *icosahedron* but you probably wouldn't find *icosagon*.

5. What do you think each of these words means?

Two Triangles. In the figure below, the vertices of the smaller triangle are the midpoints of the sides of the larger triangle, but the triangles are not equilateral.

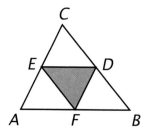

6. Are the two triangles similar?
7. How do the sides of the larger triangle compare in length with the sides of the smaller one?
8. How do the perimeters of the two triangles compare?
9. How do the two triangles compare in area?

Two Tetrahedrons. In the model pictured below, the vertices of the smaller tetrahedron are at the centers of the faces of a larger tetrahedron. Both tetrahedrons are regular.

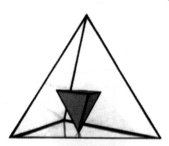

The edges of the larger tetrahedron are three times as long as the edges of the smaller one.

How do the two solids compare in

10. surface area?
11. volume?

da Vinci Polyhedron. Leonardo da Vinci built a set of wooden models of polyhedra and from them created a series of illustrations for a book published in 1509.

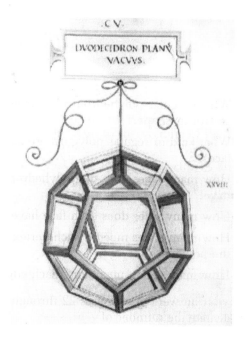

12. Which regular polyhedron did da Vinci illustrate in the picture above?
13. What kind of regular polygons are its faces?
14. How many faces does the polyhedron have?
15. How many sides does each face have?
16. How many faces meet at each vertex of the polyhedron?
17. How many faces meet along each edge?

Compare the following two calculations with your answers to exercises 14 through 17.

$$\frac{12 \times 5}{2} = 30 \qquad \frac{12 \times 5}{3} = 20$$

18. How many vertices does the polyhedron have?
19. How many edges does it have?

Escher Box. Maurits Escher designed the tin box shown here in 1963.

20. Which regular polyhedron did Escher use for its shape?

21. What kind of regular polygons are its faces?

22. How many faces does the polyhedron have?

23. How many sides does each face have?

24. How many faces meet at each vertex of the polyhedron?

25. How many faces meet along each edge?

Use your answers to exercises 22 through 25 to calculate the number of

26. vertices of the polyhedron.

27. edges of the polyhedron.

Euclid's Claim. Euclid claimed at the end of the *Elements* that "no other figure, besides the said five figures, can be constructed which is contained by equilateral and equiangular figures equal to one another."

What did he mean by

28. "equilateral and equiangular figures"?

29. "equal to one another"?

The following figures support Euclid's claim that there are only five regular polyhedra.

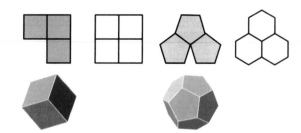

What is the sum of the angles surrounding each vertex of

30. a tetrahedron?

31. an octahedron?

32. an icosahedron?

33. Why are there no more than three regular polyhedra whose faces are equilateral triangles?

What is the sum of the angles surrounding each vertex of

34. a cube?

35. a dodecahedron? (Each angle of a regular pentagon has a measure of 108°.)

36. How does the sum of the angles surrounding a point determine whether a figure is flat?

Set II

Octahedron and Cube. In the model pictured below, the vertices of the octahedron are at the centers of the faces of a cube.

The octahedron can be viewed as consisting of two square pyramids with a common base.

37. Draw and mark the figure below as needed to find each of the following measures in terms of *e*, the length of an edge of the cube.

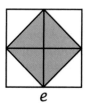

e

38. The length of an edge of the octahedron.

39. The area of the base of one of the pyramids.

40. The altitude of one of the pyramids.

41. The volume of the octahedron.

42. What fraction of the volume of the cube is the volume of the octahedron?

Dodecahedron Construction. Euclid showed how to construct a dodecahedron by starting with a cube. He did so by adding identical "rooflike" shapes to each face of the cube as shown in the figures below.*

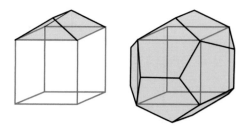

The figure below shows one of the pentagonal faces that is formed.

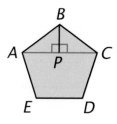

_____
**Euclid: The Creation of Mathematics*, by Benno Artmann (Springer, 1999).

43. Given that BP ⊥ AC, why does it follow that △ABP ≅ △CBP?

44. Use the fact that each angle of a regular pentagon has a measure of 108° to find the measures of ∠ABP and ∠BAP.

45. Find the ratio of the edge of the cube, AC, to the edge of the dodecahedron, AB, to the nearest thousandth.

If AC = 1 unit, the volume of each of the added rooflike shapes is about 0.135 cubic unit.

46. Find the ratio of the volume of the dodecahedron to the volume of the cube.

Round About. The first figure below is an illustration of the fact that every regular polygon is cyclic.

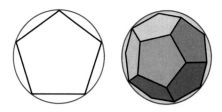

47. What does saying that a "polygon is cyclic" mean?

The second figure illustrates a comparable fact for regular polyhedra.

48. What do you think the fact is?

Suppose regular polygons having 12 and 20 sides are inscribed in the same circle.

49. Which one has an area closer to that of the circle?

Suppose regular polyhedra having 12 and 20 faces are inscribed in the same sphere.

50. Which one do you think has an area closer to that of the sphere?

Suppose the sphere in which they are inscribed has a radius of 1 unit.

51. Find its area to the nearest tenth.

A dodecahedron inscribed in this sphere has edges of length

$$e = \frac{1}{3}(\sqrt{15} - \sqrt{3}).$$

52. Find e to the nearest thousandth.

The area of a regular dodecahedron with edges of length e is

$$3e^2\sqrt{5(5 + 2\sqrt{5})}.$$

53. Find the area of the dodecahedron to the nearest tenth.

An icosahedron inscribed in the same sphere has edges of length

$$e = \frac{1}{5}\sqrt{10(5 - \sqrt{5})}.$$

54. Find e to the nearest thousandth.

The area of a regular icosahedron with edges of length e is

$$5e^2\sqrt{3}.$$

55. Find the area of the icosahedron to the nearest tenth.

56. Which polyhedron, the dodecahedron or the icosahedron, do you think has a *volume* closer to that of the sphere?

57. Find the volume of the sphere to the nearest tenth.

A regular dodecahedron having edges of length e has the following volume:

$$\frac{1}{4}e^3(15 + 7\sqrt{5}).$$

58. Find the volume of the dodecahedron inscribed in this sphere to the nearest tenth.

A regular icosahedron having edges of length e has the following volume:

$$\frac{5}{12}e^3(3 + \sqrt{5}).$$

59. Find the volume of the icosahedron inscribed in the same sphere to the nearest tenth.

60. Which inscribed polyhedron has an area and volume closer to those of the sphere: the dodecahedron or the icosahedron?

Set III

Tetrahedron Puzzle. A puzzle patented in 1940 has become so popular that it is still available for sale. It consists of two identical pieces that can be put together to form a tetrahedron.*

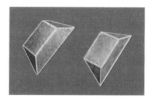

To make the puzzle, make two copies of the pattern below on stiff paper and cut them out. Fold each one along the red lines and tape the edges of each together to form a pair of identical solids.

Can you put the two solids together to form a tetrahedron? If so, make a drawing to show your solution.

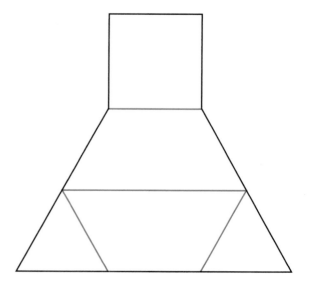

*Puzzles Old and New, by Jerry Slocum and Jack Botermans (University of Washington Press, 1986).

Basic Ideas

Altitude of a prism   640
Altitude of a pyramid   648
Cone   654
Cross section of a solid   641
Cube   629
Cylinder   655
Diagonal of a rectangular solid   629
Dodecahedron   678
Icosahedron   678
Lateral area of a prism   635
Oblique lines and planes   620
Octahedron   678
Parallel lines and planes   619
Perpendicular lines and planes   620
Polyhedron   628
Prism   634
Pyramid   647
Rectangular solid   628
Regular polyhedron   678
Similar solids   670
Skew lines   619
Sphere   662
Tetrahedron   678
Volume   640

Postulates

11. If two points lie in a plane, the line that contains them lies in the plane.   619

12. If two planes intersect, they intersect in a line.   619

13. *Cavalieri's Principle.* Consider two geometric solids and a plane. If every plane parallel to this plane that intersects one of the solids also intersects the other so that the resulting cross sections have equal areas, then the two solids have equal volumes.   641

14. The volume of any prism is the product of the area of its base and its altitude:
$V = Bh.$ 642

Theorems

79. The length of a diagonal of a rectangular solid with dimensions l, w, and h is
$\sqrt{l^2 + w^2 + h^2}.$ 629

Corollary. The length of a diagonal of a cube with edges of length e is $e\sqrt{3}.$ 629

Corollary 1 to Postulate 14. The volume of a rectangular solid is the product of its length, width, and height: $V = lwh.$ 642

Corollary 2 to Postulate 14. The volume of a cube is the cube of its edge: $V = e^3.$ 642

80. The volume of any pyramid is one-third of the product of the area of its base and its altitude: $V = \frac{1}{3}Bh.$ 648

81. The volume of a cylinder is the product of the area of its base and its altitude:
$V = Bh = \pi r^2 h.$ 655

82. The volume of a cone is one-third of the product of the area of its base and its altitude: $V = \frac{1}{3}Bh = \frac{1}{3}\pi r^2 h.$ 656

83. The volume of a sphere is $\frac{4}{3}\pi$ times the cube of its radius: $V = \frac{4}{3}\pi r^3.$ 664

84. The surface area of a sphere is 4π times the square of its radius: $A = 4\pi r^2.$ 665

85. If the ratio of a pair of corresponding dimensions of two similar solids is r, then the ratio of their surface areas is r^2.   672

86. If the ratio of a pair of corresponding dimensions of two similar solids is r, then the ratio of their volumes is r^3.   672

Exercises

Set I

Flipping Cubes. The sculpture in the photograph below is by Hungarian artist Victor Vasarely.*

Although its surfaces, numbered in the figure below, might seem to lie in 11 different planes, two of them actually lie in the same plane.

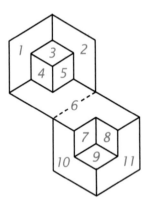

1. Which two are they?
2. If two planes intersect, in what do they intersect?
3. What relation do planes 1 and 2 appear to have?

Symmetry: A Unifying Concept, by István Hargittai and Magdolna Hargittai (Shelter Publications, 1994).

4. Which plane(s) appear to be parallel to plane 5?
5. Does plane 3 appear to be parallel to plane 9?
6. What does saying that two planes are parallel mean?

Seeing Things. The figures below, devised by psychologist Gaetano Kanizsa, are interesting because, although they look almost the same, most people see them as being very different.[†]

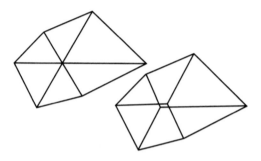

Describe in geometric terms what

7. the first figure looks like to you.
8. the second figure looks like to you.

Cord of Wood. Firewood is sold by the *cord*. A cord is the volume of a stack of wood 8 feet long, 4 feet wide, and 4 feet high.

9. How many cubic feet are contained in a cord?
10. How high would a cord of wood be if it were arranged in a stack 4 feet long and 2 feet wide?

[†] *Visual Intelligence: How We Create What We See*, by Donald D. Hoffman (Norton, 1998).

Box Pattern. The figure below is a pattern that can be cut out and folded together to form a box.* It contains six squares and two regular hexagons.

11. If the pattern is made into a box, which polygons would be its bases?

12. What kind of polyhedron would it be?

Octagonal Building. Two geometric solids were used in the design of this building in Florence, Italy. Both of them have bases that are regular octagons.

13. What are the two solids?

14. Find the volume of the lower part, given that it covers 12,000 square feet of ground and is 90 feet high.

15. Find the volume of the upper part, given that it is 20 feet high.

16. Find the total volume of the building.

The Victorian Gift Boxes, by Jane Thomson (Hearst Books, 1992).

Screen Illumination. In the figure below, light from a lens at point L illuminates two possible screens: a smaller one at A and a larger one at B twice as far away. The screens are the bases of two similar pyramids.

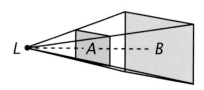

17. How do the edges of the larger screen compare in length with the corresponding edges of the smaller screen?

18. How does the area of the larger screen compare with that of the smaller screen?

According to the inverse-square law of physics, the light on the larger screen would be one-fourth as bright as that on the smaller screen.

19. Explain why this makes sense.

Stars. The circles in the figure below (not to scale) represent cross sections of two imaginary spheres centered at the sun.[†]

Sphere A has a radius of 10 light-years and sphere B has a radius of 5,000 light-years. What is the ratio of

20. the radius of sphere B to that of sphere A?

21. the surface area of sphere B to that of sphere A?

22. the volume of sphere B to that of sphere A?

[†]*Pictorial Astronomy,* by Dinsmore Alter, Clarence H. Cleminshaw, and John G. Phillips (Crowell, 1974).

23. Given that sphere A contains 10 stars, how many stars would you guess sphere B to contain?

Our galaxy is thought to have a volume 100 times that of sphere B.

24. According to this estimate, how many stars might our galaxy contain?

Divided Cube. The figure at the right shows a cube in which a diagonal of each face has been drawn.

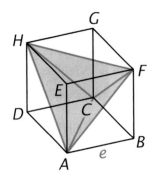

25. Find the length of each diagonal in terms of *e*, the length of an edge.

26. What can you conclude about the four triangles whose sides are these diagonals?

27. Of what regular polyhedron are these triangles the faces?

28. If the cube were cut apart along the planes of the faces of this polyhedron, how many pieces would be formed?

One of the pieces is the pyramid whose base is △ABC and whose altitude is BF.

29. Find its volume in terms of *e*.

30. Find the volume of the polyhedron that you named in exercise 27 in terms of *e*.

31. What fraction of the volume of the cube is the volume of this polyhedron?

Set II

According to Archimedes. In his book titled *On the Sphere and Cylinder*, Archimedes proved the following theorem:

> The surface area of any sphere is equal to four times the area of a great circle of the sphere.

32. What do you think Archimedes meant by "a great circle"?

33. Show why the theorem is true.

The next theorem in Archimedes' book said:

> The volume of any sphere is equal to four times the volume of the cone whose base equals a great circle of the sphere, and whose height equals the radius of the sphere.

34. Use the figure below to show that this theorem is true.

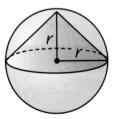

Another of Archimedes' discoveries was about a sphere and a cylinder that have the same radius and height. This figure illustrating it was even engraved on his tombstone!

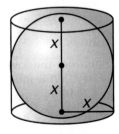

Write an expression in terms of *x* for

35. the volume of the sphere.

36. the volume of the cylinder.

37. What fraction of the volume of the cylinder is the volume of the sphere?

Write an expression in terms of x for

38. the area of the sphere.

39. the lateral area of the cylinder.

40. the total area of the cylinder.

41. How does the area of the sphere compare with the lateral area of the cylinder?

42. What fraction of the total area of the cylinder is the area of the sphere?

Twisted Ring. The "twisted ring" shown below is made from cubes that have been glued together along their faces.*

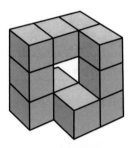

43. How many faces of each cube are glued to faces of other cubes?

Given that the edges of the cubes are 1 unit long,

44. find the volume of the ring.

45. find the surface area of the ring.

SAT Problem. The following description appeared in a problem on an SAT exam.

A closed rectangular tank 1 meter by 2 meters by 4 meters contains 4 cubic meters of water. When the tank is placed level on its various sides, the water depth changes.

Fractal Music, Hypercards, and More, by Martin Gardner (W. H. Freeman and Company, 1992).

Draw and label a sketch showing a position of the tank for which the water is

46. the deepest.

47. the shallowest.

48. What are the depths of the water for these positions?

Wine Barrel. According to Cavalieri, the volume of a wine barrel, such as the one shown below, can be estimated by the expression

$$\frac{1}{3}(2\pi R^2 + \pi r^2)h.$$

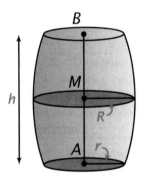

M is the midpoint of its axis, AB.

49. What does πr^2 represent?

50. What does πR^2 represent?

51. What does the wine-barrel expression become if $R = r$?

52. For what type of geometric solid does your answer to exercise 51 give the volume?

53. What does the wine-barrel expression become if $R = 0$?

54. For what type of geometric solid does your answer to exercise 53 give the volume?

55. What does the wine-barrel expression become if $r = 0$ and $h = 2R$?

56. For what type of geometric solid does your answer to exercise 55 give the volume?

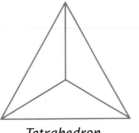
Tetrahedron

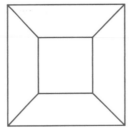
Cube

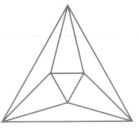
Octahedron

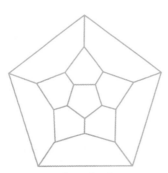
Dodecahedron

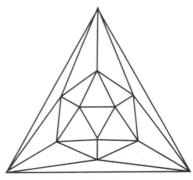
Icosahedron

Euler Characteristic. Victor Schlegel, a German mathematician, invented the diagrams above in 1883 to represent the regular polyhedra. They show the way that the edges of a polyhedron would look if the polyhedron were transparent and you viewed it from a point just above the center of a face. That face appears as the border of the diagram.

Each diagram shows all of the faces, vertices, and edges of the polyhedron.

57. A tetrahedron has four faces. Does the diagram for it contain four triangles?

58. How many vertices does a tetrahedron have?

59. How many edges does it have?

60. Refer to the diagrams to copy and complete the following table.

Regular polyhedron	faces, F	Number of vertices, V	edges, E
Tetrahedron	4	?	?
Cube	6	?	?
Octahedron	?	?	?
Dodecahedron	?	?	?
Icosahedron	?	?	?

The Euler characteristic of a geometric solid is the number $F + V - E$.

61. Find the Euler characteristic for each of the regular polyhedra.

Non-Euclidean Geometries

A remarkable thing happened in the nineteenth century. Mathematicians realized for the first time that there are geometries other than that of Euclid. These geometries are based on different assumptions and lead to theorems that seem to contradict common sense. Nevertheless, these geometries, called non-Euclidean, are logically consistent, and one of them may actually be the correct system for describing our universe!

Used by permission of Johnny Hart and Creators Syndicate, Inc.

LESSON 1

Geometry on a Sphere

Euclid defined parallel lines as "lines that, being in the same plane and being produced indefinitely in both directions, do not meet one another in either direction." In the cartoon above, one of the characters tries to prove that parallel lines never meet by tracing them on the surface of the earth. His two-pronged stick, however, has worn down to a nub by the end of the journey, and so the "parallel lines" have come together to meet in a common point.

Aside from the wearing down of the stick, the cartoon shows a way in which geometry on a sphere differs from the plane geometry that we have been studying. We think of lines as being *straight* and *infinitely long,* but "lines" drawn on the surface of a sphere are *curved* and *finite in extent.* The "plane" on which they are drawn, the surface of the sphere, is not flat but curved and is finite in extent.

Peter, the character in the cartoon who tried to prove that parallel lines never meet by tracing them around the earth, has come back to his starting point. This suggests that he walked "straight ahead," never turning either left or right. Such a path is along a *great circle* of the sphere.

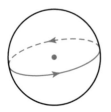

Definition
A *great circle* of a sphere is a set of points that is the intersection of the sphere and a plane containing its center.

From this definition, it follows that a great circle divides the surface of a sphere into two equal parts, called *hemispheres.* The most famous great circle on the earth is the equator, which divides the earth into the northern and southern hemispheres. Other well-known great circles on the earth are the meridians, the circles that pass through the North and South Poles. The Poles, where the axis about which the earth turns intersects the earth's surface, are an example of a pair of *antipodal points.*

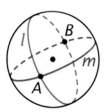

Definition

Antipodal points are the two points of intersection of a sphere with a line through its center.

At the beginning of our study of geometry, we did not define the terms "point," "line," and "plane" but gave them meaning by making postulates about them. Would these postulates still seem reasonable if we changed our ideas of these terms? For example, suppose that, in thinking about geometry on a sphere, we call great circles "lines" and the surface of the sphere a "plane."

Our first postulate said:

Two points determine a line.

If great circles are "lines," the figure at the right suggests that this postulate is no longer true. Lines *l* and *m* intersect in two antipodal points, A and B; so points A and B evidently do *not* determine a line.

Suppose, however, that we consider a pair of antipodal points to be just one "point." (Remember that, as with "line" and "plane," we did not define the term "point".) If we do consider a pair of antipodal points to be just one "point," then our first postulate is true again. Lines *l* and *m* intersect in just one point (called A and B). To determine a line, we need two points–C and D in the next figure at the right.

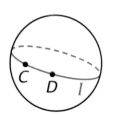

With our new ideas about points and lines comes a surprising result. The last figure on this page represents a point, P, and a line, *l*, that does not contain it. Through P, how many lines can be drawn parallel to line *l*? The answer is *none. Every* great circle of a sphere intersects all other great circles of the sphere!

What does all this mean? It means that we have the beginning of a geometry in which the Parallel Postulate that we have used in the past no longer applies, because, through a point not on a line, there are now *no lines parallel to the line.*

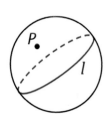

With other changes in our postulates concerning distance and betweenness and this new assumption that there are no parallel lines, we can develop a new geometry with all sorts of unexpected theorems. Although these theorems flatly contradict others that we have proved in our study of geometry, they make sense in regard to the new parallel postulate and in regard to one another. They are part of a *non-Euclidean* geometry. In this chapter, we will become acquainted with the two main non-Euclidean geometries.

Exercises

In the following exercises, we will refer to the geometry that we have been studying throughout the course as *Euclidean* geometry and to our new geometry on a sphere as *sphere* geometry. The surface that we use for our model of sphere geometry is curved in three-dimensional space, but the surface itself is two-dimensional and we will think of it as a "plane."

Set I

Our Spherical Earth. This statue at Rockefeller Center in New York City is of Atlas holding the earth on his shoulders.

The earth is represented by several *great circles*.

1. Where is the center of a great circle of a sphere?

2. What is its radius?

3. Into what does a great circle divide a sphere?

Any two great circles of a sphere intersect in a pair of *antipodal points*.

4. What type of line segment inside a sphere connects two antipodal points?

Basic Differences. The figures below illustrate some simple differences between Euclidean geometry and sphere geometry. Each figure represents three points and a line that contains them.*

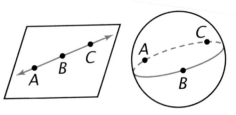

Tell whether each of the following statements seems to be true for one of the geometries (name it) or both of them.

5. Points A, B, and C are collinear.

6. Point B is between points A and C.

7. If AB = BC, then B is the midpoint of AC.

8. AB = BC = AC.

9. AB + BC = AC.

10. If two points lie in a plane, the line that contains them lies in the plane.

11. Point B separates the line into two parts.

Shortest Routes. The figure below from Euclidean geometry shows two points connected by arcs of three circles.

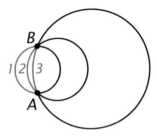

12. Which of the three numbered arcs is the shortest?

13. How does the circle of which the arc is part compare in size with the other two circles?

---

*We take the liberty of using some of the words of Euclidean geometry in sphere geometry without formal definitions when the meaning is clear by analogy or from examples given.

14. From these results, how would you describe the shortest path from A to B in sphere geometry?

15. Why is this part of sphere geometry of interest to the airlines?

Beach Ball. This beach ball has been divided by great circles into congruent triangles.

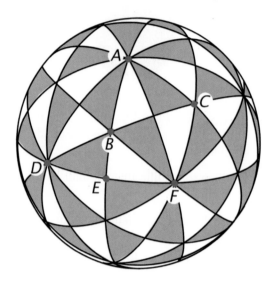

Each triangle is a 36°-60° right triangle.

16. What is the sum of the angles of one of these triangles?

17. Are the acute angles of a right triangle in sphere geometry complementary? Explain.

Find the measures of the angles in each of the following triangles and then find their sums.

18. △ABC.

19. △AEF.

20. △CDF.

21. △ADF.

22. If a triangle in sphere geometry is equiangular, does it also appear to be equilateral?

23. How does the sum of the angles of a triangle in sphere geometry seem to be related to its area?

24. What kind of triangle would you expect to have an angle sum very close to 180°?

Set II

Spherical Triangles. Menelaus, a Greek mathematician, wrote a book on sphere geometry in about 100 A.D. In it, he proved many theorems about spherical triangles.

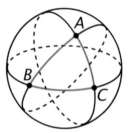

25. What figures are the sides of a triangle in sphere geometry?

Menelaus proved that the Triangle Inequality Theorem of Euclidean geometry is also true in sphere geometry.

26. What does this theorem say?

He proved that, if the angles of one triangle are equal to the angles of another triangle, then the triangles are congruent.

27. Is this statement true in Euclidean geometry? Explain.

Menelaus also proved that the sum of the angles of a triangle in sphere geometry is related to the area of the triangle.

28. What do you think the connection is?

Seemingly Parallel. The figure below seems to show two lines in sphere geometry that are parallel.

29. Why do the two curves seem to be parallel?

Parallel lines do not exist on a sphere; so something is wrong with our thinking about this figure.

30. What is it?

Euclidean and Sphere Geometries. In the figure below, lines AB and AC are both perpendicular to line BC.

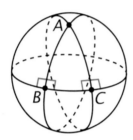

31. In Euclidean geometry, how many lines through a given point in a plane can be perpendicular to a given line in the plane?

32. Is your answer to exercise 31 also true in sphere geometry?

33. In Euclidean geometry, what can be concluded about two lines that form equal corresponding angles with a transversal?

34. Is this conclusion also true in sphere geometry? Explain.

35. In Euclidean geometry, what can be concluded about two lines that lie in a plane and are perpendicular to a third line?

36. Is this conclusion also true in sphere geometry?

37. In Euclidean geometry, what can be concluded about an exterior angle of a triangle with respect to the remote interior angles?

38. Is this conclusion also true in sphere geometry? Explain.

39. In Euclidean geometry, what can be concluded about the sum of the measures of the angles of a triangle?

40. Is this conclusion also true in sphere geometry? Explain.

Wet Paint. Obtuse Ollie's father painted a straight line on the floor of his garage. While the paint was still wet, Ollie rolled his father's bowling ball along the line.

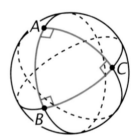

41. In what ways is a line painted on the floor different from a line in Euclidean geometry?

Acute Alice told Ollie that the ball had a line on it.

42. Does Alice's statement make any sense? Explain.

43. What determines the length of a line on a sphere?

Equilateral and Right. A triangle of the type shown in the figure below cannot exist in Euclidean geometry. △ABC is an equilateral right triangle!

In what way is it different from triangles in Euclidean geometry that are

44. equilateral?

45. right?

46. How does the line through B and C compare in length with the sides of △ABC?

Given that the radius of the sphere is 2 units, what is

47. the length of the line through B and C?

48. the perimeter of △ABC?

49. the area of the sphere?

50. the area of △ABC?

Set III

Antipodal Points. If you could dig a hole through the center of the earth from where you are to the opposite side, where would you end up? One way to find out would be to turn a world globe so that your location is at the top and then look at the bottom. Another way would be to use the map below.

1. What do you think the map represents?

2. What does the map show that is rather surprising?

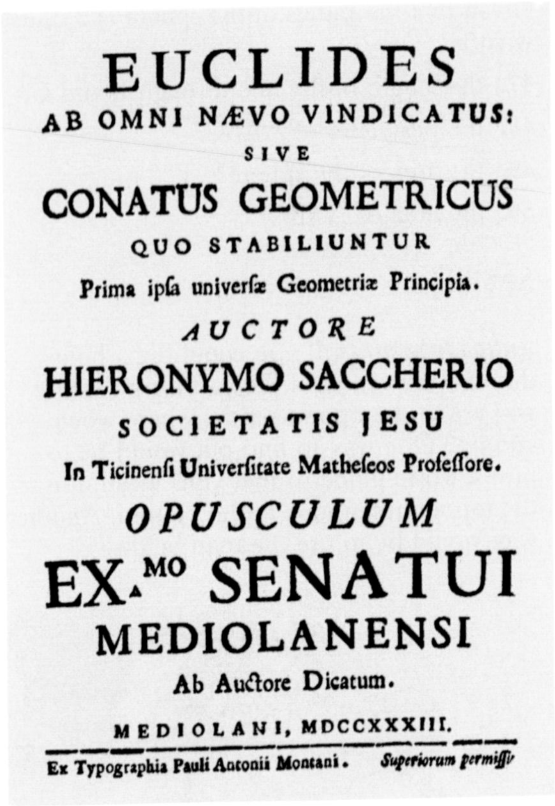

EUCLIDES

AB OMNI NÆVO VINDICATUS:

SIVE

CONATUS GEOMETRICUS

QUO STABILIUNTUR

Prima ipfa univerfæ Geometriæ Principia.

AUCTORE

HIERONYMO SACCHERIO

SOCIETATIS JESU

In Ticinenfi Univerfitate Mathefeos Profeffore.

OPUSCULUM

EX.ᴹᴼ SENATUI

MEDIOLANENSI

Ab Auctore Dicatum.

MEDIOLANI, MDCCXXXIII.

Ex Typographia Pauli Antonii Montani . *Superiorum permiffu*

LESSON 2

The Saccheri Quadrilateral

The most controversial statement in the history of mathematics was made by Euclid near the beginning of the *Elements.* After presenting a series of definitions, Euclid listed five postulates, the last of which said:

If a straight line falling on two straight lines makes the interior angles on the same side less than two right angles, the two straight lines, if produced indefinitely, meet on that side on which are the angles less than the two right angles.

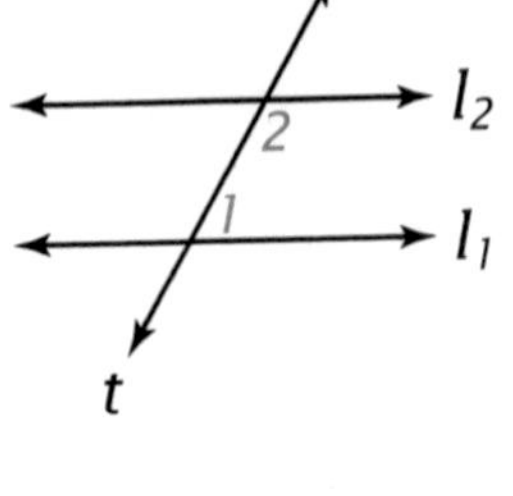

In regard to the figure at the left, this postulate says that, if $\angle 1 + \angle 2 < 180°$, then l_1 and l_2 must eventually intersect in a point on the right side of t.

Euclid's Fifth Postulate was criticized almost immediately, not only because it was much more complicated than the first four postulates, but also because many felt that he could have proved it on the basis of the first four.

A briefer statement that implies Euclid's Fifth Postulate is our Parallel Postulate:

Through a point not on a line, there is exactly one line parallel to the given line.

Among the many people who tried to prove Euclid's Fifth Postulate was an eighteenth-century Italian priest named Girolamo Saccheri. A professor of both philosophy and mathematics, Saccheri tried to use indirect reasoning to establish the postulate as a theorem. As you know, indirect reasoning begins by assuming that the opposite of what you want to prove is true and continues by showing that this assumption leads to a contradiction. In 1733, about 2,000 years after Euclid wrote the *Elements*, Saccheri wrote a book titled *Euclid Freed of Every Flaw*. He intended to prove that Euclidean geometry is the only logically consistent geometry possible.

He began his work with a quadrilateral that has a pair of sides perpendicular to a third side. We will call such a quadrilateral "birectangular."

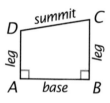

Definition

A *birectangular quadrilateral* is a quadrilateral that has two sides perpendicular to a third side.

The two sides perpendicular to the third side are the *legs*, the side to which they are perpendicular is the *base*, and the side opposite the base is the *summit*. In the first figure at the right, ∠A and ∠B are the *base angles* and ∠C and ∠D are the *summit angles* of quadrilateral ABCD. Also, ∠C is the summit angle opposite leg AD, and ∠D is the summit angle opposite leg BC.

A birectangular quadrilateral whose legs are equal might be called "isosceles," but it is usually called a *Saccheri quadrilateral* in honor of Saccheri.

A Saccheri
quadrilateral

Definition

A *Saccheri quadrilateral* is a birectangular quadrilateral whose legs are equal.

A Saccheri quadrilateral looks very much like a rectangle; that is, the summit angles look as if they must also be right angles, from which it follows that the figure is equiangular. It is easy to prove that this is so in Euclidean geometry. In a geometry with a different postulate about parallel lines, however, it can be proved that a Saccheri quadrilateral is *not* a rectangle, because its summit angles are not right angles!

Before we look into these ideas further, we will state some theorems about birectangular quadrilaterals that are true in both Euclidean and non-Euclidean geometries. Each of them can be proved without using the Parallel Postulate, and their proofs are considered in the exercises. In the next lesson, we will use these theorems to derive some strange results that Saccheri obtained.

Theorem 87

The summit angles of a Saccheri quadrilateral are equal.

Theorem 88

The line segment connecting the midpoints of the base and summit of a Saccheri quadrilateral is perpendicular to both of them.

The next two theorems are comparable to a pair of theorems about inequalities in triangles that you already know.

Theorem 89

If the legs of a birectangular quadrilateral are unequal, the summit angles opposite them are unequal in the same order.

Theorem 90

If the summit angles of a birectangular quadrilateral are unequal, the legs opposite them are unequal in the same order.

Exercises

Set I

Wyoming. The boundary of Wyoming mapped on a plane can be thought of as a Saccheri quadrilateral whose base, YO, is its southern border.

1. What are sides WY and MO called with respect to quadrilateral WYOM?

2. What are ∠Y and ∠O called?

3. What is WM called?

4. What are ∠W and ∠M called?

5. Which sides of WYOM are equal?

6. Which angles of WYOM are right angles?

Complete the proofs of the following theorems of this lesson by giving the reasons.

Theorem 87. The summit angles of a Saccheri quadrilateral are equal.

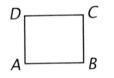 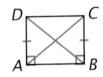

Given: Saccheri quadrilateral ABCD with base AB.
Prove: ∠C = ∠D.

Proof
7. Draw AC and BD. Why?

8. AD = BC. Why?

9. ∠BAD = ∠ABC. Why?

10. △BAD ≅ △ABC. Why?

11. BD = AC. Why?

12. △BCD ≅ △ADC. Why?

13. ∠BCD = ∠ADC. Why?

Theorem 89. If the legs of a birectangular quadrilateral are unequal, the summit angles opposite them are unequal in the same order.

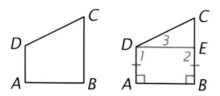

Given: Birectangular quadrilateral ABCD with base AB, CB > DA.
Prove: ∠D > ∠C.

Proof

Because ABCD is a birectangular quadrilateral with base AB, DA ⊥ AB and CB ⊥ AB. Also, CB > DA.

14. Choose point E on BC so that BE = AD. Why?

15. Draw DE. Why?

16. ABED is a Saccheri quadrilateral. Why?

17. ∠1 = ∠2. Why?

18. Because ∠ADC = ∠1 + ∠3, ∠ADC > ∠1. Why?

19. ∠ADC > ∠2. Why?

20. ∠2 > ∠C. Why?

21. ∠ADC > ∠C. Why?

Theorem 90. If the summit angles of a birectangular quadrilateral are unequal, the legs opposite them are unequal in the same order.

Given: Birectangular quadrilateral ABCD with base AB, ∠D > ∠C.
Prove: CB > DA.

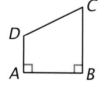

Proof (by the indirect method)

22. Either CB > DA, CB = DA, or CB < DA. Why?

Suppose CB = DA.

23. If CB = DA, what kind of quadrilateral is ABCD?

24. If your answer to exercise 23 is true, then ∠D = ∠C. Why?

25. What does this conclusion contradict?

Suppose CB < DA.

26. If CB < DA, then ∠D < ∠C. Why?

27. What does this conclusion contradict?

28. What is the only remaining conclusion about CB and DA?

Set II

Nasir Eddin. One of the many people who have tried to prove Euclid's Fifth Postulate was a Persian mathematician who was the court astronomer of the grandson of the famous Genghis Khan. His name was Nasir Eddin and he lived in the thirteenth century.

Nasir Eddin began by supposing that *l* and *m* are two lines such that perpendiculars from A and C to line *m* make ∠1 ≠ ∠2 and ∠3 ≠ ∠4.

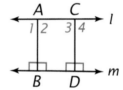

29. If ∠1 and ∠3 are acute and ∠2 and ∠4 are obtuse, which segment must be longer: AB or CD?

30. Why?

Complete the following proof of Theorem 88 by giving the reasons.

Theorem 88. The line segment connecting the midpoints of the base and summit of a Saccheri quadrilateral is perpendicular to both of them.

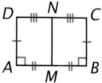

Given: Saccheri quadrilateral ABCD with MN connecting the midpoints of AB and CD.
Prove: MN ⊥ AB and MN ⊥ DC.

Proof
First, draw DM and CM.

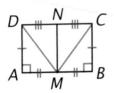

31. How can you conclude that DM = CM?

32. DN = CN. Why?

33. It follows that MN ⊥ DC. Why?

Next, draw AN and BN.

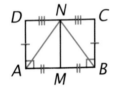

34. How can you conclude that AN = BN?

35. It follows that MN ⊥ AB. Why?

Polish Flag. The flag of Poland is shown in the figure below.

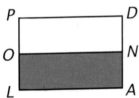

36. Copy the figure and mark the following information on it: PD = LA, ∠P and ∠L are right angles, O is the midpoint of PL, and N is the midpoint of DA.

Assuming *only* the information that you have marked on the figure and nothing about parallel lines, answer each of the following questions.

37. What kind of quadrilateral is PLAD?

38. Which side is its summit?

39. Why is ∠D = ∠A?

40. Why is ON ⊥ PL and ON ⊥ DA?

41. What kind of quadrilaterals are OPDN and LONA?

Alter Ego. In Euclidean geometry, it is easy to prove that a Saccheri quadrilateral is a rectangle.

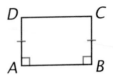

42. In Euclidean geometry, why would the legs of a Saccheri quadrilateral have to be parallel?

43. Why does it follow that a Saccheri quadrilateral is a parallelogram in Euclidean geometry?

44. Why does it follow that its summit angles are right angles?

45. Why does it follow that it is a rectangle?

46. In Euclidean geometry, what relations does the summit of a Saccheri quadrilateral have to its base?

Irregular Lots. The figure below shows an overhead view of two slightly irregular lots.

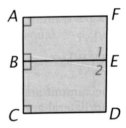

The angles at A, B, and C are right angles but the angles at D, E, and F are not; ∠1 > ∠F and ∠D > ∠2.

47. What can you conclude about the relative lengths of AF and CD? Explain.

48. If A-B-C and F-E-D, what can you conclude about the relative sizes of ∠F and ∠D? Explain.

Set III

Offsets. The jog in this road in Castleton, North Dakota, is caused by a basic problem in geometry.*

The figure at the right illustrates what the problem is. Each quadrilateral represents a "township," a unit of land used by surveyors. A township is supposedly bounded by a square measuring 6 miles on each side. If its sides lie along map directions as in the diagram, a township is effectively bounded by a Saccheri quadrilateral. The road from B to J has a jog in it from E to F.

1. Are the legs of these Saccheri quadrilaterals parallel? Explain why or why not.

Each side marked with a tick mark is 6 miles long, and DF = FH = 6 miles.

2. How do you think the summits of these quadrilaterals compare in length with their bases? Explain.

3. How do you think the summits change as the townships continue farther north?

Taking Measures Across the American Landscape, by James Corner and Alex S. MacLean (Yale University Press, 1996).

The Geometries of Lobachevsky and Riemann

Saccheri thought that he could use his quadrilaterals to prove the Parallel Postulate. Having shown that the summit angles are equal, he planned to prove indirectly that they must also be right angles. To do so, he had to eliminate the possibilities of them being either acute or obtuse.

Saccheri managed to arrive at a contradiction by assuming that the summit angles are obtuse. Rather than being able to eliminate the possibility that they are acute, however, he ended up creating the beginning of a geometry that is non-Euclidean, that is, a geometry with a different assumption about parallel lines. Saccheri missed the implications of what he had started, and so he named his book *Euclid Freed of Every Flaw*. A better name would have been *A New Kind of Geometry*.

Saccheri died in 1733, a few months after his book was published. It was nearly a century later before anyone began to realize that geometries different from Euclid's made logical sense. Three men independently reached this conclusion: the great German mathematician Carl Friedrich Gauss; a Hungarian, Janos Bolyai; and a Russian, Nicolai Lobachevsky.

The assumption that Saccheri couldn't disprove–that is, that the summit angles of a Saccheri quadrilateral are acute–is the "acute angle" hypothesis. The non-Euclidean geometry based on this hypothesis is often called *Lobachevskian geometry*, the name that we will use.

The Lobachevskian Postulate
The summit angles of a Saccheri quadrilateral are acute.

With the use of this postulate, the following theorems can be proved in Lobachevskian geometry.

Lobachevskian Theorem 1
The summit of a Saccheri quadrilateral is longer than its base.

Lobachevskian Theorem 2
A midsegment of a triangle is less than half as long as the third side.

Nicolai Lobachevsky
(1793–1856)

These theorems are false in Euclidean geometry. They contradict the theorems of Euclid that are *based on the Parallel Postulate.* The Parallel Postulate states that, through a point not on a line, there is exactly one line parallel to the given line. For the theorems stated above to hold in Lobachevskian geometry, it must be true that, through a point not on a line, there are many lines parallel to the line!

In Lesson 1, you learned that, in sphere geometry, there are *no* parallels to a line through a point not on it. However, this result contradicts other Euclidean theorems proved *before* the introduction of the Parallel Postulate. In fact, it is equivalent to assuming that the summit angles of a Saccheri quadrilateral are *obtuse*, which is why Saccheri was able to eliminate this possibility.

Nevertheless, if some other postulates related to distance and betweenness are changed in addition to the Parallel Postulate, a logically consistent non-Euclidean geometry can be developed in which there are no parallels at all. A German mathematician, Bernhard Riemann, was the first to understand this concept. We will refer to the geometry that he created as *Riemannian geometry*.

The basic differences between Euclidean geometry and these two non-Euclidean geometries are summarized in the table below. In each case, either statement can be proved to be a logical consequence of the other.

Bernhard Riemann
(1826–1866)

Statement	Euclid	Lobachevsky	Riemann
Through a point not on a line, there is	*exactly one line* parallel to the line.	*more than one line* parallel to the line.	*no line* parallel to the line.
The summit angles of a Saccheri quadrilateral are	*right.*	*acute.*	*obtuse.*

Exercises

We restrict our proofs to Lobachevskian geometry because, in this geometry, only the Parallel Postulate is changed. For this reason you can use any idea considered before Chapter 6 in this book.

Set I

Complete the proofs of the theorems of this lesson by giving the reasons. (Some of the sides of the figures have been drawn as curves to make the figures look non-Euclidean.)

Lobachevskian Theorem 1. The summit of a Saccheri quadrilateral is longer than its base.

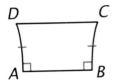

Given: Saccheri quadrilateral ABCD with base AB.
Prove: DC > AB.

Proof
Because ABCD is a Saccheri quadrilateral with base AB, DA ⊥ AB and CB ⊥ AB. Therefore, ∠A and ∠B are right angles, and so ∠A = ∠B = 90°.

1. ∠D and ∠C are acute. Why?
2. ∠D < 90° and ∠C < 90°. Why?
3. ∠D < ∠A and ∠C < ∠B. Why?

Let M and N be the midpoints of AB and DC as shown in the second figure.

4. What permits us to let M and N be these midpoints?
5. What permits us to draw MN?
6. MN ⊥ AB and MN ⊥ DC. Why?
7. AMND and BMNC are birectangular quadrilaterals. Why?

We have proved that ∠D < ∠A and ∠C < ∠B.

8. It follows that DN > AM and NC > MB. Why?
9. DN + NC > AM + MB. Why?
10. DC > AB. Why?

Lobachevskian Theorem 2. A midsegment of a triangle is less than half as long as the third side.

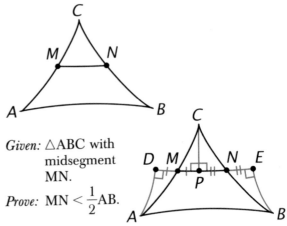

Given: △ABC with midsegment MN.
Prove: $MN < \frac{1}{2}AB$.

Proof
Through C, draw CP ⊥ MN. Choose points D and E on line MN so that MD = MP and NE = NP. Draw AD and BE.

11. △ADM ≅ △CPM and △BEN ≅ △CPN. Why?
12. AD = CP and BE = CP. Why?
13. AD = BE. Why?

Angles D and E are right angles because they are equal to the right angles at P; so AD ⊥ DE and BE ⊥ DE.

14. ADEB is a Saccheri quadrilateral. Why?
15. AB > DE. Why?

Because DE = DM + MP + PN + NE, MP = DM, and PN = NE, it follows that DE = MP + MP + PN + PN = 2MP + 2PN = 2(MP + PN).

16. DE = 2MN. Why?
17. AB > 2MN. Why?
18. $\frac{1}{2}AB > MN$, so $MN < \frac{1}{2}AB$. Why?

Set II

Lobachevsky and His Geometry. This stamp is one of two Russian stamps issued in honor of Nicolai Lobachevsky.

19. Can you guess what any of the words on the stamp mean?

Rewrite each of the following sentences from Euclidean geometry so that it is true in Lobachevskian geometry.

20. Through a point not on a line, there is exactly one line parallel to the line.

21. The summit angles of a Saccheri quadrilateral are right.

22. The summit of a Saccheri quadrilateral is equal to its base.

23. A midsegment of a triangle is half as long as the third side.

Lobachevskian Quadrilateral. ACDF is a quadrilateral in Lobachevskian geometry.

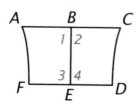

24. Copy the figure and mark the following information on it: AF ⊥ FD, CD ⊥ FD, AB = BC, FE = ED, and AF = CD.

25. What kind of quadrilateral is ACDF?

26. What kind of angles are ∠A and ∠C? Explain.

27. What kind of angles are ∠1, ∠2, ∠3, and ∠4? Explain.

28. What kind of quadrilaterals are ABEF and CBED?

29. Why is BE < AF and BE < CD?

30. State a theorem in Lobachevskian geometry about the length of the line segment that connects the midpoints of the summit and base of a Saccheri quadrilateral.

Riemannian Quadrilateral. The sphere geometry that we studied in Lesson 1 helps us understand Riemannian geometry because there are no parallel lines in either.

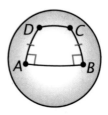

The figure above shows a Saccheri quadrilateral on a sphere.

31. What kind of angles do ∠D and ∠C seem to be?

32. Does your answer agree with the table on page 703?

33. How do DC and AB seem to compare in length?

34. State a theorem in Riemannian geometry that you think corresponds to Lobachevskian Theorem 1.

Riemannian Triangle. The figure below shows a triangle on a sphere; MN is one of the triangle's midsegments.

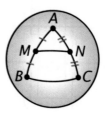

35. State a theorem in Riemannian geometry that you think corresponds to Lobachevskian Theorem 2.

36. Do you think that a midsegment of a triangle in Riemannian geometry is parallel to the third side of the triangle? Explain.

Triangular Pyramid. In the pattern below, B, D, and F are the midpoints of the sides of equilateral △ACE. The pattern can be folded to form a triangular pyramid whose properties depend on whether it is Euclidean or non-Euclidean.

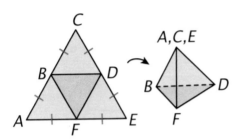

37. In Euclidean geometry, how do the edges of the pyramid compare in length with the sides of △ACE?

38. What can you conclude about the faces of the pyramid?

In Lobachevskian geometry, the pyramid formed by folding the pattern is slightly different.

39. How do the edges of its base, △BDF, compare in length with the sides of △ACE?

40. What can you conclude about its faces?

Open Box. The pattern below can be folded to form an open box in Euclidean geometry.

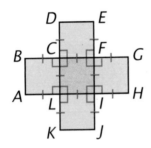

41. On the basis of the marked parts, what special shape would the box have?

42. What can you conclude about its faces?

We can show that such a pattern is impossible in Lobachevskian geometry.

43. What kind of quadrilaterals are the four faces shown in yellow?

44. How would AB, DE, GH, and JK compare in length with the sides of CFIL in Lobachevskian geometry?

45. What special type of quadrilateral is CFIL?

46. Why can't such a quadrilateral exist in Lobachevskian geometry?

Set III

Pseudosphere. The photograph below is of a model of a *pseudosphere*, a surface invented by the Italian geometer Eugenio Beltrami.*

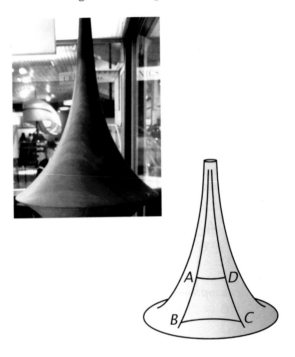

The surface of a pseudosphere can be used to represent a part of a plane in Lobachevskian geometry. In the figure above, ABCD is a Saccheri quadrilateral.

What conclusions can you draw about the figure?

Beyond the Third Dimension: Geometry, Computer Graphics, and Higher Dimensions, by Thomas F. Banchoff (Scientific American Library, 1990).

The Triangle Angle Sum Theorem Revisited

We live in a mysterious universe. Before Einstein and relativity, physical space was assumed to be Euclidean. In the nineteenth century, mathematicians realized that the geometry of Euclid is not the only one possible, but none of them would have guessed that a non-Euclidean geometry might better describe the universe. Yet Einstein's theory of relativity and the experiments confirming it suggest that a geometry other than Euclid's does.*

At about the time that Lobachevsky and Bolyai were developing the non-Euclidean geometry to which we have been referring as Lobachevskian, Karl Friedrich Gauss measured the angles of a huge triangle. You know that, in Euclidean geometry, the sum of the angles of a triangle is exactly 180°. According to the geometry of Lobachevsky, it is *less* than 180°, whereas, in Riemannian geometry, it is *more* than 180°.

Albert Einstein
(1879–1955)

---

*For more information about the possible geometries of space, see *Einstein's Legacy*, by Julian Schwinger (Scientific American Library, 1986).

The sides of the triangle that Gauss measured were formed by light rays sent between three mountain tops in Germany. The sum of the angles of the triangle turned out to be just a few seconds more than 180°. Gauss's measurements were as accurate as was possible at the time, but Gauss understood that the fact that the sum was slightly more than 180° could have been due to experimental error. Indeed, Gauss knew that the mountain-top triangle was much too small to determine whether physical space is non-Euclidean, even though the lengths of its sides ranged from 43 to 66 miles. According to both Lobachevskian and Riemannian geometry, the smaller the triangle, the closer the sum of the measures of its angles is to 180°. If space can be described by either of these non-Euclidean geometries, then a triangle with three stars as its vertices, rather than three mountain tops, would be required to determine which model is correct.

One of the consequences of the fact that the sum of the measures of the angles of a triangle in the non-Euclidean geometries is not 180° is that scale models cannot exist in these geometries. In other words, if two figures are not the same size, they cannot have the same shape!

It is no wonder that, with such surprising results as these, it took a long time for the non-Euclidean geometries to be taken seriously. We know enough about Lobachevskian geometry to be able to prove theorems that cover these observations.

Lobachevskian Theorem 3
The sum of the angles of a triangle is less than 180°.

Corollary to Lobachevskian Theorem 3
The sum of the angles of a quadrilateral is less than 360°.

Lobachevskian Theorem 4
If two triangles are similar, they must also be congruent.

Gauss, the mathematician who measured the triangle on the mountain tops, was probably the first person in history to realize that the geometry of Euclid and the geometry of our universe are not necessarily the same. At the time of the development of Lobachevskian geometry, Gauss wrote to a friend: "I am becoming more and more convinced that the necessity of our [Euclidean] geometry cannot be proved, at least not by human reason." With regard to the fact that the theorems of the non-Euclidean geometries seem to be absurd, he wrote:

> It seems to me that we know . . . too little, or too nearly nothing at all, about the true nature of space, to consider as *absolutely impossible* that which appears to us unnatural.

In the twentieth century, British scientist J. B. S. Haldane observed that the universe may not be only stranger than we imagine, but it may be stranger than we *can* imagine.

Exercises

Set I

Complete the proofs of the theorems of this lesson by answering the questions.

Lobachevskian Theorem 3. The sum of the angles of a triangle is less than 180°.

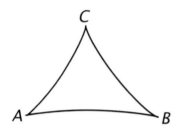

Given: △ABC.
Prove: ∠A + ∠B + ∠C < 180°.

Proof

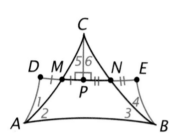

Let M and N be the midpoints of sides AC and BC, and draw MN. Through C, draw CP ⊥ MN. Choose points D and E on line MN so that MD = MP and NE = NP. Draw AD and BE.

1. △ADM ≅ △CPM and △BEN ≅ △CPN. Why?
2. Which angles of ADEB are right angles?
3. Which sides of ADEB are equal?
4. What kind of quadrilateral is ADEB?
5. ∠DAB and ∠EBA are acute. Why?
6. What can be concluded about ∠DAB + ∠EBA from the fact that ∠DAB < 90° and ∠EBA < 90°?

Because ∠DAB = ∠1 + ∠2 and ∠EBA = ∠3 + ∠4, it follows that ∠1 + ∠2 + ∠3 + ∠4 < 180°.

7. To which angles in the figure are ∠1 and ∠4 equal?
8. Why is ∠5 + ∠2 + ∠3 + ∠6 < 180°?
9. Why does it follow from this that ∠CAB + ∠CBA + ∠ACB < 180°?

Corollary to Lobachevskian Theorem 3. The sum of the angles of a quadrilateral is less than 360°.

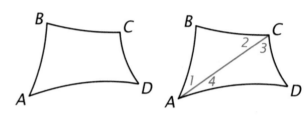

Given: Quadrilateral ABCD.
Prove: ∠A + ∠B + ∠C + ∠D < 360°.

Proof
Draw AC.

10. ∠1 + ∠2 + ∠B < 180° and ∠3 + ∠4 + ∠D < 180°. Why?
11. ∠1 + ∠2 + ∠B + ∠3 + ∠4 + ∠D < 360°. Why?
12. ∠1 + ∠4 = ∠BAD and ∠2 + ∠3 = ∠BCD. Why?
13. ∠BAD + ∠B + ∠BCD + ∠D < 360°. Why?

Lobachevskian Theorem 4. If two triangles are similar, they must also be congruent.

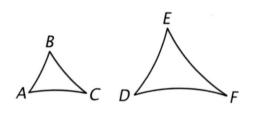

Given: △ABC ~ △DEF.
Prove: △ABC ≅ △DEF.

Proof
By hypothesis, △ABC ~ △DEF.

14. Why is ∠D = ∠A, ∠E = ∠B, and ∠F = ∠C?

Our proof will be indirect. Suppose that △ABC and △DEF are not congruent. If this is the case, then BA ≠ ED and BC ≠ EF, because, if either pair of these sides were equal, then the triangles would be congruent by ASA.

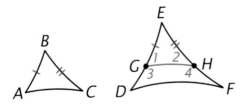

We will now copy the smaller triangle on the larger one as shown above. Choose point G on ED so that EG = BA and point H on EF so that EH = BC. Draw GH.

15. Why is △GEH ≅ △ABC?

It follows that ∠1 = ∠A and ∠2 = ∠C because they are corresponding parts of these triangles.

16. Why is ∠D = ∠1 and ∠F = ∠2?

17. Why is ∠1 + ∠3 = 180° and ∠2 + ∠4 = 180°?

18. Why is ∠1 + ∠2 + ∠3 + ∠4 = 360°?

19. Why is ∠D + ∠F + ∠3 + ∠4 = 360°?

20. If we assume from the figure that DGHF is a quadrilateral, the equation in Exercise 19 is impossible. Why?

Because we have arrived at a contradiction, our assumption that △ABC and △DEF are not congruent is false! So △ABC ≅ △DEF.

Set II

Lobachevskian Triangles. In Lobachevskian geometry, the sum of the angles of every triangle is less than 180°. The larger the triangle's area, the smaller the angle sum is.
    Use these facts to decide on answers to the following questions about triangles in Lobachevskian geometry.

21. If two angles of one triangle are equal to two angles of another triangle, can you

conclude that the angles of the third pair are equal? Explain.

22. What can you conclude about the acute angles of a right triangle?

23. What can you conclude about the measure of each angle of an equilateral triangle?

24. How does the measure of each angle of an equilateral triangle depend on the lengths of its sides?

Triangle on a Sphere. The figure below illustrates an isosceles △ABC with AB = AC on a sphere.

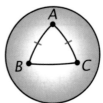

On the basis of the figure, what

25. seems to be true about ∠B and ∠C?

26. seems to be true about ∠A + ∠B + ∠C?

27. kind of geometry seems to be illustrated?

Triangle on a Pseudosphere. The figure below illustrates an isosceles △ABC with AB = AC on a pseudosphere.

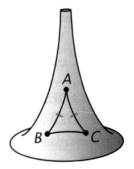

On the basis of the figure, what

28. seems to be true about ∠B and ∠C?

29. seems to be true about ∠A + ∠B + ∠C?

30. kind of geometry seems to be illustrated?

Exterior Angles. In the figure below, △ABC represents a triangle in Lobachevskian geometry and ∠1 is one of its exterior angles.

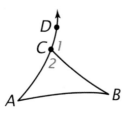

In both Euclidean geometry and Lobachevskian geometry, ∠1 > ∠A and ∠1 > ∠B.

31. What else can you conclude about ∠1 in Euclidean geometry?

32. Use the figure to show whether or not your conclusion about ∠1 is also true in Lobachevskian geometry.

Angle Inscribed in a Semicircle. In the figure below, ∠ABC is inscribed in a semicircle.

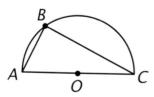

33. What can you conclude about ∠ABC in Euclidean geometry?

Radius OB has been added in the figure below.

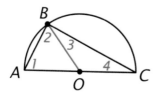

34. Use the numbered angles to show whether or not your conclusion about ∠ABC is also true in Lobachevskian geometry.

Magnification and Distortion. The following photographs are an exaggerated illustration of the fact that a figure cannot be enlarged in Lobachevskian geometry without its being distorted.

In the figure at the left below, △ABC is a right triangle with right ∠C. In the figure at the right, the triangle has been enlarged by extending line AB so that AD = 2AB and by drawing DE ⊥ line AC.

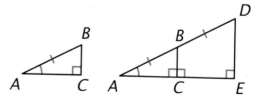

In Euclidean geometry, what can you conclude about

35. △ADE and △ABC? Why?

36. ∠D and ∠ABC?

37. the lengths of the sides of △ADE with respect to the corresponding sides of △ABC?

In the figure below, line DF has been drawn so that ∠1 = ∠A, and BC has been extended so that it intersects DF at F.

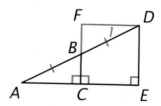

38. Copy the figure and mark this information on it.

In both Euclidean geometry and Lobachevskian geometry, what can you conclude about

39. △DBF and △ABC? Explain.

40. the lengths of BF and BC?

41. ∠F?

42. quadrilateral CFDE?

In Lobachevskian geometry, what can you conclude about

43. ∠FDE?

44. the lengths of DE and FC? Explain.

45. FC and 2BC?

46. DE and 2BC?

47. the lengths of CE and FD?

48. the lengths of CE and AC?

49. AE and 2AC?

50. How do the sides of △ADE compare in length with the corresponding sides of △ABC in Lobachevskian geometry?

Set III

Astronomical Triangle. In 1829, Lobachevsky reported that he used some astronomical measurements to find the sum of the angles of the triangle determined by Earth, the sun, and the star Sirius. He found that the sum differed from 180° by approximately 0.000000001°.

1. Does Lobachevsky's finding prove that physical space is non-Euclidean? Explain why or why not.

2. Would it be easier to prove by this method that physical space is Euclidean or that it is non-Euclidean? Explain.

CHAPTER 16 Summary and Review

Basic Ideas

Postulate

The Lobachevskian Postulate. The summit angles of a Saccheri quadrilateral are acute.   703

Theorems

87. The summit angles of a Saccheri quadrilateral are equal.   698

88. The line segment connecting the midpoints of the base and summit of a Saccheri quadrilateral is perpendicular to both of them. 698

89. If the legs of a birectangular quadrilateral are unequal, the summit angles opposite them are unequal in the same order.   698

90. If the summit angles of a birectangular quadrilateral are unequal, the legs opposite them are unequal in the same order.   698

L1. The summit of a Saccheri quadrilateral is longer than its base.   703

L2. A midsegment of a triangle is less than half as long as the third side.   703

L3. The sum of the angles of a triangle is less than 180°.   708

Corollary. The sum of the angles of a quadrilateral is less than 360°.   708

L4. If two triangles are similar, they must also be congruent.   708

Statement	Euclid	Lobachevsky	Riemann
Through a point not on a line, there is	exactly one line parallel to the line.	more than one line parallel to the line.	no line parallel to the line.
The summit angles of a Saccheri quadrilateral are	right.	acute.	obtuse.
The sum of the angles of a triangle is	180°.	less than 180°.	more than 180°.

Exercises

Set I

Sphere Geometry. The figure below appeared in a book published in 1533.*

Most of the curves on the globe are "lines" in sphere geometry.

1. What is a "line" in sphere geometry?

Tell whether each of the following statements is true or false in sphere geometry.

2. Through a point not on a line, there is exactly one line perpendicular to the line.

3. In a plane, two lines perpendicular to a third line are parallel to each other.

4. If two lines intersect, they intersect in no more than one point.

5. The sum of the angles of a triangle is 180°.

6. An exterior angle of a triangle is greater than either remote interior angle.

Introduction to Geography, by Peter Apian.

Saccheri Quadrilateral. In the figure below, ABCD is a Saccheri quadrilateral in Lobachevskian geometry; ∠B and ∠C are right angles, and AB = BC = CD.

7. Which side of ABCD is its summit?

8. What can you conclude about the length of AD?

9. Can ABCD be a rhombus? Explain.

10. What kind of angles are ∠A and ∠D?

11. Can ABCD be a rectangle? Explain.

Beach Ball. This beach ball has been divided by great circles into congruent triangles.

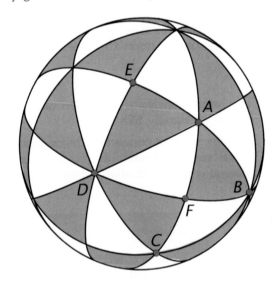

The angles at E and F are right angles, the angles at A and C are 60°, and the angles at B and D are 45°.
    What is the sum of the measures of the angles surrounding

12. point A?

13. point B?

14. point C?

15. Make a large copy of the part of the figure bounded by quadrilateral EBCD. Label the measures of all of the angles in your figure.

16. Find the measures of the angles in quadrilateral ABCD.

17. If the opposite angles of a quadrilateral in Euclidean geometry are equal, what can you conclude?

18. Does the same conclusion appear to hold in sphere geometry? Explain.

19. What can you conclude from the fact that quadrilateral ABCD is equilateral?

20. How are the diagonals of ABCD related to each other?

21. Is this relation also true for such quadrilaterals in Euclidean geometry?

22. Find the measures of the angles in quadrilateral EAFD.

Can a quadrilateral have exactly three right angles in

23. Euclidean geometry?

24. sphere geometry?

Set II

Lobachevsky's Ladder. In the figure below, l_1 and l_2 represent the two parallel side rails of a ladder. Segments AB, CD, and EF represent three rungs that are perpendicular to l_1.

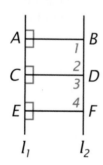

In Lobachevskian geometry, no more than two of the three rungs AB, CD, and EF can have equal lengths.

25. Copy the figure and mark it to suggest that AB = CD = EF.

26. If AB = CD = EF, what kind of quadrilaterals are ABDC and CDFE?

27. In Lobachevskian geometry, what kind of angles are ∠1, ∠2, ∠3, and ∠4?

28. What can you conclude about ∠2 + ∠3?

29. How does this conclusion contradict the fact that ∠2 and ∠3 are a linear pair?

30. What does this contradiction prove about the rungs of the ladder?

Pythagoras Meets Lobachevsky. In the figure below, △ABC is a right triangle and MN is one of its midsegments.

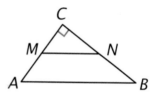

Suppose that $CA^2 + CB^2 = AB^2$ and $CM^2 + CN^2 = MN^2$.

31. On what theorem of Euclidean geometry are these equations based?

Because M and N are the midpoints of CA and CB, $CM = \frac{1}{2}CA$ and $CN = \frac{1}{2}CB$.

32. Why does it follow that
$$\left(\frac{1}{2}CA\right)^2 + \left(\frac{1}{2}CB\right)^2 = MN^2?$$

33. Use this equation and the initial assumption that $CA^2 + CB^2 = AB^2$ to show that $MN = \frac{1}{2}AB$.

34. What theorem in Lobachevskian geometry does this result contradict?

35. What does this contradiction indicate about the Pythagorean Theorem in Lobachevskian geometry?

Lobachevsky Meets Escher. The print by Maurits Escher at the beginning of this chapter illustrates a model devised by a French mathematician, Henri Poincaré, for visualizing the theorems of Lobachevskian geometry. Silvio Levy used a computer to create the above version of it.*

To understand this model, it is necessary to know what *orthogonal circles* are.

The figure at the right shows two orthogonal circles O and O′ intersecting at points A and B. The tangents to the circles at these points have been drawn.

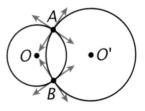

The Visual Mind: Art and Mathematics, edited by Michele Emmer (MIT Press, 1993).

36. On the basis of this figure, define *orthogonal circles.*

In Poincaré's model of Lobachevskian geometry, points of the plane are represented by points inside a circle, and lines are represented by both the diameters of the circle and the arcs of circles orthogonal to it. Examples of some lines in this model are shown in the figure below.

The figure below shows two points in a circle and the only arc through them that is orthogonal to the circle.

37. What postulate does this figure illustrate?

The figure below shows an "orthogonal arc" and several such arcs through point P that do not intersect it.

38. What idea in Lobachevskian geometry does this figure illustrate?

State a theorem or postulate in Lobachevskian geometry suggested by each of the following figures.

39.

40.

41.

The Geometry of the Universe. According to one model of the universe, called Einstein's spherical universe, the geometrical properties of space are comparable to those of the surface of a sphere.

42. If this model is correct, what conclusion follows about the volume of the space of the universe? Explain.

43. If an astronaut were to travel far enough along a straight line, what would this model predict? Explain.

Final Review

Set I

German Terms. The figure below from a German geometry book names lines and line segments related to the circle.

Kreis

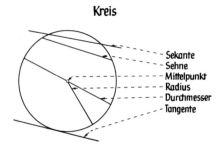

Sekante
Sehne
Mittelpunkt
Radius
Durchmesser
Tangente

1. Which word in the figure is identical in German and English?

2. It appears from the figure that a *durchmesser* is a *sehne* of a *kreis* that contains its *mittelpunkt*. Explain.

3. What is the difference between a *sekante* and a *tangente*?

Regular Polygons. The figure below consists of equilateral triangles and squares.

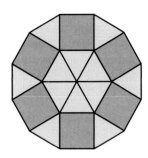

4. What other regular polygons do you see in it?

5. What properties do all regular polygons have in common?

6. What are the measures of the angles of the rhombuses in the figure that are not squares?

7. What other type of quadrilateral in the figure has angles of these measures?

8. What is the sum of the measures of the angles of a regular hexagon?

9. What is the sum of the measures of the angles of a regular dodecagon?

What Follows? Complete the statements of the following postulates and theorems.

10. The area of a parallelogram is the product of . . .

11. If a line through the center of a circle bisects a chord that is not a diameter, it . . .

12. If two points lie in a plane, the line that contains them . . .

13. If the square of one side of a triangle is equal to the sum of the squares of the other two sides, . . .

14. Triangles with equal bases and equal altitudes . . .

15. Two nonvertical lines are parallel iff their slopes . . .

16. If a line is perpendicular to a radius at its outer endpoint, it is . . .

17. If two planes intersect, they intersect in . . .

18. The length of a diagonal of a cube with edges of length *e* is . . .

19. If a line parallel to one side of a triangle intersects the other two sides in different points, it divides the sides . . .

20. Each leg of a right triangle is the geometric mean between . . .

21. The volume of a pyramid is one-third of the product of . . .

22. The ratio of the perimeters of two similar polygons is equal to . . .

23. Two nonvertical lines are perpendicular iff the product of their slopes . . .

24. A secant angle whose vertex is outside a circle is equal in measure to . . .

Pythagorean Squares. In the figure below, the squares on the legs of a right triangle have been moved so that they partly overlap the square on its hypotenuse. The letters represent the areas of the five regions that result.

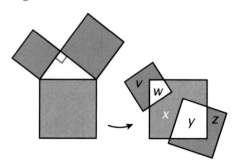

According to the Area Postulate, the area of a polygonal region is equal to the sum of the areas of its nonoverlapping parts.

25. In terms of the letters, what is the area of the largest square?

26. Which is greater: the area shaded red, $v + z$, or the area shaded blue, x? Explain.

The Value of Pi. Brahmagupta, a seventh-century Indian mathematician, proposed the following estimate for π.

AB is a diameter of the circle and $CD \perp AB$.

27. What can you conclude about $\triangle ABC$? Explain.

28. Write a proportion relating the lengths AD, CD, and DB.

29. Using the fact that AD = 2 and DB = 5, find CD.

Brahmagupta's estimate was $CD = \pi$.

30. Is this estimate correct? Explain.

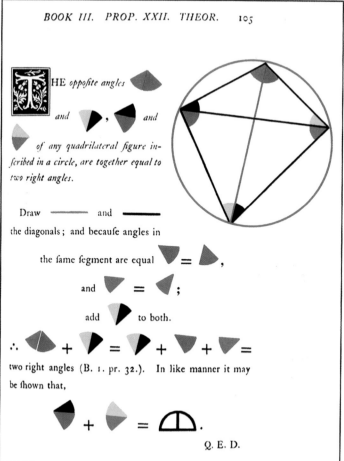

Euclid in Color. The most colorful edition of Euclid's *Elements* was published in London in 1847. The figure above shows a page from this book.

31. What theorem is being proved?

32. Why are the angles that are labeled with the same color equal?

33. Why is the part of the proof shown below true?

34. What do you think the symbol ⌓ means?

Largest Package. The rule for the largest rectangular package that you can mail at the post office is:

The length of its longest side plus the distance around its thickest part is less than or equal to 130 inches.

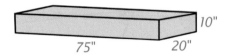

A package has dimensions 10 inches, 20 inches, and 75 inches.

35. What is its volume?

36. Would the post office accept it? Explain.

37. What is the length of the edge of the largest *cube* that you can mail?

38. What is its volume?

Four Centers. Points A, B, C, and D are the four centers of △XYZ.

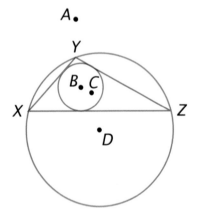

What is the name of

39. point A, the point in which the lines containing the altitudes of △ABC are concurrent?

40. point B?

41. point C, the point in which the medians of △ABC are concurrent?

42. point D?

Which of these points is

43. equidistant from the sides of the triangle?

44. equidistant from its vertices?

45. the triangle's balancing point?

46. not collinear with the other three?

Formulas. What is each of the following formulas used for?

47. $c = \pi d$.

48. $d = \sqrt{l^2 + w^2 + h^2}$.

49. $A = \dfrac{1}{2} h(b_1 + b_2)$.

50. $h = \dfrac{\sqrt{3}}{2} s$.

Kindergarten Toy. The photograph from the Milton Bradley catalog of 1889 shown below is of a toy for kindergarten children. Three basic geometric solids are suspended by strings.

51. What does each solid appear to be?

Write expressions for the volume and total surface area of

52. solid A in terms of the length, e, of each of its edges.

53. solid B in terms of its altitude, h, and the radius, r, of its bases.

54. solid C in terms of its radius, r.

Steep Roof. The steep roof of an A-frame house helps it to shed snow easily.

The figure below is a side view of an A-frame roof in a coordinate system; the units are in feet.

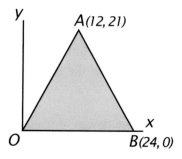

55. Find the slopes of OA and AB.

56. Find ∠AOB, the angle of inclination of the roof, to the nearest degree.

57. Find OA and AB to the nearest foot.

58. △OAB looks equilateral. Is it?

Greek Crosses. The figures below show how two congruent Greek crosses can be cut and put together to form a square.

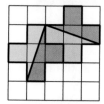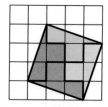

Given that the length of each side of one of the crosses is *x* units, find each of the following measures in terms of *x*.

59. The perimeter of one of the crosses.

60. The area of one of the crosses.

61. The area of the square.

62. The length of a side of the square.

63. The perimeter of the square.

Baseball in Orbit. The smaller a planet, the weaker its gravity. If the radius of the earth were 22 miles, it would be possible to throw a baseball into orbit!*

64. Given that the orbit is circular, find the distance that the ball would travel in going once around the earth.

To be put into this orbit, the ball would have to be thrown at a speed of 100 miles per hour, something that professional pitchers can easily do.

65. Approximately how many minutes would it take the ball to return to the spot from which it was thrown?

Two Quadrilaterals. ABCD represents any convex quadrilateral. The four lines that bisect its angles intersect at E, F, G, and H to form quadrilateral EFGH.

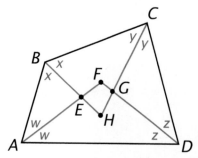

Letting the measures of the angles produced by the bisectors be *w*, *x*, *y*, and *z* as indicated, show why each of the following statements is true.

66. $w + x + y + z = 180°$.

67. $\angle F = 180° - w - z$ and $\angle H = 180° - x - y$.

68. $\angle F + \angle H = 180°$.

69. Quadrilateral EFGH is cyclic.

———————

The Cosmological Milkshake, by Robert Ehrlich (Rutgers University Press, 1994).

Long Shadows. Tall buildings cast long shadows. At 3 P.M. on the winter solstice, December 21, the Empire State Building casts a shadow more than a mile long.*

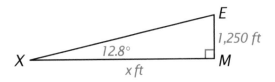

70. Given that the angle of elevation of the sun at this time is 12.8° and that the Empire State Building is 1,250 feet tall, find the approximate length of its shadow.

71. How long would the shadow cast by a person 6 feet tall be at the same time?

Tree Geometry. Galileo calculated that trees cannot grow beyond a certain size without collapsing from their own weight.

The figures at the right below represent the trunks of two trees as similar cylinders.

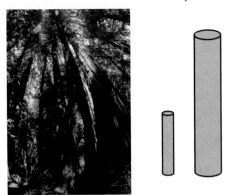

If the ratio of their diameters is k, what is the ratio of

72. their heights?

73. the areas of their bases?

74. their volumes?

75. their weights?

Suppose two trees are similar in shape and that one tree is 10 times as tall as the other.

76. How would corresponding cross sections of their trunks compare in area?

77. How would their trunks and branches compare in weight?

78. On the basis of these comparisons, which tree trunk would be more likely to fail because of the load that it bears?

SAT Problem. The figure at the right appeared in a problem on an SAT test.

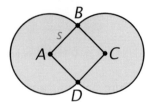

It consists of a square with side of length s and the arcs of two circles centered at A and C and having radius s.

Write an expression in terms of s for

79. the perimeter of the figure.

80. its area.

Sight Line. In the design of seating that enables each spectator to have a clear view, the sight line is projected 15 cm above the head of the spectator seated three rows below.†

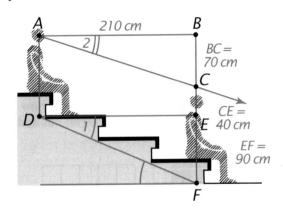

Given the measurements in the figure above, find

81. $\angle 1$, which equals the angle at which the seats rise with respect to the horizontal.

82. $\angle 2$, the angle of the sight lines with the horizontal.

*The Empire State Building, by John Tauranac (Scribner's, 1995).

†Indoor Sports Spaces, by Robin Crane and Malcolm Dixon (Van Nostrand Reinhold, 1991).

Dog Crates. Dog crates usually have the shape of rectangular solids.

Crates for beagles are 30 inches long and 22 inches high and have a volume of 12,540 cubic inches.

83. How wide are they?

Crates for boxers are 36 inches long, 26 inches high, and 23 inches wide.

84. Are the crates for beagles and boxers similar? Explain why or why not.

Crates for Great Danes are 48 inches long.

85. Given that these crates are similar to those for beagles, find the volume of such a crate to the nearest cubic inch.

Tangent Circles. The three circles in the figure below are centered on the vertices of △ABC and meet on its sides at points D, E, and F.

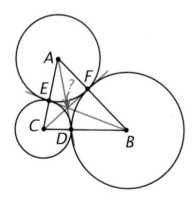

Lines AD, BE, and CF look as if they might be concurrent.

86. Write an equation relating the lengths of the segments of the sides of △ABC that, if true, would show that lines AD, BE, and CF are concurrent.

87. Would this equation be true if the three circles had equal radii? Explain.

88. Is the equation true, given that the circles have radii of different lengths? Explain.

Squares on the Legs. In the figure below, squares ABEF and BCHG have been drawn on the legs of right △ABC, and BD is the altitude to its hypotenuse.

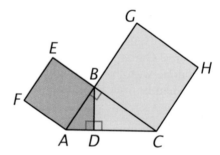

89. △ABD ~ △BCD. Why?

90. $\dfrac{a\triangle ABD}{a\triangle BCD} = \left(\dfrac{AB}{BC}\right)^2$. Why?

91. How does $\dfrac{a\triangle ABD}{a\triangle BCD}$ compare with

$\dfrac{a ABEF}{a BCHG}$? Explain.

92. Is the yellow region similar to the light red one? If so, write the similarity.

Formula Confusion. On the final exam, Obtuse Ollie started confusing different formulas with the one for the area of a triangle.

For the area of a circle, he wrote $A = \dfrac{1}{2} rc$.

93. If by *r* and *c* he meant the radius and circumference of the circle, how many points out of 5 would you give Ollie? Explain.

For the volume of a sphere, Ollie wrote

$$V = \frac{1}{2} rA.$$

94. If by r and A he meant the radius and surface area of the sphere, should Ollie get any credit for this answer? Explain.

Ollie also wrote $V = \frac{1}{2} rA$ for the volume of a right cylinder.

95. If by r and A he meant the radius and area of the lateral surface of the cylinder, should Ollie get any credit for this answer? Explain.

Regular 17-gon. The stamp shown below pictures the great German mathematician Carl Friedrich Gauss and a circle divided into 17 equal arcs. Gauss proved that this division could be done with just a straightedge and compass when he was 18 years old.

96. Find the value of $N = n \sin \dfrac{180}{n}$ for a regular 17-gon to the nearest hundredth.

97. Find the value of $M = n \sin \dfrac{180}{n} \cos \dfrac{180}{n}$ for the same polygon to the nearest hundredth.

Given that the radius of a regular 17-gon is 10 centimeters, use the formula

98. $p = 2Nr$ to find its perimeter to the nearest centimeter.

99. $A = Mr^2$ to find its area to the nearest square centimeter.

100. Without calculating the numbers, how would you expect the corresponding measurements of a circle with the same radius to compare with those of the 17-gon?

101. Check your answer to exercise 100 by calculating the circumference and area of the circle, each to the nearest square centimeter.

Packing Circles. When equal circles are packed together as closely as possible, their centers are at the vertices of equilateral triangles.

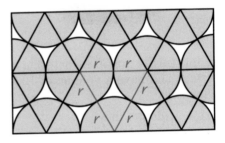

102. Find the area of one of these triangles in terms of r, the radius of the circles.

103. Find the area inside the triangle filled by the three sectors of the circles.

104. Use your answers to exercises 102 and 103 to find the percentage of the plane filled by the circles.

Rain Gutter. A rain gutter is to be constructed from a metal sheet of width 30 cm by bending upward one-third of the sheet on each side through an angle of 60°.*

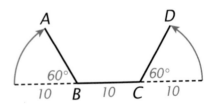

105. Copy the figure and draw perpendicular line segments from A and D to line BC to form right $\triangle AEB$ and right $\triangle DFC$. Also draw $\overline{AD}$.

---

*From a problem in *Calculus,* by James Stewart (Brooks/Cole, 1995).

106. What can you conclude about △AEB and △DFC? Explain.

107. Why is AE ∥ DF?

108. Why is AE = DF?

109. Why is AD ∥ EF?

110. Find the length of AE.

111. Find the area of ABCD (the cross section of the water when the rain gutter is full) to the nearest square centimeter.

Incircle. In right △ABC, the bisectors of ∠A and ∠B intersect in point O.

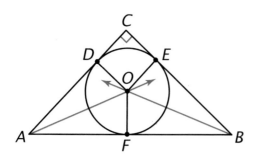

112. Why does it follow that the bisector of ∠C also passes through point O?

113. What is point O called with respect to the triangle?

The sides of the triangle are tangent to circle O at points D, E, and F.

114. Why is CD = CE?

115. Why is OD ⊥ AC and OE ⊥ CB?

116. Why is OD ∥ EC and OE ∥ DC?

117. Why does it follow that OD = EC and OE = DC?

118. Given that CA = 20 and CB = 21, find AB.

Express each of the following lengths in terms of the given side lengths and *r*, the radius of the incircle.

119. AD and AF.

120. BE and BF.

121. Use AB to write and solve an equation for *r*.

Angles and Sides. The sides opposite ∠A, ∠B, and ∠C of △ABC have lengths *a*, *b*, and *c*.

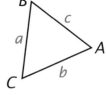

122. Why does it follow that $c^2 = a^2 + b^2 - 2ab \cos C$?

123. Solve this equation for cos C, given that $a = b = c$.

124. Use your calculator to find ∠C.

125. Is the result the number that you would expect? Explain.

126. Solve the equation of exercise 122 for cos C, given that $c^2 = a^2 + b^2$.

127. Use your calculator to find ∠C.

128. Is the result the number that you would expect? Explain.

Circular Track. The figure below shows a circular race track bordered by two concentric circles.

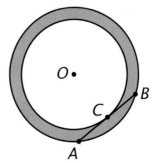

Chord AB represents one of the longest possible straight paths on the track. It is tangent to the inside of the track at C and is 200 meters long.*

129. Copy the figure and draw OA and OC. Let *R* be the length of OA and *r* be the length of OC.

130. AB ⊥ OC. Why?

131. OC bisects AB. Why?

132. $R^2 - r^2 = 10,000$. Why?

133. Find the area of the track to the nearest square meter.

———————

*Mathematical Nuts, by Samuel I. Jones (S. I. Jones Co., 1932).

da Vinci Problem. Leonardo da Vinci dedicated a hundred pages of his notebooks to geometry. He made many drawings of figures bounded by circular arcs in which the areas of the parts were related in simple ways.*

In the figure below, square ABCD is circumscribed about circle O, and square EFGH is inscribed in it. Four semicircles have been drawn with the sides of EFGH as their diameters; each diameter is 2 units long.

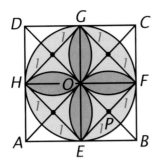

Find the area of each of the following parts of the figure.

134.

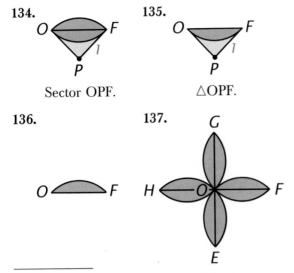

Sector OPF.

135.

△OPF.

136.

137.

138.

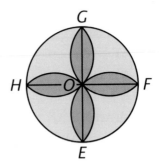

139.

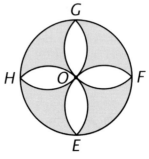

(The yellow part only.)

140.

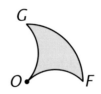

A Problem from Ancient India.[†] A fish at corner F of a rectangular pool sees a heron at corner H looking at him. As the fish swims along FB, the heron walks along the shore from H to A to B, arriving at the same time.

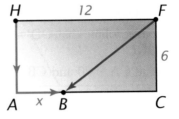

141. Given that the pool is 12 units by 6 units and that the heron and the fish move at the same speed, find the distance that the fish swam.

The Unknown Leonardo, edited by Ladislao Reti (McGraw-Hill, 1974).

[†]*Geometry Civilized: History, Culture, and Technique*, by J. L. Heilbron (Clarendon Press, 1998).

Circumradius. The figure on the blackboard can be used to derive an equation relating a triangle and its circumcircle.

The figure at the right shows △ABC with circumcircle O; OH ⊥ BC, BC = a, and OB = r.

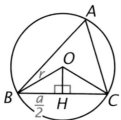

142. State the theorem that tells us that, regardless of its shape, △ABC has a circumcircle.

143. Why is BH = $\dfrac{a}{2}$?

144. Why is ∠BOH = $\dfrac{1}{2}$∠BOC?

145. Why is ∠BOC = $m\widehat{BC}$?

146. Why is ∠A = $\dfrac{1}{2}m\widehat{BC}$?

147. Why is ∠BOH = ∠A?

148. Why is sin ∠BOH = $\dfrac{\frac{a}{2}}{r}$?

149. Why does it follow that $\dfrac{a}{\sin A} = 2r$?

150. Given that the sides of △ABC opposite ∠B and ∠C have lengths b and c, why does it follow that $\dfrac{b}{\sin B} = \dfrac{c}{\sin C} = 2r$?

151. Use the equation of exercise 149 to find the radius of the circumcircle of a triangle for which $a = 3$ cm and ∠A = 30°.

152. Draw a figure to show that your answer is reasonable.

Conical Mountain. The unusual mountain in Iran in the photograph below was shaped by a gaseous spring. Its crater once contained a lake.*

In the side view of the mountain below, the crater is represented as the lower part of a circular cone, and the bowl of the crater is represented as half of a sphere.

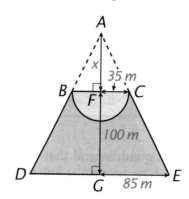

153. Use the numbers in the figure to find x, the length of AF.

Find each of the following volumes to the nearest cubic meter.

154. The volume of the solid cone whose altitude is AG.

155. The volume of the solid cone whose altitude is AF.

156. The volume of the bowl of the crater.

157. Use your answers to exercises 154 through 156 to estimate the volume of material in the actual mountain to the nearest 100,000 cubic meters.

<hr>

*_Below from Above_, by George Gerster (Abbeville Press, 1986).

Glossary

Acute angle: An angle whose measure is less than 90°. 92

Acute triangle: A triangle all of whose angles are acute. 158

Altitude of a prism: (1) A line segment that connects the planes of the bases of a prism and that is perpendicular to both of them. (2) The length of that line segment. 640

Altitude of a pyramid: (1) The perpendicular line segment from the apex of a pyramid to the plane of its base. (2) The length of that line segment. 648

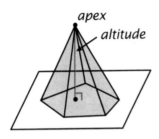

Altitude of a quadrilateral that has parallel sides: (1) A perpendicular line segment that connects points on the lines of the parallel sides. (2) The length of that line segment. 359

Altitude of a triangle: (1) A perpendicular line segment from a vertex of a triangle to the line of the opposite side. (2) The length of that line segment. 352

Angle: A pair of rays that have the same endpoint. The angle in the figure at the right can be named ∠O or ∠AOB or ∠BOA; this notation also stands for the measure of this angle. The measure might either be found by using a protractor or worked out by the geometry of a given problem. 13

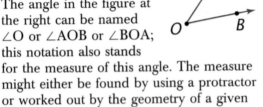

Angle of inclination: The angle that a line forms with the horizontal. 461

Antipodal points: The two points of intersection of a sphere with a line through its center. 691

Apothem of a regular polygon: A perpendicular line segment from the center of the polygon to one of its sides. 574

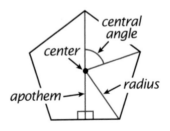

Area: Measure of extent for plane figures. Determined by using the Area Postulates for polygonal regions or as limits of the areas of polygons (as described for the area of the circle) for curved regions. The methods can be extended to finding the areas of surfaces in three dimensions, including the area of a sphere. 20, 664–665

Area of a circle: The limit of the areas of inscribed regular polygons. Archimedes extended this method to find the areas of figures bounded by curves by using areas of inscribed and circumscribed polygons. 598

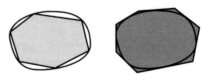

blue area < curved region area < red area

Betweenness of Points: An intuitive notion, formally defined as follows by using the Ruler Postulate. A point is between two other points on the same line iff its coordinate is between their coordinates. (More briefly, A-B-C iff $a < b < c$ or $a > b > c$.) 85

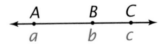

Betweenness of Rays: An intuitive notion, formally defined as follows by using the Protractor Postulate. A ray is between two others in the same half-rotation iff its coordinate is between their coordinates. (More briefly, OA-OB-OC iff $a < b < c$ or $a > b > c$.) 93

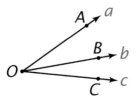

Birectangular quadrilateral: A quadrilateral that has two sides perpendicular to a third side. 697

Bisector of an angle: A line or ray that divides an angle into two equal angles. 99

Center of a regular polygon: The center of the circumscribed circle of the polygon. See *Apothem of a regular polygon*. 574

Central angle of a circle: An angle whose vertex is the center of a circle. 498

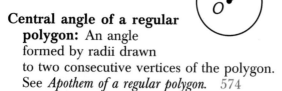

Central angle of a regular polygon: An angle formed by radii drawn to two consecutive vertices of the polygon. See *Apothem of a regular polygon*. 574

Centroid of a triangle: The point in which the medians of a triangle are concurrent. Physically, a uniform triangular region balances perfectly in any position when supported at its centroid. 549

Cevian of a triangle: A line segment that connects a vertex of a triangle to a point on the opposite side. 554

Chord of a circle: A line segment that connects two points of a circle. 485

Circle: The set of all points in a plane that are at a given distance from a given point in the plane. 484

Circumcenter of a polygon: The center of the circle circumscribed about the polygon. 531

Circumference of a circle: The limit of the perimeters of the inscribed regular polygons. 592

Circumscribed circle about a polygon: The circle that contains all of the vertices of the polygon. 531

Circumscribed polygon about a circle: A polygon each of whose sides is tangent to the circle. 542

Collinear points: Points that are contained by the same line. 9

Complementary angles: Two angles whose sum is 90°. 105

Concave polygon: A polygon that is not convex. 258

Concentric circles: Circles that lie in the same plane and have the same center. 484

Concurrent lines: Lines that contain the same point. 9

Cone: Suppose that A is a plane, R is a circular region in plane A, and P is a point not in plane A. The solid made up of all segments that connect P to a point of region R is a cone. 654

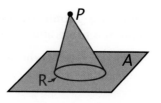

Congruent figures: Informally, two figures are congruent if they have the same size and shape so that, if one is superimposed on the other, they match exactly. Formally, two figures are congruent if there is an isometry such that one figure is the image of the other. This definition of congruence for figures in general agrees with the definition of *congruent triangles* and extends the idea of same size and same shape to all plane and solid shapes. 140, 312

Congruent triangles: Two triangles for which there is a correspondence between their vertices such that all of their corresponding sides and angles are equal. 140

Converse of a conditional statement: The statement formed by interchanging the hypothesis and conclusion of the conditional statement. 47

Convex polygon: A polygon such that every line segment that connects two points inside it lies entirely inside the polygon. More generally, a plane figure or a solid shape is convex iff every line segment connecting two points inside the figure or shape also lies inside it. 258

Coplanar points: Points that are contained in the same plane. 9

Corollary: A theorem that can be easily proved as a consequence of a definition, a postulate or another theorem. 99

Cosine of an acute angle of a right triangle: The ratio of the length of the adjacent leg to the length of the hypotenuse. More generally, see *Trigonometric functions*. 455

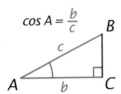

$$\cos A = \frac{b}{c}$$

Cross section of a geometric solid: The intersection of a plane and the solid. 641

Cube: A rectangular solid whose length, width, and height are equal. 629

Cyclic polygon: A polygon for which there exists a circle that contains all of the vertices of the polygon. 530

Cylinder: Suppose that A and B are two parallel planes, R is a circular region in one plane, and *l* is a line that intersects both planes but not R. The solid made up of all segments parallel to line *l* that connect a point of region R to a point of the other plane is a cylinder. 655

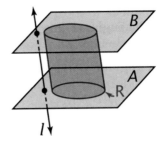

Decagon: A polygon that has 10 sides. 573

Degree measure of an arc: The measure of the central angle of an arc. 498

Diagonal of a polygon: A line segment that connects any two nonconsecutive vertices of a polygon. 259

Diameter of a circle: (1) A chord that contains the center of a circle. (2) The length of a chord that contains the center. 485

Dilation: Informally, a transformation in which a figure is reduced or enlarged. 300

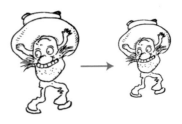

Distance between two parallel lines: In general, the length of any perpendicular segment connecting one line to the other.

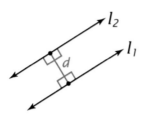

Distance between two points: An intuitive idea of what we measure by using a ruler. Formalized by the Ruler Postulate. The distance between the endpoints of a line segment gives the length of the segment. 85

Distance from a point to a line: In general, the length of the perpendicular segment from the point to the line.

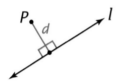

Dodecagon: A polygon that has 12 sides. 585

Dodecahedron: A polyhedron that has 12 faces. The faces of a regular dodecahedron are regular pentagons. 678

Equiangular polygon: A convex polygon all of whose angles are equal. 572

Equiangular triangle: A triangle all of whose angles are equal. 158

Equilateral polygon: A polygon all of whose sides are equal. 572

Exterior angle of a triangle: An angle that forms a linear pair with an angle of the triangle. 191

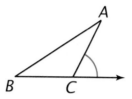

Geometric mean: The number b is the geometric mean between the numbers a and c iff a, b, and c are positive and $\frac{a}{b} = \frac{b}{c}$. 380

Glide reflection: A transformation that is the composite of a translation and a reflection in a line parallel to the direction of the translation. 313

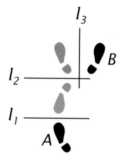

Great circle of a sphere: A set of points that is the intersection of the sphere and a plane containing its center. 690

Heptagon: A polygon that has seven sides. 573

Hexagon: A polygon that has six sides. 19

Hypotenuse of a right triangle: The side opposite the right angle of the triangle. 66

Icosahedron: A polyhedron that has 20 faces. The faces of a regular icosahedron are equilateral triangles. 678

Incenter of a polygon: The center of the inscribed circle of the polygon. 542

Inscribed angle of a circle: An angle whose vertex is on a circle and whose sides each intersect the circle in another point. 505

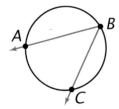

Inscribed circle in a polygon: A circle for which each side of the polygon is tangent to the circle. 542

Inscribed polygon in a circle: A polygon each of whose vertices lies on the circle. 531

Isometry: A transformation that preserves distance and angle measure. 300

Isosceles trapezoid: A trapezoid whose legs are equal. 281

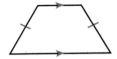

Isosceles triangle: A triangle that has at least two equal sides. 157

Lateral area of a prism: The sum of the areas of the lateral faces of a prism. Lateral area excludes the areas of the bases of a prism. 635

Length of a line segment: The distance between its endpoints. 85

Line segment: Part of a line bounded by two endpoints. If the endpoints are A and B, then the segment is written as AB (or BA). 9

Linear pair: Two angles that have a common side and whose other sides are opposite rays. 111

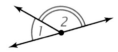

Median of a triangle: A line segment that connects a vertex of a triangle to the midpoint of the opposite side. 549

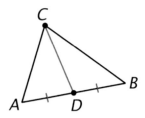

Midpoint of a line segment: The point that divides a line segment into two equal segments. 98

Midsegment of a triangle: A line segment that connects the midpoints of two of a triangle's sides. 286

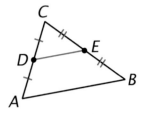

Net: A two-dimensional pattern of polygons that, when folded together, forms a polyhedron. 635

Nonagon: A polygon that has nine sides. 573

Noncollinear points: Points that do not lie on the same line. 9

Oblique line and plane (or two planes): A line and a plane (or two planes) that are neither parallel nor perpendicular. 620

Obtuse angle: An angle whose measure is more than 90° but less than 180°. 92

Obtuse triangle: A triangle that has an obtuse angle. 158

Octagon: A polygon that has eight sides. 19

Octahedron: A polyhedron that has eight faces. The faces of a regular octahedron are equilateral triangles. 678

Opposite rays: Informally, two rays are opposite rays if they have a common endpoint and point in opposite directions. Formally, rays AB and AC are opposite rays iff B-A-C. 19

Orthocenter of a triangle: The point in which the lines containing the altitudes of a triangle are concurrent. 549

Parallel line and plane: A line and a plane that do not intersect. 619

Parallel lines: Lines that lie in the same plane and do not intersect. 118

Parallel planes: Planes that do not intersect. 619

Parallelogram: A quadrilateral whose opposite sides are parallel. 265

Pentagon: A polygon that has five sides. 19

Perimeter of a polygon: The sum of the lengths of the sides of a polygon. 20

Perpendicular bisector of a line segment: The line that is perpendicular to the line segment and that divides the segment into two equal parts. 212

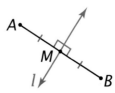

Perpendicular line and plane: A line and a plane that intersect such that the line is perpendicular to every line in the plane that passes through the point of intersection. 620

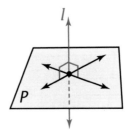

Perpendicular lines: Lines that form a right angle. 117

Perpendicular planes: Two planes such that one plane contains a line that is perpendicular to the other plane. 620

Plane: A flat unbounded surface. 9

Polygon: A connected set of at least three line segments in the same plane such that each segment intersects exactly two others, one at each endpoint. 139

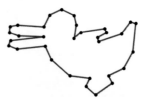

Polygonal region: The union of a polygon and its interior.   339

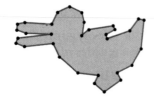

Polyhedron: A solid bounded by parts of intersecting planes.   628

Postulate: A statement that is assumed to be true without proof. We choose our postulates for their natural intuitive appeal and for their ability to capture the basic properties of space from which the rest of geometry can be developed.   61

Prism: Suppose that A and B are two parallel planes, R is a polygonal region in one plane, and *l* is a line that intersects both planes but not R. The solid made up of all segments parallel to line *l* that connect a point of region R to a point of the other plane is a prism.   634

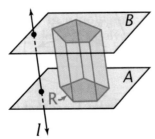

Proportion: An equality between two ratios.   379

Pyramid: Suppose that A is a plane, R is a polygonal region in plane A, and P is a point not in plane A. The solid made up of all segments that connect P to a point of region R is a pyramid. Point P is the apex of the pyramid.   647

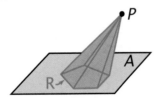

Pythagorean triple: A set of three integers that can be the lengths of the sides of a right triangle.   437

Quadrilateral: A polygon that has four sides.   19

Radius of a circle: (1) The distance between the center of a circle and any point on it. (2) A line segment that connects the center of the circle to any point on it.   485

Radius of a regular polygon: A line segment that connects the center of the polygon to a vertex of the polygon. See *Apothem of a regular polygon*.   574

Ratio: The ratio of the number *a* to the number *b* is the number $\frac{a}{b}$.   379

Ray: Part of a line that extends endlessly in one direction. If a ruler is placed on a line, points with coordinates that are zero or positive form a ray. The ray in the figure below is named ray AB.   13

Rectangle: A quadrilateral each of whose angles is a right angle.   259

Rectangular solid: A polyhedron that has six rectangular faces.   628

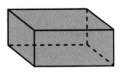

Reflection of a point through a line: The reflection of point P through line *l* is point P itself if P is on *l*. Otherwise, it is point P′ such that *l* is the perpendicular bisector of PP′.   305

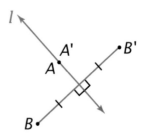

Reflection symmetry: A figure has reflection (line) symmetry with respect to a line iff it coincides with its reflection image through the line.   320

Reflex angle: An angle whose measure is more than 180°.   498

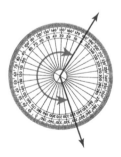

Regular polygon: A convex polygon that is both equilateral and equiangular.   572

Regular polyhedron: A convex solid having faces that are congruent regular polygons and having an equal number of polygons that meet at each vertex. Euclid showed that there are five regular polyhedra: the tetrahedron, the cube, the octahedron, the dodecahedron, and the icosahedron.   678

Rhombus: A quadrilateral all of whose sides are equal.   276

Right angle: An angle whose measure is 90°.   92

Right triangle: A triangle that has a right angle.   158

Rotation: Informally, a transformation in which a figure is rotated a certain number of degrees about a fixed point. Formally, a transformation that is the composite of two successive reflections through intersecting lines.   307

Rotation symmetry: A figure has rotation symmetry with respect to a point iff it coincides with its rotation image through less than 360° about the point.   319

Saccheri quadrilateral: A birectangular quadrilateral whose legs are equal.   697

Scalene triangle: A triangle that has no equal sides.   157

Secant: A line that intersects a circle in two points.   511

Secant angle: An angle whose sides are contained in two secants of a circle so that each side intersects the circle in at least one point other than the angle's vertex.   511

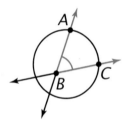

Sector of a circle: A region bounded by an arc of the circle and the two radii to the endpoints of the arc.   605

Similar figures: Informally, two figures are similar if they have the same shape, though they may differ in size. In similar figures, corresponding segments are proportional and corresponding angles are equal.   386–387

Similar solids: See *Similar figures.*   670

Similar triangles: Two triangles for which there is a correspondence between their vertices such that their corresponding sides are proportional and their corresponding angles are equal.   386

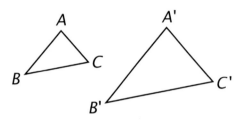

Sine of an acute angle of a right triangle: The ratio of the length of the opposite leg to the length of the hypotenuse. More generally, see *Trigonometric functions.*   455

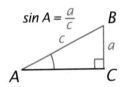

$$\sin A = \frac{a}{c}$$

Skew lines: Two lines that are not parallel and do not intersect.   619

Slope: The slope m of a nonvertical line that contains the points $P_1(x_1, y_1)$ and $P_2(x_2, y_2)$ is $m = \dfrac{\text{rise}}{\text{run}} = \dfrac{y_2 - y_1}{x_2 - x_1}$.   462

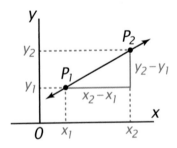

Sphere: The set of all points in space that are at a given distance from a given point.   662

Square: A quadrilateral all of whose sides and angles are equal.   276

Straight angle: An angle whose measure is 180°.   92

Supplementary angles: Two angles whose sum is 180°.   106

Symmetry with respect to a line: Two points are symmetric with respect to a line iff the line is the perpendicular bisector of the line segment connecting the two points. See *Reflection symmetry.*   212

Symmetry with respect to a point: Two points are symmetric with respect to a point iff the point is the midpoint of the line segment connecting the two points. A figure that has symmetry with respect to a point coincides with its rotation image through 180° about the point.   266

Tangent: A line in the plane of a circle that intersects the circle in exactly one point.   491

Tangent of an acute angle of a right triangle: The ratio of the length of the opposite leg to the length of the adjacent leg. More generally, see *Trigonometric functions.*   449

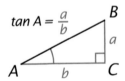

$$\tan A = \frac{a}{b}$$

Tangent segment: Any segment of a line that is tangent to a circle that has the point of tangency as one of the segment's endpoints.   517

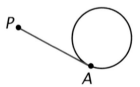

Tetrahedron: A polyhedron that has four faces. The faces of a regular tetrahedron are equilateral triangles.   678

Theorem: A statement that is proved by reasoning deductively from already accepted statements.   51

Transformation: A one-to-one correspondence between two sets of points. Examples of transformations include isometries, which preserve the size and shape of figures. Isometries give us the general definition of congruent figures. Isometries include reflections, translations, rotations, and glide reflections. Also important are dilations, which preserve shape but may alter the size of figures. 299–300

Translation: Informally, a transformation in which a figure is slid a certain distance in a given direction without being turned. Formally, a transformation that is the composite of two successive reflections through parallel lines.   307

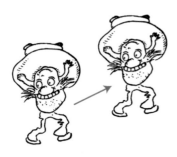

Translation symmetry: A pattern has translation symmetry if it coincides with a translation image.   320

Transversal: A line that intersects two or more lines that lie in the same plane in different points.   219

Trapezoid: A quadrilateral that has exactly one pair of parallel sides.   281

Triangle: A polygon that has three sides.   19

Trigonometric functions: For acute angles, see *Cosine, Sine,* and *Tangent.* More generally, you can discover by working with a calculator that you can find cos x, sin x, and tan x where the number of degrees of x ranges widely. The interpretation of

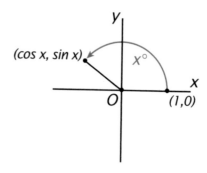

these trigonometric functions is as follows. If a unit segment with one endpoint at the origin is rotated counterclockwise through an angle of x degrees starting with its other endpoint at $(1, 0)$ on the x-axis, the other endpoint of this segment will end up at the point having coordinates $(\cos x, \sin x)$. Other trigonometric functions such as the tangent can be defined for general angles by the equations that define them in terms of sines and cosines of acute angles; for example, $\tan x = \dfrac{\sin x}{\cos x}$.

Vertical angles: Two angles such that the sides of one angle are opposite rays to the sides of the other.   111

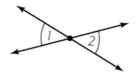

Formulary

CIRCLE

Circumference: $c = \pi d$
$c = 2\pi r$

Area: $A = \pi r^2$

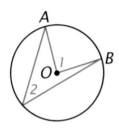

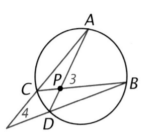

Central angle: $\angle 1 = m\widehat{AB}$

Inscribed angle: $\angle 2 = \dfrac{1}{2} m\widehat{AB}$

Secant angles: $\angle 3 = \dfrac{1}{2}(m\widehat{AB} + m\widehat{CD})$

$\angle 4 = \dfrac{1}{2}(m\widehat{AB} - m\widehat{CD})$

CONE (Circular)

Volume: $V = \dfrac{1}{3}Bh$

$V = \dfrac{1}{3}\pi r^2 h$

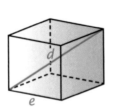

CUBE

Diagonal: $d = e\sqrt{3}$

Area: $A = 6e^2$

Volume: $V = e^3$

CYLINDER (Right circular)

Lateral area: $A = 2\pi rh$

Total area: $A = 2\pi rh + 2\pi r^2$

Volume: $V = Bh = \pi r^2 h$

DISTANCE AND SLOPE

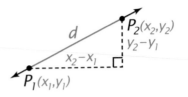

Distance: $d = \sqrt{(x_2 - x_1)^2 + (y_2 - y_1)^2}$

Slope: $m = \dfrac{\text{rise}}{\text{run}} = \dfrac{y_2 - y_1}{x_2 - x_1}$

PARALLELOGRAM

Area: $A = bh$

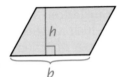

PRISM

Volume: $V = Bh$

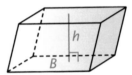

PYRAMID

Volume: $V = \dfrac{1}{3}Bh$

QUADRILATERAL (Convex)

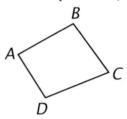

Angle sum: $\angle A + \angle B + \angle C + \angle D = 360°$

RECTANGLE

Perimeter: $p = 2l + 2w$

Area: $A = lw$

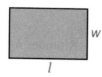

RECTANGULAR SOLID

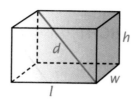

Diagonal: $d = \sqrt{l^2 + w^2 + h^2}$

Area: $A = 2lw + 2wh + 2lh$

Volume: $V = lwh$

REGULAR POLYGON (*n* sides)

$N = n \sin \dfrac{180}{n}$

$M = n \sin \dfrac{180}{n} \cos \dfrac{180}{n}$

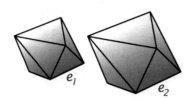

Perimeter: $p = ns = 2Nr$

Area: $A = Mr^2$

SIMILAR SOLIDS

Given the edge ratio, $\dfrac{e_2}{e_1} = r$

Area ratio: $\dfrac{A_2}{A_1} = r^2$

Volume ratio: $\dfrac{V_2}{V_1} = r^3$

SIMILAR TRIANGLES (AND POLYGONS)

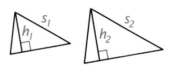

Given the side ratio, $\dfrac{s_2}{s_1} = r$

Altitude ratio: $\dfrac{h_2}{h_1} = r$

Perimeter ratio: $\dfrac{p_2}{p_1} = r$

Area ratio: $\dfrac{A_2}{A_1} = r^2$

SLOPE RELATIONS

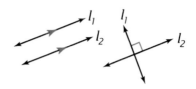

Parallel lines: $m_1 = m_2$

Perpendicular lines: $m_1 m_2 = -1$,

so $m_1 = -\dfrac{1}{m_2}$

SPHERE

Area: $A = 4\pi r^2$

Volume: $V = \dfrac{4}{3}\pi r^3$

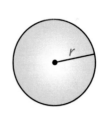

SQUARE

Diagonal: $d = s\sqrt{2}$

Perimeter: $p = 4s$

Area: $A = s^2$

TRAPEZOID

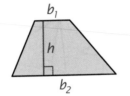

Area: $A = \dfrac{1}{2}h(b_1 + b_2)$

TRIANGLE

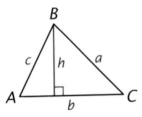

Perimeter: $p = a + b + c$

Area: $A = \dfrac{1}{2}bh$

Angle sum: $\angle A + \angle B + \angle C = 180°$

Law of sines: $\dfrac{\sin A}{a} = \dfrac{\sin B}{b} = \dfrac{\sin C}{c}$

Law of cosines: $a^2 = b^2 + c^2 - 2bc\cos A$
$$b^2 = a^2 + c^2 - 2ac\cos B$$
$$c^2 = a^2 + b^2 - 2ab\cos C$$

Side-Splitter Theorem:

$\dfrac{a}{b} = \dfrac{c}{d}$

$\dfrac{a}{a+b} = \dfrac{c}{c+d}$

$\dfrac{b}{a+b} = \dfrac{d}{c+d}$

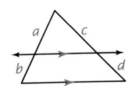

Ceva's Theorem:

$\dfrac{a}{b} \cdot \dfrac{c}{d} \cdot \dfrac{e}{f} = 1$

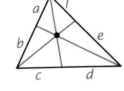

TRIANGLE, EQUILATERAL

Altitude: $h = \dfrac{\sqrt{3}}{2}s$

Area: $A = \dfrac{\sqrt{3}}{4}s^2$

TRIANGLE, RIGHT

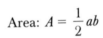

Area: $A = \dfrac{1}{2}ab$

Pythagorean Theorem: $c^2 = a^2 + b^2$

Sine ratio: $\sin A = \dfrac{a}{c}$, $\sin B = \dfrac{b}{c}$

Cosine ratio: $\cos A = \dfrac{b}{c}$, $\cos B = \dfrac{a}{c}$

Tangent ratio: $\tan A = \dfrac{a}{b}$, $\tan B = \dfrac{b}{a}$

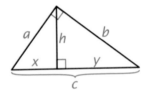

Altitude mean: $\dfrac{x}{h} = \dfrac{h}{y}$

Leg means: $\dfrac{c}{a} = \dfrac{a}{x}$, $\dfrac{c}{b} = \dfrac{b}{y}$

TRIANGLE, RIGHT (Isosceles)

Leg: a

Hypotenuse: $c = a\sqrt{2}$

TRIANGLE, RIGHT (30°–60°)

Shorter leg: a

Longer leg: $b = \sqrt{3}a = a\sqrt{3}$

Hypotenuse: $c = 2a$

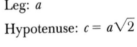

Teacher: ". . . and now I want to
  prove this theorem."
Pupil: "Why bother to prove it,
  teacher? I take your word for it."

Postulates and Theorems

Chapter 2

Chapter 3

Theorem 41 The area of a trapezoid is half the product of its altitude and the sum of its bases. 359

Theorem 42 *The Pythagorean Theorem.* The square of the hypotenuse of a right triangle is equal to the sum of the squares of its legs. 366

Theorem 43 *Converse of the Pythagorean Theorem.* If the square of one side of a triangle is equal to the sum of the squares of the other two sides, the triangle is a right triangle. 366

Chapter 10

Theorem 44 *The Side-Splitter Theorem.* If a line parallel to one side of a triangle intersects the other two sides in different points, it divides the sides in the same ratio. 393

Corollary If a line parallel to one side of a triangle intersects the other two sides in different points, it cuts off segments proportional to the sides. 394

Theorem 45 *The AA Theorem.* If two angles of one triangle are equal to two angles of another triangle, the triangles are similar. 400

Corollary Two triangles similar to a third triangle are similar to each other. 401

Theorem 46 Corresponding altitudes of similar triangles have the same ratio as that of the corresponding sides. 408

Theorem *The SAS Similarity Theorem.* If an angle of one triangle is equal to an angle of another triangle and the sides including these angles are proportional, then the triangles are similar. 412

Theorem *The SSS Similarity Theorem.* If the sides of one triangle are proportional to the sides of another triangle, then the triangles are similar. 412

Theorem 47 The ratio of the perimeters of two similar polygons is equal to the ratio of the corresponding sides. 415

Theorem 48 The ratio of the areas of two similar polygons is equal to the square of the ratio of the corresponding sides. 416

Chapter 11

Theorem 49 The altitude to the hypotenuse of a right triangle forms two triangles similar to it and to each other. 429

Corollary 1 The altitude to the hypotenuse of a right triangle is the geometric mean between the segments into which it divides the hypotenuse. 429

Corollary 2 Each leg of a right triangle is the geometric mean between the hypotenuse and its projection on the hypotenuse. 429

Theorem 50 *The Isosceles Right Triangle Theorem.* In an isosceles right triangle, the hypotenuse is $\sqrt{2}$ times the length of a leg. 442

Corollary Each diagonal of a square is $\sqrt{2}$ times the length of one side. 442

Theorem 51 *The 30°-60° Right Triangle Theorem.* In a 30°-60° right triangle, the hypotenuse is twice the shorter leg and the longer leg is $\sqrt{3}$ times the shorter leg. 442

Corollary An altitude of an equilateral triangle having side s is $\dfrac{\sqrt{3}}{2}s$ and its area is $\dfrac{\sqrt{3}}{4}s^2$. 443

Theorem 52 Two nonvertical lines are parallel iff their slopes are equal. 463

Theorem 53 Two nonvertical lines are perpendicular iff the product of their slopes is -1. 463

Theorem 54 *The Law of Sines.* If the sides opposite $\angle A$, $\angle B$, and $\angle C$ of $\triangle ABC$ have lengths a, b, and c, then
$$\frac{\sin A}{a} = \frac{\sin B}{b} = \frac{\sin C}{c}.\quad 469$$

Theorem 55 *The Law of Cosines.* If the sides opposite $\angle A$, $\angle B$, and $\angle C$ of $\triangle ABC$ have lengths a, b, and c, then
$c^2 = a^2 + b^2 - 2ab \cos C$. 469

Chapter 12

Chapter 15

Postulate 11 If two points lie in a plane, the line that contains them lies in the plane. 619

Postulate 12 If two planes intersect, they intersect in a line. 619

Postulate 13 *Cavalieri's Principle.* Consider two geometric solids and a plane. If every plane parallel to this plane that intersects one of the solids also intersects the other so that the resulting cross sections have equal areas, then the two solids have equal volumes. 641

Postulate 14 The volume of any prism is the product of the area of its base and its altitude: $V = Bh$. 642

Theorem 79 The length of a diagonal of a rectangular solid with dimensions l, w, and h is $\sqrt{l^2 + w^2 + h^2}$. 629

Corollary The length of a diagonal of a cube with edges of length e is $e\sqrt{3}$. 629

Corollary 1 to Postulate 14 The volume of a rectangular solid is the product of its length, width, and height: $V = lwh$. 642

Corollary 2 to Postulate 14 The volume of a cube is the cube of its edge: $V = e^3$. 642

Theorem 80 The volume of any pyramid is one-third of the product of the area of its base and its altitude: $V = \dfrac{1}{3}Bh$. 648

Theorem 81 The volume of a cylinder is the product of the area of its base and its altitude: $V = Bh = \pi r^2 h$. 655

Theorem 82 The volume of a cone is one-third of the product of the area of its base and its altitude: $V = \dfrac{1}{3}Bh = \dfrac{1}{3}\pi r^2 h$. 656

Theorem 83 The volume of a sphere is $\dfrac{4}{3}\pi$ times the cube of its radius: $V = \dfrac{4}{3}\pi r^3$. 664

Theorem 84 The surface area of a sphere is 4π times the square of its radius: $V = 4\pi r^2$. 665

Theorem 85 If the ratio of a pair of corresponding dimensions of two similar solids is r, then the ratio of their surface areas is r^2. 672

Theorem 86 If the ratio of a pair of corresponding dimensions of two similar solids is r, then the ratio of their volumes is r^3. 672

Chapter 16

Theorem 87 The summit angles of a Saccheri quadrilateral are equal. 698

Theorem 88 The line segment connecting the midpoints of the base and summit of a Saccheri quadrilateral is perpendicular to both of them. 698

Theorem 89 If the legs of a birectangular quadrilateral are unequal, the summit angles opposite them are unequal in the same order. 698

Theorem 90 If the summit angles of a birectangular quadrilateral are unequal, the legs opposite them are unequal in the same order. 698

The Lobachevskian Postulate The summit angles of a Saccheri quadrilateral are acute. 703

Lobachevskian Theorem 1 The summit of a Saccheri quadrilateral is longer than its base. 703

Lobachevskian Theorem 2 A midsegment of a triangle is less than half as long as the third side. 703

Lobachevskian Theorem 3 The sum of the angles of a triangle is less than 180°. 708

Corollary The sum of the angles of a quadrilateral is less than 360°. 708

Lobachevskian Theorem 4 If two triangles are similar, they must also be congruent. 708

Answers to Selected Exercises

Chapter 1, Lesson 1 (pages 10–11)
2. 12 cm. 5. 1.4 cm. 7. 3 mi. 14. Line segments. 21. Three. 25. Six; AB, AG, AC, AF, AD, AI.

Chapter 1, Lesson 2 (pages 15–17)
2. $\angle$C. 6. Rays AC and AB. 10. $\angle$B = 30°. 13. Collinear. 16. $\angle$1 = 68°. 22. $\angle$I = 117°.
25. Approximately $1\frac{3}{4}$ ft. 28. Approximately $3\frac{1}{4}$ ft. 30. 34°.

Chapter 1, Lesson 3 (pages 21–22)
2. 9 in^2. 3. 12 in. 4. 36 in^2. 5. 24 in. 13. Piece I because it has four sides. 16. Ranch A. 23. Polygons. 25. Eight. 28. Three. 30. A line. 32. 75.6 ft.

Chapter 1, Lesson 4 (pages 26–29)
5. Noncollinear. 11. The bisecting lines seem to be concurrent. 16. No. 17. West. 21. About 6 A.M. and 6 P.M. 23. OI bisects $\angle$HOJ. 25. $\angle$DOB and $\angle$EOA. 31. 60°. 33. 180°.

Chapter 1, Lesson 5 (pages 31–34)
1. 100 square units. 6. It contains 80 square units. 8. 54 square units. 11. It contains 84 square units.

Chapter 1, Review (pages 36–38)
2. Polygons (or squares). 5. 12. 8. Coplanar. 10. PQ. 13. T. 18. Constructions. 20. $\angle$DAB = 110°. 25. $\angle$DCF = $\angle$FCE = 40°.

Chapter 1, Algebra Review (page 40)
1. Associative for addition. 2. Commutative for multiplication. 3. Definition of subtraction. 4. Identity for addition. 5. Definition of division. 6. Inverse for multiplication. 7. 1,728. 8. 12,000. 9. 20. 10. −75. 11. 225. 12. 81.

13. 49π. 14. 14π. 15. $5x$. 16. x^5. 17. $5x$. 18. x^5. 19. $2x + 3y$. 20. x^2y^3. 21. $x^2 + y^3$. 22. $x^3 + y^2$. 23. $x + 2y$. 24. xy^2. 25. $7x^2$. 26. $7x^2$. 27. $5x^2$. 28. $5x^2$. 29. $4x^2 + 3x$. 30. $3x^3 + 2x^2 + x$. 31. x^{14}. 32. x^{14}. 33. $6x^5$. 34. $6x^5$. 35. $36x^2$. 36. $72x^5$. 37. $4x + 4y$. 38. $4x + 4y$. 39. $2x$. 40. $2x$. 41. 0. 42. 1. 43. $5x + 10y$. 44. $3x + 4y$. 45. $5x - 10y$. 46. $3x - 4y$. 47. $31xy$. 48. $25xy$. 49. $7 + x^3 + x^5$. 50. $10x^8$.

Chapter 2, Lesson 1 (pages 43–45)
1. A conditional statement. 4. You live in the Ozarks. 6. Yes. 14. If an animal is a koala bear, then it eats only eucalyptus leaves. 18. If I don't understand, then I ask questions. 21. If at first you don't succeed, then try again. 24. Regions 1 and 2. 28. The second. 35. Statements c and d.

Chapter 2, Lesson 2 (pages 47–49)
3. If a creature has two legs, then it is a goose. 5. You are not more than six feet tall. 9. If you do not know how to reason deductively. 13. They have the same meaning. 21. Yes. The converse must be true because this is a definition. 26. No. 28. It is the converse. 32. Sentence 2. 35. It is the converse.

Chapter 2, Lesson 3 (pages 52–54)
2. If you keep quiet, others will think you are wise. 4. All Greeks are humans. All humans are mortals. Therefore, all Greeks are mortals. 7. No. 8. The hypothesis. 12. It also may be false. 16. A theorem. 18. If you go to Dallas, you will see the yellow rows of taxis. 22. 21. 26. Red. Because the label is wrong.

Chapter 2, Lesson 4 (pages 57–59)
1. Contradiction. 3. Suppose that it would not speak foul language. 6. No. 10. It is the opposite of the theorem's conclusion. 11. The earth is not flat. 14. That it is false.

15. *Beginning assumption:* Suppose that the pupils can obey the teacher. *Contradiction:* There are 13 pupils at the black desks but only 12 brown desks. *Conclusion:* The pupils can't obey the teacher.

Chapter 2, Lesson 5 (pages 61–64)
3. You go around in circles. 6. Two points determine a line. 8. Theorems. 12. The points. 18. Converse. 20. True. 22. False. 26. A picul is 1,600 taels. 32. Statements 1 and 3. 37. Two points determine a line.

Chapter 2, Lesson 6 (pages 67–70)
1. The length of the hypotenuse of a right triangle. 5. The area of a circle. 9. No. 12. $2\pi, 4\pi, 6\pi, 8\pi$, and 10π units. 13. 9π square units. 18. 30°. 21. 70°. 24. No. 26. Approximately 50 mm². 32. Yes, because the sum of the other two angles could be 1°. 34. a^2. 38. To the left.

Chapter 2, Review (pages 71–74)
1. If something is a limerick, then it has five lines. 9. Collinear. 11. A postulate. 13. If it rains, then it pours. 18. 50°. 20. Three noncollinear points determine a plane. 23. Square. 32. Theorems. 34. 144 square units. 37. 20 ft. 41. Direct. 44. $2\pi r$. 48. $4r^2$.

Chapter 2, Algebra Review (page 76)
1. $10x$. 2. $16x^2$. 3. $6x + 5$. 4. $4x - 5$. 5. $6x^2$. 6. $-6x^2$. 7. $9x + 4y$. 8. $3x + 2y$. 9. $5x + 15$. 10. $44 - 11x$. 11. $18x + 6$. 12. $40 - 56x$. 13. $9x^2 - 18x$. 14. $20x + 6x^2$. 15. $x^2y + xy^2$. 16. $2x^2 - 4x + 8$. 17. 10. 18. 8. 19. 3. 20. 6. 21. 13. 22. 9. 23. -7. 24. 5. 25. 60. 26. 0. 27. -12. 28. 37. 29. -2. 30. 4.5. 31. 12. 32. Any number.

Chapter 3, Lesson 1 (pages 80–82)
1. Subtraction. 2. Substitution. 10. Addition. 14. No number (because there is no number when multiplied by 0 that gives 6). 19. If $a = b$ and $c \neq 0$, then $\dfrac{a}{c} = \dfrac{b}{c}$. If $c = d$,

then $\dfrac{a}{c} = \dfrac{b}{d}$ by substitution. 21. Substitution. 25. $a^2 + b^2$. 26. $2ab$. 28. $(a + b)^2$. 32. Substitution. 38. Division. 41. A direct proof.

Chapter 3, Lesson 2 (pages 86–90)
4. The definition of betweenness of points. 7. 52. 9. BC + CD = BD, or 5 + 6 = 11. 15. 92,760,000 mi. 17. 17. 20. 9 − 2 = 7. 26. A, −25; B, 15. 30. B. 35. AB + BC is greater than AC. 38. AC = AB + BC.

Chapter 3, Lesson 3 (pages 93–97)
6. The definition of betweenness of rays. 8. Rays. 11. The coordinates. 13. Acute. 16. 15. 22. Obtuse. 25. 14.4°. 26. Yes. 29. 28.8°. 31. ∠SCP + ∠PCK = ∠SCK. 35. 27. 38. They are the same. 41. Betweenness of Rays Theorem. 44. 20°. 50. 360. 51. 15.

Chapter 3, Lesson 4 (pages 100–104)
3. Figures that can be made to coincide (or fit exactly together). 7. Then it divides it into two equal segments. 9. Each is the converse of the other. 15. No. 19. 45°. 22. 67.5°. 26. The midpoint of a line segment divides it into two equal segments. 28. 1.5. 31. 2 cm. 32. 2π (or about 6.28). 42. 180. 44. They are each 36°.

Chapter 3, Lesson 5 (pages 107–109)
1. 90°. 4. 87°. 8. 30°. 9. 150°. 16. ∠DOW + ∠WOF = ∠DOF. 19. 27°. 26. Betweenness of Rays Theorem. 28. Substitution. 35. 75°. 37. ∠S seems to be 90° larger than ∠C. 42. They are supplementary.

Chapter 3, Lesson 6 (pages 112–115)
1. Because they are vertical angles. 7. They are a linear pair and they are supplementary. 12. 80°. 14. They are vertical angles. 16. No. 23. Two. 26. 180°. 30. These angles are linear pairs; so they are supplementary. 36. Vertical angles are equal. 37. ∠3 = ∠1 + 90°. 45. 179°59′58.25″.

Chapter 3, Lesson 7 (pages 119–121)

1. Two angles are complementary if their sum is 90°. 4. Supplements of the same angle are equal. 6. If the angles in a linear pair are equal, then their sides are perpendicular. 10. Vertical angles are equal. 14. DH, AE, and, if perspective is taken into account, HG, EF. 17. They are a linear pair. 21. They are perpendicular. 24. $\angle 1$ and $\angle 3$ look like vertical angles, yet they are not equal. 30. $\angle$BOX, 25°; $\angle$BOY, 65°. 33. 180°. 37. They are perpendicular.

Chapter 3, Review (pages 124–128)

1. Yes. E-F-H because $6.1 < 7.7 < 10.8$. 5. $(180 - x)$°. 8. The handle is perpendicular to the blade. 11. CE-CS-CD. 13. 41.5. 18. 110. 23. They would be perpendicular. 28. Any number is equal to itself. 34. $(6 + x)$ ft. 38. $\angle$AOB $= (90 - x + y)$°. 43. Hexagons. 46. Six. 50. 150. 53. 120 steps per minute. 56. 6,480 inches per minute.

Chapter 3, Algebra Review (page 130)

1. $6x + 1$. 2. $2x - 4y$. 3. $4x^2 + 8$. 4. $3x^2 + 6x - 5$. 5. $12x - 3$. 6. $x^3 + 4x^2 - x - 8$. 7. $14x - 5y$. 8. $7x + 4$. 9. $6x$. 10. $-x^2 - 11x$. 11. $2x^2 + 10x - 1$. 12. $2x^3 + y^3$. 13. $x^2 + 14x + 24$. 14. $6x^2 - 7x - 20$. 15. $16x^2 - 1$. 16. $x^3 - 10x^2 - 23x + 6$. 17. $4y^3 - 8y^2 + 13y - 5$. 18. $x^3 + y^3$. 19. $5x^3 + 3x^2 - 20x - 12$. 20. $x^3 + 5x^2 - 12x - 36$. 21. -49. 22. $100x^2 - 20x + 1$. 23. $x^3 + 12x^2 + 48x + 64$. 24. $-4x + 5$.

Chapter 4, Lesson 1 (pages 134–138)

3. A and E. 5. B. 7. A(4, 3), C(−3, −4). 9. On the y-axis. 12. Two. 16. The fourth (IV). 19. The hummingbirds. 23. Point A. 27. A(4, 1), B(6, 6). AB $= \sqrt{29} \approx 5.39$. 31. A$_1$(5, 2), A$_2$(15, 2). 35. (900, 200). 37. 1,000 pixels. 41. $\sqrt{18}$ or $3\sqrt{2}$.

Chapter 4, Lesson 2 (pages 141–144)

2. The vertices. 4. A 32-gon. 6. That they are congruent. 8. They are right angles (and equal). 11. Line segments AB and EF intersect two others but not at their endpoints. 12. △AEG. 17. CBEG. 25. An octagon (an 8-gon). 27. D. 31. H. 34. HBCFIE $\leftrightarrow$ MNIEHK. 40. Convex. 45. No. 48. 21 square units. 53. No.

Chapter 4, Lesson 3 (pages 148–150)

1. BF and BP. 3. $\angle$B. 5. SAS. 10. TR = AN. 11. $\angle$I = $\angle$G. 15. Two triangles congruent to a third triangle are congruent to each other. 17. All the angles are acute. 20. None of the sides are equal. 22. All three. 29. 35°. 31. They get larger. 34. About 5.9 cm. 38. Perpendicular lines form right angles. 41. ASA. 44. Both are pairs of opposite rays.

Chapter 4, Lesson 4 (pages 153–155)

2. The midpoint of a line segment divides it into two equal segments. 7. Corresponding parts of congruent triangles are equal. 10. ASA. 17. If the angles in a linear pair are equal, then their sides are perpendicular. 19. Hexagons. 20. △ABX $\cong$ △CBX. 26. No. △BDC is larger than △ADB. 35. AB = 7, AC = 4, BC $= \sqrt{65} \approx 8.1$. 37. △ABC and △DEF would coincide. 38. The x-coordinates are equal; the y-coordinates are opposites. 40. SAS. 44. Yes.

Chapter 4, Lesson 5 (pages 159–162)

3. $\angle$ABD and $\angle$ADB. 4. BD. 6. No. 8. If two sides of a triangle are equal, the angles opposite them are equal. 12. That it has at least two equal sides. 21. Addition. 22. Betweenness of Rays Theorem. 23. Substitution. 28. They appear to be parallel. 30. $\angle$S = $\angle$B = 72°. 38. 92.2°. 39. Obtuse. 43. A pentagon. 44. Because its sides intersect in points other than their endpoints. 50. They seem to be congruent. 52. It seems to be equilateral (and equiangular).

Chapter 4, Lesson 6 (pages 165–167)

1. SSS. 2. Corresponding parts of congruent triangles are equal. 5. They are a linear pair. 10. Five. 11. No. 16. CA = CB and AD = BD. 18. SSS. 24. SAS. 29. ∠ADC = ∠CBA because they are corresponding parts of congruent triangles. 38. SSS. 40. OC bisects ∠AOB. 42. Because an angle has exactly one ray that bisects it (the corollary to the Protractor Postulate).

Chapter 4, Lesson 7 (pages 172–175)

1. A compass. 2. Distances between points. 5. A line segment is bisected. 11. ∠2 is complementary to ∠1. 12. Copying an angle. 18. It means equally distant. 25. Addition. 26. Substitution. 36. SSS. 37. Height = 7.5 in; width = 10 in.

Chapter 4, Review (pages 176–180)

2. Because they have the same size and shape (they can be made to coincide). 4. They are all equal. 8. Statement 4. 13. An equilateral triangle is equiangular. 15. Substitution. 17. 60°. 19. 120°. 21. 30°. 25. SSS. 29. 90°. 33. 45°. 38. $\sqrt{4 + 16} = \sqrt{20}$ (or $2\sqrt{5} \approx 4.5$). 40. At $(-5, 3)$. 46. Seven.

Chapter 4, Algebra Review (page 182)

1. $2(3x - 1)$. 2. $3(2x - 1)$. 3. $2(3x - 2)$. 4. $4(x + 3y)$. 5. $x(x + 10)$. 6. $x^2(3x - 2)$. 7. $5(3\pi - 8)$. 8. $2x(4 + y)$. 9. $x(a + b - c)$. 10. $2\pi r(h + r)$. 11. $(x + 4)(x + 4)$ or $(x + 4)^2$. 12. $(x + 4)(x - 4)$. 13. $(x + 3)(x + 10)$. 14. $(x - 2)(x + 15)$. 15. $(x + 7)(x - 6)$. 16. $(2x - 1)(x - 7)$. 17. $(3x - 5)(x + 2)$. 18. $x(x - 4y)$. 19. $(x - 2y)(x - 2y)$ or $(x - 2y)^2$. 20. $(x + 2y)(x - 2y)$. 21. $\pi(a + r)(a - r)$. 22. $5x(x + 2)(x - 2)$. 23. $x(x + 4)(x - 3)$. 24. $z(2x - 3)$. 25. $(x + 2)(2x - 3)$.

Chapter 5, Lesson 1 (pages 186–189)

1. Either $h > w$, $h = w$, or $h < w$. 6. The transitive property. 8. Multiplication. 11. Addition. 14. AB > BC. 15. Substitution. 20. ∠APB > ∠HPI. 22. ∠PIH < ∠PBA. 26. Transitive.

Chapter 5, Lesson 2 (pages 192–194)

1. ∠BCY, ∠BAX, ∠CAD(∠YAD). 3. It gets smaller. 6. An exterior angle of a triangle is greater than either remote interior angle. 9. ∠2, ∠5, ∠8. 10. Two. 16. Two. 19. △ROS. 20. ∠ROA > ∠SRO and ∠ROA > ∠S. 25. No. It does not form a linear pair with an angle of the triangle. 26. 360°. 28. 180°. 32. A line segment has exactly one midpoint. 37. The "whole greater than part" theorem. 39. Two points determine a line. 41. The angles in a linear pair are supplementary. 43. An exterior angle of a triangle is greater than either remote interior angle.

Chapter 5, Lesson 3 (pages 197–199)

3. Each is the converse of the other. 4. BC < AC. 8. ∠A > ∠B. 10. If two sides of a triangle are unequal, the angles opposite them are unequal in the same order. 14. ∠B. 18. ∠A ≈ 29°, ∠B ≈ 104°, ∠C ≈ 47°. 19. DE. 22. DF ≈ 4.5 cm, EF ≈ 5.4 cm. 23. ∠X > ∠Y. 30. ∠BDE. 34. BE bisects ∠ABC. 36. Yes. They are congruent by ASA. 42. FG < GH because both are sides of △FGH in which GH is the longest side. 45. An equilateral triangle is equiangular. 47. The "whole greater than part" theorem.

Chapter 5, Lesson 4 (pages 202–204)

2. DP + PH > DH. 6. They are collinear. 7. Yes; 160 million miles. 10. PA + PB > 12, PA + PC > 12, and PB + PC > 12. 17. A, B, and C are not collinear. 19. AB + BC = AC. 24. An angle has exactly one line that bisects it. 27. Substitution. 28. If two angles of a triangle are unequal, the sides opposite them are unequal in the same order. 33. The sum of any two sides of a triangle is greater than the third side. 35. Substitution. 44. 5.5 m.

30. The "whole greater than part" theorem. 34. ∠A ≈ 83°, ∠B ≈ 56°, ∠C ≈ 41°. 37. 9 units. 41. That the line is "upright" (contains the center of the earth).

Chapter 5, Review (pages 206–209)
5. The "three possibilities" property.
7. Both dimensions are 2.5 in.   12. One angle has a measure of 179°, and the other two angles are each less than 1°.   16. The midpoint of a line segment divides it into two equal segments.   17. Reflexive.   20. If the angles in a linear pair are equal, their sides are perpendicular.   22. If two angles of a triangle are unequal, the angles opposite them are unequal in the same order.   24. Transitive.
26. The small angles each appear to be equal to 10°.   29. An exterior angle of a triangle is greater than either remote interior angle.
34. $n > 2$.   37. One.   39. Yes.   41. SSS.
43. Betweenness of Rays Theorem.

Chapter 5, Algebra Review (page 210)
1. $\dfrac{4}{5}$.   2. $\dfrac{3x}{8}$.   3. $\dfrac{1}{x}$.   4. $\dfrac{x+1}{2}$.   5. $\dfrac{4}{7}$.

6. $\dfrac{1}{3}$.   7. $\dfrac{1}{x-5}$.   8. $\dfrac{x}{y}$.   9. $\dfrac{x+3}{10}$.

10. $\dfrac{x-4}{x-6}$.   11. $\dfrac{4}{4x}$.   12. $\dfrac{x^3}{x^4}$.   13. $\dfrac{-3}{x-2}$.

14. $\dfrac{8}{12}$ and $\dfrac{9}{12}$.   15. $\dfrac{28}{7x}$ and $\dfrac{2}{7x}$.

16. $\dfrac{y}{xy}$ and $\dfrac{x}{xy}$.   17. $\dfrac{3x}{3x+6}$ and $\dfrac{2}{3x+6}$.

18. $\dfrac{5(x+1)}{(x-1)(x+1)}$ or $\dfrac{5x+5}{x^2-1}$ and $\dfrac{x}{(x-1)(x+1)}$

or $\dfrac{x}{x^2-1}$.   19. $\dfrac{x^2}{xyz}$ and $\dfrac{y^2}{xyz}$.

Chapter 6, Lesson 1 (pages 214–217)
4. Yes, because W and E are equidistant from the endpoints of NS.   12. 6 cm.   13. 90 ft.
15. In the west.   19. Seven.   21. Line l is the perpendicular bisector of ST.   22. If a line segment is bisected, it is divided into two equal segments.   31. 9.5 in.   34. C and E; D and F.   36. Because they are corresponding parts of congruent triangles ($\triangle ABC \cong \triangle ADC$ by SSS).   39. N.   43. Three.

Chapter 6, Lesson 2 (pages 221–224)
1. (1) $\angle 1 = \angle 2$. (2) $\angle 2 = \angle 3$. (3) $\angle 1 = \angle 3$.

(4) $a \parallel b$.   4. Alternate interior angles.
6. In a plane, two lines perpendicular to a third line are parallel.   7. Corresponding angles.
9. Equal corresponding angles mean that lines are parallel.   14. No.   18. AE $\parallel$ BF.
27. No. These angles are not formed by a transversal. They could be equal and yet lines x and y could intersect either to the left or right.   32. Four.   35. SAS.   38. No.

Chapter 6, Lesson 3 (pages 226–229)
1. 12.   2. If they form a right angle.
5. $\angle 3$.   6. Equal corresponding angles mean that lines are parallel.   12. At least, no more than, exactly.   14. No more than.
20. They form equal corresponding angles with a transversal.   22. They seem to be supplementary.   25. All four of them.
27. Down, below the figure.   30. One.
33. In a plane, two lines perpendicular to a third line are parallel.   36. Through a point not on a line, there is exactly one line parallel to the line.   37. Yes. (SAS.)   42. a and b are not parallel.   43. Given.

Chapter 6, Lesson 4 (pages 232–235)
1. They are equal.   2. Parallel lines form equal corresponding angles.   5. (1) Given.
(2) Parallel lines form equal corresponding angles. (3) Vertical angles are equal.
(4) Substitution.   9. Betweenness of Rays Theorem.   12. Equal corresponding angles mean that lines are parallel.   13. $\angle 1 = 115°$, $\angle 2 = 65°$, $\angle 3 = 115°$.   17. They must be perpendicular because, in a plane, a line perpendicular to one of two parallel lines is also perpendicular to the other.   20. 67°, 113°, 67°, and 113°.   22. $\angle 1$ and $\angle 2$ are supplementary because parallel lines form supplementary interior angles on the same side of a transversal.   24. $\angle 3 = \angle 4$ because parallel lines form equal alternate interior angles.   30. Through a point not on a line, there is exactly one line parallel to the line (the Parallel Postulate).   31. Parallel lines form equal alternate interior angles.   37. Two points determine a line.   39. In a plane, two lines perpendicular to a third line are parallel.

44. The length of a perpendicular segment between them.   46. 70°.

45°.   42. BA = CD by substitution.
48. ∠CDB = 2x°.   50. ∠ACB = 3x°.

Chapter 6, Lesson 5   (pages 238–241)
1. The sum of the angles of a triangle is 180°.
2. Substitution.   3. Substitution.
4. Subtraction.   9. An equilateral triangle is equiangular.   10. An equiangular triangle has three equal angles.   14. Through a point not on a line, there is exactly one line parallel to the line.   16. Parallel lines form equal corresponding angles.   19. ∠2 > ∠1 and ∠2 > ∠A.   24. An equilateral triangle.
27. It is a right triangle.   28. They are complementary.   34. ∠2 and ∠3 are complementary.   36. Complements of the same angle are equal.   40. An exterior angle of a triangle is equal to the sum of the remote interior angles.   41. Substitution.

Chapter 6, Lesson 6   (pages 245–248)
1. ASA.   5. HL.   6. Parallel lines form equal corresponding angles.   9. Three.
12. Yes.   19. HL.   21. If two angles of a triangle are equal, the sides opposite them are equal.   24. In a plane, two lines perpendicular to a third line are parallel.
27. Substitution.   29. AAS.   32. AB = AC, AD = AE, and ∠A = ∠A.   40. Because ∠DAP = ∠EAP (corresponding parts of congruent triangles are equal).   42. SSS.
44. 45°.   50. Substitution.

Chapter 6, Review   (pages 250–254)
1. Fold the figure along the proposed line of symmetry and see if the two halves coincide.
5. It is the perpendicular bisector of AB.
7. Equal corresponding angles mean that lines are parallel.   9. To the sum of the remote interior angles.   12. They are perpendicular.
14. Are equal, their sides are perpendicular.
16. In a plane, *two points each* equidistant from the endpoints of a line segment determine the perpendicular bisector of the line segment.
26. Equilateral.   30. In a plane, two lines perpendicular to a third line are parallel.
33. In a plane, a line perpendicular to one of two parallel lines is also perpendicular to the other.   35. Concurrent.   39. ∠B = ∠CAD =

Chapter 6, Algebra Review   (page 256)

1. $\dfrac{7}{6}$.   2. $\dfrac{x}{20}$.   3. $\dfrac{x + 10}{2x}$.   4. $\dfrac{4x - 3}{x^3}$.

5. $\dfrac{2}{3}$.   6. $\dfrac{x^6}{8}$.   7. $\dfrac{5}{7}$.   8. $\dfrac{x + 2}{2}$.

9. $\dfrac{3x}{4}$.   10. $\dfrac{1}{5}$.   11. $\dfrac{1}{6}$.   12. $\dfrac{2}{x}$.

13. $\dfrac{4x + 2y - z}{8}$.   14. $\dfrac{4\pi r^3}{3}$.   15. $\dfrac{x - y}{y}$.

16. $\dfrac{2(x - 3)}{2x - 3}$ or $\dfrac{2x - 6}{2x - 3}$.   17. $\dfrac{x + 2}{x^2 - 1}$.

18. $\dfrac{1 + x}{x - y}$.   19. 1.   20. $\dfrac{x^3}{x - 1}$.

Chapter 7, Lesson 1   (pages 260–264)
1. Two points determine a line.   3. Addition.   6. The sum of the angles of a quadrilateral is 360°.   9. A quadrilateral each of whose angles is a right angle is a rectangle.
10. Each angle of a rectangle is a right angle.
14. Lines that form right angles are perpendicular.   17. They seem to be parallel and equal.   21. They are equiangular (or each of their angles is a right angle).
26. 2x + 2y = 180°.   29. 144°.   31. SSS.
37. Triangles, quadrilaterals, and an octagon.
40. Six sides, three diagonals, and four triangles.   43. n − 3.   46. 720°.   47. 120°.
50. (n − 2)180°.   52. Their sum is 360°.
54. They all appear to be smaller.

Chapter 7, Lesson 2   (pages 267–269)
2. Point.   3. See if the figure looks exactly the same when it is turned upside down.
4. Three.   5. Yes. The opposite sides of a parallelogram are equal.   8. An exterior angle of a triangle is greater than either remote interior angle.   11. The opposite sides of a parallelogram are parallel.   15. A line segment is bisected if it is divided into two equal segments.   17. The diagonals of a parallelogram bisect each other.   18. Two points are symmetric with respect to a point if it is the midpoint of the line segment

connecting them. 26. 10. 30. About 24°.
32. $\angle AEB = x°$, $\angle CED = y°$. 35. AD = 2DC.
37. 180°. 45. All three.

Chapter 7, Lesson 3   (pages 272–275)
1. A quadrilateral is a parallelogram if its
opposite sides are equal. 3. Parallel lines
form equal corresponding angles. 4. In a
plane, if a line is perpendicular to one of two
parallel lines, it is also perpendicular to the
other. 8. Supplementary interior angles on
the same side of a transversal mean that lines
are parallel. 13. SAS. 15. A quadrilateral
is a parallelogram if its opposite sides are
equal. 20. Equal alternate interior angles
mean that lines are parallel. 21. A
quadrilateral is a parallelogram if two opposite
sides are both parallel and equal. 22. Line
symmetry. The figure can be folded along a
vertical line so that the two halves coincide.
26. No. Line symmetry (one vertical line).
29. They seem to be parallel. 32. The pairs
of opposite angles. 37. A quadrilateral is a
parallelogram if its diagonals bisect each other.
39. SSS. 43. A quadrilateral is a rectangle if
all of its angles are equal. 47. 12. 53. They
are the sides of the quadrilaterals above and
below the braced square.

Chapter 7, Lesson 4   (pages 277–280)
1. 12. 2. Three. 5. 15. 7. All of the
angles of a rectangle are equal. 10. A
quadrilateral is a parallelogram if its opposite
sides are equal. 12. All rectangles are
parallelograms. 17. All of the sides of a
rhombus are equal. 19. Two consecutive
sides. 24. No. It must be a rectangle.
31. A quadrilateral is a parallelogram if its
opposite sides are equal. 34. A quadrilateral
all of whose angles are equal is a rectangle.
36. False. 39. True. 43. Its opposite sides
are parallel.

Chapter 7, Lesson 5   (pages 282–285)
1. A trapezoid. 2. That it has exactly one
pair of parallel sides. 4. That all of its
angles are right angles (or that they are equal).
5. Yes. All rectangles are parallelograms.
8. Point. 10. They seem to be congruent.

11. Trapezoids. 13. No. The legs of a
trapezoid must be equal for it to be isosceles.
16. The bases of a trapezoid are parallel.
17. Through a point not on a line, there is
exactly one line parallel to the line. 19. The
opposite sides of a parallelogram are equal.
22. If two sides of a triangle are equal, the
angles opposite them are equal. 25. Parallel
lines form supplementary interior angles with
a transversal. 30. The base angles of an
isosceles trapezoid are equal. 36. 75°.
40. Parallel lines form equal corresponding
angles. 41. 105°. 46. AC and DB bisect each
other. 47. A quadrilateral is a parallelogram
if its diagonals bisect each other. 49. A
trapezoid has only one pair of opposite sides
parallel.

Chapter 7, Lesson 6   (pages 288–291)
2. A midsegment. 5. DE ∥ AC, and
$DE = \frac{1}{2}AC$. 8. A midsegment of a triangle
is parallel to the third side. 9. In a plane,
two lines parallel to a third line are parallel to
each other. 10. A midsegment of a triangle
is half as long as the third side. 13. MNPQ
is a parallelogram because two opposite sides
are both parallel and equal. 17. Addition.
18. Substitution. 20. The sum of its
diagonals. 24. $\angle A = \angle C$ because the base
angles of an isosceles trapezoid are equal.
28. (4, 7). 29. (8, 10). 32. 5. 35. They
should be parallel. 38. They are congruent
by SSS. 43. A rhombus. 49. MN seems to
be parallel to AB and DC, the bases of the
trapezoid.

Chapter 7, Review   (pages 292–295)
2. Both pairs of its opposite sides are parallel.
4. AAS. 7. Substitution. 9. Four.
13. All of the sides and angles of a square are
equal. 16. If a line divides an angle into
two equal parts, it bisects the angle. 21. True.
27. True. 31. The sum of the angles of a
quadrilateral is 360°. 33. The opposite
angles of a parallelogram are equal. 36. D,
E, and F. 42. GI ⊥ HM and ML ⊥ HM.
In a plane, two lines perpendicular to a third
line are parallel. 45. $2c$.

49. A trapezoid.   51. No, because a trapezoid has two parallel sides.   56. IJKL is a trapezoid because IJ ∥ LK.

Chapter 7, Algebra Review   (page 296)
1. 2.236.   2. 22.36.   3. 223.6.   4. 7.07.
5. 70.7.   6. $10\sqrt{5}$.   7. $100\sqrt{5}$.   8. $5\sqrt{2}$.
9. $50\sqrt{2}$.   10. $5\sqrt{x}$.   11. $x^2\sqrt{x}$.   12. $x\sqrt{\pi}$.
13. $2x^6\sqrt{3}$.   14. $\sqrt{49}\sqrt{3} + \sqrt{3} = 7\sqrt{3} + \sqrt{3} = 8\sqrt{3}$.   15. $\sqrt{150} = \sqrt{25}\sqrt{6} = 5\sqrt{6}$.
16. $5\sqrt{7}$.   17. $5\sqrt{21}$.   18. $2\sqrt{15}$.   19. $6\sqrt{5}$.
20. 14.   21. 10.   22. $7\sqrt{6}$.   23. 11.
24. $24\sqrt{10}$.   25. 63.   26. $3\sqrt{5}$.   27. 10.
28. 23.   29. $9 + \sqrt{3}$.   30. $4\sqrt{3} + 1$.
31. $2\sqrt{x} + 2\sqrt{y}$.   32. $x + 2\sqrt{xy} + y$.

Chapter 8, Lesson 1   (pages 300–304)
1. A translation.   3. A rotation.
6. A reflection.   16. Exercises 9, 11, and 14.
17. Each has a vertical line of symmetry.
20. Yes.   25. A translation.   28. They are parallelograms because they have two sides that are both parallel and equal.
31. The opposite sides of a parallelogram are equal.   36. Betweenness of Rays Theorem.
37. Substitution.   43. A dilation.
44. They seem to be twice as long.
52. A translation.   56. A rotation.

Chapter 8, Lesson 2   (pages 308–311)
4. $2x$ units.   5. It is the segment's perpendicular bisector.   7. A rotation.   9. 180°.   14. Its image looks the same.   18. B.   22. A reflection.   24. Yes, because it is the composite of two reflections in intersecting lines.   27. C and E.   28. 120°.   30. No. The figure does not look exactly the same upside down.   32. E.   35. E.   37. A translation.
41. A rotation.   44. If a point is reflected through a line, the line is the perpendicular bisector of the segment connecting the point and its image.   46. Its magnitude.   48. SAS.

Chapter 8, Lesson 3   (pages 314–316)
3. A reflection.   5. A glide reflection.
8. ∠PAB and ∠PCD.   10. The opposite sides of a parallelogram are equal.   14. A reflection.   17. The magnitude of the

rotation.   18. The lines bisect these angles.
22. They are the perpendicular bisectors of these line segments.   25. Two figures are congruent if there is an isometry such that one figure is the image of the other.   27. D.
29. G.   35. No, because the two dogs are not mirror images of each other.   39. A translation and a reflection.   42. B′(14, 9), C′(9, 6).
43. $6\sqrt{2}$.   46. M(11, 4), N(12, 5), P(8, 1).

Chapter 8, Lesson 4   (pages 321–324)
1. Rotation (or point) symmetry.   6. It has reflection (line) symmetry with respect to a line through home plate and second base.
12. The point itself.   14. A line looks the same if it is rotated 180°.   16. A line has reflection symmetry because it can be reflected (folded) onto itself.   19. That rays OA and OD are opposite rays and that rays OB and OC are opposite rays.   22. In a plane, two points each equidistant from the endpoints of a line segment determine the perpendicular bisector of the line segment.   25. They bisect each other.   30. Translation.   33. 22.5°.
34. No.   36. 16.   38. The y-axis.
42. Even.   45. Because it can be translated (in various directions) and look exactly the same.

Chapter 8, Review   (pages 325–329)
6. No.   8. A glide reflection.   9. A rotation.   11. That it can be rotated so that it looks the same in three positions.   17. Yes.
20. A reflection.   24. Two figures are congruent if there is an isometry such that one figure is the image of the other.   29. A translation.   31. About 47°.   36. Because △ADC is the reflection image of △ABC.
37. It has reflection (line) symmetry with respect to line AC.   41. 45°.   47. No.

Chapter 9, Lesson 1   (pages 340–342)
3. Its area is equal to the sum of the areas of its nonoverlapping parts.   7. True, because △ADC ≅ △ABC.   9. True, because $\alpha\triangle ADC - \alpha\triangle 1 - \alpha\triangle 2 = \alpha\triangle ABC - \alpha\triangle 4 - \alpha\triangle 3$.
14. $2x$ square units.   16. $(x + y)$ square units.
20. They are both concave octagons.
23. $3a + 6b$.   26. They are congruent (SSS)

and therefore equal in area. 30. No.
31. Yes. Each one contains two of the four
triangles, all of whose areas are equal.
35. $\frac{1}{6}$ square unit. 37. 2 square units.
42. It is equilateral and equiangular.
43. BFED contains four of the congruent
triangles, and ABCD contains two of them.
44. 4 square units. 49. They are both equal
to AB. 50. Because DF = DC + CF =
CF + FE = CE.

Chapter 9, Lesson 2 (pages 345–349)
1. 20 ft. 4. 3,600 in^2. 8. Four.
11. $a(b + c)$. 12. ab and ac. 14. $(a + b)^2$.
19. Two congruent triangles. 22. $\sqrt{26}$.
25. No. 28. 2,592 nails. 30. 66 ft.
34. 6,400 square chains. 37. 84 cm^2.
38. 17.5%. 40. 21.6 ft long. 43. The total
surface area of the walls. 47. 1,728 in^2.
48. 189 in^2.

Chapter 9, Lesson 3 (pages 353–357)
1. 6 square units. 5. $\frac{1}{4}c^2$. 6. The area of
a right triangle is half the product of its legs.
7. The area of a polygonal region is equal to
the sum of the areas of its nonoverlapping
parts (the Area Postulate). 9. Substitution.
15. They seem to be equal. 17. $\triangle$ABC, 40
units; $\triangle$DEF, 80 units. 21. They seem to stay
the same. 27. αABCD $\approx$ 99.87 square
chains. 29. The area of a triangle is half the
product of any base and corresponding
altitude. 31. Substitution. 33. Division.
35. 84 square units. 36. 11.2 units. 41. In
a plane, two points each equidistant from the
endpoints of a line segment determine the
perpendicular bisector of the line segment.
42. Betweenness of Points Theorem.
48. $\alpha\triangle$AMB = $\alpha\triangle$AMD = 20.25 in^2; $\alpha\triangle$BMX =
$\alpha\triangle$DMY = 6.75 in^2; $\alpha\triangle$CMX = $\alpha\triangle$CMY =
13.5 in^2. 52. About 1,200 shingles.

Chapter 9, Lesson 4 (pages 360–364)
1. That they are equal. 2. 2,800 ft^2.
6. Area = $\frac{1}{4}(s + s)(s + s) = \frac{1}{4}(2s)(2s) = s^2$.

8. 260 square units. 14. 1,369 square units.
17. A parallelogram. (Two of its opposite sides
are both parallel and equal.) 18. 1 unit.
$A = bh = (1)(1) = 1$. 23. 30,794 ft^2.
26. 4.5 ft^2. 28. 8.25 ft^2. 32. 675 m^2.
35. 3,696 m^2. 41. Its area is $(a + b)h$.
43. In a plane, two lines perpendicular to a
third line are parallel. 46. 165 square units.
50. $\triangle$EBH, FHCG (and FHCD).

Chapter 9, Lesson 5 (pages 367–370)
2. 2, 2, and 4 units. 4. The Ruler Postulate.
5. The Protractor Postulate. 8. The square
of the hypotenuse of a right triangle is equal to
the sum of the squares of its legs.
9. Substitution. 12. Substitution. 15. 12.
16. 1,225. 18. 37. 26. No. 256 + 225 =
481 ≠ 484. 33. 6 units. 35. 25 units.
37. $2ab$. 38. $(b - a)^2$. 43. The acute angles
of a right triangle are complementary (so the
sum of these angles is 90°). 45. A trapezoid.
49. It appears to bisect ABDE (that is, divide it
into two congruent parts having equal areas).

Chapter 9, Review (pages 371–375)
1. 125 m^2. 3. 525. 4. Camp A, 68 paces;
camp B, 64 paces; camp C, 60 paces.
8. 16 units. 12. The area of a polygonal
region is equal to the sum of the areas of its
nonoverlapping parts. 14. $\angle$DEY.
16. AAS. 18. Corresponding parts of
congruent triangles are equal. 20. Triangles
with equal bases and equal altitudes have
equal areas. 23. 11. 27. $4a$. 29. $4a + 4b$.
30. $a(a + 2b)$ or $a^2 + 2ab$. 34. 216 ft^2.
38. 332.5 ft^2. 40. It would be four times as
great. 44. $\alpha\triangle$AEF = $2x$ (because AF = 2AC
and BH = EG). 46. $4x^2 - xy$. 47. $4x - y$.
51. It would be rectangular.

Chapter 9, Algebra Review (page 376)
1. 500. 2. $\frac{1}{5}$ or 0.2. 3. 2.5. 4. ±10.
5. −3. 6. 42. 7. 15. 8. 20. 9. 41.
10. 3.5. 11. 0. 12. 8. 13. 5. 14. 5.
15. −36.

Chapter 10, Lesson 1 (pages 380–384)

1. 2.25.   4. The geometric mean.

5. $\dfrac{9}{6} = \dfrac{6}{4}$.   8. $h \approx 45$ ft.   9. $\dfrac{2}{7}$.

15. Division.   19. Rectangles 2 and 4.

22. 30.   28. 36 in; $\dfrac{36}{15} = 2.4$.   31. $\dfrac{19}{10}$.

36. The width of one stripe.

37. Approximately 12.3 ft.   39. Approximately

122 ft.   41. $\dfrac{9}{8}$.   42. $\dfrac{256}{243}$.   48. The means

are interchanged.   50. Division.

Chapter 10, Lesson 2 (pages 387–391)

1. They are proportional.   2. They are equal.

3. $\angle DAC = \angle FBC$.   6. $\dfrac{AD}{BF} = \dfrac{DC}{FC}$.

9. OE = 4 and OG = 8.   13. 24.2.   15. The

center of the dilation.   18. $\dfrac{1}{2}$.

20. Corresponding sides of similar polygons
are proportional.   24. A midsegment of a
triangle is parallel to the third side.
28. Division.   30. Betweenness of Points
Theorem.   34. Two triangles are similar if
their corresponding angles are equal and their
corresponding sides are proportional.
35. OC = 56 mm; $r_2 = 2.0$.   37. BF = 24 mm;

$\dfrac{BF}{AE} = \dfrac{24}{21} \approx 1.1$.   42. Approximately

840 mm.   44. Approximately 1 m². 47. $\sqrt{2}$.
49. $w = 0$.

Chapter 10, Lesson 3 (pages 394–398)

2. If a line parallel to one side of a triangle
intersects the other two sides in different
points.   7. The area of the rectangle.
8. As lengths: AC = 3, AD = 2, and AE = 6.

13. $\dfrac{AC}{CO} = \dfrac{AP}{PB}$.   17. Substitution. (Both are

equal to $\dfrac{AP}{PB}$).   18. $x = 2.4$.   22. Reasonable

because BE ∥ CF in △OCF (the Side-Splitter
Theorem).   26. It is a parallelogram because
DF ∥ EB and DF = EB.   29. If a line parallel

to one side of a triangle intersects the other
two sides in different points, it divides the
sides in the same ratio.   36. EO.   39. Point
G is the same point as point A.

41. EF = FG; so $\dfrac{EF}{FG} = 1$ by division.

43. In a plane, two lines perpendicular to a third
line are parallel.   45. The opposite sides of a
parallelogram are equal.

Chapter 10, Lesson 4 (pages 401–405)

1. Parallel lines form equal corresponding
angles.   3. AA.   6. Yes. Two triangles
similar to a third triangle are similar to each
other.   10. 30°, 30°, and 120°.
14. Corresponding sides of similar triangles
are proportional.   17. They are not
collinear.   19. That they are parallel.
21. △AHK ~ △ABD and △AKL ~ △ADE.

23. $\dfrac{HK}{BD} = \dfrac{KL}{DE}$.   27. Addition.   28. Multi-

plication.   31. △ABD ~ △CBA.   34. $x = 8$,
$y = 10$, and $z = 10$.   39. AA ($\angle A = \angle EFA$

and $\angle FHA = \angle A$).   45. $\dfrac{a}{s} = \dfrac{b}{b - s}$.

Chapter 10, Lesson 5 (pages 409–413)

1. CG and CF.   4. Corresponding altitudes.
7. CG, the distance of the fish from the
camera.   10. 7.5 cm.   12. 2.5.   15. 0.4.
18. r_2 is the reciprocal of r_1.   21. Yes.
Corresponding sides of similar triangles are
proportional.   23. No. These areas cannot be
equal if △AGB is larger.   26. B′(7, 2), C′(17, 8).
27. △A′B′C′ appears to be an enlargement of
△ABC. (Also, the corresponding sides of the
two triangles appear to be parallel.)
31. 555.4 ft.   34. Corresponding altitudes of
similar triangles have the same ratio as that of
the corresponding sides.   35. ASA.   36. AA.
40. Ruler Postulate.   41. Through a point
not on a line, there is exactly one line parallel
to the given line.   47. Parallel lines form
equal corresponding angles.   49. AA.
53. Reflexive.   55. Corresponding sides of
similar triangles are proportional.   58. SSS
Congruence Theorem.

Chapter 10, Lesson 6 (pages 416–419)

1. $\frac{1}{2}$. 2. $\frac{1}{4}$. 10. 8 m. 11. 32 m.

12. 64 m². 19. $\frac{4}{5}$. 21. $\frac{16}{25}$. 25. They

must be proportional. 28. 440.

30. $\frac{1}{63,360}$. 32. Yes. $\triangle$ADE $\sim$ $\triangle$ABC by AA.

34. No. 37. Six. 40. $\frac{1}{2}$. 44. Because all

circles have the same shape. 46. $90\pi \approx 283$ ft

and $120\pi \approx 377$ ft. 48. $\frac{3}{4} = 0.75$.

53. 921 ft.

Chapter 10, Review (pages 421–424)

1. $\frac{1}{2}$. 4. $\frac{5}{12}$. 9. 2.5. 10. It is 6.25 times

as great. 12. 6.4. 14. 12.8. 17. Concave pentagons. 18. ABHIG $\cong$ EKJGI.
20. GFEI is a parallelogram. Both pairs of its
opposite sides are equal because
GFEKJ $\cong$ EIGJK. 25. It increases. 30. 2.

32. They are multiplied by 3. 34. $\frac{10}{x} = \frac{x}{5}$.

Approximately 7.1 cm. 36. $\frac{\sqrt{2}}{2} \approx 0.71$.

41. In a plane, two lines parallel to a third line
are parallel to each other. 46. 30 ft.

48. 70 ft. 53. $\frac{EF}{20} = \frac{6}{8}$; EF = 15. 55. $\frac{4}{3}$.

56. 80. 58. $\frac{16}{9}$.

Chapter 10, Algebra Review 1 (page 425)

1. 4 and -7. 2. 1 and $-\frac{1}{5}$. 3. $4 + \sqrt{11}$ and

$4 - \sqrt{11}$. 4. 7 and -7. 5. $-2 + 2\sqrt{6}$ and

$-2 - 2\sqrt{6}$. 6. $\frac{1}{3}$. 7. $\frac{4}{3}$ and -3.

8. 2 and 5. 9. -1 and -8.

10. $\frac{1 + \sqrt{26}}{5}$ and $\frac{1 - \sqrt{26}}{5}$.

Chapter 10, Algebra Review 2 (page 426)

1. $r = \frac{c}{2\pi}$. 2. $p_1 = \frac{p_2 v_2}{v_1}$. 3. $v_2 = \frac{p_1 v_1}{p_2}$.

4. $c = \sqrt{a^2 + b^2}$. 5. $a = \sqrt{c^2 - b^2}$.

6. $h = \frac{2A}{b}$. 7. $h = \frac{V^2}{2g}$. 8. $r = \sqrt{\frac{A}{4\pi}}$ or

$r = \frac{1}{2}\sqrt{\frac{A}{\pi}}$. 9. $R = \frac{E}{I}$. 10. $h = \frac{3V}{\pi r^2}$.

11. $a = S(1 - r)$ or $a = S - Sr$. 12. $r = \frac{S - a}{S}$

or $r = 1 - \frac{a}{S}$. 13. $w = \frac{8M}{L^2}$. 14. $w_1 = \frac{W^2}{w_2}$.

15. $r = \frac{R}{A - 150}$. 16. $A = \frac{R + 150r}{r}$ or

$A = \frac{R}{r} + 150$. 17. $d = \sqrt{\frac{1}{E}}$. 18. $l = \frac{gT^2}{4\pi^2}$.

19. $A = \frac{I_n - I_x}{d^2}$. 20. $d = \sqrt{\frac{I_n - I_x}{A}}$.

21. $R = \frac{r_1 r_2}{r_1 + r_2}$. 22. $r_1 = \frac{Rr_2}{r_2 - R}$.

23. $n = -\frac{vr + vu}{ur - vu}$ or $n = -\frac{v(r + u)}{u(r - v)}$ or

$n = \frac{vr + vu}{vu - ur}$ or $n = \frac{v(r + u)}{u(v - r)}$.

24. $C = \frac{5}{9}(F - 32)$. 25. $v = c\frac{f_0^2 - f_s^2}{f_0^2 + f_s^2}$.

Chapter 11, Lesson 1 (pages 430–432)

2. The altitude to the hypotenuse. 3. AP
and PC. 5. EP. 6. EP and EG.
11. Their projections on the hypotenuse.
12. AC. 15. 4. 17. $2\sqrt{10}$ (or about 6.32).

18. 4.05. 21. 16. 26. $\frac{9}{16}$. 29. False.

33. $4\sqrt{6}$. 35. $\frac{\sqrt{2}}{1}$ (or $\sqrt{2}$). 37. 113 in².

38. $\frac{OA}{OB} = \frac{OB}{OC}$. 41. r^2. 42. r^3. 48. 5.

Chapter 11, Lesson 2 (pages 436–440)

1. 30 ft.   2. About 95 ft.   5. About 101 ft.
8. 8 cubits.   12. 20 ft.   15. About 8.7 ft.
18. $7^2 + 24^2 = 49 + 576 = 625 = 25^2$.   21. Each number in 14-48-50 is twice the corresponding number in 7-24-25.   23. 6-8-10 and 9-12-15.
28. AB.   29. $y_2 - y_1$.   31. $d = 5x$.
33. 8.4 in by 11.2 in.   35. $\dfrac{27}{14}$ or about 1.9.
38. $OH = \sqrt{45}$ or $3\sqrt{5}$, $OP = \sqrt{65}$, $PH = \sqrt{20}$ or $2\sqrt{5}$.   42. The length of AP.
43. $x^2 + 20^2 = (40 - x)^2$; $x = 15$.

53. $D = R - \sqrt{R^2 - B^2}$.

Chapter 11, Lesson 3 (pages 443–447)

1. Yes. They are similar by AA.   2. $\dfrac{a}{1} = \dfrac{c}{\sqrt{2}}$.

3. $c = a\sqrt{2}$.   4. $a = \dfrac{c}{\sqrt{2}}$.   5. In an isosceles right triangle, the hypotenuse is $\sqrt{2}$ times the length of one leg.   11. $c = \dfrac{2b}{\sqrt{3}}$.   15. $8\sqrt{2}$.

16. $5\sqrt{2}$.   17. $x = 12$, $y = 6\sqrt{3}$.   19. $x = 5\sqrt{3}$, $y = 10\sqrt{3}$.   23. $\sqrt{3}$.   24. $4\sqrt{3}$.
27. $90\sqrt{2} \approx 127$ ft.   30. $75\sqrt{3} \approx 130$ ft.
31. About 23 in.   34. 21 square units.

39. $\dfrac{x}{2}$.   43. $OA = \dfrac{1}{2}$, $AP = \dfrac{1}{2}\sqrt{3}$.

44. $\left(-\dfrac{1}{2}, \dfrac{1}{2}\sqrt{3}\right)$.   53. $\dfrac{1}{2}$ or 0.5.   54. $\dfrac{\sqrt{3}}{4}$.

Chapter 11, Lesson 4 (pages 450–453)

1. $\dfrac{c}{b}$.   3. $\dfrac{f}{d}$.   4. 0.445.   6. 57.290.

7. 5.711°.   11. $\tan A = \dfrac{a}{b} = \dfrac{a}{a} = 1$.

13. $\angle A > 45°$.   14. $\tan A > 1$.

18. $\tan 60° = \dfrac{BC}{AC} = \dfrac{b\sqrt{3}}{b} = \sqrt{3}$.   22. A right triangle because $3^2 + 4^2 = 5^2$.   24. $\dfrac{4}{3}$.

25. 37°.   27. $\angle A < \angle B$; $\angle A$ and $\angle B$ are complementary.   29. 16.5.   32. 20°.
35. 58°.   39. 197 ft.   43. About 22 ft.
46. 3.7°.   48. 26.565051°.   51. $AB = \sqrt{5}$, $BC = \sqrt{10}$, and $AC = \sqrt{5}$.   53. 40.8°.

55. About 4,172 mi.

Chapter 11, Lesson 5 (pages 456–460)

1. $\dfrac{h}{a}$ or $\dfrac{b}{x + y}$.   2. $\dfrac{h}{y}$ or $\dfrac{a}{b}$.   3. $\dfrac{y}{b}$ or $\dfrac{b}{x + y}$.

7. 0.996.   10. 82.935°.   11. 45.000°.

14. $\dfrac{12}{13}$.   15. 67°.   20. $\dfrac{5}{13}$.   23. 5.3.

25. 61°.   26. 36.5.   29. $BH = 2.6$ cm, $CI = 5.0$ cm, $DJ = 7.1$ cm, $EK = 8.7$ cm, and $FL = 9.7$ cm.   36. The sine of an acute angle of a right triangle is the ratio of the length of the opposite leg to the length of the hypotenuse.   38. In a 30°-60° right triangle, the side opposite the 30° angle is half the hypotenuse.   40. Approximately 14,500 ft, or more than 2.7 mi.   43. About 806 ft.
46. About 4°.   48. Parallel lines form equal alternate interior angles.   49. AAS.

51. 5a.   57. $\sin \angle 2 = \dfrac{d - w}{h}$.

Chapter 11, Lesson 6 (pages 463–467)

1. h.   3. The x-axis.   5. e.   6. j, $\dfrac{1}{4}$; e, -4.

11. The slope is $\tan 30° \approx 0.58$.   13. -60 m.

16. About 3.4°.   18. $\dfrac{5}{9}$ (or about 0.56).

23. $\dfrac{3}{11}$.   27. $-\dfrac{3}{2}$.   36. Its run is 550 m, and its rise is -10 m.   39. $\left(300 - \dfrac{x}{55}\right)$ m above the ground.   40. 16,500 m.   42. $Run = x - x_1$; $rise = y - y_1$.   43. $y = m(x - x_1) + y_1$.
47. From the start to about 2.5 seconds.

52. $\dfrac{AC}{BC}$.   56. Corresponding sides of similar triangles are proportional.   58. Division.
60. l_2.   62. The altitude to the hypotenuse of a right triangle is the geometric mean between the segments of the hypotenuse.

Chapter 11, Lesson 7 (pages 471–474)

2. They are opposite each other.   4. The Law of Sines.   7. They include $\angle A$.   12. 40°.
13. 17.0.   15. 60°.   16. 32.0.

18. $\dfrac{\sin \angle 1}{y} = \dfrac{\sin \angle 4}{x}$.   21. 108°.   25. 56°.

26. 27.7 mi.   28. 34.6 mi.   32. 238,000 mi.

34. $a^2 = b^2 + c^2 - 2bc \cos A$.   35. $\cos A = \dfrac{1}{2}$.

40. By multiplication.   44. $c^2 = a^2 + b^2$.

Chapter 11, Review   (pages 476–480)

1. 2.   5. $-\dfrac{4}{3}$.   8. HF $\perp$ BG.   11. $d = s\sqrt{2}$.

15. 28 ft.   16. About 24.2 ft.   19. About
195 ft.   21. About 5.7°.   26. Two.
30. 20 ft.   31. About 27.5 ft.   34. About
81.5 ft.   35. 0.87.   40. 7 units.
43. AF = BF.   47. About 44 ft.   53. About

380 times as far.   55. Approximately $\dfrac{1}{3}$ in.

57. About 600 ft.   62. $\tan \angle ABE = \dfrac{h - x}{d}$.

Chapter 11, Algebra Review   (page 482)

1. $y = -\dfrac{3}{4}x + 6$.   2. $m = -\dfrac{3}{4}$; $b = 6$.

3.

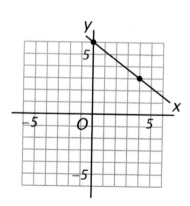

4.

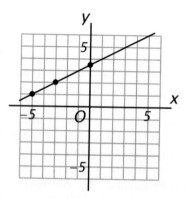

5. $y - 1 = \dfrac{1}{2}(x + 5)$.   6. $y = \dfrac{1}{2}x + \dfrac{7}{2}$.

7. $b = \dfrac{7}{2}$ (or 3.5).

8.

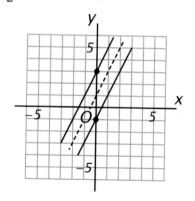

9. They have the same slope, 2.
10. $y = 2x + 1$.   11. $y = -x + 5$; $y = x - 3$.
12.

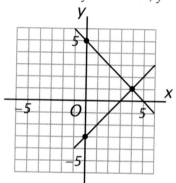

13. -1 and 1.   14. The product of their

slopes is -1.   15. $-\dfrac{1}{3}$.   16. -6.

17.

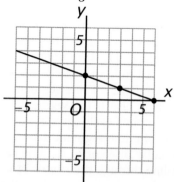

18. $y = -\dfrac{1}{3}x + 2$.   19. x-intercept, 6;

y-intercept, 2.   20. $x + 3y = 6$.

21.

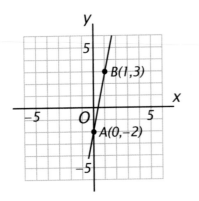

22. 5.　23. $y - 3 = 5(x - 1)$.　24. $y = 5x - 2$.

25. $5x - y = 2$.　26. $y = \frac{4}{3}x$ (or $y = \frac{4}{3}x + 0$).

27. $m = \frac{4}{3}$; $b = 0$.

28.

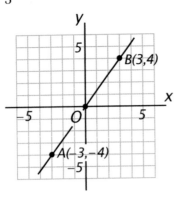

29. 0.　30. 10.

Chapter 12, Lesson 1　(pages 486–490)

2. Chords.　3. A diameter.　6. Five.
9. Six.　10. Concentric.　14. They are
perpendicular.　17. Two points determine a
line.　18. All radii of a circle are equal.
22. If a line divides a line segment into two
equal parts, it bisects the segment.　26. In a
plane, two points each equidistant from the
endpoints of a line segment determine the
perpendicular bisector of the line segment.
27. If a line through the center of a circle
bisects a chord that is not a diameter, it is also
perpendicular to the chord.　28. Through a
point not on a line, there is exactly one line
perpendicular to the line.　34. An isosceles
right triangle.　35. About 46 mm.　38. 1,000

seconds.　40. $\frac{10}{27}$, or about 0.37.　45. They
are rhombuses because all of their sides are equal.

Chapter 12, Lesson 2　(pages 493–496)

2. In a plane, two lines perpendicular to a
third line are parallel to each other.
4. OB ⊥ AC.　5. If a line through the center
of a circle bisects a chord that is not a
diameter, it is also perpendicular to the chord.

9. $\frac{4}{3}$.　10. $-\frac{3}{4}$.　15. AB is tangent to circle

O.　16. If a line is perpendicular to a radius
at its outer endpoint, it is tangent to the circle.

18. $\frac{AB}{1}$, or AB.　32. Because $\angle FDE$ is a right

angle and corresponding parts of congruent
triangles are equal.　34. Line AB.　36. If a
line is tangent to a circle, it is perpendicular
to the radius drawn to the point of contact.
41. AD = 4 cm and AF = AB = 8 cm.
42. $(8 - r)$ cm.　44. A 3-4-5 right triangle.
48. A parallelogram (also, a rectangle).

Chapter 12, Lesson 3　(pages 500–503)

1. Central angles.　2. $\overset{\frown}{PJ}$.　3. $\overset{\frown}{PCJ}$.
5. 283°.　7. 77°.　8. Two points determine
a line.　10. An arc is equal in measure to its
central angle.　16. The Arc Addition
Postulate.　19. A semicircle.　24. No. The
sum of any two sides of a triangle is greater
than the third side.　27. AB = r, BC = $r\sqrt{3}$,
AC = 2r.　31. △ABC and △ABD are
equilateral and congruent.　33. Line l is
tangent to circle A. If a line is perpendicular
to a radius at its outer endpoint, it is tangent
to the circle.　41. All of the arcs have the
same measure.

Chapter 12, Lesson 4　(pages 506–509)

2. 147°.　3. 24.5°.　4. 33°.　7. All radii of
a circle are equal.　9. An exterior angle of a
triangle is equal to the sum of the remote
interior angles.　12. A central angle is equal
in measure to its intercepted arc.
15. Betweenness of Rays Theorem.　17. Arc
Addition Postulate.　20. An inscribed angle
is equal in measure to half its intercepted arc.

22. The measure of a semicircle is 180°.
25. A 90° angle is a right angle.
28. Inscribed angles. 30. $x = 40°$, $y = 20°$, and
$z = 30°$. 33. 9°. 36. They are complementary.
37. It is a right angle. An angle inscribed in a
semicircle is a right angle. 43. $n°$. 44. $2n°$.
50. It is an altitude (to the hypotenuse) of the
triangle. 52. BF = $\sqrt{3}$ in.

Chapter 12, Lesson 5 (pages 512–515)
2. An exterior angle of a triangle is equal to
the sum of the remote interior angles. 3. An
inscribed angle is equal in measure to half its
intercepted arc. 5. 36°. 7. 54° and 126°.
10. Subtraction. 14. 40°. 15. 75°.
18. 55°. 19. A secant angle. 20. It is less
than 55°. 23. $m\overgroup{AD} + m\overgroup{CB} = 180°$.
27. 72°. 29. 36°. 34. 20°. 40. If a line
through the center of a circle bisects a chord
that is not a diameter, it is also perpendicular
to the chord. 42. 17 ft. 45. Each angle
is 90°. 48. About 92.5 days. 51. 6°.

Chapter 12, Lesson 6 (pages 517–521)
3. HL. 7. Inscribed angles that intercept the
same arc are equal. 9. Corresponding sides
of similar triangles are proportional.
12. The tangent segments to a circle from an
external point are equal. 19. Right angles.
An angle inscribed in a semicircle is a right
angle. 24. CFOE is a square. 31. PA is
tangent to circle O because it is perpendicular
to radius OA at its outer endpoint.
33. PA = PB = 10. 35. 20 units.
41. (12, 10). 45. If a line through the center
of a circle is perpendicular to a chord, it also
bisects the chord. 46. BP.

Chapter 12, Review (pages 523–526)
2. A central angle. 7. 60°. 9. 35°.
10. 16.5. 15. 30°. 18. 60°.
25. AB = AD. The tangent segments to a circle
from an external point are equal. 27. They
are similar to △ABC. 29. $\frac{1}{2}$. 34. PB $\perp$ AC.
36. Isosceles. (In the figure, they are also
obtuse.) 40. 4 cm. 42. Approximately 3.7
cm. 44. Approximately 68°. 46. 53°.
47. 74°. 51. C is the midpoint of AB.

52. Approximately 9.7 in. 53. Approxi-
mately 75.5°. 56. $\sqrt{5}$. 58. $\dfrac{\sqrt{5} + 1}{2}$.

Chapter 12, Algebra Review (page 528)
1. (8, 8). 2. (7, 14). 3. (11, 9). 4. (3, −4).
5. (0, −1). 6. (5, 14). 7. (14, 5).
8. (3.5, 10.5). 9. (45, 9). 10. (−2, 1).
11. (−19, −2). 12. (0, −5). 13. (51, −16).
14. (3, −11). 15. (18.5, 0.9). 16. (−1, −10).
17. (11, −4). 18. (7, 1). 19. (7, 3).
20. (9, 2). 21. (4, 0). 22. (−1, 5).
23. (8, −2). 24. (0, −8).

Chapter 13, Lesson 1 (pages 532–535)
4. Its circumcircle. 5. △ABC is inscribed in
circle O. 6. They are equidistant from it.
7. Minor arcs. 13. A diameter (or a chord).
17. The lines are the perpendicular bisectors
of the sides of △ABC, and the perpendicular
bisectors of the sides of a triangle are concurrent. 19. No. 24. Three. 28. OA =
2OD because, in a 30°-60° right triangle, the
hypotenuse is twice the shorter leg.
32. The circumcenter of the triangle with A,
B, and C as its vertices. 36. It is approximately
6.4 cm. 39. They are concurrent on the
hypotenuse of the triangle. 40. 7.5 cm.
42. Both ∠E and ∠ABD intercept AD.
Inscribed angles that intercept the same arc
are equal. 47. Approximately 31 mm.
48. 31.25 mm. 51. sin D = $\dfrac{a}{2r}$.

Chapter 13, Lesson 2 (pages 538–541)
1. By seeing if a pair of opposite angles are
supplementary. 4. They must be concurrent.
8. Inscribed angles that intercept the same arc
are equal. 10. Substitution. 14. They are
isosceles because all radii of a circle are equal.
18. AB ∥ DC because they are bases of a
trapezoid. 21. ∠B and ∠D are supplementary.
24. They intersect in a common point, P.
30. ABCD is not cyclic, because its
opposite angles are not supplementary.
33. Vertical angles are equal. 34. Supplements
of the same angle are equal. 40. 1,764.
42. The Protractor Postulate.
46. Multiplication. 54. Substitution.

Chapter 13, Lesson 3 (pages 544–547)

1. The angle bisectors of a triangle are concurrent. 3. Two. 4. They are perpendicular bisectors of the sides. 5. The vertices of the triangle. 7. Two angle bisectors. 10. Its incircle. 11. Its incenter. 13. They are perpendicular to the sides. If a line is tangent to a circle, it is perpendicular to the radius drawn to the point of contact. 15. They must be concurrent. 17. Only if the rectangle is a square. 21. They are the perpendicular bisectors of the sides. 25. 2π and 4π units. 28. EF seems to be tangent to the incircle. 32. Exterior angles. 38. It proves that AP bisects $\angle$DAE. 40. FDEO is a square. 42. $2\pi r$ units. 46. $\dfrac{\pi}{4}$. 49. $3 - r$. 51. $7 - 2r$. 55. π square units. 59. The area of a triangle is half the product of its base and altitude. 61. $\dfrac{2\pi r}{p}$.

Chapter 13, Lesson 4 (pages 550–553)

4. The fact that the altitudes of a triangle form right angles with the lines of its sides.
5. Two points determine a line. 6. The Ruler Postulate. 8. A midsegment of a triangle is parallel to the third side. 11. A line segment that connects a vertex of a triangle to the midpoint of the opposite side is a median. 14. Through a point not on a line, there is exactly one line parallel to the line. 18. In a plane, a line perpendicular to one of two parallel lines is also perpendicular to the other. 23. GD and EH bisect each other. The diagonals of a parallelogram bisect each other. 28. $\triangle$ABC is obtuse. 29. No. The altitude *segments* do not intersect. 32. GE, AF, and CD. 33. At point B. 41. Corresponding sides of similar triangles are proportional. 42. Substitution. 49. PD and EC are altitudes of $\triangle$APE.

Chapter 13, Lesson 5 (pages 557–560)

1. CF. 5. No. GF is not a cevian, because neither of its endpoints is a vertex of the triangle. 6. 3.2. 8. Not concurrent. 11. 2. 15. That this product is 8. 18. That this sum

is 2. 21. 3. 24. AX = 4; XB = 6. 28. $\triangle$AXZ ~ $\triangle$CPZ and $\triangle$BXY ~ $\triangle$CPY. 32. Division (and substitution). 34. If a line parallel to one side of a triangle intersects the other two sides in different points, it divides the sides in the same ratio. 41. $\dfrac{AX}{BX} \cdot \dfrac{BY}{CY} \cdot \dfrac{CZ}{AZ} = 1$ (by Ceva's Theorem). 45. In a plane, a line perpendicular to one of two parallel lines is also perpendicular to the other. 52. $\triangle$AXC ~ $\triangle$AZB.

Chapter 13, Lesson 6 (pages 562–565)

1. AB and DC. 2. $-\dfrac{3}{2}$. 4. $\sqrt{13}$ units. 7. M(9, 0); L(3, 6). 8. (8, 4). 11. CN = NB = $\sqrt{72}$ or $6\sqrt{2}$. 16. mNT = 1 and mCB = -1. 18. (9, 3). 24. At V. 27. (6, 6). 36. 48 units. 38. 150°. 45. No. AC and CB are not perpendicular, because the product of their slopes is not -1. 46. G(3, 14); I(17, 14). 53. AB = DC = 6; AD = BC = $\sqrt{10}$. 57. mXZ = 9; mWY = $-\dfrac{1}{9}$.

Chapter 13, Review (pages 566–570)

2. $\triangle$ABC is inscribed in the circle. 6. $\triangle$ABC is a right triangle because $\angle$ACB is inscribed in a semicircle. 12. F. 14. IJKL. 18. Midsegments. 24. AX = 4, YB = 3, and ZC = 2. 28. Cyclic. 34. $\dfrac{3}{4}$ in. 36. $\angle$AED + $\angle$AGD = 180°. $\angle$AED and $\angle$AGD are supplementary because they are opposite angles of a cyclic quadrilateral. 38. $\angle$EGD = $\angle$EAD because they are inscribed angles that intercept the same arc. 39. $\angle$EGD = 60° because $\angle$EGD = $\angle$EAD. 42. $\angle$BHC = 120° because it is supplementary to $\angle$BFC. 48. 125°. 53. They appear to bisect its angles. 55. DB and FB. 61. ABCD is concave.

Chapter 14, Lesson 1 (pages 574–578)

3. The radii of the polygons. 5. Yes. If a triangle is equilateral, it is also equiangular. 8. No. 10. Yes. (*All* regular polygons are cyclic.) 13. 60°. 14. Equilateral.

18. Three squares. 20. They are factors of it.
21. Equilateral triangles and regular
pentagons. 27. Regular polygons having an
even number of sides. 31. If it isn't regular,
it must not be equiangular. 33. Isosceles
right triangles. 39. 22.5°. 41. 135°.
45. Apothems. 47. 30°-60° right triangles.
52. They are equal because the sides of the
pentagon are chords of the circle, and equal
arcs in a circle have equal chords. 54. 72°.

Chapter 14, Lesson 2 (pages 581–584)
2. The number of sides. 4. 3.0902.
10. Radii. 14. PB bisects $\angle ABC$.
16. 9 sin 20°. 17. 3.078. 21. The radius of
the hexagon appears to be longer. 22. 108°.
26. 5 sin 36° $\approx$ 2.94. 28. Approximately
2.13 angstroms. 31. 74 mm. 37. $r\sqrt{3}$.
39. $p \approx 5.196r$. 41. 2. 44. By the Law of
Sines. 45. Approximately 1.9.
48. Approximately 2.2. 49. 18°.
52. 3.0901699. . . .

Chapter 14, Lesson 3 (pages 587–590)
3. 0. 5. 1.30. 9. The perimeter of the
nonagon. 14. $4a^2$. 16. $r = a\sqrt{2}$. 18. $2r^2$.
22. 628 units. 28. 31,359 square units.

31. 30°-60° right triangles. 32. $\dfrac{r}{2}$.

34. $\dfrac{r^2}{4}\sqrt{3}$. 42. They are isosceles.

43. That they are 15°. 47. All are

$(2 \sin 15°)r \approx 0.518r$. 49. $\dfrac{1}{4}r^2$. 54. 7.1 cm.

57. 38 cm.

Chapter 14, Lesson 4 (pages 593–597)
2. π. 5. The circumference of the hat.
7. Approximately 1,500,780 mi. 10. πa.
16. 704 ft/minute. 17. 14π ft. 20. 10

units. 21. 8 units. 24. AC $= \dfrac{1}{2}$AB. If a

line through the center of a circle is
perpendicular to a chord, it also bisects the
chord. 26. 3.1415927. 28. $2\sqrt{2}$.
29. 2.83. 35. Approximately 24,880 mi.
36. Approximately 1,040 mi. 37. 1,040
mi/hour. 42. Approximately 19 mi/second.

45. $r^2 = \dfrac{5}{4}x^2$. 46. $r^2 = \dfrac{1}{2}y^2$.

49. $2a + 2b + 2c$. 52. 825 ft.
53. $\pi \approx 3.14$ in.

Chapter 14, Lesson 5 (pages 600–604)
1. 300 mi. 2. 940 mi. 3. 71,000 mi².
4. 15 mi. 5. 90 mi. 9. x^2. 12. 100
circular inches. 14. $3,600\pi$ cm². 15. $60t$
cm. 19. 36π square units. 23. π^2.
25. 6 units. 27. 3.1425. 31. $3\pi x^2$.
33. $(4 - \pi)x^2$. 35. $(5\pi - 8)x^2$.
36. $(3\sqrt{3} - \pi)x^2$. 42. 72.6. 43. 290.
47. $a + b$. 48. $\pi a^2 + \pi ab$ or $\pi a(a + b)$.

Chapter 14, Lesson 6 (pages 606–611)
1. A sector. 2. 45°. 3. $\dfrac{1}{4}\pi r$. 4. $\dfrac{1}{8}\pi r^2$.

5. The length of AB in meters.
8. 15,700 m². 9. About 6,220 mi.
12. 2,009 ft². 13. 887 ft². 16. πr^2. 18. 60°.

19. $\dfrac{1}{3}\pi x$. 22. x. 23. About 9 in.

25. About 0.0007 second. 27. 360°. 28. $\dfrac{1}{2\pi}$.

30. 57.3°. 31. 46 in. 32. 469 in².
34. 53°. 37. About 93 square units.
39. About 45 square units. 41. 63.66 m.
43. 103.77 m. 45. About 188 m. 47. $2\sqrt{2}$.
49. 4π. 50. 8. 51. $4\pi - 8$. 53. π.
58. 1,256.64 in². 62. 34.64 in.
64. 246 in². 66. $2a + b$. 67. $2a + 2b$.

Chapter 14, Review (pages 612–616)
2. It must be convex, equilateral, and
equiangular. 4. 120°. 6. 48°. 9. 3.12.
10. 3.05. 12. 6.24r. 15. About 420 turns.

18. $2\pi^2$. 20. 4π. 21. $\dfrac{\pi}{8}a^2$, $\dfrac{\pi}{8}b^2$, and $\dfrac{\pi}{8}c^2$.

24. $\dfrac{1}{2}\pi r^2$. 28. $\sqrt{3} \approx 1.732$. 29. $\dfrac{2}{3}\pi \approx 2.094$.

31. $\dfrac{4}{3}\pi - \sqrt{3} \approx 2.457$. 33. 45°. 34. 0.79.

35. $\sqrt{2} - 1$. 37. 0.98. 39. About 1,037 mi.
40. About 3,034 mi. 42. About 794 mi.
45. $\sqrt{2}$ (or about 1.414). 47. 8.78.
52. $\pi R^2 - \pi r^2$ or $\pi(R^2 - r^2)$. 55. 4π.

58. $(360 - 2x)°$. 59. $\dfrac{180 - x}{90}\pi$.

63. About 83 ft.

Chapter 15, Lesson 1 (pages 620–624)
1. The second. 7. It appears to be oblique to the ground. 8. A vertical plane.
10. That they lie in a horizontal plane.
11. No. AB is perpendicular to the floor if it is perpendicular to *every* line in the floor that passes through point B. 13. Parallelograms.
15. EFGH. 21. They intersect in line l (or they both contain it). 23. One plane must contain a line that is perpendicular to the other plane. 25. CF is perpendicular to plane EFGH. 27. If a plane intersects two parallel planes, it intersects them in parallel lines. 32. Three noncollinear points determine a plane. 33. If two points lie in a plane, the line that contains them lies in the plane. 34. They lie in it. 40. No. Two horizontal lines can be skew. They can also intersect. 42. About 91 cm. 43. About 62°. 45. SAS. 47. A quadrilateral is a parallelogram if its diagonals bisect each other.
55. Nine.

Chapter 15, Lesson 2 (pages 630–633)
1. Six. 2. Eight. 3. 12. 4. F.
7. CG, DH, EH, and FG. 10. 0.025 cm.
12. 0.225 cm^2. 14. 185 units. 15. 697 units. 18. $8x + 10 = 106$. 20. A regular hexagon. 21. $\triangle$HEM and $\triangle$HEN are congruent right triangles. 25. $\angle$EAC is a right angle. 28. An isosceles trapezoid.
30. 6 cm. 32. 45°. 33. 60°. 35. About 35°. 39. $3\sqrt{2}$ cm. 44. $\dfrac{\ell}{2}\sqrt{3}$. 46. 54.74°.
49. One. The structure appears to contain $27 + 1 = 28$ cubes.

Chapter 15, Lesson 3 (pages 635–638)
1. L, I, and E. 3. Prisms. 5. Two.
6. Three. 10. The bases. 12. n.
13. $n + 2$. 18. 1,624 ft^2. 19. A parallelogram. 20. BAB'C. 23. EDE'F.
26. They appear to be parallel and equal.
29. Pentagons. 33. 1,458 ft^2. 35. They are rectangles. 38. Yes. The bases of *every* prism are congruent. 44. AX > AE. 46. A right triangular prism. 50. $2n$.

Chapter 15, Lesson 4 (pages 642–646)
2. "x cubed." 4. Its volume. 5. 27.
7. 36. 8. 1,296. 12. About 1.6 ft^3.
14. 1,518,750 ft^3. 16. 1 m^3. 17. 6 m^2.
20. 12 m^2. 27. A right hexagonal prism and an oblique hexagonal prism. 31. 108 cubic units. 33. 288 cubic units. 34. 79 cm^3.
36. 55 cm^3. 38. 0.004 in. 40. 187.156 in^2.
41. $(a + b)^3$. 43. Two of them. 44. a^2b.
49. $ab + ac + bc + c\sqrt{a^2 + b^2}$. 51. 3 cm.
54. 236.5 ft^2. 55. 4,730 ft^3. 57. 9 ft^3.

Chapter 15, Lesson 5 (pages 649–653)
1. A pyramid. 2. Its apex. 4. A cross section. 5. A lateral face. 10. 128 cubic units. 12. 70 cubic units. 13. They are equal. 19. 576 yd^3. 22. $V = \dfrac{1}{3}Bh$.
23. 55.125 square units. 25. 385.875 cubic units. 28. $\dfrac{1}{6}x^3$. 30. $\dfrac{1}{2}x$. 33. 231,000 ft^2.
34. 612 ft. 35. 231,000 ft^2. 37. 92,000,000 ft^3. 38. $n + 1$. 43. It is a pyramid.
45. Isosceles right triangles. 46. $\dfrac{3}{4}s^2$.
47. $\dfrac{1}{6}s^3$. 48. $\dfrac{1}{3}a^2(x + h)$. 51. OM $= \dfrac{1}{2}a$ and PN $= \dfrac{1}{2}b$. 52. Corresponding sides of similar triangles are proportional.
53. $\dfrac{x + h}{x} = \dfrac{a}{b}$.

Chapter 15, Lesson 6 (pages 656–661)
6. Product. 10. Its axis. 11. The altitude.
12. The lateral surface. 13. The bases.
15. 45π in^3. 19. 7 in^2. 22. 4,800 m^3.
25. They have equal volumes.
26. Cavalieri's Principle. 27. 35π cm^2.
28. 110 cm^3. 31. 65%. 34. That they have the same length. 38. The diameter of its base. 41. 352 in^3. 42. πh^2. 44. It is multiplied by four. 48. 285 in^3. 52. $2\pi rh$.
54. A sector of a circle. 55. $2\pi r$. 57. πrl.

Chapter 15, Lesson 7 (pages 665–669)

1. They are equal. 2. It is four times as large. 3. About 12.6 km². 4. About 4.2 km³. 7. $\frac{1}{3}\pi x^3$. 11. All radii of a sphere are equal. 12. If a line is perpendicular to a plane, it is perpendicular to every line in the plane that passes through the point of intersection. 18. It decreases. 19. 212 cm³. 21. 0.7 gram/cm³. 28. $\frac{2}{3}\pi r^3$. 30. $\frac{3}{2}\pi r^2$. 33. Either leg of a right triangle is the geometric mean between the hypotenuse and its projection on the hypotenuse. 35. 3,895 mi. 38. About 15 hours. 39. About 13 hours. 44. 325,000,000 mi³. 47. The second expression.

Chapter 15, Lesson 8 (pages 672–676)

2. Two cubes are always similar. 6. It is multiplied by 9. 7. It is multiplied by 27. 10. It is multiplied by n^2. 11. It is multiplied by n^3. 13. 10.24. 14. 32.768. 17. That Gulliver's body was similar to their bodies. 20. About 3.6 times. 23. About 22 mm. 25. About 1.8 times. 30. $24x^2$. 32. $8x^3$. 35. The square. 38. $x = \sqrt[3]{2}$; $y = \sqrt[3]{4}$. 39. PA, 1; PB, 2; PC, 4; PD, 8. 40. It is twice as large. 45. Eight. 51. About 47 pounds. 52. About 93 pounds.

Chapter 15, Lesson 9 (pages 678–682)

1. Eight. 3. Quadrilateral. 6. Yes. 9. The area of the larger triangle is four times the area of the smaller one. 10. The surface area of the larger tetrahedron is $3^2 = 9$ times the surface area of the smaller one. 14. 12. 16. Three. 18. 20. 20. An icosahedron. 26. 12. 29. That they are congruent. 30. 180°. 34. 270°. 38. $\frac{\ell}{2}\sqrt{2}$. 41. $\frac{1}{6}e^3$. 44. $\angle ABP = 54°$ and $\angle BAP = 36°$. 45. 1.618. 46. About 1.8. 52. 0.714 unit. 53. 10.5 square units. 58. 2.8 cubic units.

Chapter 15, Review (pages 684–688)

1. 4 and 8. 3. They appear to be perpendicular. 10. 16 ft. 13. A prism and a pyramid. 15. 80,000 ft³. 18. It is four times as large. 21. 250,000. 23. 1,250,000,000. 25. $e\sqrt{2}$. 27. A regular tetrahedron. 29. $\frac{1}{6}e^3$. 30. $\frac{1}{3}e^3$. 36. $2\pi x^3$. 37. $\frac{2}{3}$. 40. $6\pi x^2$. 45. 40 square units. 50. The area of the horizontal cross section halfway up the barrel. 51. $\pi r^2 h$. 58. Four. 59. Six.

Chapter 16, Lesson 1 (pages 692–695)

1. At the center of the sphere. 2. A radius of the sphere. 3. Two hemispheres. 7. Euclidean geometry. 10. Both geometries. 16. 186°. 18. $\angle A = 72°$, $\angle B = \angle C = 60°$; $\angle A + \angle B + \angle C = 192°$. 22. Yes. 25. Arcs of great circles. 30. Both curves cannot correspond to lines. 31. One. 32. No. 40. No. The sum of the angles of $\triangle ABC$ is greater than 180°. 45. It has three right angles rather than one. 46. It is four times as long.

Chapter 16, Lesson 2 (pages 698–700)

1. Its legs. 2. The base angles. 3. The summit. 5. WY and MO. 6. $\angle Y$ and $\angle O$. 7. Two points determine a line. 9. All right angles are equal. 14. The Ruler Postulate. 16. It is a birectangular quadrilateral whose legs are equal. 17. The summit angles of a Saccheri quadrilateral are equal. 20. An exterior angle of a triangle is greater than either remote interior angle. 23. A Saccheri quadrilateral. 25. The fact that $\angle D > \angle C$. 26. If the legs of a birectangular quadrilateral are unequal, the summit angles opposite them are unequal in the same order. 29. CD. 31. DM = CM because $\triangle ADM \cong \triangle BCM$ (SAS). 33. In a plane, two points each equidistant from the endpoints of a line segment determine the perpendicular bisector of the line segment. 38. DA. 40. The line segment connecting the midpoints of the base and summit of a Saccheri quadrilateral is perpendicular to both of them.

42. In a plane, two lines perpendicular to a third line are parallel.   44. The opposite angles of a parallelogram are equal.

Chapter 16, Lesson 3   (pages 704–706)

1. The summit angles of a Saccheri quadrilateral are acute in Lobachevskian geometry.   3. Substitution.   4. A line segment has exactly one midpoint.   6. The line segment connecting the midpoints of the base and summit of a Saccheri quadrilateral is perpendicular to both of them.   7. A quadrilateral that has two sides perpendicular to a third side is birectangular.   9. The Addition Theorem of Inequality.   14. A birectangular quadrilateral whose legs are equal is a Saccheri quadrilateral.   15. The summit of a Saccheri quadrilateral is longer than its base in Lobachevskian geometry.   20. Through a point not on a line, there is more than one line parallel to the line.   28. Birectangular.   34. In Riemannian geometry, the summit of a Saccheri quadrilateral is shorter than its base.   37. They are all half as long.   42. They are congruent squares.

Chapter 16, Lesson 4   (pages 709–712)

2. $\angle D$ and $\angle E$.   4. A Saccheri quadrilateral.

5. The summit angles of a Saccheri quadrilateral are acute in Lobachevskian geometry.   8. Substitution.   10. The sum of the angles of a triangle is less than $180°$ in Lobachevskian geometry.   14. Corresponding angles of similar triangles are equal.   17. The angles in a linear pair are supplementary.
21. No. The sums of the angles of the two triangles may not be equal.   26. $\angle A + \angle B + \angle C > 180°$.   27. Riemannian geometry.
31. $\angle 1 = \angle A + \angle B$.   35. $\triangle ADE \sim \triangle ABC$ (AA).
41. $\angle F$ is a right angle.   42. CFDE is a birectangular quadrilateral (in two different ways).   43. $\angle FDE$ is acute.   46. $DE > 2BC$.

Chapter 16, Review   (pages 714–717)

1. A great circle.   2. False.   4. True (because antipodal points are considered to be identical).   7. AD.   12. $360°$.
16. $\angle ABC = 90°$; $\angle BCD = 120°$; $\angle CDA = 90°$; $\angle DAB = 120°$.   17. The quadrilateral is a parallelogram.   19. It is a rhombus.
23. No.   26. Saccheri quadrilaterals.
27. Acute.   32. Substitution.   34. A midsegment of a triangle is less than half as long as the third side.   37. Two points determine a line.   40. The sum of the angles of a triangle is less than $180°$.

Illustration Credits

Introduction

p. 1: From *Collected Poems* by Vachel Lindsay (Macmillan, 1914) copyright renewed 1942 by Elizabeth C. Lindsay.

Chapter 1

p. 17: *(upper right)* Lowell Observatory; **p. 18:** *(top)* Adam C. Sylvester/Photo Researchers; **p. 24:** Courtesy of http:www.indias-best.com; **p. 30:** Georg Gerster; **p. 35:** *Dido Purchases Land for the Foundation of Carthage (1630)*. Engraving by Matthäus Merian in Historische Chronica, Frankfurt a.M. 1630. Staats und Stadtbibliothek Augsburg; **p. 36:** *(top left)* Réunion des Musées/Art Resource *(upper left)* Department of Anthropology, Smithsonian Institution.

Chapter 2

p. 41: *The Art of Optical Illusions* by Al Seckel (Illusion Works, 2000), Jos De Mey; **p. 42:** Photofest; **p. 45:** *(top and bottom)* From *The Animal Mind* by James L. Gould and Carol Grant Gould © 1994 by Scientific American Library; **p. 46:** Los Angeles Times, 8/15/91 *(left)* Stockbyte/Picture Quest, *(center)* Gemma Giannini/Grant Heilman Photography, *(right)* Peggy Koyle/Index Stock Imagery; **p. 50:** *(left)* Comic Strip Classics Stamp Sheet; *(right)* From Scientific American, April 1998, Vol. 278, No. 4, p. 108; **pp. 55 and 56:** From *Anno's Hat Tricks* by Akihiro Nozaki and Mitsumasa Anno. Published by Philomel Books, 1985. Used with permission of Anno/Dowaya Ltd., Japan; **p. 58:** *(top right)* From "Architecture of Molecules" by Linus Pauling and Roger Hayward, plate 11 © 1964 by W. H. Freeman and Company; **p. 62:** *(left)* Photofest, *(right)* From *The Complete Manual of Woodworking* by Albert Jackson, © 1989 by Wm Collins Sons Ltd. Used with permission of Alfred A. Knopf, a division of Random House, Inc.; **p. 69:** *(top left)* From *Light & Vision* by Conrad Mueller (Time Science Library, 1966), front cover; **p. 70:** *(right) Dissections, Plane and Fancy* by Greg N. Frederickson (Cambridge University Press, 1997). Reprinted with the permission of Cambridge University Press; **p. 72:** *(top)* W. H. Freeman and Company, *(bottom)* Courtesy of Bogen Photo Corp., Ramsey, NJ.

Chapter 3

p. 83: Drawing by Harry Furniss. National Portrait Gallery, London; **p. 86:** Modified from *Rules of the Game,* Diagram Group (St. Martin's Press, 1990); **p. 88:** *(bottom left)* Harold Edgerton; **p. 94:** *(bottom left) Dutton's Navigation and Piloting,* 14th ed., Elbert S. Maloney (Naval Institute Press, 1985), p. 61, *(bottom right)* G. C. Kelley/Photo Researchers; **p. 95:** Numbers Facts, Figures and Fiction, Richard Phillips (Cambridge University Press, 1994); **p. 96:** *(top left)* Alex S. McLean/Landslides, *(right)* The NBC® peacock is a registered trademark of NBC Broadcasting, Inc.; **p. 98:** *(top)* Lester Lefkowitz/Corbis; **p. 102:** *(top and middle left)* Photodisc/W. H. Freeman and Company, *(bottom left)* Modified "Architecture of Molecules" by Linus Pauling and Roger Hayward. © 1964 by W. H. Freeman and Company; **p. 103:** *(top right)* James W. Richardson/Visuals Unlimited; **p. 105:** *(top)* Joseph Daniel; **p. 107:** *(right)* Adapted from *The Physics of Skiing,* David Lind and Scott P. Sanders (AIP Press/Springer-Verlag, 1996), p. 78; **p. 108:** *(left)* From *Sports, The Complete Visual Reference,* Francois Fortin (Firefly Books, 2000); **p. 110:** *(top right)* Alex S. McLean/Landslides; **p. 117:** Historical Atlas of the United States,

National Geographic Society, 1988; **p. 119:** *(top right)* From *Rules of the Game,* Diagram Group (St. Martin's Press, 1990), p. 65; **p. 120:** *(top left)* From *Mathematical Snapshots,* by Hugo Steinhaus (Oxford University Press, 1969); **p. 121:** *(top right)* Photo courtesy of Elizabeth Bryarly; **p. 122:** *(left)* From *New Book of Puzzles* by Jerry Slocum and Jack Botermans (W. H. Freeman and Company, 1992), p. 12; **p. 124:** *(top left)* James A. Sugar/Corbis, *(bottom left) The Complete Manual of Woodworking* by Albert Jackson, David Day, and Simon Jennings (Alfred A. Knopf, 1996), p. 76; **p. 126:** *(top left)* Colin Garratt/ Corbis, *(bottom left)* A painting by Francisco de Goya. Prado, Madrid (photograph by Sem Presser), *(middle right)* From *The Complete Manual of Woodworking* by Albert Jackson, David Day, and Simon Jennings (Alfred A. Knopf, 1996); **p. 127:** *(left)* Chip Clark.

Chapter 4

p. 132: *(middle left)* Detail from Addams cartoon *(at top of page).* © The New Yorker Collection 1974, Charles Addams, from cartoonbank.com. All rights reserved; **p. 137:** *(top)* From *Architecture–Form, Space, and Order* by Francis D. K. Ching (Wiley, 1996); **p. 139:** *(top)* Alex S. McLean/Landslides; **p. 144:** *(bottom right)* Internet: members.tripod.com/jeff560.sierpin.jpg. Original stamp issued by Poland on Nov. 23, 1982; **p. 146:** *(top)* Sheet Music courtesy of The Dam Busters March; **p. 156:** *(top right)* Adapted from a problem by Henry Ernest Dudeny, *Amusements in Mathematics* (1917); **p. 160:** *(top left)* Dwayne Newton/PhotoEdit; **p. 161:** From "Architecture of Molecules" by Linus Pauling and Roger Hayward. © 1964 by W. H. Freeman and Company; **p. 162:** *(top right)* From M. C. Escher's detail from "Lizard E25"© 2002 Cordon Art B. V.–Baarn-Holland. All rights reserved, *(bottom right)* Detail of "Lizard E25" courtesy of Cordon Art B. V.–Baarn-Holland; **p. 163:** *(top)* Smithsonian Institution; **p. 176:** *(top right)* Detail of "La Symetrie Bidimensionnelle et le Canada" courtesy of Francois Brisse, *(bottom right)* "La Symetrie Bidimensionnelle et le Canada" by Francois Brisse, *The Canadian Mineralogist,* Vol. 19, p. 217, 1981. Used by permission of the author; **p. 179:** The Rock Art Museum of Tanum, Sweden. Gerhard Milstreu.

Chapter 5

p. 183: From *The Playful Eye* by Julian Rothenstein and Mel Gooding (Chronicle Books, 1999). Used with permission of Redstone Press, UK; **p. 184:** *(top left)* Photography by William Vandivert and Scientific American. (From Scientific American Library: *Perception,* p. 84); **p. 186:** *(middle left) The Snark Puzzle Book* by Martin Gardner (Simon & Schuster, 1973), p. 101. Used with permission of the author; **p. 187:** *(top)* Pictor International/PictureQuest; **p. 190:** *(top)* From *Industrial Light and Magic–The Art of Special Effects,* Thomas G. Smith (Ballantine Books, 1986); **p. 195:** *(top and top right)* Scrots, William, *Edward VI,* 1546, National Portrait Gallery, London; **p. 197:** *(bottom right)* Kip Peticolas/Fundamental Photographs; **p. 200:** *(top)* Lowell Observatory; **p. 206:** *(left)* Adapted from *Sam Loyd's Cyclopedia of 5,000 Puzzles* (Pinnacle Books, 1976), p. 248, *(right)* Vladimir Pcholkin/Taxi; **p. 209:** *(top left) Information Visualization: Perception for Design,* Colin Ware (Morgan Kaufmann, 2000).

Chapter 6

p. 211: *The Art of Optical Illusion* by Al Seckel (Illusion Works, 2000), p. 111; **p. 215:** *(top left)* From *Wild Animal Paper Chains,* Stewart and Sally Walton (Tupelo Books/Wm. Morrow & Co., 1993); **p. 217:** *(left)* Used with permission of Scott Kim; **p. 222:** Michael and Patricia Fogden; **p. 223:** *(middle left) Can You Believe Your Eyes?* J. R. Block and Harold E. Yuker (Brunner/Mazel, 1992); **p. 225:** *(top left and top right)* From *Laughing Camera II* (Hill & Wang, New York, 1969), pp. 66 and 67; **p. 228:** *(bottom left)* Rendered from *Architecture: Form, Space, and Order* by Francis D. K. Ching (Wiley, 1996); **p. 230:** *(top)* Tom Bean/Corbis; **p. 232:** *(top left)* Adapted from *Challenge!* By Charles Rice, Hallmark Editions, 1968; **p. 233:** *(top left)* The Photo Works; **p. 234:** *(top left)* From *Puzzles: Old & New* by Jerry Slocum and Jack Botermans (University of Washington Press–Seattle, 1986), p. 21, *(middle right)* Terrence Moore/USGS; **p. 236:** *(top) Historical Atlas of the United States: Centennial Edition* (National Geographic Society, 1988), p. 115, *(bottom left)* Map courtesy of U.S.C.G.S.; **pp. 242 and 243:** *(top)* From *Visualization* by Richard Mark Friedhoff and William Benzon (Harry N. Abrams Inc., 1989), pp. 120 and 121; **p. 245:** *(top left)* Steve Satushek/Getty; **p. 246:** *(top right)* Courtesy of DSH Inc., manufacturer of quality hardware for sliding and bifold mirror doors; **p. 250:** *(top right)* Alex S. McLean/Landslides.

Chapter 7

p. 258: *(top)* Courtesy of Marvin Windows and Doors © 1988; **p. 260:** *(right)* Georg Gerster/Photo Researchers; **p. 267:** *(top left)* Courtesy of the Margaret Woodbury Strong Museum, Rochester, New York; **p. 269:** *(right)* From *Games of the World*, Frederic V. Grunfeld, ed. (Holt, Rinehart & Winston, 1975), p. 126. Dutch Tax Museum, Rotterdam; **p. 270:** *(top)* From *The Mind*, John Rowan Wilson (Time-Life Books, 1969), pp. 50–51. Three Photographs: Norman Snyder, courtesy Animal Talent Scouts Inc., NY; **p. 272:** *(top left)* From *Mathematics Meets Technology* by Brian Bolt (Cambridge University Press, 1991). Reprinted with the permission of Cambridge University Press; **p. 276:** Neil Leifer/Sports Illustrated; **p. 278:** *(middle right)* Georg Gerster/Photo Researchers; **p. 279:** *(top left)* Gary Russ/Getty; **p. 281:** *(top)* Maya murals from Bonampak, Chiapas, 9th c. A.D., paintings copied by Antonio Tejeda for the Carnegie Institution of Washington, DC (Robert Kafka); **p. 282:** *(bottom left)* Adapted from *Architecture: Form, Space, and Order* by Francis D. K. Ching (Wiley, 1996); **p. 288:** *(bottom)* Modified from *The Hammond-Doubleday Illustrated World Atlas;* **p. 290:** *(top left)* Detail from an ad published in *Scientific American*, November 1990, for *Envisioning Information* by Edward R. Tufte (Graphics Press, 1990); **p. 292:** *(left) Modified Geometry from Africa*, Paulus Gerdes (The Mathematical Association of America, 1999), p. 100. Fig. 3.34, described as "wall of a bag"; **p. 294:** *(top left)* From *Mathematics Meets Technology*, Brian Bolt (Cambridge University Press, 1991), p. 66. Reprinted with the permission of Cambridge University Press, *(top right)* From *Creative Puzzles of the World*, Pieter van Delft and Jack Botermans (Abrams, 1978).

Chapter 8

p. 300: *(bottom)* M. C. Escher's "Fish E20" © 2002 Cordon Art B. V.–Baarn-Holland. All rights reserved; **p. 301:** *(top left) The Galactic Club*, Ronald N. Bracewell (W. H. Freeman and Company, 1975), p. 15, rendered at studio, *(bottom right) Adobe Illustrator 9.0 User Guide* (Adobe, 2000), pp. 20–21; **p. 302:** *(top left)* Douglas Hofstadter design adapted from Games Column by Scot Morris, *Omni*, June 1988, p. 136; **p. 305:** *(bottom)* **and p. 307:** *(top and bottom)* Details from Charles Addams cartoon, courtesy of Charles Addams © 1957, 1985, The New Yorker Magazine, Inc.; **p. 308:** *(top left)* Bob Carey/*Los Angeles Times* 1/8/87, Part II, p. 8.; **p. 309:** *(bottom left) Can You Believe Your Eyes?* J. R. Blocker and Harold E. Yuker (Brunner/Mazel, 1992), p. 208, Fig. 17.22. Courtesy of David Moser, *(top and bottom right)* Al Freni; **p. 310:** *(bottom right)* **and p. 311:** *(top left)* From *The Boomerang Book,* John Cassidy (Klutz Press, 1985), p. 1; **p. 312:** "Turning the Tables," modified from *Mind Sights*, Roger N. Shepard (W. H. Freeman and Company, 1990), p. 48; **p. 314:** *(bottom left)* Stuart Westmorland/Corbis, *(top right)* From *Can You Believe Your Eyes?* J. R. Blocker and Harold E. Yuker (Brunner/Mazel, 1992), p. 212, Fig. 17.25. Courtesy of Paul Agule, *(bottom right)* Courtesy of Baby Harold Jacobs; **p. 316:** *(top left)* M. C. Escher's "Bull Dog E97" © 2002 Cordon Art B. V.–Baarn-Holland. All rights reserved, *(bottom left and top right)* Details from Escher drawing,

p. 316; **p. 321:** *(top left) Algebra* is adapted from *Wordplay* by John Langdon (Harcourt Brace Jovanovich, 1992), p. 127, *(lower right)* Bettmann/Corbis; **p. 323:** *(bottom right)* **and p. 324:** *(top right)* Georg Gerster/Photo Researchers; **p. 324:** *(middle left, middle right, and bottom) Thinking Upside Down—An Activity Guide for Inversions*, Scott Kim (a pamphlet published by Dale Seymour Publications, 1984); **p. 325:** Kaiser Porcelain Ltd.; **p. 326:** *(top left)* From C. C. Mayer, *Masterpieces of Western Textiles*, Chicago, The Art Institute of Chicago, 1969, *(right)* First measure from First Prelude (BWV 846) from *The Well-Tempered Clavier*, Vol. 1; **p. 327:** *(top left)* M. C. Escher's "Two Fish E41" © 2002 Cordon Art B. V.–Baarn-Holland. All rights reserved, *(middle and bottom left)* Details from Escher drawing, p. 327, *(right) Keep Your Eye on the Ball*, Robert G. Watts and A. Terry Bahill (W. H. Freeman and Company, 1990), p. 116; **p. 329:** *(left) Wordplay*, John Langdon (Harcourt Brace Jovanovich, 1992), p. 179.

Midterm Review

p. 332: © 1997–2001 Andrew Bayuk

Chapter 9

p. 337: © 1968, W. A. Elliot Co., Toronto, Canada; **p. 340:** *(top left)* From *Symbols of America*, Hal Morgan (Viking, 1986), p. 179; **p. 341:** *(right)* From *Wheels, Life and Other Mathematical Amusements*, Martin Gardner (W. H. Freeman and Company, 1983). Used by permission of the author; **p. 343:** From *New Book of Puzzles* by Jerry Slocum and Jack Botermans (W. H. Freeman and Company, 1992), p. 119; **p. 344:** *(top)* Alex S. McLean/Landslides; **p. 345:** *(bottom)* Artist: Ad Reinhardt, in Museum of Modern Art; **p. 347:** *(top right)* From *The Cosmological Milkshake*, Robert Ehrlich (Rutgers University Press, 1994), p. 5. Drawing by Gary Ehrlich, *(bottom right)* Arnold E. Palmer/Arrowhead Images; **p. 348:** *(bottom left)* From *The Thomas Guide: Los Angeles County Street Guide and Directory* (Thomas Bros. Maps, Irvine, CA); **p. 349:** *(top)* From *Wood Handbook*, Forest Products Laboratory (U. S. Department of Agriculture, 1974), *(top right)* From *The Best of Better Homes and Gardens Home Plans*, Fall 1997, p. 54. [Plan No. 24700]; **p. 350:** *(top)* Painting by Mary Russel; **p. 354:** *(top right)* By permission of Vahan Shirvanian; **p. 357:** *(top right)* Modified from *The Best of Better Homes and Gardens Home Plans*, Fall 1997, p. 109 [Plan No. 90966]; **p. 358:** Modified from drawing by D'Arcy Thompson "On the theory of transformations, or the comparison of related forms," *On Growth and Form*, edited by J. T. Bonner, Cambridge University Press © 1966; **p. 360:** *(left top and bottom)* Georg Gerster/Photo Researchers; **p. 361:** *(bottom left) Geometry and the Imagination*, David Hilbert and S. Cohen-Vossen (American Mathematical Society reprint, 1999), *(top right)* Thomas A. Heinz/Corbis; **p. 367:** *(left)* Annagret Haake, University of Frankfurt; **p. 369:** *(bottom left)* Bettmann/Corbis; **p. 374:** *(top left)* NASA Dryden Flight Research Center.

Chapter 10

p. 378: Roy Lichtenstein, *Mural with Blue Brushstroke*, 1984–86. Photographed by Robert McKeever; **p. 380:** *(top left)* PhotoDisc/Getty; **p. 381:** *(top left)* From *Architecture: Form, Space, and Order*, Francis D. K. Ching (Wiley, 1996), p. 294, *(bottom left)* Peter Raedschelders, *Turtles Forever;* **p. 383:** *(left)* J. Pat Carter/AP; **p. 384:** *(top)* Yann Arthus-Bertrand/Corbis; **p. 385 and p. 386:** *(top and top left)* Photofest; **p. 387:** *(bottom left)* ESO/ESA, *(bottom right)* John Chumack/Photo Researchers; **p. 390:** *(top left)* Adapted from *Size and Life* by Thomas A. McMahon and John Tyler Bonner. © 1983 by Thomas A. McMahon and John Tyler Bonner; **p. 391:** *(bottom left)* Francis G. Mayer/Corbis, *(top right)* From *Architecture: Form, Space, and Order* by Francis D. K. Ching (Wiley, 1996), p. 291; **p. 397:** *(bottom left)* Courtesy of the HNTB Companies; **p. 398:** *(middle left)*

Courtesy of Rockler.com; **p. 403:** *(top left)* Piero della Francesca, *Il trionfo di Federico di Montefeltro.* Alinari/Art Resource; **p. 409:** *(top left)* Photography by Andrew Brilliant, © 1983; **p. 410** *(right)* **and p. 413:** *(top right)* PhotoDisc/Getty; **p. 414:** *(top)* Joseph Sohm, Visions of America/Corbis; **p. 418:** *(top left)* Barbara Dean, Chantilly, VA, *(top right)* Alex S. McLean/Landslides; **p. 419:** *(top left)* Don S. Montgomery, USN (Ret.)/Corbis, *(right)* Granger Collection; **p. 421:** *(top left)* Adapted from *Cat's Paws and Catapults,* Steven Vogel (W. W. Norton 1998), p. 44. Fig. 3.3, *(bottom left)* Detail from B.C. Cartoon (p. 420). Used by permission of Johnny Hart and Creators Syndicate, Inc.

Chapter 11

p. 428: *(top left)* From Rutherford Platt, *(bottom left)* Jonathan Blair/Corbis; **p. 430:** *(top left)* PeterLilja/Getty; **p. 434:** *(top)* By permission of the British Library, 1007628.011; **p. 438:** *(top left)* Bettmann/Corbis; **p. 439:** *(top right)* Adapted from *Why Buildings Fall Down: How Structures Fail,* by Matthys Levy and Mario Salvadori (Norton, 1992); **p. 440:** *(top left)* Adapted from *Energy,* Mitchell Wilson and the editors of LIFE (Life Science Library, 1963), p. 142; **p. 441:** *(top)* Yale Babylonian Collection (YBC 7289); **p. 445:** *(top left)* Modified from *Traffic Engineering for Better Roads,* Military Traffic Management Command, Washington, DC, 1978, *(bottom left)* Drawing by J. Bertolli, *(top right)* Modified from *Sports: The Complete Visual Reference* by Francois Fortin © 2000 published by Firefly Books; **p. 446:** *(bottom right)* The Unexpected Hanging and Other Mathematical Diversions, Martin Gardner (Simon & Schuster, 1969); **p. 448:** Galen Rowell/Corbis; **p. 451:** *Sport Science: Physical Laws and Optimum Performance,* Peter Brancazio (Simon & Schuster, 1984). Used with permission of the author; **p. 452:** *(top left)* Painting by Mario Larrinaga, *(bottom left)* "Reconstruction" by A. Thiersch. Plate taken from his book "Der Pharos von Alexandrien," 1909, *(top right)* From Internet: www.nebogear.com/108-720.html. Olympus Trooper Zoom DPS R 7-15x35 Binocular; **p. 453:** *(bottom right)* Georg Gerster/Photo Researchers; **p. 454:** *(left)* Nick Bergkessel, *(right)* Adapted from *Exploring Biomechanics* by R. McNeill Alexander © 1992 by Scientific American Library; **p. 458:** *(bottom left)* © Richard Synergy; *(bottom right)* Adapted from *Invention by Design,* Henry Petroski (Harvard University Press, 1996), p. 138, Fig. 7.8; **p. 459:** *(bottom left)* Corbis; **p. 461:** *(top)* Courtesy of Erwin Purucker; **p. 464:** *(top left)* ImageState, *(bottom left)* *Environmental Geology,* Dorothy J. Merritts et al. (W. H. Freeman and Company, 1998), p. 241. Used with permission, *(right)* Pictor International/PictureQuest; **p. 465:** *(top right)* Stock Boston; **p. 468:** *(top)* Adapted from LA Times 10/11/99; **p. 472:** *(right)* *The Great Arc,* John Keay (HarperCollins, 2000), p. xv. Part of a map titled "The Great Arc and Associated Series"; **p. 473:** *(bottom left)* From nssdc.gsfc.nasa.gov/image/planetary/earth/apollo 17_earth.jpg [NASA ID is 72-HC-928, 72-H-1578, or AS17-148-22727]; **p. 477:** *(top left)* *Sport Science: Physical Laws and Optimum Performance,* Peter Brancazio (Simon & Schuster, 1984). Used with permission of the author; **p. 479:** *(middle right)* Courtesy of American Optical Company; **p. 480:** *(right)* Columbia University.

Chapter 12

p. 483: *The Science of Illusions* by Jaques Ninio (Cornell University Press, 2001); **p. 484:** T. C. Schneirla, *Army Ants,* H. R. Topoff (ed.) (W. H. Freeman and Company, 1971); **p. 486:** *(right)* Gary W. Carter/Corbis; **p. 488:** *(middle left)* The CBS and CBS Eye Design are registered trademarks of CBS Broadcasting Inc., *(top right)* From *The Book of Ingenious and Diabolical Puzzles* by Jerry Slocum and Jack Botermans (Times Books, 1994), p. 32; **p. 489:** *(left)* Rex Elliot; **p. 490:** *(left)* Hulton Getty Picture Collection; **p. 491:** *(top)* From *Sports–The Complete Visual Reference,* Francois Fortin (Firefly Books, 2000), p. 6; **p. 494:** *(top left)* Mark Meinders; **p. 496:** *(right)* GSFC/NASA; **p. 497:** *(top)* Raymond Gehman/Corbis; **p. 501:** *(bottom right)* Corbis; **p. 502:** *(top right)* Douglas

Kirkland/Corbis; **p. 504:** *(top)* Corbis; **p. 506:** *(top left)* Adapted from *Rules of the Game,* Diagram Group (St. Martin's Press, 1990), p. 78; **p. 508:** *(top left)* From *Pioneers of Science,* Sir Oliver Lodge (Macmillan, London, 1893), p. 61; **p. 514:** *(top left)* Photography by Kathryn Abbe, 1979; **p. 515:** *(bottom right)* Detail from B. C. Cartoon (top, p. 515). Used by permission of Johnny Hart and Creators Syndicate, Inc.; **p. 516:** *(top)* Fred Espenak; **p. 521:** *(left)* From Everett Hale's story "The Brick Moon" published originally in Atlantic Monthly in 1869–1870; **p. 522:** Courtesy of Elmer Atkins © 1963 Saturday Review, Inc.; **p. 523:** *(top)* Frederick von Martens/George Eastman House; **p. 525:** *(top left)* Corbis.

Chapter 13

p. 529: Exhibition by Four Graphic Designers. Shigeo Fukakan, 1975; **p. 530:** *(top)* Jason Hawkes/Corbis; **p. 542:** *(top)* Courtesy of Professor H. Hashimoto, Okayama University of Science, Ohtsu, Japan; **p. 561:** *(top)* "The Shade of Napoleon," A popular print, UK 1831 (pub. R. Ackerman).

Chapter 14

p. 571: Treat Davidson/Photo Researchers; **p. 574:** *(bottom left)* Max Bill (The Buffalo Fine Arts Gallery and Albright-Knox Art Gallery, 1974), p. 63–15 Variations on a Single Theme, Variation 14, *(bottom right)* Variation 8; **p. 575:** *(top left)* From Dr. Benjamin M. Shaub, *(bottom left)* Chip Clark, *(top right)* Manuel Velarde, Universidade Comp-Lutense, Madrid; **p. 577:** *(right)* Museo Diocesano, Mantua, Italy, Scala/Art Resource; **p. 579:** *(top)* Stone/Getty, *(right)* *Euclid–The Creation of Mathematics,* Benno Artman (Springer, 1999), p. 291. Labeled: "After Bousquet (1993), p. 294 and Charbonneaux (1925); **p. 582:** *(top left)* *The Self-Made Tapestry–Pattern Formation in Nature,* Philip Ball (Oxford University Press, 1999), p. 245. Labeled: "The Radial Design of the Renaissance City of Palma Nuova in Italy, from *Fractal Cities: A Geometry of Form and Function,* M. Batty and P. A. Longley (Academic Press, 1994), after Morris (1979), *(bottom left)* From "Architecture of Molecules" by Linus Pauling and Roger Hayward, plate 11 © 1964 by W. H. Freeman and Company, *(bottom right)* The U. S. Mint; **p. 583:** *(top left)* Adapted from *National Geographic's How Things Work,* John Langone (National Geographic, 1999), p. 216; **p. 584:** *(top right)* Jeff Lepore/Photo Researchers; **p. 588:** *(top right)* Treat Davidson/Photo Researchers; **p. 591:** *(top)* Rod Planck; **p. 594:** *(bottom left)* Granger Collection; **p. 596:** *(right)* Adapted from *Scientific American: How Things Work Today,* Michael Wright (Crown, 2000), p. 104; **p. 597:** *(right)* *Auto Math Handbook* by John Lawlor (HP Books, a division of Price Stern Sloan, 1991); **p. 600:** *(top left)* Science VU/GSFC/NASA, *(top right)* PhotoDisc/Getty, *(bottom right)* *Calculus* by James Stewart (Brooks/Cole, 1995); **p. 601:** *(middle left)* Alex S. McLean/Landslides; **p. 606:** *(bottom)* Travis Amos; **p. 606:** *(middle)* **and p. 609:** *(bottom right)* Adapted from *Sports–The Complete Visual Reference,* Francois Fortin (Firefly Books, 2000), p. 28; **p. 613:** *(left)* Courtesy of Hans-Erich Dechant; **p. 614:** *(bottom left)* Elio Ciol/Corbis.

Chapter 15

p. 617: *The Art of Optical Illusions* by Al Seckel (Illusion Works, 2000), © Bruno Ernst; **p. 618–620:** M. C. Escher's "Ascending and Descending" © 2002 Cordon Art B. V.–Baarn-Holland. All rights reserved.; **p. 621:** *(left)* From *Architecture: Form, Space, and Order* by Francis D. K. Ching (Wiley, 1996), *(top right)* Adapted from Science, Vol. 262, pp. 2042–2044 (Fig. 3A), "Perceptual Organization and the Judgment of Brightness," Edward H. Adelson by permission of Edward H. Adelson and © 1993 The American Association for the Advancement of Science; **p. 622:** *(bottom left)* "Illusions of the Third Dimension" by Martin Gardner (Psychology Today, August 1993), reprinted in *Gard-*

ner's Why's and Wherefores (University of Chicago Press, 1989), p. 60; **p. 623:** *(left) The Unique World of Mitsumasa Anno–Selected Works (1968-1977)* by Mitsumasa Anno (Philomel Books, 1980), p. 35, Plate 29. A section of a cube; **p. 624:** *(top right)* José Yturralde; **p. 625:** M. C. Escher's "Belvedere" © 2002 Cordon Art B.V.–Baarn-Holland. All rights reserved; **p. 628:** *(top)* Photofest; **p. 630:** *(top left)* From *Mathematical Circus* by Martin Gardner (Knopf, 1979). Used with permission of the author; **p. 631:** *(top left)* Susan Schwartzenberg/Exploratorium; **632:** *(right)* From "Architecture of Molecules" by Linus Pauling and Roger Hayward, plate 11 © 1964 by W. H. Freeman and Company; **p. 634:** *(top)* George D. Lepp/Corbis; **p. 637:** *(left) Architecture: Form, Space, and Order* by Francis D. K. Ching (Wiley, 1996), p. 200; **p. 639:** *(top left)* Mark A. Schneider/Photo Researchers; **pp. 642, 644:** *(top right)* courtesy of the Science Museum of Minnesota; **p. 646:** *(top left)* Modified from *200% of Nothing* by A. K. Dewdney (Wiley, 1993), p. 18, Fig. 1, *(bottom left)* PhotoDisc/Getty, *(bottom right) Envisioning Information* by Edward R. Tufte (Graphics Press, 1990), p. 14, Mary C. Dickerson, *(right)* Michael Ambrosino; **p. 649:** *(top left)* Adapted from *Scientific American: How Things Work Today,* Michael Wright and M. N. Patel (Crown, 2000), p. 196, *(bottom left)* From "Architecture of Molecules" by Linus Pauling and Roger Hayward, plate 11 © 1964 by W. H. Freeman and Company; **p. 652:** *(top left)* Modified from *Geometry from Africa,* Paulus Gerges (The Mathematical Association of America, 1999), p. 101, Fig. 3.39, Eheleo-funnel; **p. 661:** Alex S. McLean/Landslides; **p. 662:** NASA; **p. 654:** *(top)* René Magritte, "Euclidean Promenade," 1955, William Hood Dunwoody Fund, Minneapolis Museum of Arts; **p. 657:** *(bottom right)* QA Photos; **p. 659:** *(left) Auto Math Handbook,* John Lawlor (HP Books, Price Stern Sloan, 1991), *(bottom right)* Photo by Elizabeth Bryarly; **p. 665:** *(left) The Unique World of Mitsumasa Anno–Selected Works (1968-1977),* Mitsumasa Anno (Philomel Books, 1980), p. 45, plate 39. The Shadow of the Earth; **p. 667:** *(bottom right) Fractal Music, Hypercards and More,* by Martin Gardner (W. H. Freeman and Company, 1992), p. 122, Fig. 50. Used with permission of the author; **p. 668:** Koreshan State Historic Site; **p. 669** *(top right)* **and p. 670:** Photofest; **p. 672:** *(right)* Corbis; **p. 673:** *(left)* Gougeon Brothers, Inc. *(bottom right)* Hubble Heritage Team/NASA; **p. 674:** *(bottom left)* Michael DiBella/Words & Pictures/Picture Quest; **p. 676:** Vermont Teddy Bear Company; **p. 679:** *(right)* From *Science and Society;* **p. 680:** *(top left)* M. C. Escher's "Verblifa Tin" © 2002 Cordon Art B. V.–Baarn-Holland. All rights reserved; **p. 684:** *(top left) Symmetry–A Unifying Concept,* I. Hargittai and M. Hargittai (Shelter Publications, 1994), p. 1041, *(bottom right)* © Photofest; **p. 685:** *(top left)* Photo taken from *The Victorian Gift Boxes,* by Jane Thomson (Hearst Books, 1992), p. 19, *(bottom left)* MaryAnn & Bryan Hemphill/Index Stock.

Chapter 16

p. 692: *(left)* Paul Katz/Index Stock; **p. 703:** *(top)* Boyer-Viollet, *(bottom)* Courtesy of AIP/Niels Bohr Library; **p. 706:** *(top left)* From Gerd Fischer, *Mathematical Models,* Vieweg-Verlag, 1986; **p. 707:** *(top)* AURA/STScl/NASA; *(bottom)* Bettmann/Corbis; **p. 711:** *(top right)* Photo courtesy of Elizabeth Bryarly; **p. 714:** *(left)* By permission of the British Library; **p. 716:** *(top)* M. C. Escher's "Circle Limit III" © 2002 Cordon Art B. V.–Baarn-Holland. All rights reserved.

Final Review

p. 721: *(top left)* Image compliments of Homeplans.com; **p. 722:** *(bottom left)* David Lorenz/Brand X Pictures/PictureQuest; **p. 723:** *(top left)* Dogbedworks; **p. 727:** *(top right)* Georg Gerster/Photo Researchers.

Index

Syllogism, 51
Symmetry
   line, 212
   point, 265–266
   reflection, 320
   rotation, 319–320
   translation, 320
Systems of equations, solving of, 527–528

Tangent (ratio), 448–449
Tangent line, 491
   construction of, 518–519
Tangent segment, 516–517
Tangent Segments Theorem, 517
Tangrams, 372
Terms of a proportion, 379
Tetrahedron, 178, 290, 678
Theorem, 51
Theorems and corollaries, list of, 741–746
30°-60° right triangle, lengths of sides of, 442
Three possibilities property, 185
Torus (doughnut), 669
Transformation, 298–300
   dilation, 300, 408
   glide reflection, 313
   isometry, 300
   reflection, 299
   rotation, 299, 307
   translation, 299, 306–307
Transitive property, 185
Translation, 299
   as composite of two reflections, 306–307
Translation symmetry, 320
Transversal, 219
Trapezoid, 281
   area of, 359
Trapezoidal rule, 363, 375
Triangle, 19
   area of, 351–353, 459
   classification of, 157–158
   construction of, 171
   equilateral, construction of, 2
   side and angle inequalities, 195–196
Triangle Angle Sum Theorem, 66, 237, 707–708
Triangle Inequality Theorem, 200–201
Triangulation, 236, 473
Trigonometric angles, 446
Trigonometric functions, 737
Trisection problems, 32–34

Undefined terms, 60–61

Vectors
   force components, 458
   force triangles, 165
   gliding bird, 68
   parallelogram rule, 268
   skier forces, 107
   tidal current, 136
Vertical angles, 110–111
Vertical lines, 110, 188
Vertices of a polygon, 139
Volume, 640
   of a cone, 656
   of a cube, 642
   of a cylinder, 655
   of a prism, 642
   of a pyramid, 648
   of a rectangular solid, 642
   of a sphere, 663–664

"Whole greater than part" theorem, 185, 188